Table of Values

Value and Units	Item	Symbol or Abbreviation
General		
10^{-8} cm	$\equiv$ 1 angstrom	Å
1 kxu $=$ 1.0020 Å	$=$ 1 kilo-x-unit	
10^{-4} cm	$\equiv$ 1 micron	μ
2.998×10^{2} volts	$\cong$ 1 statvolt	
2.998×10^{10} cm/sec	Speed of light in vacuum	c
Atomic		
6.626×10^{-27} erg-sec	Planck's constant	h
1.054×10^{-27} erg-sec	Planck's constant/2π	$\hbar$
1.6019×10^{-12} erg $\rbrace$ 23.05 kilocal/mole	Energy associated with 1 electron volt	ev
13.60 electron volts	Energy associated with 1 rydberg	
1.98×10^{-16} erg	Energy associated with unit wave number	hc
1.24×10^{-4} cm	Wavelength associated with 1 electron volt	λ_0
8066 cm^{-1}	Wave number associated with 1 electron volt	
2.42×10^{14} sec^{-1}	Frequency associated with 1 electron volt	ν_0
11605°K	Temperature associated with 1 electron volt	
0.529×10^{-8} cm	Bohr radius of the ground state of hydrogen $\hbar^2/me^2$	a_0
0.927×10^{-20} erg/gauss	Bohr magneton $e\hbar/2mc$	μ_B
0.505×10^{-23} erg/gauss	Nuclear magneton $e\hbar/2M_pc$	μ_n
137.04	Reciprocal of fine-structure constant	$\hbar c/e^2$
Particles		
0.911×10^{-27} gm	Electron rest mass	m
1.6725×10^{-24} gm	Proton rest mass	M_p
1.6747×10^{-24} gm	Neutron rest mass	M_n
1.66042×10^{-24} gm	One unified atomic mass unit ($\equiv \frac{1}{12}$ mass of C^{12})	u
1836	Proton mass/electron mass	M_p/m
2.82×10^{-13} cm	Classical radius of the electron e^2/mc^2	r_0
4.803×10^{-10} esu	Charge on the proton	e
3.86×10^{-11} cm	Electron Compton wavelength $\hbar/mc$	λ_C
Gases		
22.4×10^{3} cm^3/mole	Molar volume at STP	V_0
2.69×10^{19} cm^{-3}	Loschmidt's number	n_0
6.0225×10^{23} mole^{-1}	Avogadro's number	N_0
8.31×10^{7} erg mole^{-1} deg^{-1}	Gas constant	R_0
1.381×10^{-16} erg/°K	Boltzmann's constant	k_B
1.01×10^{6} dynes/cm^2	Atmospheric pressure	

INTRODUCTION TO SOLID STATE PHYSICS

CHARLES KITTEL

Introduction
to
Solid State
Physics

THIRD EDITION

John Wiley & Sons, Inc., New York, London, Sydney

SECOND PRINTING, FEBRUARY, 1967

Library of Congress Catalog Card Number: 66-21055

Preface to the Third Edition

This volume gives an elementary account of central aspects of the physics of solids. The volume was written as a textbook for senior undergraduate and beginning graduate students of science and engineering. The necessary background is a course in modern atomic physics.

Solid state physics is concerned with the remarkable properties exhibited by atoms and molecules because of their association and regular periodic arrangements in crystals. These properties may be understood in terms of simple models of solids. Real solids are more complicated, but the power and utility of simple models can hardly be overestimated.

The third edition follows ten years after the second edition. These ten years have seen a vigorous growth in solid state physics. The new edition represents an extensive modernization of the second edition. Almost every chapter was entirely rewritten, and more than three hundred new drawings and photographs were added. The great advances in energy band studies, superconductivity, magnetic resonance, and neutron scattering methods are reflected in the text. Emphasis is given to elementary excitations: phonons, plasmons, polarons, magnons, and excitons.

Along with the modernization an equal effort was made to produce a clear, intelligible, and well-illustrated text directed to students' needs. Criticism and student feedback was solicited and used widely to this end. The sequence of subjects exploits from the beginning the concept of the reciprocal lattice. The new sequence also makes it easy to select material for a one semester course. This might include most of the material in Chapters 1 through 10, with additional topics from the later chapters or elsewhere, according to taste and time.

The articles in the excellent Seitz-Turnbull series should be consulted for subjects not treated in this book and for detailed bibliographies. There are in the literature perhaps ten thousand articles of high quality which could usefully be cited. I have tried to give a helpful, but small, sample of those most accessible in English.

Problems of appreciable length or difficulty are marked by an asterisk. The symbol e denotes the charge on the proton: $e = +4.80 \times 10^{-10}$ esu. The notation (18) refers to equation number 18 of the current chapter, while (3.18) refers to equation 18 of Chapter 3; figures are referred to in the same way. A caret or "hat" over a vector, as in $\hat{\mathbf{k}}$, denotes a unit vector.

The preparation of this edition was made possible by the cooperation of many colleagues and friends. I would like to mention some of their contributions; there is not space to list all. The entire manuscript was strongly influenced by detailed criticism by Marvin L. Cohen and Michael Millman; my debt to them is indeed great. Successive drafts were kindly read by Ching Yao Fong and Joseph Ryus, and the problems were checked by Leonard Sander. Individual chapters were reviewed by Adolf Pabst, Charles S. Smith, David Templeton, Raymond Bowers, Sidney Abrahams, Earl Parker, G. Thomas, and M. Tinkham. Walter Marshall very kindly prepared an extensive selection of neutron diffraction results. The preparation of the historical introduction was assisted by Adolf Pabst, P. P. Ewald, Elizabeth Huff, Muriel Kittel, Georgianne Titus, and the physics librarian of the Ecole Normale Supérieure.

For their experienced advice in the selection of experimental data for tables of values I am grateful to Leo Brewer, R. M. Bozorth, Norman Phillips, Bernd Matthias, Vera Compton, M. Tinkham, Charles S. Smith, E. Burstein, F. P. Jona, and S. Strässler.

The illustrations were developed in their final form by Felix Cooper, with early help by Ellis Myers. Credits are given with the individual photographs and figures; exceptional help in their collection was given by Robert van Nordstrand, T. Geballe, W. Parrish, Betsy Burleson, I. M. Templeton, and G. Thomas; also by H. McSkimin, H. J. Williams, R. W. De Blois, E. L. Hahn, A. von Hippel, B. N. Brockhouse, R. C. Miller, R. C. Le Craw, E. W. Müller, P. R. Swann, G. E. Bacon, G. M. Gordon, and Alan Holden.

I am deeply grateful to Mrs. Madeline Moore for her infinite skill in typing the manuscript and in organizing all related matters.

Berkeley, California   *C. Kittel*
April, 1966

Note to the Reader

Chapters 1 and 2 on crystal structure analysis are fundamental. Every concept developed in Chapter 2 is exploited heavily in the chapters on energy bands and semiconductors; this is particularly true of the reciprocal lattice and of Brillouin zones. The general method developed in Appendix A for x-ray diffraction is repeated in Chapter 9 as the basis of the theory of electron energy bands. Chapters 4, 5, and 6 are concerned with the velocity, quantization, and interaction of elastic waves in crystals; among the topics used later are the enumeration of states in a Brillouin zone and the number of states per unit energy range. Chapters 7, 8, and 9 are concerned with electrons in metals. Chapter 9 on energy bands is the most important single chapter in the book; the line of development is somewhat new in a textbook, but reflects the attitude of current research in the field. The proof of the Bloch theorem is central for the understanding of the chapter. The discussion of the properties of holes is carried out with particular care as preparation for Chapter 10 on semiconductors.

Chapter 11 on superconductivity gives the essential experimental facts as viewed in the light of the BCS theory, but at this level it is impossible to give a meaningful derivation of the theory; the author's *Quantum theory of solids* may be consulted. Chapters 12 through 16 are devoted to the dielectric and magnetic properties of solids. Chapter 16 on magnetic resonance is tightly written: please work through it slowly. The final three chapters (17, 18, 19) are concerned largely with imperfections in solids and may be read at any convenient stage.

Contents

Some General References

Atomic physics background
    Max Born, *Atomic physics*, Hafner, New York, 7th ed., 1962.
    R. L. Sproull, *Modern physics*, Wiley, 2nd ed., 1963.

Crystallography
    F. C. Phillips, *An introduction to crystallography*, Wiley, 3rd ed., 1963.
    J. F. Nye, *Physical properties of crystals: their representation by tensors and
        matrices*, Oxford, 1957.

Elementary texts
    J. C. Slater, *Introduction to chemical physics*, McGraw-Hill, 1939.
    A. J. Dekker, *Solid state physics*, Prentice-Hall, 1957.

Advanced series
    F. Seitz and D. Turnbull, *Solid state physics, advances in research and applications*,
        Academic Press. Cited as Solid state physics.
    Encyclopedia of physics, Springer.

Advanced texts
    R. E. Peierls, *Quantum theory of solids*, Oxford, 1955.
    C. Kittel, *Quantum theory of solids*, Wiley, 1963. Cited as QTS.

INTRODUCTION TO SOLID STATE PHYSICS

1

Crystal Structure

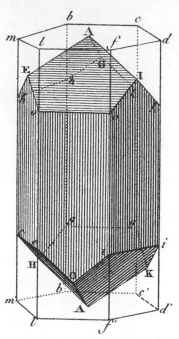

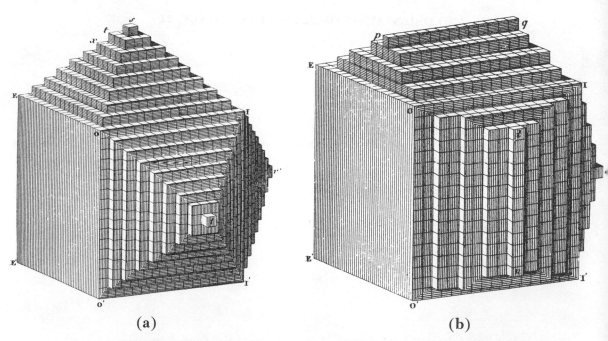

Figure 1 Sketch of a crystal, selected at random from an early mineralogy treatise. (Haüy.)

(a)

(b)

Figure 2 Relation of the external form of crystals to the form of the elementary building blocks. The building blocks are identical in (a) and (b), but different crystal faces are developed. (Haüy, from the atlas to the 1822 edition of his *Traité de cristallographie*.)

The study of the physical properties of the solid state, viewed as a branch of atomic physics, began in the early years of this century. Solid state physics has come to mean the study of crystals and of electrons in crystals. A century ago the study of crystals was concerned only with the external form of crystals and with geometrical symmetry relationships among the various coefficients which describe the physical properties. After 1910 physicists became deeply concerned with atomic models of crystals, following the discovery of x-ray diffraction by crystals and the publication of a series of simple and reasonably successful calculations and predictions of crystalline properties.

Many crystalline minerals and gems, particularly quartz, have been known and described for several thousand years. One of the earliest drawings of a crystal appears in a Chinese pharmacopeia of the eleventh century A.D. A quartz crystal has been preserved in the Shosoin in Nara (Japan) at least since the eighth century. The word crystal itself referred only to quartz until the late middle ages when the word acquired a more general meaning.

The regularity of the appearance and of the external form of the crystals found in nature (Fig. 1) or grown in the laboratory has disposed observers since the seventeenth century toward the belief that crystals are formed by a regular repetition of identical building blocks (Fig. 2). When a crystal grows in a constant environment the shape often remains unchanged during growth, as if identical elementary building blocks were added continuously to the crystal. We now know the elementary building blocks are atoms or groups of atoms: crystals are a three-dimensional periodic array of atoms.

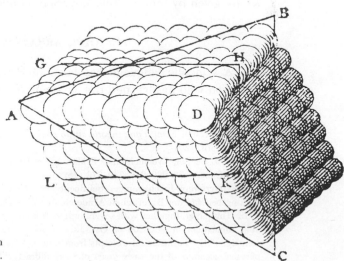

Figure 3   Model of calcite ($CaCO_3$) from C. Huyghens, *Traité de la lumiere*, 1690.

In the eighteenth century mineralogists made the important discovery that the index numbers (on a certain scheme of indexing to be described later) of the directions of all faces of a crystal were exact integers. Haüy[1] showed that the arrangement of identical particles in a three-dimensional periodic array could account for this law of rational indices. A. L. Seeber[2] of Freiburg suggested in 1824 that the elementary building blocks of crystals were small spheres, and he proposed an empirical law of interatomic force with both attractive and repulsive regions as needed to cause a lattice array to be the stable equilibrium state of a system of identical atoms.

Probably the most important date in the history of the physics of solids is June 8, 1912, when a paper[3] entitled "Interference effects with Röntgen rays" was laid before the Bavarian Academy of Sciences in Munich. In the first part of the paper Laue develops an elementary theory of diffraction of x-rays by a periodic array of atoms. In the second part Friedrich and Knipping report the first experimental observations of x-ray diffraction by crystals.

The work demonstrated that x-rays are waves, because they can be diffracted. The work also proved decisively that crystals are composed of a periodic array of atoms. This experimental proof marks the beginning of the field of solid state physics as we know it today. With an established atomic model of a crystal, physicists could think or calculate further. Much important pioneer work in physics of solids was done in the years immediately following 1912.

The first determinations of crystal structures by x-ray diffraction analysis were reported by W. L. Bragg in 1913: the structures of KCl, NaCl, KBr and KI are given by him in Proc. Roy. Soc. (London) **A89**, 248 (1913).

PERIODIC ARRAYS OF ATOMS

A symbolic language has been built up to describe crystal structures. A person who has learned the language of crystallography can reconstruct a

[1] R. J. Haüy, *Essai d'une théorie sur la structure des cristaux*, Paris, 1784; *Traité de cristallographie*, Paris, 1801.

[2] A. L. Seeber, "Versuch einer Erklärung des inneren Baues der festen Körper," Annalen der Physik (Gilbert) **76**, 229–248, 349–372 (1824).

[3] "Interferenz-Erscheinungen bei Roentgenstrahlen," W. Friedrich, P. Knipping, and M. Laue, Sitzungsberichte der Bayerischen Akademie der Wissenschaften, Math.-phys. Klasse, pp. 303–322, 1912. This paper, together with several others from the group around Laue, is reprinted with valuable annotations in Vol. 204 of Ostwald's *Klassiker der exakten Wissenschaften*, Akad. Verlag, Leipzig, 1923; the historical excerpts from Laue's Nobel prize lecture are of special interest. For personal accounts of the early years of x-ray diffraction studies of crystals, see P. P. Ewald, ed., *Fifty years of x-ray diffraction*, A. Oosthoek's Uitgeversmij., Utrecht, 1962. Shrewd guesses about the structures of a number of crystals had been made much earlier by W. Barlow, Nature **29**, 186, 205, 404 (1883); he argued from considerations of symmetry and packing (the filling of space).

crystal structure from a few printed symbols. We give here several elementary ideas about the language, sufficient to describe the geometry of simple crystal structures.

An ideal crystal is constructed by the infinite regular repetition in space of identical structural units in the form of parallelepipeds. In the simplest crystals such as copper, silver, gold, and the alkali metals the structural unit contains a single atom. More generally the structural unit contains several atoms or molecules, up to perhaps 100 in inorganic crystals[4] and 10^5 in protein crystals. A crystal may be composed of more than one chemical element (as in NaCl) or it may contain associated groups of identical atoms (as in H_2). We describe the structure of all crystals in terms of a single periodic lattice, but with a group of atoms attached to each lattice point or situated in each elementary parallelepiped. This group of atoms is called the **basis**; the basis is repeated in space to form the crystal. We now make these definitions more precise.

Crystal Translation Vectors and Lattices

An ideal crystal is composed of atoms arranged on a lattice defined by three **fundamental translation vectors a, b, c** such that the atomic arrangement looks the same in every respect when viewed from any point **r** as when viewed from the point

$$\mathbf{r}' = \mathbf{r} + n_1\mathbf{a} + n_2\mathbf{b} + n_3\mathbf{c}, \tag{1}$$

where n_1, n_2, n_3 are arbitrary integers (Fig. 4).

The set of points **r'** specified by (1) for all values of the integers n_1, n_2, n_3 defines a **lattice**. A lattice[5] is a regular periodic arrangement of points in space. A lattice is a mathematical abstraction: the crystal structure is formed only when a basis of atoms is attached identically to each lattice point. The logical relation is

lattice + basis = crystal structure.

The lattice and the translation vectors **a, b, c** are said to be **primitive** if *any* two points **r, r'** from which the atomic arrangement looks the same[6]

---

[4] The intermetallic compound $NaCd_2$ has a cubic cell of 1192 atoms as its smallest structural unit; see S. Samson, Nature **195**, 259 (1962).

[5] We use the words *lattice* and *lattice points* interchangeably. Bravais noted that the lattice points are the roots of the equation

$$\sin^2(\pi\xi/a) + \sin^2(\pi\eta/b) + \sin^2(\pi\zeta/c) = 0,$$

where ξ, η, ζ are spatial coordinates referred to a system of three coordinate axes, in general oblique. The unit vectors of the coordinate system are denoted by $\hat{a}$, $\hat{b}$, $\hat{c}$.

[6] This definition may sound clumsy, but it guarantees that there is no cell of smaller volume which could serve as a building block for the structure.

An octahedron of fluorite, CaF$_2$. (Courtesy of Optovac.)

Cleaving a crystal of rocksalt, NaCl. (Courtesy of Optovac.)

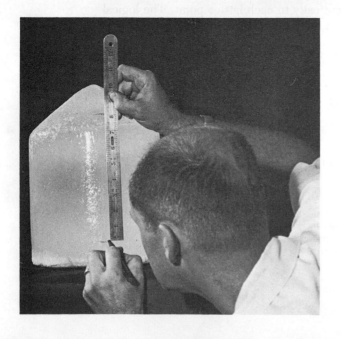

Large single crystal of sodium iodide, with thallium impurity added for use as a detector of gamma radiation. (Courtesy of Crystal Division, Isotopes, Inc.)

Cesium iodide single crystal boule being raised from Kyropoulos-Czolchralski type growing furnace. The 60-pound crystal is hanging from the small seed crystal. Support frame over furnace is automatically controlled so that the boule revolves continuously to assure even growth. The boule is slowly raised from melt at rate of about 1 inch per day to assure even vertical growth. Arrow points to boule. (Courtesy of Crystal Division, Isotopes, Inc.)

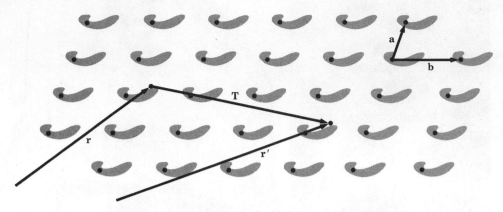

Figure 4 Portion of a crystal of an imaginary protein molecule, in a two-dimensional world. (We picked a protein molecule because it is likely to have no special symmetry of its own.) The atomic arrangement in the crystal looks exactly the same to an observer at $\mathbf{r}'$ as to an observer at $\mathbf{r}$, provided that the vector $\mathbf{T}$ which connects $\mathbf{r}'$ and $\mathbf{r}$ may be expressed as an integral multiple of the vectors $\mathbf{a}$ and $\mathbf{b}$. In this illustration $\mathbf{T} = -\mathbf{a} + 3\mathbf{b}$. The vectors $\mathbf{a}$ and $\mathbf{b}$ are primitive translation vectors of the two-dimensional lattice.

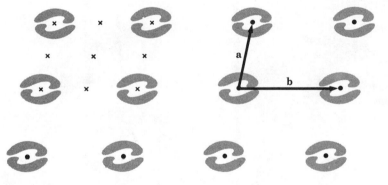

Figure 5 Similar to Fig. 4, but with protein molecules associated in pairs. The crystal translation vectors are $\mathbf{a}$ and $\mathbf{b}$. A rotation of π radians about any point marked × will carry the crystal into itself.

always satisfy (1) with a suitable choice of the integers n_1, n_2, n_3. For a given crystal structure the density of lattice points is greater for a primitive lattice than for a nonprimitive lattice. Correspondingly, the basis of the primitive lattice contains fewer atoms than the basis of a nonprimitive lattice.

We often use the primitive translation vectors to define the **crystal axes** **a, b, c** although nonprimitive crystal axes may be used when they are more convenient or simpler. The crystal axes **a, b, c** form three adjacent edges of a parallelepiped. If there are lattice points only at the corners of the parallelepiped, then it is a primitive parallelepiped.

A **lattice translation operation** or **crystal translation operation** is defined as the displacement of a crystal parallel to itself by a crystal translation vector

$$\mathbf{T} = n_1\mathbf{a} + n_2\mathbf{b} + n_3\mathbf{c}. \tag{2}$$

A vector **T** connects any two lattice points.

Symmetry Operations

In describing a crystal structure there are four important questions to answer: What is the lattice?[7] What crystal axes **a, b, c** do we wish to use to describe the lattice? What is the basis? What are the symmetry operations which carry the crystal structure into itself?

Among the symmetry operations there are the crystal translation operations specified by (2). There are rotation and reflection operations, called **point operations**. About various points in space (lattice points or special points within an elementary parallelepiped) it may be possible to apply rotation and reflection operations that "carry the crystal structure into itself"; these operations are in addition to the translation operations. There may be still other symmetry operations, called compound operations, made up of combined translations and point operations. The language of crystallography is largely devoted to the concise description of symmetry operations.

The crystal structure of Fig. 4 has been drawn in such a way that it has only translation symmetry operations, apart from the trivial point operation of rotation by 360°. The crystal structure of Fig. 5 has both translational and point symmetry operations. The primitive translation vectors are **a** and **b**. If we rotate the crystal by π radians (180°) about any point marked x, the crystal structure is carried into itself. This occurs also for equivalent points in other cells, but we have marked the points x only within one cell.

---

[7] More than one lattice is always possible for a given structure and more than one set of crystal axes is always possible for a given lattice. We cannot pick the basis until we have selected the lattice and the axes we wish to use. Everything (such as the x-ray diffraction pattern) works out the same in the end as long as the basis is chosen properly for whatever crystal axes we use.

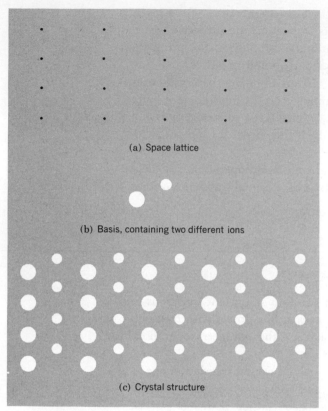

(a) Space lattice

(b) Basis, containing two different ions

(c) Crystal structure

Figure 6 The crystal structure is formed by the addition of the basis (b) to every lattice point of the lattice (a). By looking at (c), you can recognize the basis and then you can abstract the space lattice. It does not matter where the basis is put in relation to a lattice point.

Figure 7a Lattice points of a space lattice in two dimensions. All pairs of vectors **a**, **b** are translation vectors of the lattice. But a_4, b_4, are not *primitive* translation vectors because we cannot form the lattice translation **T** from integral combinations of a_4 and b_4. All other pairs shown of **a** and **b** may be taken as the primitive translation vectors of the lattice. The parallelograms 1, 2, 3 are equal in area and any of them could be taken as the primitive cell. The parallelogram 4 has twice the area of a primitive cell.

Figure 7b Primitive cell of a space lattice in three dimensions.

Figure 7c What are the primitive axes of this "lattice"? The question is meaningless because this is not a lattice in the sense of our definition: the points shown cannot all be reached by vectors of the form $n_1\mathbf{a} + n_2\mathbf{b}$ for all values of the integers n_1, n_2. But suppose these points were identical atoms: sketch in on the figure a set of lattice points, a choice of primitive axes, a primitive cell, and the basis of atoms associated with a lattice point.

Figure 7d Three linear crystal structures. Lattice points are denoted by x: For structure I we have arbitrarily taken the lattice points to be halfway between two atoms; we might have taken them at any other position, while preserving the length and direction of **a**. In all three structures the lattice points are connected by the translation vector **a**, where **a** is a primitive translation vector for each of the three lattices. The primitive (smallest) basis of structure I consists of one atom at $\frac{1}{2}\mathbf{a}$. The primitive basis of structure II consists of two identical atoms, one at $u_1\mathbf{a}$ and the other at $u_2\mathbf{a}$. The primitive basis of structure III consists of two different atoms, one at $u_1\mathbf{a}$ and the other at $u_2\mathbf{a}$. If we wish to describe structure I in terms of the nonprimitive lattice translation vector $\mathbf{a}'\ (=2\mathbf{a})$, then the basis associated with $\mathbf{a}'$ consists of two identical atoms, one at $\frac{1}{4}\mathbf{a}'$ and the other at $\frac{3}{4}\mathbf{a}'$. If we had taken the origin of $\mathbf{a}'$ at one of the atoms, the basis would consist of one atom at 0 and a second atom of $\frac{1}{2}\mathbf{a}'$. The lattice associated with $\mathbf{a}'$ has half the number of lattice points as the lattice associated with **a**.

The Basis and the Crystal Structure

We attach to every lattice point a basis of atoms; every basis is identical in composition, arrangement, and orientation. The formation of a crystal structure by the addition of a basis to every point of a lattice is shown in Fig. 6. In the structures of Figs. 4 and 5 the lattice was indicated by dots; in Fig. 6c the dots are omitted. The description of a crystal structure as a lattice plus a basis is very well suited for analysis of the structure by x-ray or neutron diffraction, as we shall see in Chapter 2.

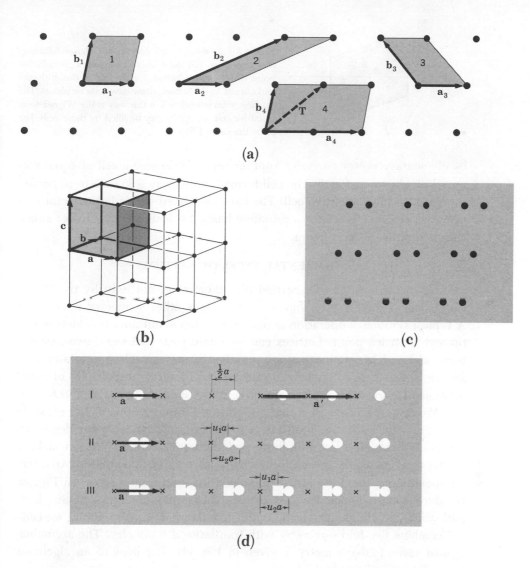

(a)

(b)   (c)

(d)

Primitive Lattice Cell

The parallelepiped (Fig. 7b) defined by primitive axes **a, b, c** is called a **primitive cell**. A primitive cell is a type of **unit cell**. A unit cell will fill all space under the action of suitable crystal translation operations; a primitive cell is a minimum-volume unit cell.[8] There is a density of one lattice point per primitive cell.[9] There are lattice points at the eight corners of the parallelepiped, but each corner point is shared among the eight cells which touch there. The volume V_c of a primitive cell defined by primitive axes **a, b, c** is

$$V_c = |\mathbf{a} \times \mathbf{b} \cdot \mathbf{c}|, \tag{3}$$

---

[8] There are many ways of choosing the primitive axes and primitive cell for a given lattice; sketch on Fig. 6a the axes for two or three different primitive parallelograms.

[9] The number of atoms in a primitive cell is given by the number of atoms in the basis.

11

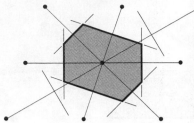

Figure 8 A primitive cell may also be chosen following this procedure: (1) draw lines to connect a given lattice point to all nearby lattice points; (2) at the midpoint and normal to these lines, draw new lines or planes. The smallest volume enclosed in this way is the Wigner-Seitz primitive cell. All space may be filled by these cells, just as by the cells of Fig. 7.

by elementary vector analysis. Another way of choosing a cell of equal volume V_c is shown in Fig. 8. The cell formed in this way is known to physicists as a **Wigner-Seitz primitive cell.** The basis associated with a lattice point of a primitive cell may be called a primitive basis. No basis contains fewer atoms than a primitive basis contains.

FUNDAMENTAL TYPES OF LATTICES[10]

Crystal lattices can be carried into themselves not only by the lattice translations **T** of Eq. (2), but also by various other symmetry operations. A typical symmetry operation is that of rotation about an axis which passes through a lattice point. Lattices can be found such that one-, two-, three-, four-, and six-fold rotation axes are permissible, corresponding to rotations by 2π, $2\pi/2$, $2\pi/3$, $2\pi/4$, and $2\pi/6$ radians and by integral multiples of these rotations. The **rotation axes** are denoted by the symbols 1, 2, 3, 4, and 6.

We cannot find a lattice that goes into itself under other rotations, such as by $2\pi/7$ radians or $2\pi/5$ radians. A single molecule can have any degree of rotational symmetry, but an infinite periodic lattice cannot. We can make a crystal from molecules which individually have a five-fold rotation axis, but we should not expect the lattice to have a five-fold rotation axis. In Fig. 9a we show what happens if we try to construct a periodic lattice having five-fold symmetry: the pentagons do not fit together neatly. We see that we cannot combine five-fold symmetry with translational symmetry. The argument against seven-fold symmetry is given in Fig. 9b. The lines of an algebraic argument are indicated in Fig. 10.

A **lattice point group** is defined as the collection of the symmetry operations which, when applied *about a lattice point,* leave the lattice invariant. The possible rotations have been given earlier. We can also have **mirror reflections** m about a plane through a lattice point. The **inversion operation** is made up of a rotation of π followed by reflection in a plane normal to the rotation axis; the total effect is to replace **r** by $-$**r**.

[10] The original 1848 study by A. Bravais is reprinted in his *Etudes crystallographiques,* Gautier-Villars, Paris, 1866; a German translation appears in Ostwald's *Klassiker der exakten Wissenschaften* **90**, (1897). For a full discussion of crystal symmetry, see F. Seitz, Z. Krist. **88**, 433 (1934); **90**, 289 (1935); **91**, 336 (1935); **94**, 100 (1936); and Vol. 1 of *International tables for x-ray crystallography,* Kynoch Press, Birmingham, 1952. A particularly readable discussion of space groups is given by F. C. Phillips, *An introduction to crystallography,* Wiley, 1963, 3rd ed.

Figure 9a A five-fold axis of symmetry cannot exist in a lattice because it is not possible to fill all space with a connected array of pentagons.

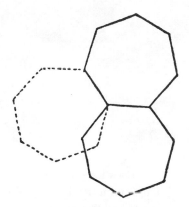

Figure 9b Kepler's demonstration (*Harmonice mundi,* 1619) that a seven-fold axis of symmetry cannot exist in a lattice. (*Gesammelte Werke,* Vol. 6, Beck, Munich, 1940.)

Figure 10 The crystal lattice is rotated by an angle φ about a lattice point. The vector **a** is carried into **a'** by the rotation. For special values of φ the rotated lattice coincides with the original lattice. For a square lattice these special values are $\varphi = \frac{1}{2}\pi$ and multiples thereof, so that the point group of the square lattice includes a four-fold rotation. Wherever the rotated lattice coincides with the original lattice, the vector $\mathbf{a}' - \mathbf{a}$ will be a lattice vector. Such a lattice vector will never be shorter than **a**, because there is no lattice vector shorter than **a**, except zero. Similar requirements determine the special values of φ for all possible lattices.

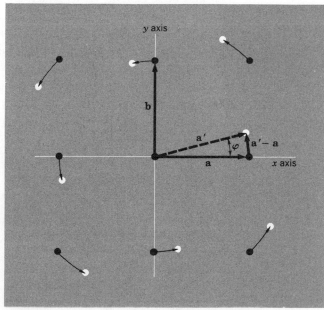

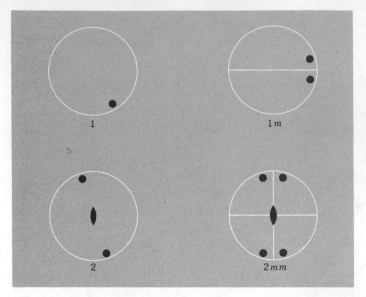

Figure 11 Diagrams illustrating four point groups. The dots denote equivalent points. The point group 1 has no symmetry elements, so here a point has no other point equivalent to it. For 1*m* there is a mirror plane: one dot on reflection across the mirror plane becomes the second dot. With a two-fold axis 2, a rotation of π takes one dot into the other. With a two-fold axis and one mirror plane there is automatically a second mirror plane normal to the first, and we have 2*mm* with four equivalent points.

Locations of equivalent points are shown for four point groups in Fig. 11. The symmetry operations of the group carry one point into all the equivalent positions. The points themselves must not be thought of as possessing symmetry elements; they may be scalene triangles or molecules with no symmetry elements. The symmetry axes and planes of a cube are shown in Fig. 12.

Two-Dimensional Lattice Types

There is an unlimited number of possible lattices because there is no natural restriction on the lengths a, b of the lattice translation vectors or on the angle φ between them. The lattice in Fig. 7a was drawn for arbitrary **a** and **b**. A general lattice such as this is known as an **oblique lattice**. The lattice is invariant under rotations of π and 2π about any lattice point.

But lattices of the oblique type are not necessarily invariant under rotations of $2\pi/3$, $2\pi/4$, or $2\pi/6$, or under mirror reflection. We must impose restrictive conditions on **a** and **b** if we want to construct a lattice which will be invariant under one or more of these new operations. Such restrictions are found below: there are four distinct types of restriction, and each leads to what we may call a **special lattice type**.

Thus there are five distinct lattice types in two dimensions, the oblique lattice and the four special lattices. **Bravais lattice** is the common phrase[11] for a distinct lattice type; we say that there are five Bravais lattices in two dimensions.

The point operation 4 requires a square lattice (Fig. 13a). The point operations 3 and 6 require a hexagonal lattice (Fig. 13b). This lattice is invariant under a rotation $2\pi/6$ about an axis through a lattice point and normal to the plane.

[11] We have not succeeded in finding or constructing a definition which starts out "A Bravais lattice is . . ."; the sources we have looked at say "That was a Bravais lattice." The phrase "fundamental type of lattice" is more suggestive.

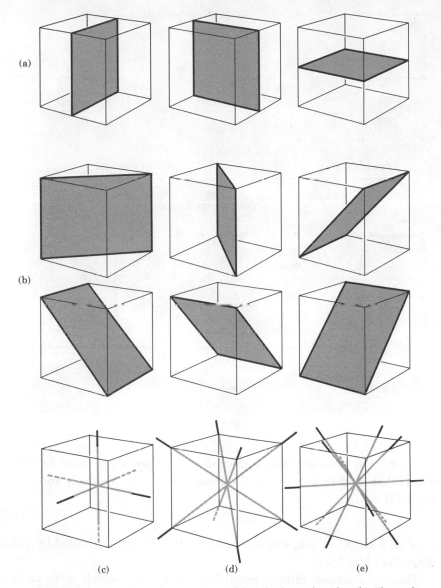

Figure 12 (a) The three planes of symmetry parallel to the faces of a cube. (b) The six diagonal planes of symmetry in a cube. (c) The three tetrad axes of a cube. (d) The four triad axes of a cube. (e) The six diad axes of a cube. The inversion center is not shown.

The mirror reflection m has important consequences. We write the primitive translation vectors $\mathbf{a}, \mathbf{b}$ in terms of the unit vectors $\hat{\mathbf{x}}, \hat{\mathbf{y}}$ along the x, y axes:

$$\mathbf{a} = a_x\hat{\mathbf{x}} + a_y\hat{\mathbf{y}}; \qquad \mathbf{b} = b_x\hat{\mathbf{x}} + b_y\hat{\mathbf{y}}. \tag{4}$$

If the primitive vectors are mirrored in the x axis, then $\mathbf{a}, \mathbf{b}$ are transformed by the reflection operation into new vectors $\mathbf{a}', \mathbf{b}'$ given by

$$\mathbf{a}' = a_x\hat{\mathbf{x}} - a_y\hat{\mathbf{y}}; \qquad \mathbf{b}' = b_x\hat{\mathbf{x}} - b_y\hat{\mathbf{y}}. \tag{5}$$

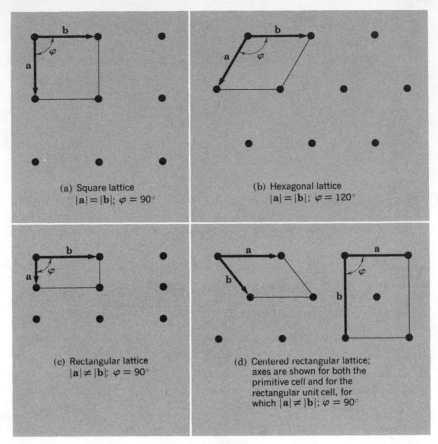

(a) Square lattice
$|\mathbf{a}| = |\mathbf{b}|$; $\varphi = 90°$

(b) Hexagonal lattice
$|\mathbf{a}| = |\mathbf{b}|$; $\varphi = 120°$

(c) Rectangular lattice
$|\mathbf{a}| \neq |\mathbf{b}|$; $\varphi = 90°$

(d) Centered rectangular lattice; axes are shown for both the primitive cell and for the rectangular unit cell, for which $|\mathbf{a}| \neq |\mathbf{b}|$; $\varphi = 90°$

Figure 13

If the lattice is invariant under the reflection, then $\mathbf{a}'$, $\mathbf{b}'$ must be lattice vectors; that is, they must be of the form $n_1\mathbf{a} + n_2\mathbf{b}$, where n_1 and n_2 are integers. If we take

$$\mathbf{a} = a\hat{\mathbf{x}}; \qquad \mathbf{b} = b\hat{\mathbf{y}}; \qquad (6)$$

then $\mathbf{a}' = \mathbf{a}$ and $\mathbf{b}' = -\mathbf{b}$, which is satisfactory. The lattice defined by (6) is rectangular (Fig. 13c).

There is a second distinct possibility for $\mathbf{a}$ and $\mathbf{b}$ which gives another type of lattice invariant under reflection. Note that $\mathbf{b}'$ will be a lattice vector if

$$\mathbf{b}' = \mathbf{a} - \mathbf{b}; \qquad (7)$$

then using (5) we have

$$b_x' = a_x - b_x = b_x; \qquad b_y' = a_y - b_y = -b_y. \qquad (8)$$

These equations have a solution if $a_y = 0$; $a_x = 2b_x$; thus a possible choice of primitive translation vectors for a lattice with mirror symmetry is

$$\mathbf{a} = a\hat{\mathbf{x}}; \qquad \mathbf{b} = \tfrac{1}{2}a\hat{\mathbf{x}} + b_y\hat{\mathbf{y}}. \qquad (9)$$

This choice gives a centered rectangular lattice (Fig. 13d).

Table 1   The five two-dimensional lattice types

(The notation *mm* means that two mirror lines are present)

Lattice	Conventional unit cell	Axes of conventional unit cell		Point-group symmetry of lattice about lattice points
Oblique	Parallelogram	$a \neq b$,	$\varphi \neq 90°$	2
Square	Square	$a = b$,	$\varphi = 90°$	*4mm*
Hexagonal	60° rhombus	$a = b$,	$\varphi = 120°$	*6mm*
Primitive rectangular	Rectangle	$a \neq b$,	$\varphi = 90°$	*2mm*
Centered rectangular	Rectangle	$a \neq b$,	$\varphi = 90°$	*2mm*

Table 2   The fourteen lattice types in three dimensions

System	Number of lattices in system	Lattice symbols	Restrictions on conventional unit-cell axes and angles
Triclinic	1	*P*	$a \neq b \neq c$ $\alpha \neq \beta \neq \gamma$
Monoclinic	2	*P, C*	$a \neq b \neq c$ $\alpha = \gamma = 90° \neq \beta$
Orthorhombic	4	*P, C, I, F*	$a \neq b \neq c$ $\alpha = \beta = \gamma = 90°$
Tetragonal	2	*P, I*	$a = b \neq c$ $\alpha = \beta = \gamma = 90°$
Cubic	3	*P* or sc *I* or bcc *F* or fcc	$a = b = c$ $\alpha = \beta = \gamma = 90°$
Trigonal	1	*R*	$a = b = c$ $\alpha = \beta = \gamma < 120°, \neq 90°$
Hexagonal	1	*P*	$a = b \neq c$ $\alpha = \beta = 90°$ $\gamma = 120°$

We have now exhausted the two-dimensional Bravais lattices which are consistent with the point-group operations applied to lattice points. The five possibilities in two dimensions are summarized in Table 1. The point symmetry given is that of the *lattice;* an actual crystal structure may have lower symmetry than its lattice. Thus it is possible for a crystal with a square lattice to have the operation 4 without having all of the operations 4 *mm*.

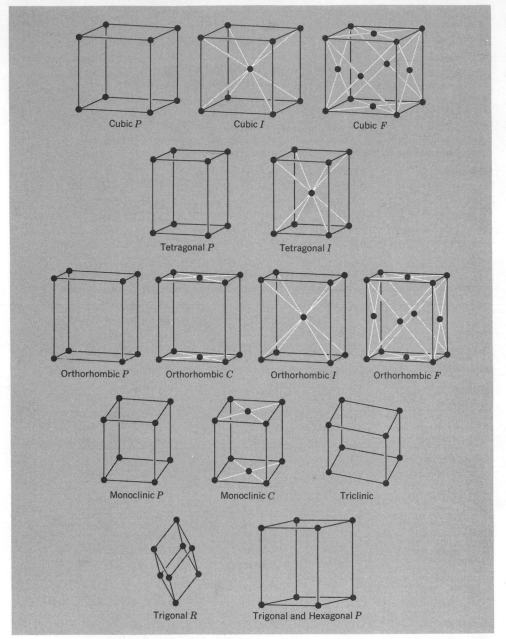

Figure 14 The fourteen Bravais or space lattices. The cells shown are the conventional unit cells, which are not always the primitive cells.

Three-Dimensional Lattice Types

In two dimensions the point groups are associated with five different types of lattices. In three dimensions the point symmetry groups require the fourteen different (one general and thirteen special) lattice types shown in Fig. 14 and listed in Table 2. The general lattice type is the triclinic lattice.

The fourteen lattice types are conveniently grouped into seven **systems** according to the seven types of conventional unit cells: triclinic, monoclinic,

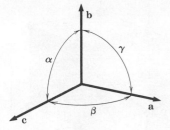

Figure 15 Crystal axes **a**, **b**, **c**. The angle α is included between **b** and **c**.

orthorhombic, tetragonal, cubic, trigonal, and hexagonal. The division into systems is summarized conveniently in terms of the special axial relations for the conventional unit cells. The axes **a**, **b**, **c** and angles α, β, γ are defined in Fig. 15.

The unit cells shown in Fig. 14 are the conventional unit cells, and they are not always primitive cells. Sometimes a nonprimitive cell has a more obvious connection with the point symmetry elements than has a primitive cell. We now discuss the various lattices by their classification in systems.

1. In the **triclinic** system the single lattice type has a primitive (P) unit cell, with three axes of unequal lengths and unequal angles.

2. In the **monoclinic** system there are two lattice types, one with a primitive unit cell and the other with a nonprimitive conventional cell which may be base-centered (C) with lattice points at the centers of the cell faces normal to the c axis.

3. In the **orthorhombic** system there are four lattice types: one lattice has a primitive cell; one lattice is base-centered; one is body-centered (I = German *Innenzentrierte*); and one is face-centered (F).

4. In the **tetragonal** system the simplest unit is a right square prism; this is a primitive cell and is associated with a tetragonal space lattice. A second tetragonal lattice type is body-centered.

5. In the **cubic** system there are three lattices: the simple cubic (sc) lattice which is primitive; the body-centered cubic (bcc) lattice, and the face-centered cubic (fcc) lattice. The characteristics of the three cubic lattices are summarized in Table 3.

Table 3   Characteristics of cubic lattices

	Simple	Body-centered	Face-centered
Volume, conventional unit cell	a^3	a^3	a^3
Lattice points per cell	1	2	4
Volume, primitive cell	a^3	$\frac{1}{2}a^3$	$\frac{1}{4}a^3$
Lattice points per unit volume	$1/a^3$	$2/a^3$	$4/a^3$
Number of nearest neighbors°	6	8	12
Nearest-neighbor distance	a	$3^{1/2}a/2$	$a/2^{1/2}$
Number of second neighbors	12	6	6
Second neighbor distance	$2^{1/2}a$	a	a

°"Neighbors" refers to the nearest lattice points to any given lattice point.

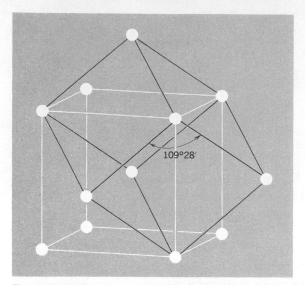

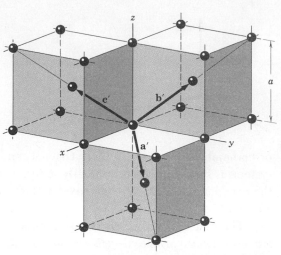

Figure 16 Body-centered cubic lattice, showing a primitive unit cell. The primitive cell shown is a rhombohedron of edge $\frac{1}{2}\sqrt{3}\,a$, and the angle between adjacent edges is 109°28′.

Figure 17 Primitive translation vectors of the body-centered cubic lattice; these vectors connect the lattice point at the origin to lattice points at the body centers. The primitive cell is obtained on completing the rhombohedron. In terms of the cube edge a the primitive translation vectors are

$$\mathbf{a}' = \frac{a}{2}(\hat{\mathbf{x}} + \hat{\mathbf{y}} - \hat{\mathbf{z}}); \quad \mathbf{b}' = \frac{a}{2}(-\hat{\mathbf{x}} + \hat{\mathbf{y}} + \hat{\mathbf{z}});$$

$$\mathbf{c}' = \frac{a}{2}(\hat{\mathbf{x}} - \hat{\mathbf{y}} + \hat{\mathbf{z}}).$$

These primitive axes make angles of 109°28′ with each other.

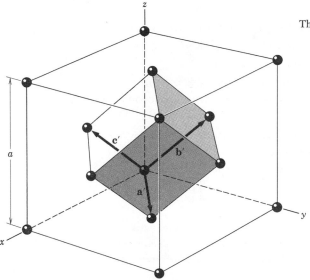

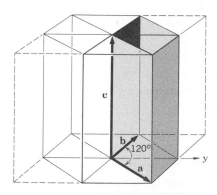

Figure 18 The rhombohedral primitive cell of the face-centered cubic crystal. The primitive translation vectors $\mathbf{a}'$, $\mathbf{b}'$, $\mathbf{c}'$ connect the lattice point at the origin with lattice points at the face centers. As drawn, the primitive vectors are:

$$\mathbf{a}' = \frac{a}{2}(\hat{\mathbf{x}} + \hat{\mathbf{y}}); \quad \mathbf{b}' = \frac{a}{2}(\hat{\mathbf{y}} + \hat{\mathbf{z}}); \quad \mathbf{c}' = \frac{a}{2}(\hat{\mathbf{z}} + \hat{\mathbf{x}}).$$

The angles between the axes are 60°.

Figure 19 Relation of the primitive cell in the hexagonal system (heavy lines) to a prism of hexagonal symmetry. Here $a = b \neq c$.

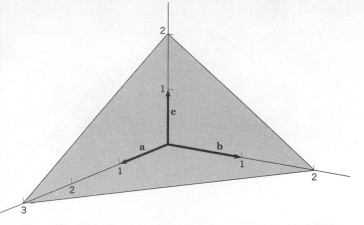

Figure 20 This plane intercepts the **a, b, c** axes at 3a, 2b, 2c. The reciprocals of these numbers are $\frac{1}{3}$, $\frac{1}{2}$, $\frac{1}{2}$. The smallest three integers having the same ratio are 2, 3, 3, and thus the Miller indices of the plane are (233).

A primitive unit cell of the body-centered cubic lattice is shown in Fig. 16; the primitive translation vectors are shown in Fig. 17. The primitive translation vectors of the face-centered cubic lattice are shown in Fig. 18. The primitive cells contain only one lattice point, but the conventional cubic unit cells contain two lattice points (bcc) or four lattice points (fcc).

6. In the **trigonal** system a rhombohedron is usually chosen as the unit cell. The lattice is primitive.

7. In the **hexagonal** system the conventional unit cell chosen is a right prism based on a rhombus with an angle of 60°. The lattice is primitive. The relation of the rhombic cell with a hexagonal prism is shown in Fig. 19.

POSITION AND ORIENTATION OF PLANES IN CRYSTALS

The position and orientation of a crystal plane are determined by any three points in the plane, provided the points are not collinear. If each of the points lies on a crystal axis, the plane may be specified by giving the positions of the points along the axes in terms of the lattice constants. If, for example, the atoms determining the plane have coordinates (4, 0, 0), (0, 1, 0), (0, 0, 2) relative to the axis vectors from some origin, the plane may be specified by the three numbers 4, 1, 2.

But it is more useful for structure analysis to specify the orientation of a plane by **Miller indices**,[12] determined as in Fig. 20:

1. Find the intercepts on the axes **a, b, c** in terms of the lattice constants. The axes may be primitive or nonprimitive.

2. Take the reciprocals of these numbers and then reduce to three integers having the same ratio, usually the smallest three integers. The result is enclosed in parentheses: (hkl).

[12] At first sight the usefulness of the Miller indices seems improbable, but Chapter 2 makes clear their convenience and elegance.

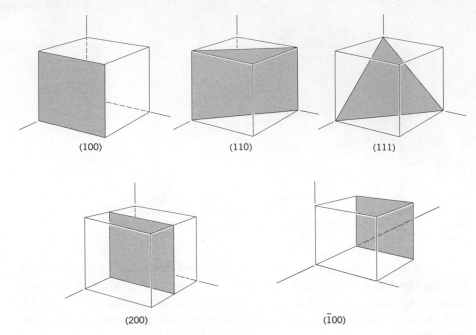

Figure 21 Miller indices of some important planes in a cubic crystal. The plane (200) is parallel to (100), but it divides the unit cube in two equal parts.

For the plane whose intercepts are 4, 1, 2 the reciprocals are $\frac{1}{4}$, 1, and $\frac{1}{2}$ and the Miller indices are (142). If an intercept is at infinity, the corresponding index is zero. The Miller indices of some important planes in a cubic crystal are illustrated by Fig. 21.

The indices (*hkl*) may denote a single plane or a set of parallel planes.[13] If a plane cuts an axis on the negative side of the origin, the corresponding index is negative and is indicated by placing a minus sign above the index: ($h\bar{k}l$). The cube faces of a cubic crystal are (100), (010), (001), ($\bar{1}$00), ($0\bar{1}0$), and ($00\bar{1}$). Planes equivalent by symmetry may be denoted by curly brackets (braces) around Miller indices; the set of cube faces is {100}. We often speak simply of the 100 faces. If we speak of the (200) plane we mean a plane parallel to (100) but cutting the **a** axis at $\frac{1}{2}$**a**.

The indices of a direction in a crystal are expressed as the set of the smallest integers which have the same ratios as the components of a vector in the desired direction referred to the axis vectors. The integers are written between square brackets [*hkl*]. In a cubic crystal the *x* axis is the [100] direction; the $-y$ axis is the [$0\bar{1}0$] direction. Often we speak of the [*hkl*] and equivalent directions, or simply of the [*hkl*] directions. In cubic crystals the direction [*hkl*] is always perpendicular to a plane (*hkl*) having the same indices (Problem 3), but this is not generally true in other crystal systems.

[13] Other symbols are frequently used by crystallographers: they may use *u*, *v*, *w* in place of our *h*, *k*, *l*, and *x*, *y*, *z* in place of our *u*, *v*, *w*.

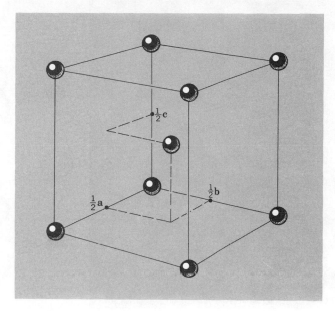

Figure 22 The coordinates of the central point of a cell are $\frac{1}{2}\frac{1}{2}\frac{1}{2}$, in terms of the length of the axes.

POSITION IN THE UNIT CELL

The positions of points in a unit cell are specified in terms of **atomic coordinates** u, v, w in which each coordinate is a fraction of the axial length, a, b, or c, in the direction of the coordinate, with the origin taken at a corner of a unit cell. Thus (Fig. 22) the coordinates of the central point of a cell are $\frac{1}{2}\frac{1}{2}\frac{1}{2}$, and the face-centered positions include $\frac{1}{2}\frac{1}{2}0$; $0\frac{1}{2}\frac{1}{2}$; $\frac{1}{2}0\frac{1}{2}$. The coordinates of fcc and bcc lattices are usually given in terms of the conventional cubic cell.

SIMPLE CRYSTAL STRUCTURES

We discuss briefly a small number of simple crystal structures of general interest, including the sodium chloride, cesium chloride, hexagonal close-packed, diamond, and cubic zinc sulfide structures.

Sodium Chloride Structure

The sodium chloride, NaCl, structure is shown in Figs. 23 and 24. The Bravais lattice is face-centered cubic; the basis consists of one Na atom and one Cl atom separated by one-half the body diagonal of a unit cube. There are four units of NaCl in each unit cube, with atoms in the positions

$$\text{Na:} \qquad 0\,0\,0; \quad \tfrac{1}{2}\tfrac{1}{2}0; \quad \tfrac{1}{2}0\tfrac{1}{2}; \quad 0\tfrac{1}{2}\tfrac{1}{2}.$$
$$\text{Cl:} \qquad \tfrac{1}{2}\tfrac{1}{2}\tfrac{1}{2}; \quad 0\,0\tfrac{1}{2}; \quad 0\tfrac{1}{2}0; \quad \tfrac{1}{2}0\,0.$$

Each atom has as nearest neighbors six atoms of the opposite kind.

Figure 23 Model of sodium chloride. The sodium ions are smaller than the chlorine ions. (Courtesy of A. N. Holden and P. Singer, from *Crystals and crystal growing.*)

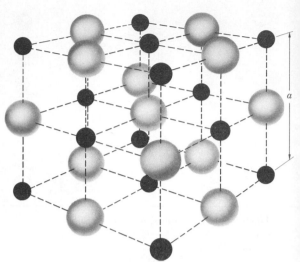

Figure 24 The sodium chloride crystal structure. The space lattice is fcc, and the basis has one Na$^+$ ion at 0 0 0 and one Cl$^-$ ion at $\frac{1}{2}$ $\frac{1}{2}$ $\frac{1}{2}$.

Figure 25 Natural crystals of lead sulfide, PbS, which has the NaCl crystal structure. (Photograph by Betsy Burleson.)

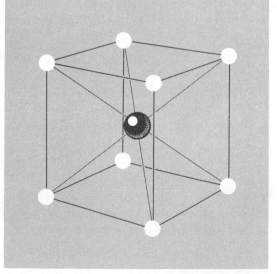

Figure 26 The cesium chloride crystal structure. The space lattice is simple cubic, and the basis has one Cs$^+$ ion at 0 0 0 and one Cl$^-$ ion at $\frac{1}{2}$ $\frac{1}{2}$ $\frac{1}{2}$.

Representative crystals having the NaCl arrangement include those in the following table:

Crystal	a	Crystal	a
LiH	4.08 Å	AgBr	5.77 Å
NaCl	5.63	MgO	4.20
KCl	6.29	MnO	4.43
PbS	5.92	UO	4.92

Figure 25 is a photograph of crystals of galena (PbS) from Joplin, Missouri. The Joplin specimens form in beautiful cubes.

Cesium Chloride Structure

The cesium chloride, CsCl, structure is shown in Fig. 26. There is one molecule per unit cell, with atoms in the body-centered positions:

$$\text{Cs:} \quad 0\,0\,0 \quad \text{and} \quad \text{Cl:} \quad \tfrac{1}{2}\tfrac{1}{2}\tfrac{1}{2}.$$

The space lattice is simple cubic.[14] Each atom is at the center of a cube of atoms of the opposite kind, so that the coordination number is eight. Representative crystals having the CsCl arrangement include those in the following table:

Crystal	a	Crystal	a
CsCl	4.11 Å	CuZn (β-brass)	2.94 Å
TlBr	3.97	AgMg	3.28
TlI	4.20	LiHg	3.29
NH$_4$Cl	3.87	AlNi	2.88
RbCl (190°C)	3.74	BeCu	2.70

Hexagonal Close-packed Structure (hcp)

There are two ways (Fig. 27a) of arranging equivalent spheres in a regular array to minimize the interstitial volume. One way leads to a structure with cubic symmetry and is the face-centered cubic (cubic close-packed) structure; the other has hexagonal symmetry and is called the hexagonal close-packed structure (Fig. 27b). The fraction of the total volume filled is 0.74 for both the fcc and hcp structures.

Spheres may be arranged in a single closest-packed layer by placing each sphere in contact with six others. Such a layer can be either the basal plane of a hcp structure or the (111) plane of the fcc structure. A second similar layer is packed on top of this by placing each sphere in contact with three spheres of the bottom layer, as in Fig. 27a. Next a third layer can be added in two ways: in the fcc structure the spheres in the third layer are placed over the holes in the first layer not occupied by the second layer; in the hexagonal

[14] Crystal structures with simple cubic Bravais lattices are not rare, but no common *element* crystallizes in a sc structure, which is favored neither by density of packing nor by directed bonds.

26

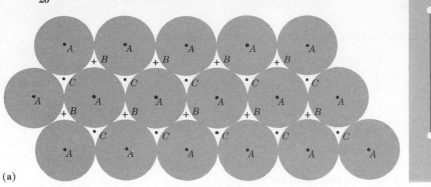

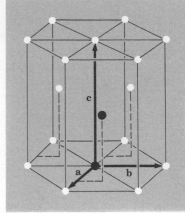

(a)

(b)

Figure 27a A close-packed layer of spheres is shown, with centers at points marked A. A second and identical layer of spheres can be placed over this, with centers over the points marked B (or, equivalently, over the points marked C). If the second layer goes in over B, there are two nonequivalent choices for a third layer. It can go in over A or over C. If it goes in over A the sequence is $ABABAB$ . . . and the structure is hexagonal close-packed. If the third layer goes in over C the sequence is $ABCABCABC$ . . . and the structure is face-centered cubic; the plane is a [111] plane.

Figure 27b The hexagonal close-packed structure. The atom positions in this structure do not constitute a space lattice. The space lattice is *simple hexagonal* with two identical atoms associated with each lattice point. The two atoms of one basis are shown as solid in the figure. One atom of the basis is at the origin, 0 0 0; the other atom is at $\frac{2}{3} \frac{1}{3} \frac{1}{2}$, which means at $\mathbf{r} = \frac{2}{3}\mathbf{a} + \frac{1}{3}\mathbf{b} + \frac{1}{2}\mathbf{c}$.

structure the spheres in the third layer are placed directly over the spheres in the first layer. We say that the packing in the fcc structure is $ABCABC$ . . . , whereas in the hcp structure the packing is $ABABAB$. . . . The unit cell of the hcp structure is the hexagonal primitive cell; the basis contains two atoms, as shown in Fig. 27b. The fcc primitive cell in Fig. 18 contains one atom.

The c/a ratio for hexagonal closest-packing of spheres is $(\frac{8}{3})^{1/2} = 1.633$. By convention we refer to crystals as hcp even if the actual c/a ratio departs somewhat from the theoretical value. Thus zinc with $c/a = 1.85$ ($a = 2.66$ Å; $c = 4.94$ Å) is referred to commonly as hcp, although the interatomic bond angles are quite different from the ideal hcp structure. Magnesium with $c/a = 1.62$ is close to ideal hcp. Many metals transform easily at appropriate temperatures between fcc and hcp structures. We note that the **coordination number,** defined as the number of nearest-neighbor atoms, is the same for the two structures. If the binding energy depended only on the number of nearest-neighbor bonds, then there would be no difference in energy between the fcc and hcp structures.

Diamond Structure

The space lattice of diamond is face-centered cubic. A primitive basis of two identical atoms at 0 0 0; $\frac{1}{4} \frac{1}{4} \frac{1}{4}$ is associated with each lattice point,[15] as

[15] The conventional unit cube contains eight atoms; if we describe the structure in terms of the lattice points at the corners of the unit cube, then the basis will contain eight atoms. There is no way of choosing a primitive cell such that the basis of diamond contains only one atom.

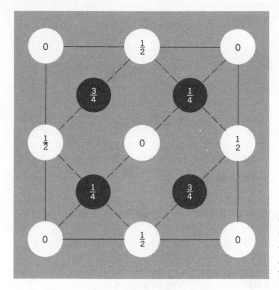

Figure 28 Atomic positions in the unit cell of the diamond structure projected on a cube face; fractions denote height above base in units of a cube edge. The points at 0 and $\frac{1}{2}$ are on the fcc lattice; those at $\frac{1}{4}$ and $\frac{3}{4}$ are on a similar lattice displaced among the body diagonal by one-fourth of its length. With a fcc space lattice, the basis consists of two identical atoms at 0 0 0; $\frac{1}{4}\frac{1}{4}\frac{1}{4}$.

shown in Fig. 28. The tetrahedral bonding of the diamond structure is represented in Fig. 29. Each atom has four nearest neighbors and twelve next nearest neighbors. There are eight atoms in a unit cube. The diamond lattice is relatively empty; the maximum proportion of the available volume which may be filled by hard spheres is only 0.34, or about 46 percent of the filling factor for a closest-packed structure. Carbon, silicon, germanium, and gray tin crystallize in the diamond structure, with lattice constants 3.56, 5.43, 5.65, and 6.46 Å, respectively. The diamond structure is the result of covalent bonding, as discussed in Chapter 3.

Cubic Zinc Sulfide Structure

We have seen that the diamond structure is composed of two fcc lattices displaced from each other by one-quarter of a body diagonal. The cubic zinc sulfide or zinc blende structure results from the diamond structure when Zn atoms are placed on one fcc lattice and S atoms on the other fcc lattice, as in Fig. 30. The coordinates of the Zn atoms are 0 0 0; $0\frac{1}{2}\frac{1}{2}$; $\frac{1}{2}0\frac{1}{2}$; $\frac{1}{2}\frac{1}{2}0$; the coordinates of the S atoms are $\frac{1}{4}\frac{1}{4}\frac{1}{4}$; $\frac{1}{4}\frac{3}{4}\frac{3}{4}$; $\frac{3}{4}\frac{1}{4}\frac{3}{4}$; $\frac{3}{4}\frac{3}{4}\frac{1}{4}$. The space lattice is fcc. There are four molecules of ZnS per unit cell. About each atom there are four equally distant atoms of the opposite kind arranged at the corners of a regular tetrahedron.

The diamond structure possesses a center of inversion symmetry at the midpoint of each line connecting nearest-neighbor atoms; the ZnS structure does not have inversion symmetry.[16] This is particularly evident if we look at

[16] In the inversion operation we carry each point **r** into the point −**r**. Note that a tetrahedron does not have inversion symmetry about its center.

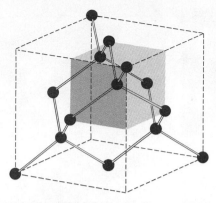

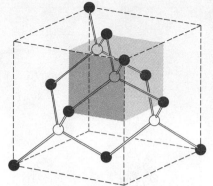

Figure 29 Crystal structure of diamond, showing the tetrahedral bond arrangement.

Figure 30 Crystal structure of cubic zinc sulfide.

the arrangement of atoms along a body diagonal. In diamond (Figs. 28 and 29) the order is CC··CC··CC, where the dots represent vacancies. In ZnS (Fig. 30) the order is ZnS··ZnS··ZnS; this order is not invariant under inversion about any point.

Examples of the cubic zinc sulfide structure are

Crystal	a	Crystal	a
CuF	4.26 Å	CdS	5.82 Å
CuCl	5.41	InAs	6.04
AgI	6.47	InSb	6.46
ZnS	5.41	SiC	4.35
ZnSe	5.65	AlP	5.42

Collections of Crystal Structure Data

The reader who wishes to look up the crystal structure of a substance may profitably consult the excellent compilation by Wyckoff listed in the references. *Strukturbericht, Structure Reports,* and the journal Acta Crystallographica are valuable aids.

In Table 4 we list for convenience the common crystal structures and lattice constants of a number of elements. Hume-Rothery[17] has given a useful series of tables of crystal structures of elements arranged according to the groups in the periodic table.

[17] W. Hume-Rothery, *Structure of metals and alloys*, Institute of Metals, London, 4th ed., 1962.

Table 4 Cell dimensions of selected elements, at room temperature

Element	Structure	Density at 20°C, gm/cm³	a, Å	c, Å	Atomic volume, cm³/mole	Nearest-neighbor distance, Å
Aluminum	fcc	2.70	4.04		9.99	2.86
Argon	fcc		5.43(20°K)		24.	3.83
Barium	bcc	3.5	5.01		39.	4.34
Beryllium	hcp	1.82	2.27	3.59	4.96	2.22
Cadmium	hcp	8.65	2.97	5.61	13.0	2.97
Calcium	fcc	1.55	5.56		25.9	3.93
Carbon	diamond	3.51	3.56		3.4	1.54
Cerium	fcc	6.9	5.14		20.	3.64
Cesium	bcc	1.9	6.05(92°K)		70.	5.24
Chromium	bcc	7.19	2.88		7.23	2.49
Cobalt	hcp	8.9	2.51	4.07	6.6	2.50
Copper	fcc	8.96	3.61		7.09	2.55
Gadolinium	hcp	7.95	3.62	5.75	19.7	3.55
Germanium	diamond	5.36	5.65		13.5	2.44
Gold	fcc	19.32	4.07		10.2	2.88
Helium (He⁴)	hcp		3.57(2°K)	5.83		3.57
Iron	bcc	7.87	2.86		7.1	2.48
Lanthanum	fcc	6.15	5.29		22.5	3.73
Lead	fcc	11.34	4.94		18.27	3.49
Lithium	bcc	0.53	3.50		13.	3.03
Magnesium	hcp	1.74	3.20	5.20	14.0	3.19
Molybdenum	bcc	10.2	3.14		9.41	2.72
Neon	fcc		4.52(20°K)		13.7	3.20
Nickel	fcc	8.90	3.52		6.59	2.49
Niobium	bcc	8.57	3.29		10.8	2.85
Palladium	fcc	12.0	3.88		8.89	2.74
Platinum	fcc	21.45	3.92		9.10	2.77
Potassium	bcc	0.86	5.33		45.	4.62
Rubidium	bcc	1.53	5.62(92°K)		55.9	4.87
Silicon	diamond	2.33	5.43		12.0	2.35
Silver	fcc	10.49	4.08		10.28	2.88
Sodium	bcc	0.97	4.28		24.0	3.71
Strontium	fcc	2.6	6.05		34.	4.30
Tantalum	bcc	16.6	3.30		10.9	2.85
Tin (gray)	diamond	5.75	6.46			
Titanium	hcp	4.54	2.95	4.73	10.6	2.91
Tungsten	bcc	19.3	3.16		9.53	2.73
Uranium	complex	18.7			12.7	2.76
Vanadium	bcc	6.0	3.03		8.5	2.63
Xenon	fcc		6.24(92°K)		36.4	4.41
Zinc	hcp	7.13	2.66	4.94	9.17	2.66
Zirconium	bcc	6.5	3.61(850°C)		14.	3.16

Problems

1. **Diamond structure.** (a) How many atoms are there in the primitive cell of diamond? (b) What is the length in angstroms of a primitive translation vector? (c) Show that the angle between the tetrahedral bonds of diamond is $109°28'$. (*Hint:* As in Fig. 16, this is the angle between the body diagonals of a cube.) (d) How many atoms are there in the conventional cubic unit cell?

2. **Five-fold axis.** A lattice cannot have five-fold rotational symmetry. Give an algebraic proof of this statement by considering a vector **a** taken to be the shortest nonvanishing translation of the lattice; show that the vector $\mathbf{a}'' + \mathbf{a}'$ is shorter than **a**, where $\mathbf{a}'$, $\mathbf{a}''$ are vectors obtained from **a** by rotations of $\pm 2\pi/5$.

3. **Perpendicular to plane.** Prove that in a cubic crystal a direction $[hkl]$ is perpendicular to a plane (hkl) having the same indices.

4. **Packing fraction.** Show that the maximum proportion of the available volume which may be filled by hard spheres arranged on various lattices is: simple cubic, 0.52; body-centered cubic, 0.68; face-centered cubic, 0.74.

5. **Hcp structure.** (a) Show that the c/a ratio for an ideal hexagonal close-packed structure is $(\tfrac{8}{3})^{1/2} = 1.633$. (b) Compare this with the experimental values of the ratios for three hcp crystals. (c) Show that no hcp space lattice exists (with a basis of *one* atom per lattice point). *Hint:* Show that no lattice vectors **a**, **b**, **c** can be found such that the set of translations **T** of Eq. (2) forms a hcp lattice. We can choose **a**, **b** to form a hexagonal net in a basal plane, but the problem is with **c**.

6. **Crystal structures.** Describe the crystal structures of hexagonal ZnO, NiAs, and α-quartz. Specify the lattice and the basis which you use.

7. **Sublattices.** Show that a bcc lattice may be decomposed into two sc lattices A, B with the property that none of the nearest-neighbor lattice points to a lattice point on A lie on A, and similarly for the B lattice. Show that to obtain the same property a sc lattice is decomposed into two fcc lattices, and a fcc lattice into four sc lattices. These considerations are of interest for antiferromagnetism (Chapter 15).

8. **Closest-packing of fibers.** Find the closest-packing arrangement of identical infinite straight fibers of circular cross-section. What is the packing fraction for this arrangement?

9. **Three-fold axes and cubic crystals.** Show that a crystal which has four three-fold point symmetry axes making tetrahedral angles (Problem 1) with each other must have a cubic lattice. (This is the minimum symmetry requirement for a cubic crystal.)

References

ELEMENTARY

A. Holden, *Nature of solids*, Columbia University Press, 1965.

A. Holden and P. Singer, *Crystals and crystal growing* (Anchor S7) Doubleday, 1960.

L. G. Berry and B. Mason, *Mineralogy*, Freeman, 1959.

B. Chalmers, J. G. Holland, K. A. Jackson, and R. B. Williamson, *Crystallography: A programmed course in three dimensions*, Books 1 through 6. Appleton, 1965.

CRYSTALLOGRAPHY

M. J. Buerger, *Elementary crystallography*, Wiley, 1963.

F. C. Phillips, *An introduction to crystallography*, Wiley, 3rd ed., 1963.

CRYSTAL GROWTH

W. D. Lawson and S. Nielsen, *Preparation of single crystals*, Butterworths, 1958.

A. Smakula, *Einkrystalle*, Springer, 1962.

J. J. Gilman, *The art and science of growing crystals*, Wiley, 1963.

CLASSICAL TABLES AND HANDBOOKS

P. H. Groth, *Chemische Krystallographie*, 5 volumes, W. Englemann, Leipzig, 1906.

International tables for x-ray crystallography, 3 volumes, Kynoch Press, Birmingham, 1952–1962.

C. Palache, H. Berman, and C. Frondel, *Dana's system of mineralogy*, Vols. I, II, and III, Wiley, 7th ed., 1944, 1951, 1962.

R. W. G. Wyckoff, *Crystal structures*, Interscience, 2nd ed., 1963.

2

Crystal Diffraction and the Reciprocal Lattice

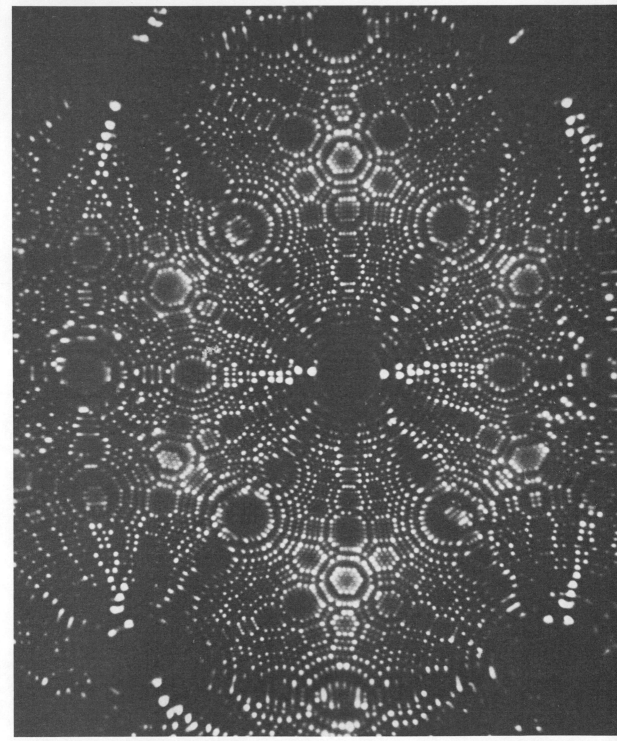

Figure A Field ion microscope image of a clear tungsten tip of radius approximately 450 Å. (Courtesy of E. W. Müller.)

In rare situations it is possible to form a direct microscope image of the structure of a crystal. A remarkable direct image[1] of the atoms on the surface of a tip of tungsten is shown in Fig. A. But in general to explore the structure of crystals we use the diffraction of waves which interact with atoms and which have a wavelength comparable with the interatomic spacing (10^{-8} cm) in crystals. Radiation of longer wavelength cannot resolve the details of structure on an atomic scale, and radiation of much shorter wavelength is diffracted through inconveniently small angles. Our object is to determine the size of the unit cell, the position of the nuclei within the cell, and the distribution of electrons within the cell. This is a very important chapter.

The Incident Beam

We study crystal structure through the diffraction of photons, neutrons, and, less often, electrons. The angle through which a wave is diffracted by a crystal depends chiefly on the crystal structure and on the wavelength of the radiation.

X-rays. The energy of an x-ray photon is related to its wavelength λ by $\epsilon = h\nu = hc/\lambda$, where $h = 6.62 \times 10^{-27}$ erg-sec is Planck's constant. In laboratory units,

$$\lambda(\text{Å}) = \frac{12.4}{\epsilon(\text{kev})}, \tag{1}$$

where λ is the wavelength in angstrom units (1 Å = 10^{-8} cm) and ϵ is the energy in kilo-electron-volts (1 ev = 1.60×10^{-12} erg). We see from Fig. 1 that for crystal studies we require photon energies in the 10 to 50 kev range. X-rays are generated both by the deceleration of electrons in metal targets and by the inelastic excitation of the core electrons in the atoms of the target. The first process gives a broad continuous spectrum; the second gives sharp lines. The radiation from a copper target bombarded by electrons shows a strong line (the $K\alpha_1$ line) at 1.541 Å; a molybdenum target has its $K\alpha_1$ line at 0.709 Å.

When an atom is exposed to electromagnetic radiation, the atomic electrons may scatter part or all of the radiation elastically, at the frequency of the incident radiation. At optical wavelengths such as 5000 Å the superposition of the waves scattered elastically by the individual atoms in a crystal results in ordinary optical refraction. But when the wavelength of the radia-

---

[1] A review of the method of field emission microscopy is given by R. H. Good and E. W. Müller, *Encyclo. of physics* **21**, 176–231 (1956); see also E. W. Müller, ASTM Special Tech. Publ. No. 340, pp. 80–98 (1962).

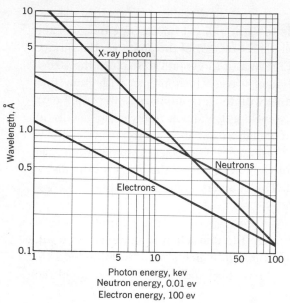

Figure 1 Wavelength versus particle energy, for photons, neutrons, and electrons.

tion is comparable with or smaller than the lattice constant, we may find one or more diffracted beams in directions quite different from the incident direction.

Neutrons. The energy of a neutron is related to its de Broglie wavelength λ by $\epsilon = h^2/2M_n\lambda^2$, where $M_n = 1.675 \times 10^{-24}$ gm is the mass of the neutron. (We recall that $\epsilon = p^2/2M_n$, and the wavelength λ is related to the momentum p by $\lambda = h/p$.) In laboratory units

$$\lambda(\text{Å}) \cong \frac{0.28}{[\epsilon(\text{ev})]^{1/2}}, \tag{2}$$

where ϵ is the neutron energy in ev. From Fig. 1 we see that $\lambda = 1$ Å for $\epsilon \approx 0.08$ ev.

Because of their magnetic moment, neutrons interact with the magnetic electrons of a solid, and neutron methods are exceedingly valuable in structural studies of magnetic crystals. In nonmagnetic materials the neutron interacts with the nuclei of the constituent atoms.

Electrons. The energy of an electron is related to its de Broglie wavelength λ by $\epsilon = h^2/2m\lambda^2$, where $m = 0.911 \times 10^{-27}$ gm is the mass of the electron. In laboratory units

$$\lambda(\text{Å}) \cong \frac{12}{[\epsilon(\text{ev})]^{1/2}}. \tag{3}$$

Electrons are charged and interact strongly with matter; they penetrate a relatively short distance into a crystal. Structural studies by electron diffraction are important for surfaces, films, very thin crystals, and gases (see Problem 7d).

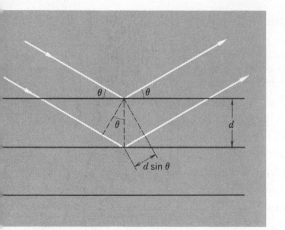

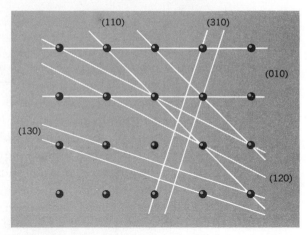

Figure 2   Derivation of the Bragg equation $2d \sin \theta = n\lambda$; here d is the spacing of parallel atomic planes and $2n\pi$ is the difference in phase between reflections from successive planes. What do we mean by a set of parallel reflecting planes? Any set of parallel planes will do, provided each plane passes through at least three non-colinear lattice points! See Fig. 3 for several examples. *The reflecting planes have nothing to do with the surface planes bounding the particular specimen*, because the x-rays or neutrons see all!

Figure 3   Several types of reflecting planes in a simple cubic crystal lattice. The planes shown are labeled by their Miller indices. We have shown in each case a set of two parallel planes. Distances between parallel planes decrease as the indices increase; thus high index reflections require shorter wavelengths. In principle the number of different types of reflecting planes is unlimited if the crystal is infinite.

Bragg Law

W. L. Bragg[2] presented a simple explanation of the observed angles of the diffracted beams from a crystal. Suppose that the incident waves are reflected specularly[3] from parallel planes of atoms in the crystal, with each plane reflecting only a very small fraction of the radiation, as with a very lightly silvered mirror. The diffracted beams are found only when the reflections from parallel planes of atoms interfere constructively, as in Fig. 2. We consider elastic scattering, so that the wavelength of the photon or neutron is not changed on reflection. Inelastic scattering (scattering accompanied by the excitation of elastic waves in the crystal) is considered in Chapter 5.

Consider a series of parallel lattice planes spaced equal distances d apart. The radiation is incident in the plane of the paper. The path difference for rays reflected from adjacent planes is $2d \sin \theta$, where θ is measured from the plane. Constructive interference of the radiation reflected from successive planes occurs whenever the path difference is an integral number n of wave-

[2] W. L. Bragg, Proc. Cambridge Phil. Soc. **17**, 43 (1913). The Bragg derivation is simple but is convincing only because it reproduces the results of Laue, Eqs. (32) and (39). Diffraction from a single plane of atoms is the subject of Problem 7.

[3] In specular (mirrorlike) reflection the angle of incidence is equal to the angle of reflection.

lengths λ. Thus the condition for constructive reflection of the incident radiation is

$$2d \sin \theta = n\lambda. \tag{4}$$

This is the **Bragg law.** Observe that although the reflection from each plane is assumed to be specular, only for certain values of θ will the reflections from all parallel planes add up in phase to give a strong reflected (diffracted) beam. By contrast, if each plane were perfectly reflecting, then only the first plane of a parallel set would see the radiation and any wavelength would be reflected.

The Bragg law is a consequence of the periodicity of the space lattice. The law does not refer to the arrangement or basis of atoms associated with each lattice point. The composition of the basis determines the relative intensity of the various orders n of diffraction from a given set of parallel planes.

Bragg reflection can occur only for wavelengths $\lambda \leq 2d$. This is why we cannot use visible light! Consider 1.54 Å radiation incident on a cubic crystal with a lattice constant 4.00 Å. In the first-order ($n = 1$) reflection from parallel (100) planes of the crystal we have

$$\theta = \sin^{-1}(\lambda/2d) = \sin^{-1}(1.54/8.00) = 11°.$$

As the wavelength is decreased, the angle is decreased. For gamma-rays glancing angles must be used.

EXPERIMENTAL DIFFRACTION METHODS

The Bragg law (4) requires that θ and λ be matched: *x-rays of wavelength λ striking a three-dimensional crystal at an arbitrary angle of incidence will in general not be reflected.* To satisfy the Bragg law it is necessary to scan in either wavelength or angle. We do this experimentally by providing for a continuous range of values of either λ or θ, usually of θ. The standard methods of diffraction used in crystal structure analysis are designed expressly to accomplish this. Three methods are employed, sometimes with elaborate modifications, in current research.

Laue Method

In the **Laue method** a single crystal is held stationary in a beam of x-ray or neutron radiation of continuous wavelength. The crystal selects out and diffracts the discrete values of λ for which planes exist of spacing d and incidence angle θ satisfying the Bragg law. The Laue method is convenient for the rapid determination of crystal orientation and symmetry. It is also used to study the extent of crystalline imperfection under mechanical and thermal treatment.

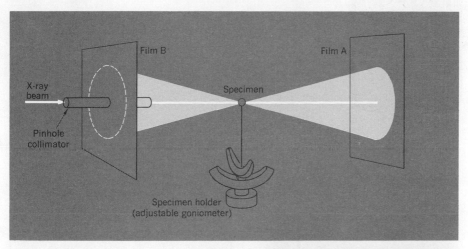

Figure 4 (*above*)   A flat plate camera. With a continuous spectrum x-ray beam and a single crystal specimen, the camera produces Laue patterns. The adjustable mount is convenient for the orientation of single crystals, as is often needed in other solid state experiments. The film B is used for back-reflection Laue patterns. (Courtesy of Philips Electronic Instruments.)

Figure 5 (*right*)   Laue pattern of a silicon crystal in approximately the [100] orientation. Note that the pattern is nearly invariant under a rotation of $2\pi/4$. The invariance follows from the four-fold symmetry of silicon about a [100] axis. The black center is a cut-out in the film. (Courtesy of J. Washburn.)

A Laue x-ray camera is illustrated schematically in Fig. 4. A source is used which produces a beam of x-rays over a wide range of wavelengths, perhaps from 0.2 Å to 2 Å. A pinhole arrangement produces a well-collimated beam. The dimensions of the single-crystal specimen need not be greater than 1 mm. Flat film is placed to receive either the transmitted diffracted beams or the reflected diffracted beams. The diffraction pattern consists of a series of spots, shown for a silicon crystal in Fig. 5.

Each reflecting plane in the crystal selects from the incident beam a wavelength satisfying the Bragg equation $2d \sin \theta = n\lambda$. The pattern will show the symmetry of the crystal: if a crystal with four-fold axial symmetry is

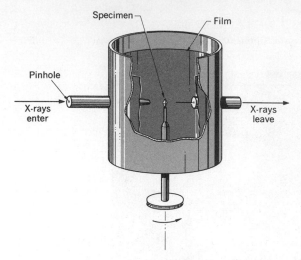

Specimen — — Film

Pinhole

X-rays
enter

X-rays
leave

Figure 6 (*left*) A rotating-crystal camera. (By permission from *Structure of metals*, by C. S. Barrett.)

Figure 7 (*below*) (a) Intensity versus wavelength distribution for x-rays from a Mo target bombarded by 30 kev electrons; (b) for the neutron beam emerging from a reactor with the wavelength band selected by a crystal monochromator. (After G. Bacon.)

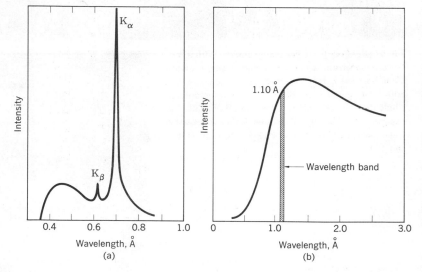

K_α

K_β

Intensity

Wavelength, Å

(a)

1.10 Å

Intensity

Wavelength band

Wavelength, Å

(b)

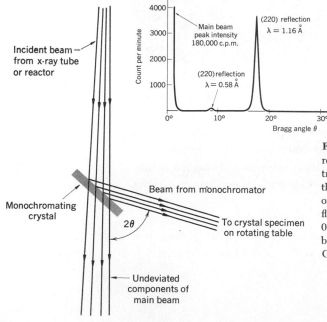

Count per minute

Main beam
peak intensity
180,000 c.p.m.

(220) reflection
$\lambda = 1.16$ Å

(220) reflection
$\lambda = 0.58$ Å

(440)
$\lambda = 1.16$ Å

Bragg angle θ

Incident beam —
from x-ray tube
or reactor

Monochromating
crystal

2θ

Beam from monochromator

To crystal specimen
on rotating table

Undeviated
components of
main beam

Figure 8 Sketch of a monochromator which by Bragg reflection selects a narrow spectrum from a broad spectrum incident beam. The upper part of the figure shows the analysis (obtained by reflection from a second crystal) of the purity of a 1.16 Å beam of neutrons from a calcium fluoride crystal monochromator. The peak intensity at 0.58 Å is less than 1 percent of that at 1.16 Å. The main beam is that not reflected from the second crystal. (After G. Bacon.)

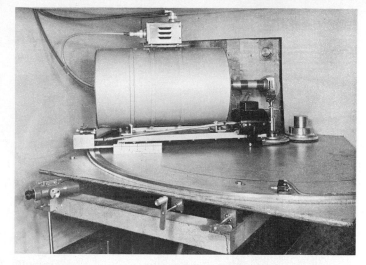

Figure 9 A small rotating-crystal neutron spectrometer at Harwell. The large can contains a counter surrounded by shielding material. Most counters used in neutron diffraction studies are filled with boron trifluoride enriched in B^{10}. (Courtesy of G. Bacon.)

oriented with the axis parallel to the beam, then the Laue pattern will show the four-fold symmetry, as in Fig. 5. The Laue pattern is widely used to orient crystals for solid state experiments.

The Laue method is practically never used for crystal structure determination. Because of the wide range of wavelengths, it is possible for several wavelengths to reflect in different orders from a single plane, so that different orders of reflection may superpose on a single spot. This makes difficult the determination of reflected intensity, and thus the determination of the basis.

Rotating-Crystal Method

In the **rotating-crystal method** a single crystal is rotated about a fixed axis in a beam of monoenergetic x-rays or neutrons. The variation in the angle θ brings different atomic planes into position for reflection. A modified rotating-crystal method is used for structure determination when a single-crystal specimen is available.

A simple rotating-crystal x-ray camera is shown in Fig. 6. The film is mounted in a cylindrical holder concentric with a rotating spindle on which the single crystal specimen is mounted. The dimensions of the crystal usually need not be greater than 1 mm. The incident x-ray beam is made nearly monochromatic by a filter or by reflection from an earlier crystal. The beam is diffracted from a given crystal plane whenever in the course of rotation the value of θ satisfies the Bragg equation. Beams from all planes parallel to the vertical rotation axis will lie in the horizontal plane. Planes with other orientations will reflect in layers above and below the horizontal plane.

The intensity distribution of the radiation from a 30 kev x-ray tube with a molybdenum target is shown by Fig. 7a. The distribution of neutrons emerging from a nuclear reactor is shown by Fig. 7b. If we reflect the x-ray or neutron beam from a monochromating crystal, as in Fig. 8, we get the crosshatched distribution of Fig. 7b. A simple rotating-crystal neutron spectrometer at Harwell is shown in Fig. 9.

41

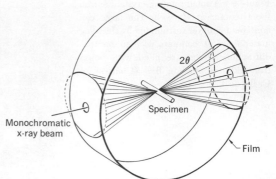

Figure 10 X-ray powder diffraction camera. The specimen is a polycrystalline powder. (Courtesy of Philips Electronic Instruments.)

Several variations of the rotating-crystal method are in common use. In *oscillating-crystal* photographs the crystal is oscillated through a limited angular range, instead of being rotated through 360°. The limited range reduces the possibility of overlapping reflections. The *Weissenberg goniometer* and also the *precession cameras* shift the film in synchronism with the oscillation of the crystal. Modern methods use diffractometers in which scintillation counters or proportional counter tubes are used to detect the diffracted radiation. These methods allow automatic collection of data: complex structures may exhibit 10,000 diffracted rays.

Powder Method

In the **powder method** (Fig. 10) the incident monochromatic radiation strikes a finely powdered specimen or a fine-grained polycrystalline specimen contained in a thin-walled capillary tube. The distribution of crystallite orientations will be nearly continuous. The powder method is convenient because single crystals are not required. Diffracted rays go out from individual crystallites which happen to be oriented with planes making an incident angle θ with the beam satisfying the Bragg equation. An early neutron powder spectrometer as used at Oak Ridge is shown in Fig. 11. Figures 12 and 13 are examples of powder-pattern results. Diffracted rays leave the specimen along the generators of cones concentric with the original beam. The generators make an angle 2θ with the direction of the original beam, where θ is the Bragg angle. The cones intercept the film in a series of concentric rings.

An important use of the powder method is in the study of phase diagrams of alloy systems. Special cameras permit the specimen to be at an elevated temperature.

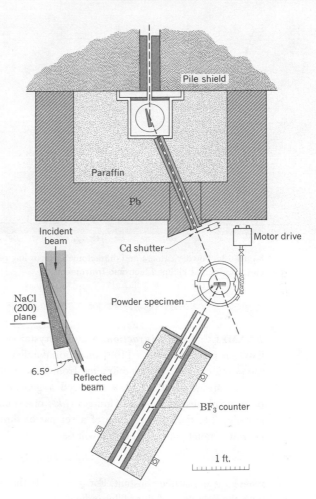

Figure 11 An early neutron spectrometer for powder studies, after E. O. Wollan and C. G. Shull, Phys. Rev. **73**, 830 (1948). The sketch shows the monochromating crystal (detailed in left center) collimating slits, shielding, second spectrometer with location of powder specimen and counter.

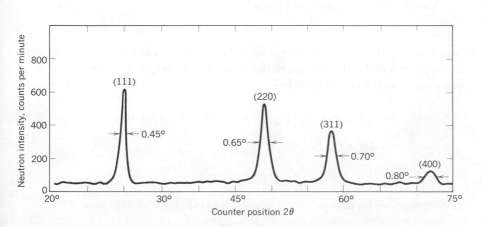

Figure 12 Neutron diffraction pattern for powdered diamond. (After G. Bacon.)

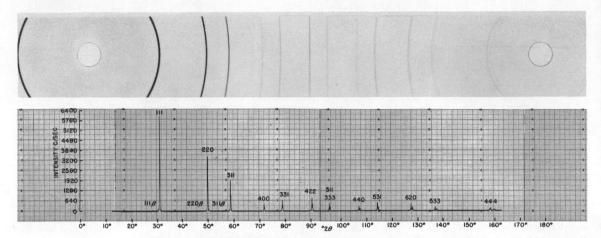

Figure 13 Powder camera and diffractometer recording of silicon. (Courtesy of W. Parrish, Philips Laboratories and Philips Electronic Instruments.)

EXAMPLE: *Laue Diffraction.* A cubic crystal (as determined by its shape or growth habit) is mounted with a [100] direction parallel to the incident x-ray beam. What are the positions of the beams diffracted from some of the low-index reflection planes?

To apply the Bragg law we need a general expression for the distance $d(hkl)$ between planes[4] of any set of indices (hkl) of a simple cubic lattice. Note from Fig. 1.20 and Fig. 14a that if one plane of a set passes through the origin, the equation of the nearest parallel plane to this one will be

$$hx + ky + lz = a, \tag{5}$$

where a is the lattice constant. For $y = z = 0$, the equation gives $x = a/h$, in agreement with the definition of the Miller indices hkl.

Now the general equation of a plane is

$$\hat{n} \cdot r = d, \tag{6}$$

from Fig. 14b. Here $\hat{n}$ is a unit vector normal to the plane, r is a vector from the origin to the plane, and d is the distance of the plane from the origin. The unit normal to the plane (5) is, according to (42) below,

$$\hat{n} = \frac{1}{(h^2 + k^2 + l^2)^{1/2}} (h\hat{x} + k\hat{y} + l\hat{z}), \tag{7}$$

and then $\hat{n} \cdot r = d$ is of the form (5) if

$$d = \frac{a}{(h^2 + k^2 + l^2)^{1/2}}. \tag{8}$$

For (110) planes we have $d(110) = a/2^{1/2}$; for (111) planes, $d(111) = a/3^{1/2}$.

---

[4] The result for a general lattice is derived in (44).

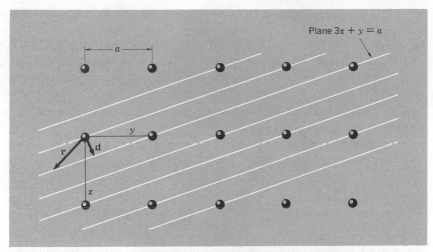

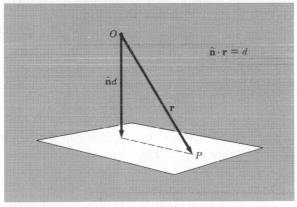

Figure 14a (*above*) Construction showing interplanar distance between (310) planes of a simple cubic lattice. Note the positions of the x and y axes.

Figure 14b (*right*) Equation of a plane; $\hat{n}d$ is the normal to the plane from the origin O. Let $\mathbf{r}$ be an arbitrary vector from the origin O to any point P in the plane. The projection $\mathbf{r}$ on $\hat{n}d$ must be equal in magnitude to d. Thus the equation of the plane is $\hat{n} \cdot \mathbf{r} = d$.

The (110) planes will appear in Laue reflection from our assumed [100] oriented crystal when the angle θ between the beam and a plane is $\pi/4$, for which $\sin \theta = 1/2^{1/2}$. The diffracted beam will appear at right angles to the incident beam because $2\theta = \pi/2$. From the Bragg law and the spacing $d(110)$, the required wavelength is given by

$$n\lambda = 2\left(\frac{a}{2^{1/2}}\right)\left(\frac{1}{2^{1/2}}\right) = a. \tag{9}$$

For the (111) planes in this orientation $\sin \theta = 1/3^{1/2}$. The Bragg law gives

$$n\lambda = 2\left(\frac{a}{3^{1/2}}\right)\left(\frac{1}{3^{1/2}}\right) = \frac{2}{3}a. \tag{10}$$

For special arrangements of the atoms within a cubic cell it is possible to have zero intensity for reflections from certain planes in certain orders. The actual diffraction patterns are quite different in appearance for sc, bc, and fcc lattices. This is discussed later in connection with Eqs. (66) and (67).

LAUE DERIVATION OF AMPLITUDE OF SCATTERED WAVE

The Bragg derivation of the diffraction condition is neat and physically clear,[5] particularly for scattering from point charges arranged on a space lattice. But when we are concerned with the intensity of scattering from a spatial distribution of electrons within each unit cell, then we must carry out a more detailed analysis. The simplest procedure is that due to Laue. A deeper analysis is given in Appendix A.

Suppose that a plane wave is incident on a small crystal, as in Fig. 15. The primitive axes of the space lattice are $\mathbf{a}$, $\mathbf{b}$, $\mathbf{c}$; we suppose there are M^3 primitive cells in the crystal. Let the amplitude F of the wave in free space at a point $\mathbf{x}$ be given by

$$F(\mathbf{x}) = F_o \exp\left[i(\mathbf{k} \cdot \mathbf{x} - \omega t)\right], \tag{11}$$

referred to an origin at $\mathbf{x} = 0$. This expression describes a traveling wave of wavevector $\mathbf{k}$ and angular frequency ω; the wavelength is $\lambda = 2\pi/k$. If we like, we may avoid complex numbers and work entirely in terms of real quantities, but complex numbers are convenient here.

We place the crystal in the beam, with the origin O chosen anywhere within the crystal. We suppose that the incident beam is not greatly disturbed by the crystal, neither by the refractive index of the crystal (which is very close to unity for neutrons and for x-rays) nor by loss of energy through scattering. Then the wave amplitude of the incident beam as seen at a point $\boldsymbol{\rho}$ within the crystal of Fig. 15 is

$$F(\boldsymbol{\rho}) = F_o \exp(i\mathbf{k} \cdot \boldsymbol{\rho}). \tag{12}$$

Here and later we consider only the instant of time $t = 0$.

The atom at $\boldsymbol{\rho}$ will scatter some of the radiation out of the incident beam. As in Figs. 16 and 17, the contribution of the atom at $\boldsymbol{\rho}$ to the amplitude of the *scattered* radiation at a point P at $\mathbf{R} = \boldsymbol{\rho} + \mathbf{r}$ outside the crystal involves the phase factor $\exp(i\mathbf{k} \cdot \boldsymbol{\rho})$ of the incident radiation at $\boldsymbol{\rho}$ and the phase factor $\exp(ikr)$ of the scattered radiation as observed at $\mathbf{R}$. Here $\mathbf{R}$ is the vector from a fixed origin in the crystal to the point of observation. The total phase factor at $\mathbf{R}$ of the radiation scattered from the atom at $\boldsymbol{\rho}$ is the product of the two phase factors:

$$\exp(i\mathbf{k} \cdot \boldsymbol{\rho}) \exp(ikr) = \exp(i\mathbf{k} \cdot \boldsymbol{\rho} + ikr). \tag{13}$$

[5] Provided that we are willing to assume specular reflection (geometrical optics) for the reflection from a single plane and wave optics thereafter.

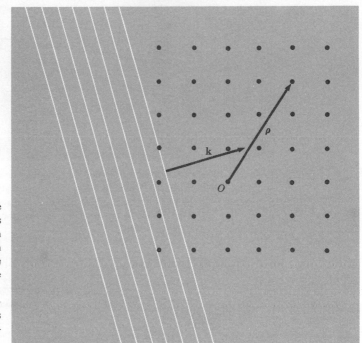

Figure 15 An electromagnetic wave of wavevector **k** and wavelength λ is incident upon a small crystal. One atom is selected as the origin O. At a given instant of time the phase of the wave at ρ is advanced with respect to the phase at O by the phase angle $\mathbf{k} \cdot \boldsymbol{\rho} = (2\pi/\lambda) \cos(\boldsymbol{\rho}, \mathbf{k})$. Thus the phase factor in the wave amplitude at ρ is $\exp(i\mathbf{k} \cdot \boldsymbol{\rho})$ with respect to the amplitude at O.

Figure 16 The atom at ρ will scatter some of the radiation in the incident beam. The amplitude of the scattered radiation as seen at a point distant **r** from ρ will be proportional to

$$\left(F_o\, e^{i\mathbf{k}\cdot\boldsymbol{\rho}}\right)\left(\frac{e^{ikr}}{r}\right),$$

where the first parenthesis contains the amplitude and phase factor of the incident beam and the second parenthesis describes the spatial variation of the radiation scattered from a point atom at ρ.

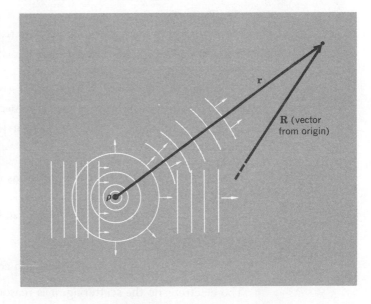

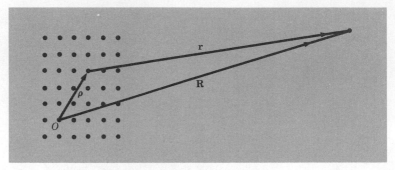

Figure 17 The wave scattered from the atom at an arbitrary origin O is received at a point $\mathbf{R}$ with the phase factor exp (ikR). The wave scattered from the atom at $\boldsymbol{\rho}$ starts out with the phase factor exp $(i\mathbf{k} \cdot \boldsymbol{\rho})$ and in transversing the distance $\mathbf{r}$ it acquires the additional phase factor exp (ikr), so that the total phase factor on arriving at $\mathbf{R}$ is exp $(i\mathbf{k} \cdot \boldsymbol{\rho} + ikr)$.

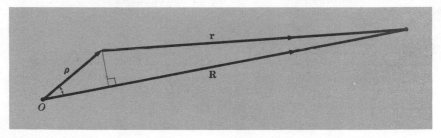

Figure 18 The length of $\mathbf{r}$ is

$$r^2 = (\mathbf{R} - \boldsymbol{\rho})^2 = R^2 + \rho^2 - 2\rho R \cos{(\boldsymbol{\rho}, \mathbf{R})}.$$

If $\mathbf{R}$ is sufficiently distant so that $\rho/R \ll 1$, we may expand the square root of the right-hand side to obtain

$$r \cong R[1 - (2\rho/R) \cos{(\boldsymbol{\rho}, \mathbf{R})}]^{1/2} \cong R - \rho \cos{(\boldsymbol{\rho}, \mathbf{R})}.$$

Thus the total phase factor of the scattered wave on arriving at $\mathbf{R}$ is, from Fig. 17,

$$\exp{[i\mathbf{k} \cdot \boldsymbol{\rho} + ikR - ik\rho \cos{(\boldsymbol{\rho}, \mathbf{R})}]}.$$

If R is much larger than the dimensions of the crystal, the argument of Fig. 18 shows that

$$r \cong R - \rho \cos{(\boldsymbol{\rho}, \mathbf{R})}, \tag{14}$$

whence (13) becomes

$$\exp{[i\mathbf{k} \cdot \boldsymbol{\rho} + ikR - ik\rho \cos{(\boldsymbol{\rho}, \mathbf{R})}]}. \tag{15}$$

The electrons do the scattering; it is reasonable to assume that the amplitude of the wave scattered from an element of volume of the crystal is proportional to the electron concentration $n(\boldsymbol{\rho})$ in the volume element. (See also the analysis of Appendix A.) Then the amplitude of the radiation scattered from the crystal and received at the outside point $\mathbf{R}$ will be proportional to the integral

$$\int dV \, n(\boldsymbol{\rho}) \, \exp\left[i\mathbf{k} \cdot \boldsymbol{\rho} - ik\rho \cos\left(\boldsymbol{\rho}, \mathbf{R}\right)\right], \tag{16}$$

where in (16) we omit the factor $\exp(ikR)$ from (15) because it is constant over the volume; we also omit $1/R$ and we neglect the difference between $1/r$ and $1/R$ in the expression given in Fig. 16 for the amplitude of the scattered wave.

The argument of the exponential in (16) may be written more compactly as

$$i\mathbf{k} \cdot \boldsymbol{\rho} - ik\rho \cos\left(\boldsymbol{\rho}, \mathbf{R}\right) \equiv i\boldsymbol{\rho} \cdot (\mathbf{k} - \mathbf{k}') \equiv -i\boldsymbol{\rho} \cdot \Delta\mathbf{k}, \tag{17a}$$

where $\mathbf{k}'$ is the wavevector in the scattering direction $\mathbf{R}$ and

$$\Delta\mathbf{k} \equiv \mathbf{k}' - \mathbf{k} \tag{17b}$$

is the difference between the scattered wavevector $\mathbf{k}'$ and the initial wavevector $\mathbf{k}$. The vector $\Delta\mathbf{k}$ plays an important part in the theory. Our assumption that the magnitude of the wavevector is unchanged on scattering is equivalent to the statement that the frequency is unchanged in elastic scattering.

Scattering from Lattice of Point Atoms

Suppose in a finite crystal there are identical point scattering centers at every lattice point

$$\boldsymbol{\rho} = m\mathbf{a} + n\mathbf{b} + p\mathbf{c}, \tag{18}$$

where m, n, p are integers.[6] Then the integral in (16) reduces to a sum over the discrete lattice points; the total scattered radiation amplitude seen at $\mathbf{R}$ will be proportional to

$$\mathfrak{a} \equiv \sum_{\rho} \exp\left(-i\boldsymbol{\rho} \cdot \Delta\mathbf{k}\right) = \sum_{mnp} \exp\left[-i(m\mathbf{a} + n\mathbf{b} + p\mathbf{c}) \cdot \Delta\mathbf{k}\right]$$

$$= \left(\sum_{m} \exp\left[-im(\mathbf{a} \cdot \Delta\mathbf{k})\right]\right)\left(\sum_{n} \exp\left[-in(\mathbf{b} \cdot \Delta\mathbf{k})\right]\right)\left(\sum_{p} \exp\left[-ip(\mathbf{c} \cdot \Delta\mathbf{k})\right]\right). \tag{19}$$

The intensity of the scattered wave involves the square of the wave amplitude, or

$$|\mathfrak{a}|^2 = \left|\sum_{m} \exp\left[-im(\mathbf{a} \cdot \Delta\mathbf{k})\right]\right|^2 \left|\cdots\right|^2 \left|\cdots\right|^2. \tag{20}$$

[6] We may let m, n, and p run from 0 to $M - 1$; the crystal will then have M^3 primitive cells.

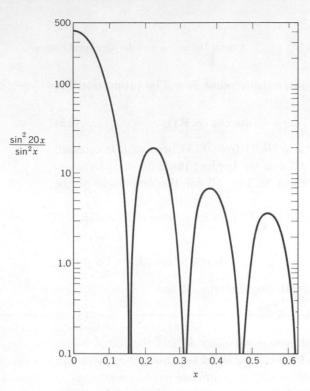

$$\frac{\sin^2 20x}{\sin^2 x}$$

Figure 19 Plot of the function in Eq. (24) for $M = 20$. The vertical scale is logarithmic.

Now consider the value of one of the sums in (20) for a crystal of dimension Ma in the direction $\mathbf{a}$, where M is an integer. We take the sum over the M values of the index m:

$$\sum_{m=0}^{M-1} \exp\left[-im(\mathbf{a} \cdot \Delta\mathbf{k})\right] = \frac{1 - \exp\left[-iM(\mathbf{a} \cdot \Delta\mathbf{k})\right]}{1 - \exp\left[-i(\mathbf{a} \cdot \Delta\mathbf{k})\right]}, \tag{21}$$

using the series

$$\sum_{m=0}^{M-1} x^m = \sum_{m=0}^{\infty} x^m - \sum_{m=M}^{\infty} x^m = \frac{1}{1-x} - \frac{x^M}{1-x}, \tag{22}$$

with $x \equiv \exp\left[-i(\mathbf{a} \cdot \Delta\mathbf{k})\right]$.

The sum in (21) may be written as

$$\frac{\exp\left[-\tfrac{1}{2}iM(\mathbf{a} \cdot \Delta\mathbf{k})\right]}{\exp\left[-\tfrac{1}{2}i(\mathbf{a} \cdot \Delta\mathbf{k})\right]} \cdot \frac{\exp\left[\tfrac{1}{2}iM(\mathbf{a} \cdot \Delta\mathbf{k})\right] - \exp\left[-\tfrac{1}{2}iM(\mathbf{a} \cdot \Delta\mathbf{k})\right]}{\exp\left[\tfrac{1}{2}i(\mathbf{a} \cdot \Delta\mathbf{k})\right] - \exp\left[-\tfrac{1}{2}i(\mathbf{a} \cdot \Delta\mathbf{k})\right]}. \tag{23}$$

Multiply (23) by its complex conjugate; we see that the scattered intensity (20) involves the product of three factors each of the form

$$\left| \sum_m \exp\left[-im(\mathbf{a} \cdot \Delta\mathbf{k})\right] \right|^2 = \frac{\sin^2 \tfrac{1}{2}M(\mathbf{a} \cdot \Delta\mathbf{k})}{\sin^2 \tfrac{1}{2}(\mathbf{a} \cdot \Delta\mathbf{k})}. \tag{24}$$

This function of $\mathbf{a} \cdot \Delta\mathbf{k}$ is steeply peaked, as in Fig. 19. The absolute maxima occur whenever each term in the sum on the left has the value unity; that is, when

$$\mathbf{a} \cdot \Delta\mathbf{k} = 2\pi q, \tag{25}$$

where q is an integer. At these values (24) has the value M^2.

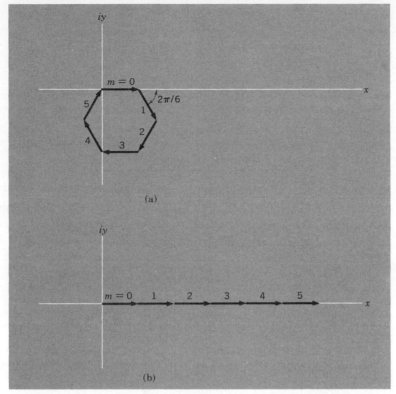

Figure 20 (a) In the direction of the first zero of the diffraction pattern the individual waves from neighboring atoms have phase differences of 60° and the sum of all six amplitudes is zero. Each vector in the diagram in the complex plane represents one term in the sum on the left-hand side of Eq. (22). (b) In the direction of the central maximum in the diffraction pattern from six regularly spaced atoms, the waves scattered from each atom are in phase and the sum of their amplitudes in Eq. (22) or (24) is a maximum.

What is the width of the maximum as we slightly vary the value of $\mathbf{a} \cdot \Delta\mathbf{k}$? The first zero of $\sin \frac{1}{2}M(\mathbf{a} \cdot \Delta\mathbf{k})$ occurs when $\Delta\mathbf{k}$ has changed from (25) to a nearby value

$$\mathbf{a} \cdot \Delta\mathbf{k} = 2\pi q + \epsilon, \tag{26}$$

where ϵ is the smallest nonzero number such that

$$\sin \tfrac{1}{2}M\epsilon = 0, \tag{27}$$

or $\qquad\qquad \tfrac{1}{2}M\epsilon = \pi; \qquad \epsilon = 2\pi/M. \tag{28}$

Thus the width of the maximum is proportional to $1/M$ and can be extremely narrow for an ideal crystal of macroscopic dimensions. The area under the central maximum of (24) is given by the height ($\propto M^2$) times the width ($\propto 1/M$), so that the area is proportional to M, the number of atoms in the line. If the crystal in three dimensions has M^3 atoms, the scattered intensity will be directly proportional to M^3.

The graphical construction of the first zero is shown in Fig. 20 for $M = 6$.

It is very helpful to look at a sum of the form $\sum_m \exp(-im\varphi)$ as a vector sum in the complex plane.

Diffraction Conditions

We see from (20) and (25) that to form a strong diffracted beam the following three equations must be satisfied simultaneously for integral values of q, r, s:

$$\mathbf{a} \cdot \Delta \mathbf{k} = 2\pi q; \qquad \mathbf{b} \cdot \Delta \mathbf{k} = 2\pi r; \qquad \mathbf{c} \cdot \Delta \mathbf{k} = 2\pi s. \tag{29}$$

These equations (known as **Laue equations**) may be solved for the vector $\Delta \mathbf{k}$ defined by (17b). We shall show in (46) that they are equivalent to the Bragg law.[7] The solution of (29) is particularly simple if the crystal axes **a, b, c** are mutually orthogonal, for then

$$\Delta \mathbf{k} = 2\pi \left(\frac{q}{a} \hat{\mathbf{a}} + \frac{r}{b} \hat{\mathbf{b}} + \frac{s}{c} \hat{\mathbf{c}} \right) \tag{30}$$

is the solution, where $\hat{\mathbf{a}}$, $\hat{\mathbf{b}}$, $\hat{\mathbf{c}}$ are unit vectors along the crystal axes and q, r, s are integers.

If the crystal axes are not orthogonal, the result (30) is not a solution of (29), for now quantities such as $\mathbf{a} \cdot \mathbf{b}$ are not all zero. For this problem we need to develop the concept of vectors in the reciprocal lattice. This concept is so useful, elegant, and general that we shall use it throughout the text for the expression of all the results of wave problems in crystals, including the theory of energy bands. The concept is due to J. Willard Gibbs.

RECIPROCAL LATTICE

Consider the expression

$$\Delta \mathbf{k} = q\mathbf{A} + r\mathbf{B} + s\mathbf{C}, \tag{31}$$

where q, r, s are the integers of Eq. (29) and **A, B, C** are vectors to be determined. On direct substitution we see that (31) will be a solution of (29) if all these relations are satisfied:

$$
\begin{array}{lll}
\mathbf{A} \cdot \mathbf{a} = 2\pi, & \mathbf{B} \cdot \mathbf{a} = 0, & \mathbf{C} \cdot \mathbf{a} = 0; \\
\mathbf{A} \cdot \mathbf{b} = 0, & \mathbf{B} \cdot \mathbf{b} = 2\pi, & \mathbf{C} \cdot \mathbf{b} = 0; \\
\mathbf{A} \cdot \mathbf{c} = 0, & \mathbf{B} \cdot \mathbf{c} = 0, & \mathbf{C} \cdot \mathbf{c} = 2\pi.
\end{array} \tag{32}
$$

We see from the first column of (32) that **A** must be perpendicular to **b** and to **c**. A vector perpendicular to **b** and **c** is given by the vector product

---

[7] Like the Bragg law, the Laue equations are necessary conditions for a diffracted beam; if the crystal cell contains more than one atom the equations are not sufficient conditions, for we must also have a nonzero value of the structure factor (69).

b × **c**; to form **A** there remains only the question of normalizing **b** × **c** to satisfy the equation **A** · **a** = 2π. We can satisfy all the equations (32) by choosing

$$
\boxed{\mathbf{A} = 2\pi\,\frac{\mathbf{b}\times\mathbf{c}}{\mathbf{a}\cdot\mathbf{b}\times\mathbf{c}}\,;\qquad \mathbf{B} = 2\pi\,\frac{\mathbf{c}\times\mathbf{a}}{\mathbf{a}\cdot\mathbf{b}\times\mathbf{c}}\,;\qquad \mathbf{C} = 2\pi\,\frac{\mathbf{a}\times\mathbf{b}}{\mathbf{a}\cdot\mathbf{b}\times\mathbf{c}}\,.}\qquad (33)
$$

These[8] are the **fundamental vectors of the reciprocal lattice.** They are orthogonal only if **a, b, c** are orthogonal. We have written all the denominators as **a** · **b** × **c**, because by elementary vector algebra

$$
\mathbf{b}\cdot\mathbf{c}\times\mathbf{a} = \mathbf{c}\cdot\mathbf{a}\times\mathbf{b} = \mathbf{a}\cdot\mathbf{b}\times\mathbf{c},\qquad (34)
$$

whose magnitude is the volume of the cell of the crystal lattice. The vectors **a, b, c** are not necessarily primitive translation vectors of the crystal but may correspond to a conventional unit cell.

It is as important to be able to visualize the reciprocal lattice as to visualize the real crystal lattice. Every crystal structure has two important lattices associated with it, the crystal lattice and the reciprocal lattice. The two lattices are related by the definitions (33). When we rotate a crystal, we rotate both the direct lattice and the reciprocal lattice. Vectors in the crystal lattice have the dimensions of [length]; vectors in the reciprocal lattice have the dimensions of [length]$^{-1}$. The crystal lattice is a lattice in real or ordinary space; the reciprocal lattice is a lattice in Fourier space. The term **Fourier space** is motivated by Eq. (38) and by Problem 5.

The points ρ of the crystal lattice are given by

$$
\rho = m\mathbf{a} + n\mathbf{b} + p\mathbf{c},\qquad (m, n, p = \text{integers}).\qquad (35)
$$

Similarly, we define the **reciprocal lattice points** or **reciprocal lattice vectors G** in Fourier space as

$$
\mathbf{G} = h\mathbf{A} + k\mathbf{B} + l\mathbf{C},\qquad (h, k, l = \text{integers}).\qquad (36)
$$

Every position in Fourier space has a meaning, but there is a special importance to the reciprocal lattice points defined by (36).

To see the significance of the **G**'s, form the scalar product:

$$
\begin{aligned}
\mathbf{G}\cdot\rho &= (h\mathbf{A} + k\mathbf{B} + l\mathbf{C})\cdot(m\mathbf{a} + n\mathbf{b} + p\mathbf{c})\\
&= 2\pi(hm + kn + lp) = 2\pi(\text{integer}).
\end{aligned}\qquad (37)
$$

It follows that

$$
\exp(i\mathbf{G}\cdot\rho) = 1,\qquad (38)
$$

---

[8] Crystallographers usually omit the factor of 2π from the definitions, but most solid state physicists include the factor.

because exp $[i2\pi(\text{integer})] = 1$. We see from (29) that *if* Δk *is equal to any reciprocal lattice vector* $\mathbf{G}$, *then the Laue equations for wave diffraction are satisfied.* The diffraction condition is

$$\boxed{\Delta k = G.} \tag{39}$$

A diffraction pattern is a map of the reciprocal lattice of the crystal, in contrast to a microscope image which is a map of the real crystal structure.

EXAMPLE: *Reciprocal Lattice in Two Dimensions.* A particular two-dimensional lattice (Fig. 21) has the basis vectors $\mathbf{a} = 2\hat{x}$; $\mathbf{b} = \hat{x} + 2\hat{y}$. Find the basis vectors of the reciprocal lattice.

We can use our three-dimensional definitions in this two-dimensional problem if we suppose that $\mathbf{c}$ is parallel to the z axis, for then the plane of the reciprocal lattice vectors $\mathbf{A}$ and $\mathbf{B}$ will be in the plane of $\mathbf{a}$ and $\mathbf{b}$. Let us take $\mathbf{c} = \hat{z}$. Now

$$\mathbf{c} \times \mathbf{a} = \hat{z} \times (2\hat{x}) = 2\hat{y};$$

$$\mathbf{b} \times \mathbf{c} = \hat{x} \times \hat{z} + 2\hat{y} \times \hat{z} = -\hat{y} + 2\hat{x}; \qquad \mathbf{a} \cdot \mathbf{b} \times \mathbf{c} = 4.$$

These results substituted in (33) give

$$\mathbf{A} = \pi\hat{x} - \tfrac{1}{2}\pi\hat{y}; \qquad \mathbf{B} = \pi\hat{y},$$

as sketched in Fig. 21.

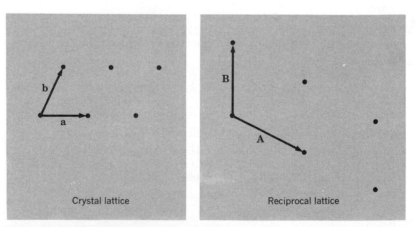

Crystal lattice   Reciprocal lattice

Figure 21 Reciprocal lattice in two dimensions: $\mathbf{A}$ and $\mathbf{B}$ are perpendicular to sets of planes (lines) in the crystal lattice, namely, to the lines parallel to $\mathbf{b}$ and $\mathbf{a}$, respectively. Any vector between reciprocal lattice points is perpendicular to some lattice plane in the crystal lattice.

Normal to Plane of Crystal Lattice

THEOREM: Every reciprocal lattice vector is normal to a lattice plane of the crystal lattice.

PROOF. A vector

$$\mathbf{G}(hkl) \equiv h\mathbf{A} + k\mathbf{B} + l\mathbf{C} \tag{40}$$

will be normal to the plane through the three points $m\mathbf{a}$, $n\mathbf{b}$, $p\mathbf{c}$ of the crystal lattice if $\mathbf{G}$ is normal to any vector which lies in the plane. The vectors $m\mathbf{a} - n\mathbf{b}$; $m\mathbf{a} - p\mathbf{c}$; $n\mathbf{b} - p\mathbf{c}$ lie in the plane, so that we must have

$$\mathbf{G} \cdot (m\mathbf{a} - n\mathbf{b}) = \mathbf{G} \cdot (m\mathbf{a} - p\mathbf{c}) = \mathbf{G} \cdot (n\mathbf{b} - p\mathbf{c}) = 0. \tag{41}$$

The left-hand expression is just $(h\mathbf{A} + k\mathbf{B} + l\mathbf{C}) \cdot (m\mathbf{a} - n\mathbf{b}) = hm - kn = 0$. Similarly, the set of equations (41) becomes

$$mh = nk; \qquad mh = pl; \qquad nk = pl;$$

which are satisfied if, for example,

$$m = 1/h; \qquad n = 1/k; \qquad p = 1/l. \tag{42}$$

But the Miller indices of the crystal plane through the three points, $m\mathbf{a}$, $n\mathbf{b}$, $p\mathbf{c}$, are the (hkl) of (42), apart from a possible integral factor, so that the vector $\mathbf{G}(hkl)$ in the reciprocal lattice is normal to the plane (hkl) of the crystal lattice.

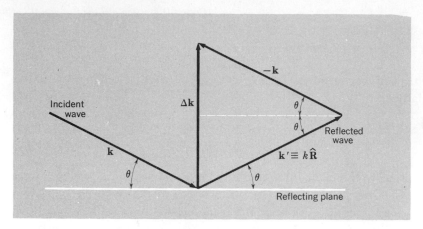

Figure 22 Construction for $\Delta\mathbf{k} = \mathbf{k}' - \mathbf{k}$ in terms of the reflection angles θ of Fig. 2. Observe that $|\Delta\mathbf{k}| = 2k \sin \theta = (4\pi/\lambda) \sin \theta$.

Spacing of Planes of Crystal Lattice

THEOREM: The spacing $d(hkl)$ of the planes (hkl) of the crystal lattice is equal to $2\pi/|\mathbf{G}(hkl)|$.

PROOF. If $\mathbf{r}$ is any vector from the origin of the crystal lattice to the plane (hkl), then by (6) and (40)

$$\mathbf{r} \cdot \hat{\mathbf{G}} = d(hkl), \tag{43}$$

where $\hat{\mathbf{G}}$ is the unit vector in the direction $\mathbf{G}(hkl)$ which, by the preceding theorem, is normal to the plane. It is sufficient to consider one particular $\mathbf{r}$, say $\mathbf{r} = \mathbf{a}/h$. By (40) we have $\mathbf{a} \cdot \mathbf{G} = 2\pi h$. Now $\hat{\mathbf{G}} \equiv \mathbf{G}/|\mathbf{G}|$ so that $\mathbf{r} \cdot \hat{\mathbf{G}} = 2\pi/|\mathbf{G}|$, whence on comparison with (43) we have

$$d(hkl) = 2\pi/|\mathbf{G}(hkl)|, \tag{44}$$

as desired.

The diffraction condition (39) is $\Delta\mathbf{k} = \mathbf{G}$, or $2\pi/|\Delta\mathbf{k}| = d(hkl)$. But from Fig. 22

$$|\Delta\mathbf{k}| = (4\pi/\lambda) \sin \theta, \tag{45}$$

where θ is the angle of reflection. Thus (45) becomes

$$\lambda = 2d(hkl) \sin \theta, \tag{46}$$

which is a form of the Bragg law, but without the factor n which appears in (4). If h, k, l have a common factor n, the diffracted ray is an nth order reflection from lattice planes with their true spacing. The nth point from the origin in a given row in the reciprocal lattice corresponds to the nth order reflection from the associated crystal planes. *Every point in the reciprocal lattice corresponds to a possible reflection from the crystal lattice.* Diffraction experiments give us the reciprocal lattice points, and from these we reconstruct the crystal lattice.

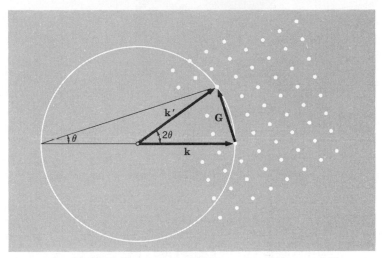

Figure 23 The points on the right hand side are reciprocal lattice points of the crystal. The vector **k** is drawn in the direction of the incident x-ray beam and it terminates at any reciprocal lattice point. We draw a sphere of radius $k = 2\pi/\lambda$ about the origin of **k**. A diffracted beam will be formed if this sphere intersects any other point in the reciprocal lattice. The sphere as drawn intercepts a point connected with the end of **k** by a reciprocal lattice vector **G**. The diffracted x-ray beam is in the direction $\mathbf{k}' = \mathbf{k} + \mathbf{G}$. The reflection planes in the crystal lattice are normal to **G**, according to the theorem following Eq. (40). The spacing in the crystal lattice of these reflection planes is $d = 2\pi/G$, according to (44). We see from the figure that $2k \sin\theta = G$ or $2d \sin\theta = \lambda$, which is the Bragg law in the form (46). This construction is due to P. P. Ewald.

Ewald Construction

The Bragg equation has an elegant geometrical significance in the reciprocal lattice, as shown in Fig. 23. This construction is the geometrical expression of our earlier result (39) that the diffraction condition is

$$\Delta\mathbf{k} = \mathbf{G}. \tag{47}$$

In terms of the definition (17b) of $\Delta\mathbf{k}$ as $\mathbf{k}' - \mathbf{k}$, we have

$$\mathbf{k} + \mathbf{G} = \mathbf{k}', \tag{48}$$

where **k**' is the wavevector of the wave after reflection and **G** connects any two points of the reciprocal lattice. In effect, (48) is a selection rule; it is the form the momentum conservation law assumes in a periodic structure. We discuss momentum further in Chapter 5.

On squaring (48) we have $(\mathbf{k} + \mathbf{G})^2 = k'^2$. Now $k = k'$ in elastic scattering; this is a statement of the conservation of energy. Thus we may write the diffraction law as

$$\boxed{2\mathbf{k} \cdot \mathbf{G} + G^2 = 0.} \tag{49}$$

We shall encounter this equation again and again in wave propagation problems in crystal lattices.

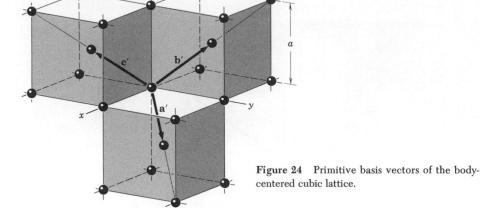

Figure 24 Primitive basis vectors of the body-centered cubic lattice.

Reciprocal Lattice to bcc Lattice. The primitive translation vectors of the bcc lattice as shown in Fig. 24 are

$$\mathbf{a}' = (a/2)(\hat{\mathbf{x}} + \hat{\mathbf{y}} - \hat{\mathbf{z}});$$
$$\mathbf{b}' = (a/2)(-\hat{\mathbf{x}} + \hat{\mathbf{y}} + \hat{\mathbf{z}}); \tag{50}$$
$$\mathbf{c}' = (a/2)(\hat{\mathbf{x}} - \hat{\mathbf{y}} + \hat{\mathbf{z}});$$

where a is the side of the conventional unit cube and $\hat{\mathbf{x}}$, $\hat{\mathbf{y}}$, $\hat{\mathbf{z}}$ are orthogonal unit vectors parallel to the cube edges. The volume of the primitive cell is

$$V = |\mathbf{a}' \cdot \mathbf{b}' \times \mathbf{c}'| = \tfrac{1}{2}a^3. \tag{51}$$

The primitive translations $\mathbf{A}$, $\mathbf{B}$, $\mathbf{C}$ of the reciprocal lattice are defined by (33). We have, using (50) and (51),

$$\mathbf{A} = (2\pi/a)(\hat{\mathbf{x}} + \hat{\mathbf{y}}); \quad \mathbf{B} = (2\pi/a)(\hat{\mathbf{y}} + \hat{\mathbf{z}}); \quad \mathbf{C} = (2\pi/a)(\hat{\mathbf{x}} + \hat{\mathbf{z}}). \tag{52}$$

Note by comparison with Fig. 1.18 that these are just the primitive vectors of an fcc lattice. Thus *the fcc lattice is the reciprocal lattice of the bcc lattice.*

If h, k, l are integers, the general reciprocal lattice vector is

$$\mathbf{G} = h\mathbf{A} + k\mathbf{B} + l\mathbf{C} = (2\pi/a)[(h + l)\hat{\mathbf{x}} + (h + k)\hat{\mathbf{y}} + (k + l)\hat{\mathbf{z}}]. \tag{53}$$

The shortest nonzero $\mathbf{G}$'s are the following twelve vectors, where all choices of sign are independent:

$$(2\pi/a)(\pm\hat{\mathbf{x}} \pm \hat{\mathbf{y}}); \quad (2\pi/a)(\pm\hat{\mathbf{y}} \pm \hat{\mathbf{z}}); \quad (2\pi/a)(\pm\hat{\mathbf{x}} \pm \hat{\mathbf{z}}). \tag{54}$$

The primitive cell of the reciprocal lattice may be taken to be the parallelepiped described by $\mathbf{A}$, $\mathbf{B}$, and $\mathbf{C}$ defined by (52). The parallelepiped contains one reciprocal lattice point, because each of the eight corner points is shared among eight parallelepipeds, and thus one parallelepiped contains one-eighth of each of eight corner points. But it is customary in solid state physics to take the primitive cell of the reciprocal lattice as the smallest volume bounded by planes normal to each of the (shorter) $\mathbf{G}$'s at its midpoint.

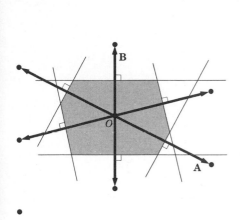

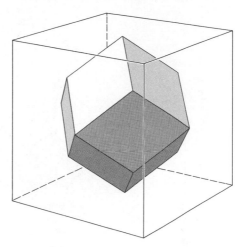

Figure 25b (*above*)   First Brillouin zone of the body-centered cubic lattice. The figure is a regular rhombic dodecahedron.

Figure 25a (*left above*)   Construction of the first Brillouin zone for an oblique lattice in two dimensions. The crystal lattice is somewhat similar to that of Fig. 21. We first draw an adequate number of reciprocal lattice vectors from O to nearby points in the reciprocal lattice. Next we construct lines perpendicular to these vectors at their midpoints. The smallest enclosed area is the first Brillouin zone.

This is just another method for dividing space up into identical cells which fill it uniformly. Each of the new cells contains one lattice point; the point is at the center of the cell. This cell is essentially the Wigner-Seitz cell (Chapter 1), but in the reciprocal lattice.

Brillouin Zones

The primitive cell formed in this way (Fig. 25a) in the reciprocal lattice is called the **first Brillouin zone** for historical reasons. Brillouin zones are not used particularly in x-ray analysis, but they are absolutely essential in the theory of electronic energy bands in crystals (Chapter 9).

The first Brillouin zone of the bcc crystal lattice is the primitive cell formed from the planes normal to the twelve vectors of Eq. (54) at their midpoints. [Sometimes we need more than just the shortest vectors—see Eq. (60).] The zone thus formed is a regular twelve-faced solid, a rhombic dodecahedron, as shown in Fig. 25b. The vectors from the origin to the center of each face are one-half of the vectors (54), or

$$(\pi/a)(\pm\hat{\mathbf{x}} \pm \hat{\mathbf{y}}); \qquad (\pi/a)(\pm\hat{\mathbf{y}} \pm \hat{\mathbf{z}}); \qquad (\pi/a)(\pm\hat{\mathbf{x}} \pm \hat{\mathbf{z}}). \qquad (55)$$

All choices of sign are independent, giving twelve vectors.

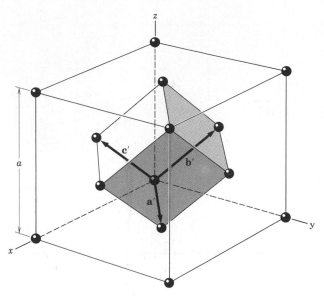

Figure 26 Primitive basis vectors of the face-centered cubic lattice.

Reciprocal Lattice to fcc Lattice. The primitive translation vectors of the fcc lattice as shown in Fig. 26 are:

$$\mathbf{a'} = (a/2)(\hat{\mathbf{x}} + \hat{\mathbf{y}}); \qquad \mathbf{b'} = (a/2)(\hat{\mathbf{y}} + \hat{\mathbf{z}}); \qquad \mathbf{c'} = (a/2)(\hat{\mathbf{z}} + \hat{\mathbf{x}}); \qquad (56)$$

which are parallel to those of (52).

From the definitions (33) the primitive translation vectors $\mathbf{A}$, $\mathbf{B}$, $\mathbf{C}$ of the reciprocal lattice to the fcc lattice are

$$\mathbf{A} = (2\pi/a)(\hat{\mathbf{x}} + \hat{\mathbf{y}} - \hat{\mathbf{z}});$$
$$\mathbf{B} = (2\pi/a)(-\hat{\mathbf{x}} + \hat{\mathbf{y}} + \hat{\mathbf{z}}); \qquad (57)$$
$$\mathbf{C} = (2\pi/a)(\hat{\mathbf{x}} - \hat{\mathbf{y}} + \hat{\mathbf{z}}).$$

These are primitive translation vectors of a bcc lattice, so that the bcc lattice is the reciprocal lattice of the fcc lattice. We have now

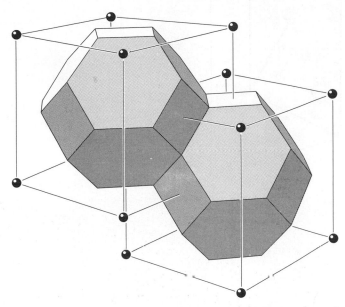

Figure 27 Brillouin zones of the face-centered cubic lattice. The cells are in reciprocal space, and the reciprocal lattice is body-centered, as drawn.

$$\mathbf{G} = (2\pi/a)\,[(h - k + l)\hat{\mathbf{x}} + (h + k - l)\hat{\mathbf{y}} + (-h + k + l)\hat{\mathbf{z}}]. \quad (58)$$

The shortest nonzero $\mathbf{G}$'s are the eight vectors

$$(2\pi/a)\,(\pm\hat{\mathbf{x}} \pm \hat{\mathbf{y}} \pm \hat{\mathbf{z}}). \quad (59)$$

The boundaries of a primitive cell in the reciprocal lattice may be determined for the most part by the eight planes normal to these vectors at their midpoints. But the corners of the octahedron thus formed are truncated by the planes which are the perpendicular bisectors of the six reciprocal lattice vectors[8a]

$$(2\pi/a)\,(\pm 2\hat{\mathbf{x}}); \qquad (2\pi/a)\,(\pm 2\hat{\mathbf{y}}); \qquad (2\pi/a)\,(\pm 2\hat{\mathbf{z}}). \quad (60)$$

The primitive cell is then the truncated octahedron shown in Fig. 27. This is the first Brillouin zone of the fcc crystal lattice.

[8a] Note that $(2\pi/a)(2\hat{\mathbf{x}})$ is a reciprocal lattice vector because it is equal to $\mathbf{A} + \mathbf{C}$.

62

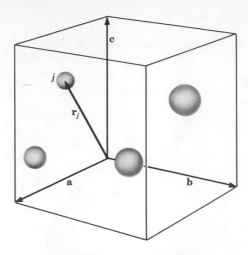

Figure 28 Position of the jth atom within the unit cell is specified by $\mathbf{r}_j = u_j\mathbf{a} + v_j\mathbf{b} + w_j\mathbf{c}$, where u_j, v_j, w_j are constants.

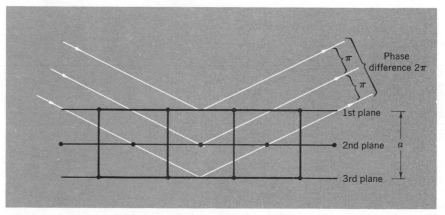

Figure 29 Explanation of the absence of a (100) reflection from a body-centered cubic lattice. The phase difference between successive planes is π, so that the reflected amplitude is $1 + e^{-i\pi} = 1 - 1 = 0$.

GEOMETRICAL STRUCTURE FACTOR

Equations (4) or (29) or (49) determine all the reflections (hkl) possible for a given crystal lattice. The possible reflections are described by the reciprocal lattice points $\mathbf{G}(hkl) = h\mathbf{A} + k\mathbf{B} + l\mathbf{C}$. The relative intensities of the various reflections depend on the contents of the unit cell: on the number, position, and electronic distribution of the atoms in the unit cell. We want to develop the connection.

Let there be s atoms within each cell, with the nucleus of the jth atom of the cell at the position (Fig. 28) specified by

$$\mathbf{r}_j = u_j\mathbf{a} + v_j\mathbf{b} + w_j\mathbf{c}, \tag{61}$$

relative to a lattice point as the origin of $\mathbf{r}_j$. Suppose (for the present) that all the electrons of the jth atom are concentrated at the position r_j. Let f_j be a measure of the scattering power of the jth atom.

Then the expression $\mathcal{a} = \Sigma \exp{(-i\boldsymbol{\rho} \cdot \Delta\mathbf{k})}$ in (19) for the total scattered amplitude becomes, for the present more general problem,

$$\begin{aligned} \mathfrak{a} &= \sum_{\rho}\sum_{j} f_j \exp\left[-i(\rho + \mathbf{r}_j)\cdot\Delta\mathbf{k}\right] \\ &= \left(\sum_{\rho}\exp\left(-i\rho\cdot\Delta\mathbf{k}\right)\right)\left(\sum_{j} f_j \exp\left(-i\mathbf{r}_j\cdot\Delta\mathbf{k}\right)\right). \end{aligned} \tag{62}$$

This differs from (19) by the right-hand factor, which we call the **geometrical structure factor**, denoted by $\mathcal{S}$:

$$\mathcal{S} \equiv \sum_{j} f_j \exp\left(-i\mathbf{r}_j\cdot\Delta\mathbf{k}\right) = \sum_{j} f_j \exp\left(-i\mathbf{r}_j\cdot\mathbf{G}\right), \tag{63}$$

where we have used the Bragg condition (39). For the reflection (hkl) we have

$$\begin{aligned} \mathbf{r}_j\cdot\mathbf{G} &= (u_j\mathbf{a} + v_j\mathbf{b} + w_j\mathbf{c})\cdot(h\mathbf{A} + k\mathbf{B} + l\mathbf{C}) \\ &= 2\pi(u_j h + v_j k + w_j l), \end{aligned} \tag{64}$$

so that the geometrical structure factor is given by

$$\boxed{\mathcal{S}(hkl) = \sum_{j} f_j \exp\left[-i2\pi(u_j h + v_j k + w_j l)\right].} \tag{65}$$

The structure factor need not be real; the *intensity* involves $\mathcal{S}^*\mathcal{S}$, where $\mathcal{S}^*$ is the complex conjugate of $\mathcal{S}$.

Structure Factor of the bcc Lattice. The basis of the bcc structure referred to the usual cubic unit cell has identical atoms at $0\,0\,0$ and $\frac{1}{2}\frac{1}{2}\frac{1}{2}$. For one atom $u_1 = v_1 = w_1 = 0$ and for the other atom $u_2 = v_2 = w_2 = \frac{1}{2}$. Thus (65) becomes

$$\mathcal{S}(hkl) = f\{1 + \exp\left[-i\pi(h + k + l)\right]\}, \tag{66}$$

where f is the scattering power of an atom. The value of $\mathcal{S}$ is zero whenever the exponential has the value -1. Now the exponential has the value -1 whenever its argument is $-i\pi$ times an odd integer. We have

$$\begin{aligned} \mathcal{S} &= 0 & &\text{when } h + k + l = \text{odd integer;} \\ \mathcal{S} &= 2f & &\text{when } h + k + l = \text{even integer.} \end{aligned}$$

Metallic sodium has a bcc structure. The diffraction spectrum does not contain lines such as (100), (300), (111), or (221), but lines such as (200), (110), and (222) will be present; here the planes (hkl) are referred to a cubic unit cell.

What is the physical interpretation of the result that the (100) reflection vanishes for the bcc lattice? The (100) reflection normally occurs when the reflections from the first and third planes in Fig. 29 differ in phase by 2π.

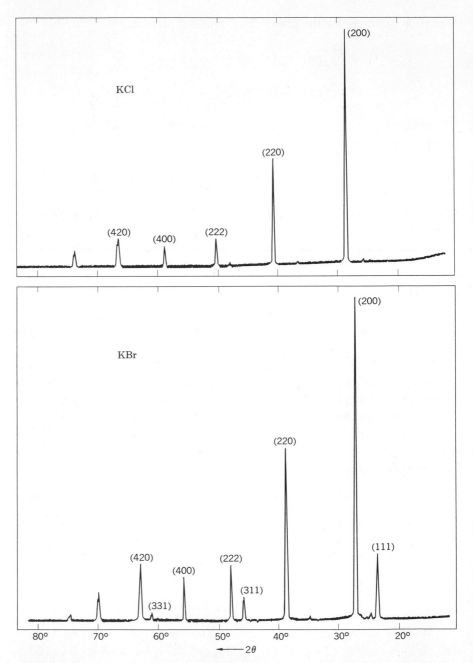

Figure 30 Comparison of x-ray reflections from KCl and KBr powders. In KCl the form factors of K^+ and Cl^- ions are almost exactly equal, so that the crystal looks to x-rays as if it were a monatomic simple cubic lattice of lattice constant $a/2$. Only even integers occur in the reflection indices when these are based on a cubic lattice of lattice constant a. In KBr the form factor of Br^- is quite different than that of K^+, and all reflections of the fcc lattice are present. (Courtesy of Robert van Nordstrand.)

These planes bound the unit cube. In the bcc lattice there is an intervening plane of atoms, labeled the second plane in the figure, which is equal in scattering power to the other planes. Situated midway between them, it gives a reflection retarded in phase by π with respect to the first plane, thereby canceling the contribution from that plane. The cancellation of the (100) reflection occurs in the bcc lattice because the planes are identical in composition. In the CsCl structure (Fig. 1.26) this cancellation does not occur: the planes of Cs and Cl ions alternate, but the scattering power of Cs is much greater than the scattering power of Cl, because Cs^+ has 54 electrons and Cl^- has only 18 electrons.

Structure Factor of the fcc Lattice. The basis of the fcc structure referred to the usual cubic unit cell has identical atoms at $0\,0\,0$; $0\,\frac{1}{2}\,\frac{1}{2}$; $\frac{1}{2}\,0\,\frac{1}{2}$; $\frac{1}{2}\,\frac{1}{2}\,0$. Thus (65) becomes

$$S(hkl) = f\{1 + \exp\left[-i\pi(k+l)\right] + \exp\left[-i\pi(h+l)\right] + \exp\left[-i\pi(h+k)\right]\}. \qquad (67)$$

If all indices are even integers, $S = 4f$; similarly if all indices are odd integers. But if only one of the integers is even, two of the exponents will be odd multiples of $-i\pi$ and S will vanish. If only one of the integers is odd, the same argument applies and S will also vanish. Thus in the fcc lattice no reflections can occur for which the indices are partly even and partly odd. The point is beautifully illustrated by Fig. 30: both KCl and KBr have an fcc lattice, but KCl simulates an sc lattice because the K^+ and Cl^- ions have equal numbers of electrons. Diffraction patterns for two crystals, diamond and aluminum, having an fcc Bravais lattice are given in Figs. 12 and 31.

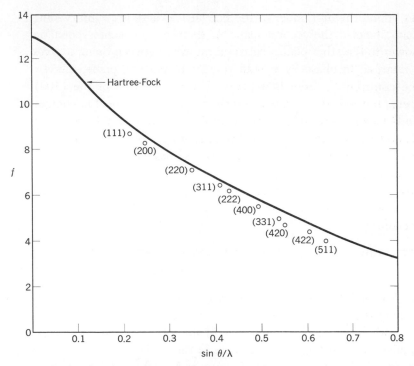

Figure 31 Absolute experimental atomic scattering factors for metallic aluminum, after Batterman, Chipman, and DeMarco. Each observed reflection is labeled. The incident radiation was MoK$_\alpha$, with $\lambda = 0.709$ Å. Note that no reflections occur for which the indices are partly even and partly odd; this is what we expect for an fcc crystal, according to (67).

ATOMIC SCATTERING FACTOR OR FORM FACTOR

In the expression (65) for the geometrical structure factor there occurs the quantity f_j, which we said was a measure of the scattering power of the jth atom in the unit cell. What determines f_j? For x-rays the scattering power involves only the atomic electrons, because the nuclei are too heavy to respond significantly to an x-ray photon.

The value of f involves the number and distribution of atomic electrons, and it also involves the wavelength and angle of scattering of the radiation. These factors enter because of interference effects arising from the finite extent of the atoms. We now give a classical calculation of the scattering factor.

Consider the expressions (16) and (17) applied to the scattered radiation from a single atom. We want to account for interference effects within the atom. For a single atom we define a quantity f by

$$f = \int dV\, n(\boldsymbol{\rho})\, \exp\left(-i\boldsymbol{\rho} \cdot \Delta\mathbf{k}\right), \tag{68}$$

where $n(\rho)$ is the electron concentration. We call f the **atomic scattering factor** or **form factor**.[9] Let ρ make an angle α with Δk; then $\boldsymbol{\rho} \cdot \Delta \mathbf{k} = \rho \, \Delta k \cos \alpha$. If the electron distribution is spherically symmetric about the origin, then

$$f \equiv 2\pi \int \rho^2 \, d\rho \, d(\cos \alpha) \, n(\rho) \exp\left(-i\rho \, \Delta k \cos \alpha\right)$$

$$= 2\pi \int d\rho \, \rho^2 \, n(\rho) \cdot \frac{e^{i\rho \, \Delta k} - e^{-i\rho \, \Delta k}}{i\rho \, \Delta k}.$$

Thus the atomic scattering factor is given by

$$\boxed{f = 4\pi \int d\rho \, n(\rho) \, \rho^2 \, \frac{\sin \mu\rho}{\mu\rho},} \tag{69}$$

where $\mu \equiv \Delta k = (4\pi/\lambda) \sin \theta$, by the expression (45) for Δk. [For a Bragg reflection $\mu = G$, by (45).]

If the same total electron density were concentrated at the origin where $\rho = 0$, then in the integral in (69) only $\mu\rho = 0$ would contribute to the integrand. In this limit $(\sin \mu\rho)/\mu\rho = 1$, and

$$f_o = 4\pi \int d\rho \, n(\rho) \, \rho^2 = Z, \tag{70}$$

the number of atomic electrons. Therefore f is the ratio of the radiation amplitude scattered by the actual electron distribution in an atom to that scattered by one electron localized at a point.

At $\theta = 0$ we see by the same argument that $\mu = 0$, and f reduces to the value Z. We also see from the solution of Problem 4 that at very short wavelengths interference effects reduce the scattered amplitude drastically.[10]

The overall electron distribution in a solid is fairly close to that of the appropriate free atoms. This statement does not mean that the outermost or valence electrons are not redistributed in forming the solid; it means only that the x-ray reflection intensities are represented well by the free atom values of the form factors. As an example, Batterman and co-workers[11] find agreement within 1 percent in a comparison of the x-ray intensities of Bragg reflections of metallic iron, copper, and aluminum with the theoretical free atom values from wavefunction calculations. The results for aluminum are shown in Fig. 31, where we see also that $f \to Z$ as $\theta \to 0$, as required.

There have been many attempts to obtain direct x-ray evidence about the actual electron distribution in a covalent chemical bond, particularly in

---

[9] This is also discussed in Appendix A.

[10] In a more accurate treatment one finds that the amplitude and phase of scattering are rather different for those inner electrons whose binding energies approach, or exceed the energy of the x-ray photons. This effect, widely referred to as "anomalous dispersion," introduces complications which can be very useful in structure determinations.

[11] B. W. Batterman, D. R. Chipman, and J. J. DeMarco, Phys. Rev. **122**, 68 (1961); see also L. D. Jennings et al., Phys. Rev. **135**, 1612 (1964).

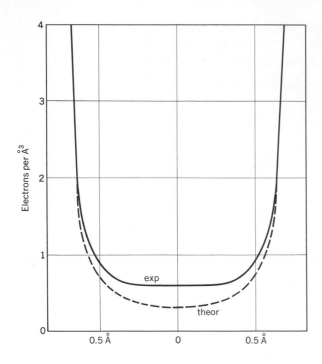

Figure 32 Electron density in vicinity of midpoint between two neighboring Si atoms in the [111] direction in the lattice. The solid curve is calculated from the observed f values; the dashed curve is the superposition of calculated free atom charge densities. Part of the difference is due to the expansion of charge distributions in the crystal, and part is due to an extra concentration of charge in the chemical bond (see Problem 5c). (After Göttlicher et al.)

crystals having the diamond structure.[12] The question lies near the limits of what can be explored by x-ray diffraction methods. There is some indication in silicon that midway between two nearest-neighbor atoms there is an appreciable increase in electron concentration over what is expected from the overlap of the electron densities calculated for two free atoms of Si (see Fig. 32).

Temperature Dependence of the Reflection Lines

As the temperature of the crystal is increased, the intensity of the Bragg-reflected beams decreases, but the angular width of the reflected line is unchanged. Experimental results for a reflection line of copper are shown in Fig. 33. It is surprising that we can get a sharp x-ray reflection from atoms in large amplitude random thermal motion,[13] with instantaneous nearest-neighbor spacings differing by perhaps 10 percent at room temperature. Before the Laue experiment was done, but when the proposal was being discussed[14] in coffee houses in Munich, the objection was made that the instantaneous posi-

---

[12] For diamond, see G. B. Carpenter, J. Chem. Phys. **32**, 525 (1960); for silicon, see S. Göttlicher et al., Z. f. Physikalische Chemie **21**, 133 (1959).

[13] Using concepts to be developed in Chapters 4 and 6, we can make an estimate of the thermal variation of interatomic spacing. Suppose there is one atom in a cell of volume $V = (2 \times 10^{-8} \text{ cm})^3$. If C is the elastic stiffness and e the strain, then in thermal equilibrium (except at low temperatures) we have $Ce^2V \approx k_BT$, where k_B is the Boltzmann constant. Thus at 300°K we might expect the root-mean-square strain to be of the order

Figure 33 Temperature dependence of the integrated x-ray intensity of MoKα radiation reflected from the (800) planes of copper, after P. A. Flinn, G. M. McManus, and J. A. Rayne, Phys. Rev. **123**, 809 (1961).

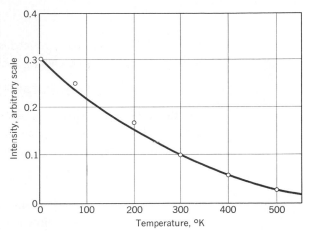

tions of the atoms in a crystal at room temperature are very far from a regular periodic array, because of this large thermal fluctuation. Therefore, the argument went, one should not expect a well-defined diffracted beam.

Why is there a well defined diffracted beam? Consider the expression (16) or (19) for the radiation amplitude scattered by a crystal: let the position of the atom nominally at ρ_0 contain a term $\mathbf{u}(t)$ fluctuating in time:

$$\rho(t) = \rho_0 + \mathbf{u}(t). \tag{71}$$

We suppose that each atom fluctuates independently about its own equilibrium position.[15] Then the thermal-average scattered amplitude of (19) can be written

$$\langle \mathcal{A} \rangle = \mathcal{A}_0 \langle \exp\,(-i\mathbf{u} \cdot \Delta \mathbf{k}) \rangle, \tag{72}$$

where $\Delta \mathbf{k}$ is the change in wavevector on reflection and $\langle \cdots \rangle$ denotes thermal average. The appearance of $\mathcal{A}_0$ assures us that all diffraction lines will be sharp. The exponential factor in (72) will be shown to reduce the intensity. The series expansion of the exponential is

$$\langle \exp\,(-i\mathbf{u} \cdot \Delta \mathbf{k}) \rangle = 1 - i\langle \mathbf{u} \cdot \Delta \mathbf{k} \rangle - \tfrac{1}{2}\langle (\mathbf{u} \cdot \Delta \mathbf{k})^2 \rangle + \cdots. \tag{73}$$

But $\langle \mathbf{u} \cdot \Delta \mathbf{k} \rangle = 0$, because $\mathbf{u}$ is a random motion uncorrelated with the direction of $\Delta \mathbf{k}$. Further,

$$e_{\text{rms}} \approx (k_B T/CV)^{1/2} \approx \left[\frac{(1.4 \times 10^{-16}\ \text{erg/deg})(3 \times 10^2\ \text{deg})}{(10^{11}\ \text{ergs/cm}^3)(8 \times 10^{-24}\ \text{cm}^3)} \right]^{1/2} \approx 0.2,$$

which means that the rms thermal fluctuation in the lattice constant is 20 percent at room temperature, for this example.

[14] P. P. Ewald, private communication.

[15] This is the Einstein model of a solid; it is not a very good model at low temperatures, but it works well at high temperatures (Chapter 6). For our present purpose it leads us to a simple result. For a more realistic treatment, see *QTS*, Chap. 20.

$$\langle (\mathbf{u} \cdot \Delta\mathbf{k})^2 \rangle = \tfrac{1}{3}\langle u^2 \rangle (\Delta k)^2. \tag{74}$$

The factor $\tfrac{1}{3}$ arises by geometrical averaging in three dimensions, because only the component of $\mathbf{u}$ along $\Delta\mathbf{k}$ is involved. Now the function

$$\exp\left[-\tfrac{1}{6}\langle u^2 \rangle (\Delta k)^2\right] = 1 - \tfrac{1}{6}\langle u^2 \rangle (\Delta k)^2 + \cdots \tag{75}$$

has the same series expansion as (73) for the first two terms shown here. For a harmonic oscillator all terms in the series can be shown to be identical. Thus the scattered intensity, which is the square of the amplitude, is

$$I = I_0 \exp\left[-\tfrac{1}{3}\langle u^2 \rangle (\Delta k)^2\right], \tag{76}$$

where I_0 is the scattered intensity from the rigid lattice as treated earlier. The exponential factor is known as the **Debye-Waller factor**; it is often written as $\exp(-2W)$, where $2W$ is defined by (76) as $\tfrac{1}{3}\langle u^2 \rangle (\Delta k)^2$.

Here $\langle u^2 \rangle$ is the mean square displacement of an atom. The average potential energy $\langle U \rangle$ of a classical harmonic oscillator is $\tfrac{1}{2}k_B T$, whence

$$\langle U \rangle = \tfrac{1}{2}C\langle u^2 \rangle = \tfrac{1}{2}M\omega^2\langle u^2 \rangle = \tfrac{1}{2}k_B T, \tag{77}$$

where C is the force constant, M is the mass of an atom, and ω is the frequency of the oscillator. We have used the result $\omega^2 = C/M$. Thus the scattered intensity is

$$I(hkl) = I_0 \exp\left[-\frac{k_B T (\Delta k)^2}{3M\omega^2}\right]. \tag{78}$$

where hkl are the indices of $\Delta\mathbf{k} = h\mathbf{A} + k\mathbf{B} + l\mathbf{C}$. This classical result is a good approximation at high temperatures. For quantum oscillators $\langle u^2 \rangle$ does not vanish even at $T = 0$ because of zero-point motion. The evaluation of (76) at low temperatures is discussed in books on x-ray diffraction.

We see from (78) and from Fig. 33 that the intensity of the diffracted line decreases (but not catastrophically) as the temperature is increased. The reflections of low Δk are less affected than the reflections of high Δk. The intensity we have calculated is that of the coherent diffraction or elastic scattering in the well-defined Bragg directions. That part of the intensity lost from the main beam as the temperature is increased appears as a somewhat diffuse background. The lost intensity is the inelastic photon scattering discussed in Chapter 5; in the inelastic scattering process the x-ray photon causes the excitation or de-excitation of a lattice vibration, and the photon changes direction and energy.

The theory we have worked out here for x-ray reflection describes equally well the **Mössbauer effect**,[16] the recoilless emission of gamma rays by nuclei bound in crystals. The theory also applies to neutron scattering.

[16] *QTS*, Chap. 20.

SUMMARY

This has been a long and important chapter. It is good to summarize the steps which relate the crystal structure to the relative intensities of the diffraction pattern produced by the structure. Suppose that we have guessed the structure. We want to predict the diffraction pattern of the assumed structure and test the prediction against the observed diffraction pattern. The observed pattern is available in the form of a map in reciprocal space giving the values of $\Delta \mathbf{k} \equiv \mathbf{k}' - \mathbf{k}$ for which diffracted beams are found. [See (17b).]

First: We choose a set of translation vectors $\mathbf{a}, \mathbf{b}, \mathbf{c}$ for the assumed structure. The vectors need not necessarily be primitive translation vectors. From $\mathbf{a}, \mathbf{b}, \mathbf{c}$ we form the vectors $\mathbf{A}, \mathbf{B}, \mathbf{C}$ which are the fundamental vectors of the reciprocal lattice. We plot the points $\mathbf{G} = h\mathbf{A} + k\mathbf{B} + l\mathbf{C}$ for integral values of h, k, l. Some or all of these points should coincide with the points of the experimental map of $\Delta \mathbf{k}$. If no points coincide, we have most probably chosen incorrect magnitudes for the lengths of $\mathbf{a}, \mathbf{b}, \mathbf{c}$. We can adjust the magnitudes until some points $\mathbf{G}$ coincide with the observed $\Delta \mathbf{k}$. The corresponding $\mathbf{a}, \mathbf{b}, \mathbf{c}$ define the crystal lattice. If this does not work, we have started with the wrong symmetry. [See (33) and (39).]

Second: Every $\Delta \mathbf{k}$ now falls on some $\mathbf{G}$, but some $\mathbf{G}$'s will not fall on a $\Delta \mathbf{k}$ if the structure factor $\mathcal{S}$ is zero for these values of $\mathbf{G}$. We calculate $\mathcal{S}$ for our assumed basis $\mathbf{a}, \mathbf{b}, \mathbf{c}$ and see if the zeros of $\mathcal{S}$ fall at the values of $\mathbf{G}$ for which no diffracted beam was observed. We adjust the positions u, v, w of the atoms in the assumed basis until the zeros of $\mathcal{S}$ coincide with the positions of the "absent" reflections. The corresponding atomic coordinates u, v, w define the basis associated with the crystal lattice. [See (65).]

Third: Values of the atomic form factor f for the atoms and G's of interest may be found in the *International tables for x-ray crystallography*.[16a] The exact indices of the zeros of $\mathcal{S}$ usually may be found without specific use of the f's. We should compare at least qualitatively the predicted and observed values of the relative intensities of the diffracted beams. To make this comparison we use the f's to calculate $|\mathcal{S}(hkl)|^2$. After we multiply this by the Debye-Waller temperature factor $\exp[-2W(hkl)]$ we obtain a rough measure of the approximate relative intensity expected for a given reflection hkl. [See (69) and (78).]

[16a] Vol. III, pp. 201–227.

Problems

1. **Planar spacing.** Show that (44) is consistent with (8), for a simple cubic lattice of lattice constant a. *Hint:* Note that for this lattice

$$\mathbf{G}(hkl) = h\mathbf{A} + k\mathbf{B} + l\mathbf{C} = (2\pi/a)(h\hat{\mathbf{a}} + k\hat{\mathbf{b}} + l\hat{\mathbf{c}}).$$

2. **Hexagonal space lattice.** The primitive translation vectors of the hexagonal space lattice as shown in Fig. 1.19 may be taken as

$$\mathbf{a} = (a/2)\hat{\mathbf{x}} + (3^{1/2}a/2)\hat{\mathbf{y}}; \qquad \mathbf{b} = -(a/2)\hat{\mathbf{x}} + (3^{1/2}a/2)\hat{\mathbf{y}}; \qquad \mathbf{c} = c\hat{\mathbf{z}}.$$

   (a) Show from (34) that the volume of the primitive cell is $(3^{1/2}/2)a^2c$.
   (b) Show using (33) that the primitive translations of the reciprocal lattice are

$$\mathbf{A} = (2\pi/a)\hat{\mathbf{x}} + (2\pi/3^{1/2}a)\hat{\mathbf{y}}; \qquad \mathbf{B} = -(2\pi/a)\hat{\mathbf{x}} + (2\pi/3^{1/2}a)\hat{\mathbf{y}}; \qquad \mathbf{C} = (2\pi/c)\hat{\mathbf{z}},$$

   so that the lattice is its own reciprocal, but with a rotation of axes. (c) Describe and sketch the first Brillouin zone of the hexagonal space lattice.

3. **Neutron diffraction.** A crystal of calcium fluoride was used in Fig. 8 to analyze the output of the monochromator. By early x-ray measurements it is known that the value of the lattice constant of the cubic unit cell of CaF_2 is 5.45 Å. From the values of the Bragg angles on the graph, calculate the neutron wavelength and compare with the value 1.16 Å printed on the figure.

4. **Form factor of uniform sphere.** (a) Find the atomic form factor f for a uniform distribution of Z electrons inside a sphere of radius R. *Hint:* In (69) set $n(\rho) = n = Z/(4\pi R^3/3)$; then $f = (4\pi n/\mu^3)\int_0^{\mu R} x \sin x \, dx$; now evaluate the integral. (b) Let $\mathbf{G}$ be the reciprocal lattice vector for a Bragg reflection $\mu R = GR \gg 1$; show that the form factor is proportional to

$$f \propto G^{-2} \cos GR,$$

   so that the scattering amplitude decreases as G increases.

5. **Structure factor of diamond.** The crystal structure of diamond is described in Chapter 1. If the unit cell is taken as the conventional cube the basis consists of eight atoms. (a) Find the structure factor (65) of this basis. (b) Find the zeros of $\mathcal{S}$ and show that the allowed reflections of the diamond structure satisfy $h + k + l = 4n$ where all indices are even and n is any integer; or else all indices are odd. (c) Show that the forbidden reflection (222) will be observed if there is an extra concentration of electrons midway between two nearest neighbor carbon atoms (see Fig. 34).

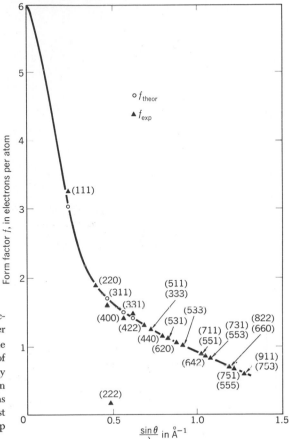

Figure 34 Experimental and theoretical atomic form factors from x-ray reflections of diamond, after S. Göttlicher and E. Wölfel, Z. Elektrochemie **63**, 891 (1959). The theoretical form factors are for a lattice of atoms of spherically symmetric charge density, as calculated by the Hartree method. The presence of the (222) forbidden reflection indicates an extra concentration of electrons (perhaps 0.4 electron) in the bond between nearest neighbors, above what one finds from the simple overlap of two spherical charge distributions.

6. *Fourier analysis of periodic array.* The electron charge density $n(\mathbf{r})$ in a crystal may be expressed as a Fourier series

$$n(\mathbf{r}) = \sum_k n_{\mathbf{k}} e^{i\mathbf{k}\cdot\mathbf{r}}.$$

If we write $\mathbf{k}$ in terms of the primitive translations $\mathbf{A}$, $\mathbf{B}$, $\mathbf{C}$ of the reciprocal lattice $\mathbf{k} = h\mathbf{A} + k\mathbf{B} + l\mathbf{C}$, show that the requirement that $n(\mathbf{r}) = n(\mathbf{r} + \mathbf{T})$ under all translations by crystal lattice vectors of the form $\mathbf{T} = n_1\mathbf{a} + n_2\mathbf{b} + n_3\mathbf{c}$ may be satisfied by setting h, k, l equal to integers. Thus

$$n(\mathbf{r}) = \sum_{\mathbf{G}} n_{\mathbf{G}} e^{i\mathbf{G}\cdot\mathbf{r}}.$$

The only values of $\mathbf{k}$ which occur in the Fourier series are the vectors $\mathbf{G}$ to the lattice points of the reciprocal lattice. That is, the charge density everywhere is described completely by values of $n_{\mathbf{k}}$ at the reciprocal lattice points $\mathbf{G}$. (The identical result applies to the Fourier analysis of any function which is invariant under all crystal lattice translations $\mathbf{T}$.)

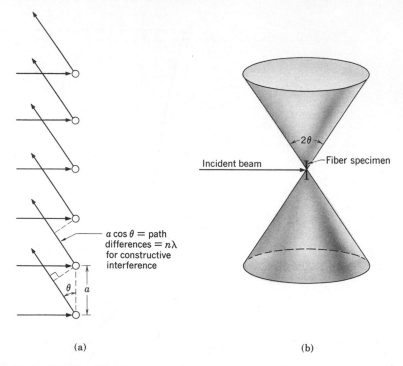

a cos θ = path
differences = nλ
for constructive
interference

Incident beam

Fiber specimen

(a)

(b)

Figure 35 The diffraction pattern from a single line of lattice constant a in a monochromatic x-ray beam perpendicular to the line. (a) The condition for constructive interference is $a \cos \theta = n\lambda$, where n is an integer. (b) For given n the diffracted rays lie on the surface of a cone.

7. *Diffraction from a linear array and a square array.* The diffraction pattern of a linear structure of lattice constant a is explained[17] in Fig. 35. Somewhat similar structures are important in molecular biology: DNA and many proteins are linear helices[18]. (a) A cylindrical film is exposed to the diffraction pattern of Fig. 35b; the axis of the cylinder is coincident with the axis of the linear structure or fiber. Describe the appearance of the diffraction pattern on the film. (b) A flat photographic plate is placed behind the fiber and normal to the incident beam. Sketch roughly the appearance of the diffraction pattern on the plate. (c) A single plane of atoms forms a square lattice of lattice constant a. The plane is normal to the incident x-ray beam. Sketch roughly the appearance

[17] Another viewpoint is useful: for a linear lattice the diffraction pattern is described [see (29)] by the single Laue equation $\mathbf{a} \cdot \Delta\mathbf{k} = 2\pi q$, where q is an integer. The lattice sums which led to the other Laue equations do not occur for a linear lattice. Now $\mathbf{a} \cdot \Delta\mathbf{k} = $ const. is the equation of a plane; thus the reciprocal lattice becomes a set of parallel planes normal to the line of atoms. What happens to the reciprocal lattice for a single plane of atoms? (Now there are two Laue equations.)

[18] The diffraction pattern of a helix is treated by W. Cochran, F. H. C. Crick, and V. Vand, Acta Cryst. **5**, 581 (1952); A. Klug, F. H. C. Crick, and H. W. Wyckoff, Acta Cryst. **11**, 199 (1958).

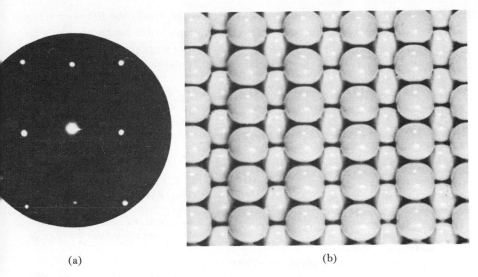

(a)   (b)

Figure 36   (a) Backward scattering pattern of 76 ev electrons incident normally on the (110) face of a nickel crystal; a model of the surface is shown in (b). (Courtesy of A. U. MacRae.)

of the diffraction pattern[19] on the photographic plate. *Hint:* The diffraction from a plane of atoms can be inferred from the patterns for two perpendicular lines of atoms. (d) Figure 36 shows the electron diffraction pattern in the backward direction from the nickel atoms on the (110) surface of a nickel crystal. Explain the orientation of the diffraction pattern in relation to the atomic positions of the surface atoms shown in the model. Assume that only the surface atoms are effective in the reflection of low-energy electrons.

8. *Diatomic line.* Consider a line of atoms $ABAB \ldots AB$, with an A—B *bond length of* $\frac{1}{2}a$. The form factors are f_A, f_B for atoms A, B, respectively. The incident beam of x-rays is perpendicular to the line of atoms. (a) Show that the interference condition is $n\lambda = a \cos \theta$, where θ is the angle between the diffracted beam and the line of atoms. (b) Show that the intensity of the diffracted beam is proportional to $|f_A - f_B|^2$ for n odd, and to $|f_A + f_B|^2$ for n even. (c) Explain what happens if $f_A = f_B$.

9. *Reciprocal lattice (110) plane.* (a) Consider the (110) plane of the lattice (58) reciprocal to the fcc lattice. Let the plane pass through the origin of the reciprocal lattice. Locate twelve lattice points about the origin, and label these points with indices hkl which refer to the reciprocal lattice to the conventional cubic cell, namely $A_c = (2\pi/a)\hat{x}$; $B_c = (2\pi/a)\hat{y}$; $C_c = (2\pi/a)\hat{z}$. Notice that not all points $G = hA_c + kB_c + lC_c$ occur. (The (110) plane is understood to be defined in terms of these hkl.) (b) Divide up the plane in the reciprocal lattice into identical Wigner-Seitz cells.

[19] See L. H. Germer, "Structure of crystal surfaces," Sci. American, March 1965, p. 32.

10. *Forbidden reflections of cubic lattices.* (a) Indicate graphically the 10 lowest values of sin θ at which x-ray diffraction occurs for a simple cubic lattice of cube edge a, taking $\lambda/a = 0.2$. *Hint:* Use Eq. (8). (b) Indicate in strips parallel to the one you have just constructed which of these ten lines will be allowed for bcc and fcc lattices of the same cube edge.

References

X-RAY DIFFRACTION

L. V. Azaroff and M. J. Buerger, *Powder methods in x-ray crystallography,* McGraw-Hill, 1958.

W. H. Bragg and W. L. Bragg, "Structure of the diamond," Proc. Roy. Soc. (London) **A89**, 277 (1913).

W. L. Bragg, "Structure of some crystals as indicated by their diffraction of x-rays," Proc. Roy. Soc. (London) **A89**, 248 (1913). (A careful treatment and analysis; the first correct structure determinations are given here.)

M. J. Buerger, *Crystal structure analysis,* Wiley, 1960.

A. Guinier, *X-ray diffraction in crystals, imperfect crystals and amorphous bodies,* Freeman, 1963.

R. W. James, *The optical principles of the diffraction of x-rays,* G. Bell and Sons, Ltd., London, new ed., 1950.

R. W. James, "Dynamical theory of x-ray diffraction," *Solid state physics* **15**, 53–220 (1963).

H. Lipson and C. A. Taylor, *Fourier transforms and x-ray diffraction,* G. Bell and Sons, Ltd., London, 1958.

H. Lipson and W. Cochran, *The determination of crystal structures,* Macmillan, New York, 1954.

W. H. Zachariasen, *Theory of x-ray diffraction in crystals,* Wiley, 1945.

NEUTRON DIFFRACTION

G. E. Bacon, *Neutron diffraction,* Oxford, 2nd ed., 1962.

ELECTRON DIFFRACTION

R. Gevers, in Strumane et al., ed., *Interaction of radiation in solids,* North-Holland, Amsterdam, 1964.

3

Crystal Binding

Table 1   Cohesive Energies° of the Elements

Energy required to form separated neutral atoms from the solid at 0°K; values in parentheses are at 298.15°K or at the melting point, whichever temperature is lower. Upper figure in ev/atom; lower in kcal/mole.

°Data furnished by Leo Brewer and reduced by S. Strässler.

Li	Be											B	C	N	O	F	Ne
1.65	3.33											5.81	7.36	(114)	(60)	(20)	(0.50)
38.0	76.9											134.	170.				
Na	Mg											Al	Si	P	S	Cl	Ar
1.13	1.53											3.34	4.64	(79.2)	2.86	(32.2)	0.080
26.0	35.3											76.9	107		66.1		1.85

K	Ca	Sc	Ti	V	Cr	Mn	Fe	Co	Ni	Cu	Zn	Ga	Ge	As	Se	Br	Kr
0.941	1.825	3.93	4.855	5.30	4.10	2.98	4.29	4.387	4.435	3.50	1.35	2.78	3.87	3.0	2.13	1.22	0.116
21.7	42.1	90.6	112.0	122.	94.5	68.7	98.9	101.2	102.3	80.8	31.1	64.2	89.3	69.	49.2	(28.2)	2.67
Rb	Sr	Y	Zr	Nb	Mo	Tc	Ru	Rh	Pd	Ag	Cd	In	Sn	Sb	Te	I	Xe
0.858		4.387	6.316	7.47	6.810		6.615	5.752	3.936	2.96	1.160	2.6	3.12	2.7	2.0		
19.8	(39.1)	101.2	145.7	172.	157.1		152.6	132.7	90.8	68.3	26.76	59	71.9	62.	46	(25.6)	(3.57)
Cs	Ba	La	Hf	Ta	W	Re	Os	Ir	Pt	Au	Hg	Tl	Pb	Bi	Po	At	Rn
0.827	1.86	4.491	6.35	8.089	8.66	8.10		6.93	5.852	3.78	(0.694)	1.87	2.04	2.15			
19.1	(42.8)	103.6	146.	186.6	200.	187.	(187)	160.	135.0	87.3	(16.0)	43.2	47.0	49.6	(34.5)		
Fr	Ra	Ac															

Ce	Pr	Nd	Pm	Sm	Eu	Gd	Tb	Dy	Ho	Er	Tm	Yb	Lu
4.77	3.9	3.35		2.11	1.80	4.14	4.1	3.1	3.0	3.3	2.6	1.6	(4.4)
110	89	77.2		48.6	41.5	95.4	94	71	70	77	59	36	(102)
Th	Pa	U	Np	Pu	Am	Cm	Bk	Cf	Es	Fm	Md		Lw
5.926	5.46	5.405	4.55	4.0	2.6								
136.7	126	124.7	105	92	60								

The world about us contains condensed matter in very many forms. There are biological materials, from DNA to enzymes, and geological materials, from granite to mica. There are the thousands of metallic alloys of the metallurgists and the millions of compounds of the organic chemists. All these are built up from atoms of one hundred chemical elements. Solid state physics at present is largely concerned only with single crystals of the elements and of simple compounds; of these we have gained a deep understanding and insight. Measurements on single crystals are always much more significant and informative than are measurements on polycrystalline specimens.

The observed differences between the forms of condensed matter are caused by differences in the distribution of the electrons and nuclei, or particularly of the outermost electrons and the ion cores. In studying a crystal we first ask ourselves "Where are the nuclei and the electrons?" The determination of the structure of the solid often can be handled by the diffraction methods of Chapter 2.

In this chapter we are concerned with the question: What holds a crystal together? *The attractive electrostatic interaction between the negative charges of the electrons and the positive charges of the nuclei is entirely responsible for the cohesion of solids.* Magnetic forces have only a weak effect on cohesion, and gravitational forces are negligible. Given a knowledge of the spatial distribution and velocity distribution of electrons and nuclei in a crystal (as determined in principle by quantum mechanics), we can calculate the binding energy of the crystal. Specialized terms are employed only to categorize distinctive situations: exchange energy, van der Waals forces, resonance stabilization energy, and covalent bonds.

To bind atoms into solids by the electrostatic attraction between the valence electrons and the ion cores we can do four things, which are not all compatible:

1. The positive ions should be kept apart, in order to minimize the Coulomb repulsion of like charges.

2. The valence electrons should also be kept apart.

3. The valence electrons should be kept close to the positive ions, to maximize the Coulomb attraction of unlike charges.

4. These three suggestions may lower the potential energy of the system, but they must be carried out in such a way that the kinetic energy of the system is not much increased. By quantum theory any localization of electrons tends to increase the kinetic energy.[1]

---

[1] Suppose we localize an electron in one dimension in a region of extent Δx; the Heisenberg uncertainty principle tells us that the related spread in momentum $\Delta(mv) \geq h/2\pi \Delta x$, where h is Planck's constant. Thus the value of the kinetic energy $\frac{1}{2}mv^2$ is at least $h^2/2m(2\pi \Delta x)^2$. If $\Delta x \approx 10^{-8}$ cm, then the kinetic energy is $\approx 5 \times 10^{-12}$ erg ≈ 3 ev.

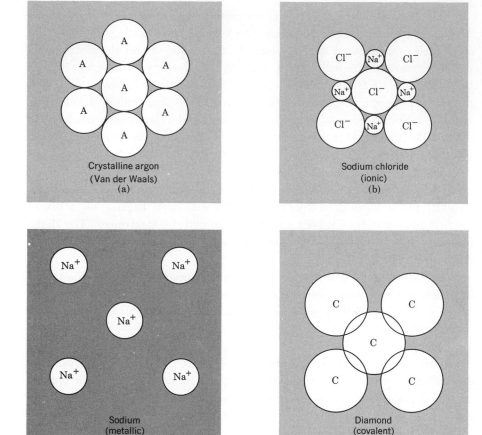

Figure 1 The principal types of crystalline binding forces. In (a) neutral atoms are bound together weakly by the van der Waals forces associated with fluctuations in the charge distributions. In (b) electrons are transferred from the alkali atoms to the halogen atoms, and the resulting ions are held together by attractive electrostatic forces between the positive and negative ions. In (c) the valence electrons are taken away from each alkali atom to form a community electron sea in which the positive ions are dispersed. In (d) the neutral atoms appear to be bound together by the overlapping parts of their electron distributions.

To discuss cohesion we compare the total energy of the solid, kinetic plus potential, with the energy of the same number of free neutral atoms at infinite separation. A crystal can only be stable if its total energy is lower than the total energy of the atoms or molecules when free. The difference (free atom energy) — (crystal energy) is defined as the **cohesive energy.**

Values of the cohesive energy of the crystalline elements, referred to separated neutral atoms, are given in Table 1. The values are usually obtained from a combination of thermodynamic and spectroscopic data. Notice the wide variation in cohesive energy between different columns of the table. The inert gas crystals (at the right) are weakly bound, with cohesive energies less than a few percent of the elements in the C, Si, Ge . . . column. The alkali metal crystals (at the left) have intermediate values of the cohesive energy. The transition element metals (in the middle columns) are quite strongly bound. Ionic compounds (not shown) are also strongly bound.

In Fig. 1 we picture the principal types of crystalline binding forces. In this chapter we shall try to understand at least qualitatively the reasons for some of the differences in the binding forces.

CRYSTALS OF INERT GASES

In many respects the inert gases form the simplest crystals known to us. The properties of inert gas crystals at absolute zero are summarized in Table 2. The crystals are transparent insulators and are weakly bound, with low melting temperatures. The crystals are composed of atoms which have very high ionization energies. The outermost electronic shells of the atoms are completely filled, and the distribution of electronic charge in the free atom is spherically symmetric. In the crystal there is every reason for the inert gas atoms to pack together as closely as possible: the crystal structures

Table 2   Properties of inert gas crystals
(Extrapolated to 0°K and zero atmospheres pressure)

	Nearest-neighbor distance, in Å	Cohesive energy°		Melting point, deg K	Ionization† potential of free atom, ev	Parameters in Lennard-Jones potential,‡ Eq. (4)	
		kcal/mole	ev/atom			ϵ in $10^{-16} \times$ erg	σ, in Å
Ne	3.13	0.45 ± 0.01	0.02	24	21.56	50	2.74
Ar	3.76	1.85	0.080	84	15.76	167	3.40
Kr	4.01	2.67	0.116	117	14.00	225	3.65
Xe	4.35	3.83 ± 0.05	0.17	161	12.13	320	3.98

°See E. R. Dobbs and G. O. Jones, Rpts. Prog. Phys. **20**, 516 (1957); the values for Ar and Kr were furnished by L. Brewer.

†See C. E. Moore, *Atomic energy levels*, Circular of the National Bureau of Standards 467 Vol. I, p. XL. These volumes are the canonical source for data about the electronic energy states of free atoms.

‡N. Bernardes, Phys. Rev. **112**, 1534 (1958).

Figure 2 Cubic close-packed (fcc) crystal structure of crystals of the inert gases Ne, Ar, Kr, and Xe. The lattice parameters of the unit cubes are 4.42, 5.32, 5.67, and 6.15 Å, respectively.

(Fig. 2) actually are all cubic close-packed (fcc), except[2] for He^3 and He^4.

What holds an inert gas crystal together? We believe that the electron distribution in the crystal cannot be significantly distorted from the electron distribution around the free atoms, because the cohesive energy of an atom in the crystal is only one percent or less of the ionization energy of an atomic electron, from Table 2. Thus not much energy is available to distort the free atom charge distributions.

Van der Waals–London Interaction

Consider two identical inert gas atoms at a separation R large in comparison with any reasonable measure of the radii of the atoms. What interactions exist between the two neutral atoms?

[2] Zero-point motion (kinetic energy at absolute zero) is a quantum effect which plays a dominant role in He^3 and He^4. They do not solidify at zero pressure even at absolute zero. The average fluctuation at $0°K$ of an He atom from its equilibrium position is of the order of 30–40 percent of the nearest-neighbor distance. See L. H. Nosanow and G. L. Shaw, Phys. Rev. **128**, 546 (1962). The heavier the atom, the less important are the zero-point effects, as we can see from mass dependence of the expression for the kinetic energy in footnote 1.

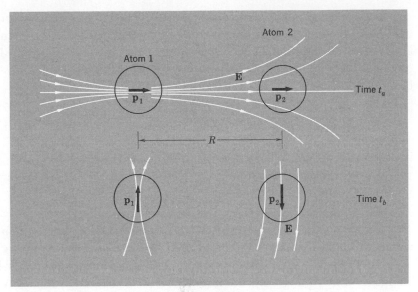

Figure 3 Origin of the van der Waals interaction, according to a classical argument. At one instant of time there is a dipole moment p_1 on atom 1. This produces an electric field E at atom 2, which acquires an induced dipole moment p_2. Diagrams are shown for two times, t_a and t_b. The interaction is always attractive: the closer the atoms, the tighter the binding.

If the charge distributions on the atoms were rigid, the interaction between atoms would be zero, because the electrostatic potential of a spherical distribution of electronic charge is canceled outside a neutral atom by the electrostatic potential of the charge on the nucleus. Then the inert gas atoms could show no cohesion and could not condense, contrary to experiment. It is true that the time-average electric moments are all zero. But the electrons are in motion around the nucleus even in the lowest electronic state, and at any instant of time there is likely to be a nonvanishing electric dipole moment from this motion.[3] An instantaneous dipole moment of magnitude p_1 on one atom (Fig. 3) produces an electric field E of magnitude $2p_1/R^3$ at the center of the second atom distant R from the first atom. This field will induce an instantaneous dipole moment $p_2 = \alpha E = 2\alpha p_1/R^3$ on the second atom; here α is the electronic polarizability (Chapter 12). The potential energy of the dipole moments is

$$U(R) \approx -\frac{2p_1 p_2}{R^3} = -\frac{4\alpha p_1{}^2}{R^6}. \tag{1}$$

The interaction is attractive.

---

[3] The semiclassical model leads to the correct result, but the language is not to be taken entirely literally.

The coefficient αp_1^2 may be estimated as follows: Electronic polarizabilities have dimensions [length]^3 as we see from the relation $p_2 = 2\alpha p_1/R^3$ above; and the relevant length is an atomic radius, denoted by r_0. Dipole moments have dimensions [charge] $\times$ [length] and have magnitudes of the order of er_0. Thus

$$U(R) \approx -\frac{4e^2r_0^5}{R^6} \approx -\frac{4(5 \times 10^{-10})^2(1 \times 10^{-8})^5}{R^6} \approx -\frac{10^{-58}}{R^6}, \quad (2)$$

in ergs for R in cm. We have taken $r_0 \approx 10^{-8}$ cm.

We write the interaction as

$$U(R) = -C/R^6. \quad (3)$$

This is known variously as the **van der Waals interaction**,[4] the London interaction, or the fluctuating dipole interaction. It is the principal attractive interaction in crystals of inert gases and also in crystals of many organic molecules. Taking $C \approx 10^{-58}$ erg-cm^6, the interaction[5] at a separation $R = 4$ Å as for krypton has the value $U \approx 10^{-58}/4 \times 10^{-45} \approx 2 \times 10^{-14}$ erg $\approx 100°$K, which is the order of magnitude of the melting temperature of inert gas crystals.

Because of the R^{-6} dependence the interaction increases rapidly at shorter distances. For example, at the interatomic separation, 2.55 Å, of metallic copper the van der Waals interaction between the Cu$^+$ ion cores is $\approx 2 \times 10^{-13}$ ergs for the above value of C. A better value of C may be as much as ten times greater, which would account for a substantial part of the high cohesive energy of copper (Table 1).

Repulsive Interaction

As the two atoms are brought together their charge distributions gradually overlap (Fig. 4), thereby changing the energy of the system. At sufficiently close separations the overlap energy is repulsive. For atoms with filled electronic shells the overlap energy may be repulsive[6] at all distances of interest (say 0.5 Å to 5 Å), in large part because of the Pauli exclusion principle.

[4] An elegant semiclassical derivation is given in Appendix 39 of M. Born, *Atomic physics*, Hafner, 1962, 7th ed. The quantum-mechanical theory is discussed by H. Margenau, Revs. Mod. Phys. **11**, 1 (1939). In the London approximation for identical molecules $C \approx \hbar\omega_0\alpha^2$, where $\hbar\omega_0$ is the energy of the strongest optical absorption line and α is the electronic polarizability. The discussion we have given above is essentially correct, but the language is not good quantum mechanics.

[5] It is easier to grasp the magnitude of an interaction energy U if it is expressed in terms of an effective temperature which we define by the relation $k_BT = U$, where k_B is the Boltzmann constant.

[6] The overlap energy naturally depends on the radial distribution of charge about each atom. The mathematical calculation is always complicated even if the charge distribution is known. For a clear discussion for two hydrogen atoms, see Chapter 12 of L. Pauling and E. B. Wilson, *Introduction to quantum mechanics*, McGraw-Hill, 1935.

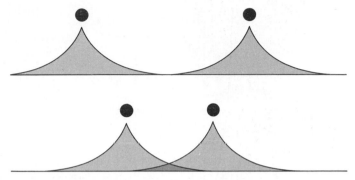

Figure 4 Electronic charge distributions overlap as atoms approach. The solid circles denote the nuclei.

The elementary statement of the **Pauli exclusion principle** is that no two electrons can have all their quantum numbers equal. The Pauli principle prevents two electrons from occupying the same quantum state: when the charge distributions of two atoms overlap there is a tendency for electrons from atom B to occupy in part states of atom A already occupied by electrons of atom A, and vice versa. The Pauli principle prevents multiple occupancy, and electron distributions of atoms with closed shells can overlap only if accompanied by the partial promotion of electrons to unoccupied higher energy states of the atoms. Thus the electron overlap increases the total energy of the system and gives a repulsive contribution to the interaction.[7]

We make no attempt here to evaluate the repulsive interaction from first principles. Experimental data on the inert gases can be fitted well by an empirical repulsive potential of the form B/R^{12}, where B is a positive constant, when used together with a long-range attractive potential of the form of (3). The constants B and C are empirical parameters determined from measurements made in the gas phase; the data used include the virial coefficients and the viscosity. It is usual to write the total potential energy of two atoms at separation R as

$$U(R) = 4\epsilon\left[\left(\frac{\sigma}{R}\right)^{12} - \left(\frac{\sigma}{R}\right)^{6}\right], \tag{4}$$

where ϵ and σ are now the parameters, with $4\epsilon\sigma^6 \equiv C$ and $4\epsilon\sigma^{12} \equiv B$. The potential (4) is known as the Lennard-Jones potential, and is plotted in

[7] A simple example of repulsion due only to the increase of kinetic energy as forced by the Pauli principle can be understood from Eq. (7.13). Suppose first that we have two identical systems each of N electrons confined to a line of length L. The total kinetic energy is $(2\hbar^2/3m)(1/2L)^3 \cdot (N/2)^3$. The energy is unchanged if we combine the systems and place $2N$ electrons on a line of length $2L$. If we now compress the combined systems we see that the energy increases proportional to $1/L^2$.

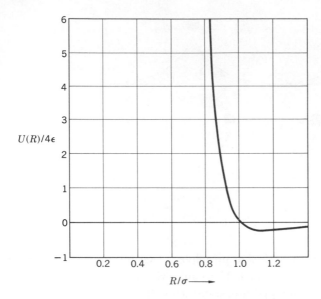

$U(R)/4\epsilon$

$R/\sigma \longrightarrow$

Figure 5 Form of the Lennard-Jones potential (4) which describes the interaction of two inert gas atoms. The minimum occurs at $R/\sigma = 2^{1/6} \cong$ 1.12. Notice how steep the curve is inside the minimum, and how flat it is outside the minimum. The value of U at the minimum is $-\epsilon$; and $U = 0$ at $R = \sigma$. The minimum of V is at $R \cong 1.122\sigma$.

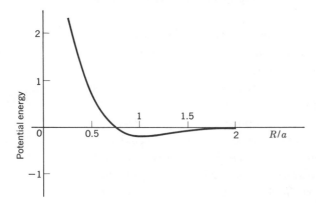

Potential energy

R/a

Figure 6 Coulomb energy of two spheres of radius a, as a function of the distance R between their centers. Each sphere carries a charge $+q$ at its center, and has a charge $-q$ uniformly distributed throughout the volume of the sphere. The charges are taken as rigid, so that van der Waals and polarization effects are not included in this model. (Courtesy of C. Y. Fong.)

Fig. 5. The force between the two atoms is given by $-dU/dR$. Values of ϵ and σ as recommended by Bernardes are given in Table 2; the values can be obtained from gas-phase data, so that calculations on properties of the solid do not involve any disposable parameters.

Other empirical forms for the repulsive interaction are widely used,[8] in particular the exponential form $\lambda \exp(-R/\rho)$, where ρ is a measure of the range of the interaction. This is generally as easy to handle analytically as the inverse power law form. The classical Coulomb energy of two neutral atoms with static electrons distributed uniformly inside spheres is plotted in Fig. 6.

[8] For discussions of repulsive terms, see M. P. Tosi, *Solid state physics* **16**, 1 (1964); Hirschfelder, Curtiss, and Bird, *Molecular theory of gases and liquids*, Wiley, 1954; F. G. Fumi and M. P. Tosi, J. Phys. Chem. Solids **25**, 31, 45 (1964).

Equilibrium Lattice Constants

If we neglect the kinetic energy of the inert gas atoms, the cohesive energy of an inert gas crystal is given by summing the Lennard-Jones potential (4) over all pairs of atoms in the crystal. If there are N atoms in the crystal, the total potential energy is

$$U_{\text{tot}} = \tfrac{1}{2}N(4\epsilon)\left[\sum_{j}{}'\left(\frac{\sigma}{p_{ij}R}\right)^{12} - \sum_{j}{}'\left(\frac{\sigma}{p_{ij}R}\right)^{6}\right], \tag{5}$$

where $p_{ij}R$ is the distance between reference i atom and any other atom j, expressed in terms of the nearest neighbor distance R. The factor $\tfrac{1}{2}$ occurs with the N to avoid counting twice each pair of atoms. The summations in (5) have been evaluated,[9] and for the fcc structure

$$\sum_{j}{}'p_{ij}^{-12} = 12.131; \qquad \sum_{j}{}'p_{ij}^{-6} = 14.454. \tag{6}$$

There are twelve nearest-neighbor sites in the fcc structure; we see that the series are rapidly converging and have values not far from twelve. Thus the nearest neighbors contribute most of the interaction energy of inert gas crystals.

If we take U_{tot} in (5) as the total energy of the crystal, the equilibrium value R_0 is given by requiring that U_{tot} be a minimum with respect to variations in the nearest neighbor distance R:

$$\frac{dU_{\text{tot}}}{dR} = 0 = -2N\epsilon\left[(12)(12.13)\frac{\sigma^{12}}{R^{13}} - (6)(14.45)\frac{\sigma^{6}}{R^{7}}\right], \tag{7}$$

whence

$$R_0/\sigma = 1.09, \tag{8}$$

the same for all elements with an fcc structure. The observed values of R_0/σ, using the independently determined values of σ given in Table 2, are:

	Ne	Ar	Kr	Xe
R_0/σ	1.14	1.11	1.10	1.09

The agreement with (8) is remarkable. The slight departure of R_0/σ from the universal value 1.09 predicted for inert gases can be explained by quantum effects.[10]

Cohesive Energy

The cohesive energy of inert gas crystals at absolute zero and at zero pressure is obtained by substituting (6) and (8) in (5):

---

[9] J. E. Lennard-Jones and A. E. Ingham, Proc. Roy. Soc. (London) **A107**, 636 (1925).

[10] N. Bernardes, Phys. Rev. **112**, 1534 (1958); see also L. H. Nosanow and G. L. Shaw, Phys. Rev. **128**, 546 (1962).

$$U_{tot}(R) = 2N\epsilon \left[(12.13) \left(\frac{\sigma}{R} \right)^{12} - (14.45) \left(\frac{\sigma}{R} \right)^{6} \right], \tag{9}$$

and, at $R = R_0$,

$$U_{tot}(R_0) = -(2.15)(4N\epsilon), \tag{10}$$

the same for all inert gases. This is the calculated cohesive energy if the kinetic energy is zero. Bernardes has calculated quantum-mechanical corrections including kinetic energy contributions; the corrections act to reduce the binding and amount to 28, 10, 6, and 4 percent of Eq. (10) for Ne, Ar, Kr, and Xe, respectively. The heavier the atom, the smaller the correction, because the kinetic energy of particles of equal wavelength is inversely proportional to their masses.[11] The final calculated cohesive energies agree with the experimental values of Table 2 within 1 to 7 percent.

Compressibility and Bulk Modulus

An independent test of the theory is provided by the **bulk modulus**, defined as

$$B = -V \frac{dp}{dV}, \tag{11}$$

where V is the volume and p the pressure. The compressibility is defined as the reciprocal of the bulk modulus. At absolute zero the entropy is constant, so that $dU = -p\, dV$ is the change in energy accompanying a change dV in volume. Thus $dp/dV = -d^2U/dV^2$, whence

$$B = V \frac{d^2U}{dV^2}. \tag{12}$$

The volume occupied by N atoms in an fcc lattice of lattice constant a is $V = \frac{1}{4}Na^3$, because $\frac{1}{4}a^3$ is the volume per atom (Chapter 1). In terms of the nearest-neighbor distance $R = a/\sqrt{2}$, we have $V = NR^3/\sqrt{2}$. The potential energy (9) may be written as

$$U_{tot}(V) = \frac{b_{12}}{V^4} - \frac{b_6}{V^2}, \tag{13}$$

where the parameters b_{12} and b_6 follow from (5) and (6):

$$b_{12} \equiv \tfrac{1}{2}(12.13)N^5\epsilon\sigma^{12}; \qquad b_6 \equiv (14.45)N^3\epsilon\sigma^6.$$

At equilibrium under zero pressure

[11] For free particles $E = p^2/2M = (h/\lambda)^2/2M$, using the de Broglie relation.

$$\frac{dU_{\text{tot}}}{dV} = 0 = -\frac{4b_{12}}{V^5} + \frac{2b_6}{V^3},$$ (14)

whence the equilibrium volume is given by

$$V_0 = (2b_{12}/b_6)^{1/2}.$$ (15)

The bulk modulus from (13) is

$$B = \left(V\frac{d^2U}{dV^2}\right)_{V_0} = \frac{20b_{12}}{V_0^5} - \frac{6b_6}{V_0^3} = \sqrt{2}\frac{b_6^{5/2}}{b_{12}^{3/2}},$$ (16)

which is of the order of magnitude ϵ/σ^3. The values of B from (16) are in very good agreement with the available experimental results.

With the empirical two-atom potential (4) inferred from gas-phase data we can give an excellent account of the observed properties of the inert gas crystals Ne, Ar, Kr, and Xe. Quantum corrections improve the agreement further.

IONIC CRYSTALS

Ionic crystals are made up of positive and negative ions. The ions arrange themselves with the Coulomb attraction between ions of opposite sign stronger than the Coulomb repulsion between ions of the same sign. The **ionic bond** is the bond resulting from the electrostatic interaction of oppositely charged ions. Two common crystal structures found for ionic crystals, the sodium chloride and the cesium chloride structures, were shown in Figs. 23 to 26 of Chapter 1.

The electronic configurations of all ions of a simple ionic crystal correspond to closed electronic shells, as in the inert gas atoms. In lithium fluoride the configuration of the neutral atoms are, according to the periodic table in the front end papers of this book,

$$\text{Li:} \quad 1s^22s; \qquad \text{F:} \quad 1s^22s^22p^5.$$

The singly charged ions have the configurations

$$\text{Li}^+: \quad 1s^2, \qquad \text{F}^-: \quad 1s^22s^22p^6,$$

as for helium and neon, respectively. Inert gas atoms have closed shells, and the charge distributions are spherically symmetric. We expect that the charge distributions on each ion in an ionic crystal will have approximately spherical symmetry, with some distortion near the region of contact with neighboring atoms. This picture is confirmed by x-ray studies of electron distributions

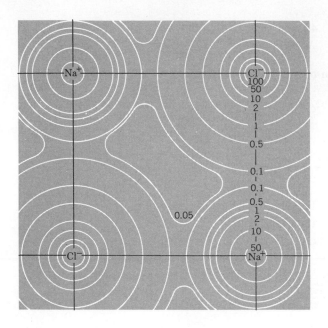

Figure 7 Electron density distribution in the base plane of NaCl, after x-ray studies by G. Schoknecht, Z. Naturforschg. **12a**, 983 (1957).

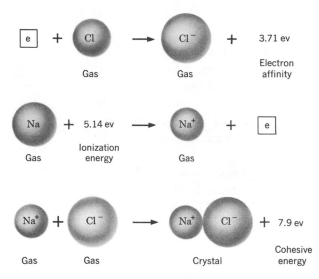

Figure 8 The energy per molecule unit of a crystal of sodium chloride is $(7.9 - 5.1 + 3.7) = 6.5$ ev lower than the energy of separated neutral atoms. The cohesive energy with respect to separated *ions* is 7.9 ev per molecule unit. All values on the figure are experimental.

(Fig. 7); distortions from spherical symmetry will appear as extra x-ray reflections, as in Problem 2.5.

A quick estimate suggests that we are not misguided in looking to electrostatic interactions for a large part of the binding energy of an ionic crystal. The distance between a positive ion and the nearest negative ion in crystalline sodium chloride is 2.81×10^{-8} cm, so that the attractive part of the potential energy of the two ions by themselves is

$$\frac{e^2}{r_0} = \frac{(4.8 \times 10^{-10})^2}{2.81 \times 10^{-8}} = 8.2 \times 10^{-12} \text{ erg} = 5.1 \text{ ev}.$$

This value may be compared (Fig. 8) with the known value from Table 3 of 7.9 ev per molecule unit for the cohesive energy of crystalline NaCl with respect to separated Na^+ and Cl^- ions. The order of magnitude agreement between the values is quite suggestive. We now calculate the lattice energy more closely.

ELECTROSTATIC OR MADELUNG ENERGY

The long range interaction between ions with charge $\pm q$ is the electrostatic interaction $\pm q^2/r$, attractive between ions of opposite charge and repulsive between ions of the same charge. The ions arrange themselves in whatever crystal structure gives the strongest attractive interaction compatible with the repulsive interaction which sets in at short distances between ion cores. The repulsive interactions between ions with inert gas configurations are similar to those between inert gas atoms. The van der Waals part of the attractive interaction in ionic crystals makes a relatively small contribution to the cohesive energy, of the order of 1 or 2 percent. The main contribution to the binding energy of ionic crystals is electrostatic and is called the **Madelung energy.**

If U_{ij} is the interaction energy between ions i and j, the total energy of any one ion i is

$$U_i = \sum_j{}' U_{ij}, \tag{17}$$

where the summation includes all ions except $j = i$. We suppose that U_{ij} may be written as the sum of a central field repulsive potential of the form $\lambda \exp(-r/\rho)$, where λ and ρ are empirical parameters, and a Coulomb potential $\pm q^2/r$. Thus

$$U_{ij} = \lambda \exp(-r_{ij}/\rho) \pm \frac{q^2}{r_{ij}}, \tag{18}$$

where the $+$ sign is taken for the like charges and the $-$ sign for unlike charges. The repulsive term describes the fact that filled electronic shells act as if they are fairly hard, and each ion resists overlapping with the electron distributions of neighboring ions. We have seen that this is in large measure an effect of the Pauli exclusion principle. We regard the strength λ and range ρ as constants to be determined from observed values[12] of the lattice constant

---

[12] For the ions we do not have gas-phase data available to permit the independent determination of λ and ρ.

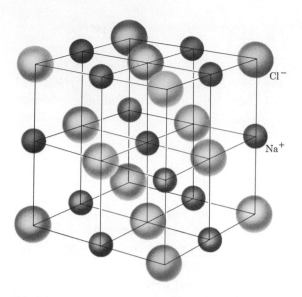

Cl⁻

Na⁺

Figure 9 We may construct the sodium chloride crystal structure by arranging Na⁺ and Cl⁻ ions alternately at the lattice
points of a simple cubic lattice. In the crystal each ion is surrounded by six nearest neighbors of the opposite charge and
twelve next-nearest neighbors of the same charge as the reference ion. The Na⁺ ion carries a single positive charge, so that
the electronic configuration is identical with neon, and the Cl⁻
ion carries a single negative charge and is in the argon configuration. The space lattice is fcc, as discussed in Chap. 1.

and compressibility; we have used the exponential form of the empirical
repulsive potential rather than the R^{-12} form used for the inert gases. The
change of form is made partly for variety in the discussion and partly because
it may give a better representation of the repulsive interaction.

In the NaCl structure (Fig. 9) the value of U_i does not depend on
whether the reference ion i is a positive or a negative ion. The sum (17) can
be arranged to converge rapidly, so that its value will not depend on the particular location of the reference ion in the crystal, as long as it is not near the
surface. Neglecting surface effects, we may write the total lattice energy U_{tot}
of a crystal composed of N molecules or $2N$ ions as

$$U_{\text{tot}} = NU_i. \tag{19}$$

Here N, rather than $2N$, occurs because in taking the total lattice energy we
must count each *pair* of interactions only once. The total lattice energy (19)

is the energy required to separate the crystal into individual ions at an infinite distance apart.

It is convenient again to introduce quantities p_{ij} such that $r_{ij} \equiv p_{ij}R$, where R is the nearest-neighbor separation in the crystal. If we include the repulsive interaction only among nearest neighbors, we have

$$U_{ij} = \begin{cases} \lambda \exp\ (-R/\rho) - \dfrac{q^2}{R} & \text{(nearest neighbors)} \\[2ex] \pm \dfrac{1}{p_{ij}} \dfrac{q^2}{R} & \text{(otherwise).} \end{cases} \tag{20}$$

Thus

$$U_{\text{tot}} = NU_i = N\left(z\lambda e^{-R/\rho} - \frac{\alpha q^2}{R}\right), \tag{21}$$

where z is the number of nearest neighbors of any ion and

$$\boxed{\alpha \equiv \sum_j \frac{(\pm)}{p_{ij}} \equiv \textbf{Madelung constant.}} \tag{22}$$

The sum should include the nearest-neighbor contribution, which is just z. The $(\pm)$ sign is discussed just before (26). The value of the Madelung constant is of central importance in the theory of an ionic crystal. Methods for its calculation are discussed below.

At the equilibrium separation $dU_{\text{tot}}/dR = 0$, so that

$$N\frac{dU_i}{dR} = -\frac{Nz\lambda}{\rho} \exp\ (-R/\rho) + \frac{N\alpha q^2}{R^2} = 0, \tag{23}$$

or

$$R_0^2 \exp\ (-R_0/\rho) = \frac{\rho\alpha q^2}{z\lambda}. \tag{24}$$

This determines the equilibrium separation R_0 if the parameters ρ, λ of the repulsive interaction are known.

The total lattice energy of the crystal of $2N$ ions at their equilibrium separation R_0 may be written, using (21) and (24), as

$$U_{\text{tot}} = -\frac{N\alpha q^2}{R_0}\left(1 - \frac{\rho}{R_0}\right). \tag{25}$$

The term $-N\alpha q^2/R_0$ is the Madelung energy. We shall find in (33) that ρ is of the order of $0.1R_0$, so that the cohesive energy is dominated by the Madelung contribution. The low value of ρ/R_0 means that the repulsive interaction is steep and has a very short range.

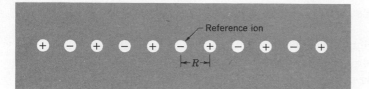

Figure 10 Line of ions of alternating signs, with distance R between ions.

Evaluation of the Madelung Constant[13]

The first calculation of the Coulomb energy constant α was made by Madelung.[14] A powerful general method for lattice sum calculations was developed by Ewald,[15] and Evjen and Frank[16] have given simple methods which arrange the counting in rapidly convergent ways.

The definition (22) of the Madelung constant α is

$$\alpha = \sum_j{}' \frac{(\pm)}{p_{ij}}.$$

If we take the reference ion as a negative charge the plus sign will be used for positive ions and the minus sign for negative ions. An equivalent definition is

$$\frac{\alpha}{R} = \sum_j{}' \frac{(\pm)}{r_j}, \tag{26}$$

where r_j is the distance of the jth ion from the reference ion and R is the nearest-neighbor distance. It must be emphasized that the value given for α will depend on whether it is defined in terms of the nearest-neighbor distance R or in terms of the lattice parameter a or in terms of some other relevant length. *Beware!*

As an example, we compute the value of the Madelung constant for the infinite line of ions of alternating sign in Fig. 10. We pick a negative ion as reference ion, and let R denote the distance between adjacent ions. Then

$$\frac{\alpha}{R} = 2\left[\frac{1}{R} - \frac{1}{2R} + \frac{1}{3R} - \frac{1}{4R} + \cdots\right],$$

or

$$\alpha = 2\left[1 - \frac{1}{2} + \frac{1}{3} - \frac{1}{4} + \cdots\right];$$

the factor 2 occurs because there are two ions, one to the right and one to the left, at equal distances r_j. We sum this series by the expansion

---

[13] A detailed review and bibliography is given by M. P. Tosi, *Solid state physics* **16**, 1 (1964).

[14] E. Madelung, Physik. Z. **19**, 524 (1918).

[15] P. P. Ewald, Ann. Physik **64**, 253 (1921); see also Appendix A to the second edition of this book.

[16] H. M. Evjen, Phys. Rev. **39**, 675 (1932); F. C. Frank, Phil. Mag. **41**, 1287 (1950).

$$\log (1 + x) = x - \frac{x^2}{2} + \frac{x^3}{3} - \frac{x^4}{4} + \cdots .$$

Thus for the one-dimensional chain the Madelung constant is

$$\alpha = 2 \log 2. \tag{27}$$

In three dimensions the series presents greater difficulty. It is not possible to write down the successive terms by a casual inspection. More important, the series will not converge unless the successive terms in the series are arranged so that the contributions from the positive and negative terms nearly cancel.

In the sodium chloride structure (Fig. 9) the nearest neighbors to the negative reference ion are six positive ions at $p = 1$, giving a positive contribution to α of $6/1$; there are twelve negative ions at $p = 2^{1/2}$, giving $-12/2^{1/2}$; eight positive ions at $p = 3^{1/2}$, giving $8/3^{1/2}$; six negative ions at $p = 2$, giving $-6/2$; etc. Thus

$$\alpha = \frac{6}{1} - \frac{12}{2^{1/2}} + \frac{8}{3^{1/2}} - \frac{6}{2} + \cdots$$

$$= 6.000 - 8.485 + 4.620 - 3.000 + \cdots .$$

The convergence is obviously poor.

We may improve the convergence by arranging to work with neutral, or nearly neutral, groups of ions, if necessary dividing an ion among different groups and using fractional charges. The physical motivation for working with a neutral group is that its potential falls off faster[17] at a distance than if the group has an excess of charge.

In the sodium chloride structure we obtain nearly neutral groups by considering the charges on cubes, counting charges on cube faces as shared between two cells, on edges as shared between four cells, and on corners as shared between eight cells. The first cube (Fig. 11) surrounding the negative reference ion intercepts six positive charges on cube faces, twelve negative charges on cube edges, and eight positive charges at cube corners. The contribution to α from the first cube is

$$\frac{\frac{6}{2}}{1} - \frac{\frac{12}{4}}{2^{1/2}} + \frac{\frac{8}{8}}{3^{1/2}} = 1.46.$$

On taking into account in similar fashion the ions in the next larger cube[18] enclosing the original cube, we get $\alpha = 1.75$, which is close to the accurate value $\alpha = 1.747558$ for sodium chloride.

Typical values of the Madelung constant are listed below, based on unit

---

[17] The potential of a charge goes as $1/r$; of a dipole as $1/r^2$; of a quadrupole as $1/r^3$, etc.

[18] The remainder of fractional charges not counted in the first cube is to be counted as part of the second cube.

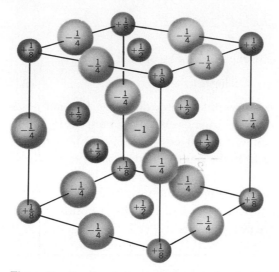

Figure 11 Fractional charge assignments for the NaCl structure, arranged according to the Evjen method for calculating the Madelung constant. Face atoms carry charge $+\frac{1}{2}$; edge atoms $-\frac{1}{4}$; corner atoms $+\frac{1}{8}$.

charges and *referred to the nearest-neighbor distance:*

Structure	α
Sodium chloride, NaCl	1.747558
Cesium chloride, CsCl	1.762670
Zinc blende, cubic ZnS	1.6381

The cesium chloride structure is shown in Fig. 1.26. Each ion is at the center of a cube formed by eight ions of the opposite charge. For the same nearest-neighbor distance the cesium chloride structure has a slightly ($\sim$1 percent) stronger Madelung contribution to the cohesive energy than in the sodium chloride structure, as the value of the Madelung constant α is higher for cesium chloride. But there are more nearest neighbors in CsCl, so that the repulsive energy is higher. Each ion has eight nearest neighbors contributing to the repulsive energy, whereas there are only six in sodium chloride. The repulsive energy is about 10 percent of the total energy of sodium chloride; roughly, we might expect the repulsive energy to be perhaps $\frac{8}{6} \times 10$ percent ≈ 13 percent of the total energy in cesium chloride. This increase outweighs the Madelung energy difference and may favor the sodium chloride structure by a small amount. Problem 3 involves a comparison of the NaCl and cubic ZnS structures.

Many more ionic crystals are known with the sodium chloride structure than with the cesium chloride structure, but the differences in binding energy are small. We can decide which structure will be stable for a particular salt only by a consideration of second-order contributions to the energy. A detailed discussion of the stability of the two lattices is given in the review article by Tosi.

Bulk Modulus

We found in (12) that the bulk modulus at absolute zero is given by $B = V \, d^2U/dV^2$, where V is the volume. For the NaCl structure the volume occupied by N molecules is $V = 2NR^3$, where R is the nearest-neighbor distance. This follows because the volume per molecule is $\frac{1}{4}a^3$ and $a = 2R$, as in Fig. 11.

Now

$$\frac{dU}{dV} = \frac{dU}{dR}\frac{dR}{dV}; \qquad \frac{dR}{dV} = \frac{1}{dV/dR} = \frac{1}{6NR^2}; \qquad (28)$$

$$\frac{d^2U}{dV^2} = \frac{d^2U}{dR^2}\left(\frac{dR}{dV}\right)^2 + \frac{dU}{dR}\frac{d^2R}{dV^2}. \qquad (29)$$

At the equilibrium separation $R = R_0$ and $dU/dR = 0$, whence

$$B = V\frac{d^2U}{dR^2}\left(\frac{1}{6NR^2}\right)^2 = \frac{1}{18NR_0}\frac{d^2U}{dR^2}. \qquad (30)$$

By (21) and (24),

$$\left(\frac{d^2U}{dR^2}\right)_{R_0} = \frac{Nz\lambda}{\rho^2}e^{-R_0/\rho} - \frac{2N\alpha q^2}{R_0^3} = \frac{N\alpha q^2}{R_0^3}\left(\frac{R_0}{\rho} - 2\right),$$

whence

$$B = \frac{\alpha q^2}{18R_0^4}\left(\frac{R_0}{\rho} - 2\right). \qquad (31)$$

We may solve (31) for ρ using observed values of R_0 and the bulk modulus. We may then calculate the cohesive energy from (25) and compare with experimental results. Let us carry out the calculation for KCl. The experimental value of the bulk modulus of KCl extrapolated to absolute zero temperature is $B = 1.97 \times 10^{11}$ dynes/cm^2, using Eq. (4.29) and Table 4.1. The nearest-neighbor separation R_0 is 3.14×10^{-8} cm; α is 1.75; and thus (31) gives

$$\frac{R_0}{\rho} = \frac{18R_0^4B}{\alpha q^2} + 2 \cong 10.4, \qquad (32)$$

so that the range of the repulsive interaction is $\rho \cong 0.30 \times 10^{-8}$ cm.

With this value of R_0/ρ, the calculated cohesive energy (25) becomes

$$\frac{U_{\text{tot}}}{N} = -\frac{\alpha q^2}{R_0}\left(1 - \frac{\rho}{R_0}\right) \cong -1.16 \times 10^{-11} \text{ erg} \cong -7.26 \text{ ev}, \qquad (33)$$

Table 3   Properties of alkali halide crystals with the NaCl structure.

[Data from various tables by M. P. Tosi, *Solid state physics* **16**, 1 (1964).]

All values (except those in brackets) at room temperature and atmospheric pressure, with no correction for changes in R_0 and U from absolute zero. Values in brackets at absolute zero temperature and zero pressure, from private communication by L. Brewer.

	Nearest-neighbor separation R_0, in Å	Bulk modulus B, in 10^{11} dynes/cm^2	Repulsive energy parameter° $z\lambda$, in 10^{-8} erg	Repulsive range parameter† ρ, in Å	Cohesive energy compared to free ions, in kcal/mole	
					Experimental	Calculated‡
LiF	2.014	6.71	0.296	0.291	−242.3 [−246.8]	−242.2
LiCl	2.570	2.98	0.490	0.330	−198.9 [−201.8]	−192.9
LiBr	2.751	2.38	0.591	0.340	−189.8	−181.0
LiI	3.000	(1.71)	0.599	0.366	−177.7	−166.1
NaF	2.317	4.65	0.641	0.290	−214.4 [−217.9]	−215.2
NaCl	2.820	2.40	1.05	0.321	−182.6 [−185.3]	−178.6
NaBr	2.989	1.99	1.33	0.328	−173.6 [−174.3]	−169.2
NaI	3.237	1.51	1.58	0.345	−163.2 [−162.3]	−156.6
KF	2.674	3.05	1.31	0.298	−189.8 [−194.5]	−189.1
KCl	3.147	1.74	2.05	0.326	−165.8 [−169.5]	−161.6
KBr	3.298	1.48	2.30	0.336	−158.5 [−159.3]	−154.5
KI	3.533	1.17	2.85	0.348	−149.9 [−151.1]	−144.5
RbF	2.815	2.62	1.78	0.301	−181.4	−180.4
RbCl	3.291	1.56	3.19	0.323	−159.3	−155.4
RbBr	3.445	1.30	3.03	0.338	−152.6	−148.3
RbI	3.671	1.06	3.99	0.348	−144.9	−139.6

° Calculated from B and R_0, using Eqs. (24) and (31); for the NaCl structure $z = 6$.

† Calculated from B and R_0, using Eq. (31).

‡ Calculated from B and R_0, using Eq. (33).

in excellent agreement with the observed value -7.397 ev for KCl near $0°$K (Table 3).

The repulsive energy parameter λ may be found from (24):

$$z\lambda = \frac{\rho \alpha q^2}{R_0^2} e^{R_0/\rho} \cong 3.8 \times 10^{-8} \text{ erg}, \qquad (34)$$

with $z = 6$ for the number of nearest neighbors. The Madelung and repulsive contributions to the binding of a KCl crystal are shown in Fig. 12.

Properties of alkali halide crystals having the sodium chloride structure are given in Table 3. The values of the repulsive parameters λ and ρ are very sensitive to the values of the input data B and R_0, but the cohesive energy turns out to be relatively insensitive[19] to the value adopted for ρ. The calculated values of the cohesive energy are in exceedingly good agreement with the observed values.

[19] Notice that in our example (33) to (35) we used a value of the bulk modulus of KCl at $0°$K which differs by 10 percent from that given in Table 3 for room temperature. A 10 percent change in B changes λ by perhaps a factor of 3. The cohesive energy is not very sensitive to the value of the bulk modulus.

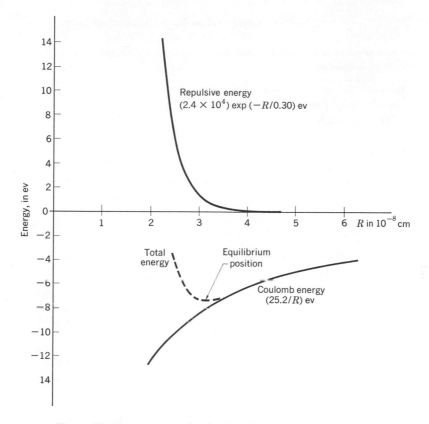

Figure 12 Energy per molecule of KCl crystal, showing Madelung and repulsive contributions.

COVALENT CRYSTALS

The covalent bond is the classical electron pair or homopolar bond of chemistry, particularly of organic chemistry. It is a strong bond: the bond between two carbon atoms in diamond has a cohesive energy of 7.3 ev with respect to separated neutral atoms. This is comparable with the bond strength in ionic crystals, in spite of the fact that the covalent bond acts between neutral atoms. The covalent bond has strong directional properties. Thus carbon, silicon, and germanium have the diamond structure,[20] with atoms joined to four nearest neighbors at tetrahedral angles, even though this arrangement gives a low filling of space. For spheres the diamond structure fills 0.34 of the available space, compared with 0.74 for a close-packed structure (Problem 1.4). The tetrahedral bond allows only four nearest neighbors, whereas a close-packed structure has twelve.

[20] We should not overemphasize the similarity of the bonding of carbon and silicon. It has been said that carbon gives biology, but silicon gives quartz.

Table 4   Energy values for single covalent bonds
(After Pauling)

Bond	Bond energy		Bond	Bond energy	
	ev	kcal/mole		ev	kcal/mole
H—H	4.5	104	P—P	2.2	51
C—C	3.6	83	O—O	1.4	33
Si—Si	1.8	42	Te—Te	1.4	33
Ge—Ge	1.6	38	Cl—Cl	2.5	58

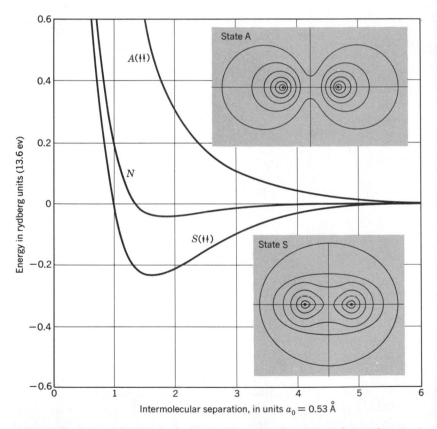

Figure 13   Energy of molecular hydrogen (H_2) referred to separated neutral atoms. A negative energy corresponds to binding. The curve N refers to a classical calculation with free atom charge densities; A is the result for parallel electron spins, taking the Pauli exclusion principle into account, and S (the stable state) for antiparallel spins. The density of charge is represented by contour lines for the states A and S.

The covalent bond is usually formed from two electrons, one from each atom participating in the bond. The electrons forming the bond tend to be partly localized in the region between the two atoms joined by the band. The spins of the two electrons in the bond are antiparallel.

The Pauli principle gives a repulsive interaction between atoms with filled shells. If the shells are not filled, electron overlap can be accommodated without excitation of electrons to high energy states. Compare the bond length (2 Å) of Cl_2 with the interatomic distance (3.76 Å) of Ar in solid Ar; also compare the cohesive energies given in Table 1. The difference between Cl_2 and Ar_2 is that the Cl atom has five electrons in the 3p shell and the Ar atom has six, filling the shell. The repulsive interaction is stronger in Ar than in Cl.

The elements C, Si, and Ge lack four electrons with respect to filled shells, and thus these elements (for example) can have an attractive interaction associated with charge overlap. The electron configuration of carbon is $1s^2 2s^2 2p^2$. Further details can be found in works on quantum chemistry.

There is apparently a continuous range of crystals between the ionic and the covalent limits. It is often of importance to estimate the extent to which a given bond is ionic or covalent, but this may be difficult to do with any confidence. We think of NaF as an ionic crystal and perhaps of GaAs[21] as largely covalent. Atoms with nearly filled shells (Na, Cl) tend to be ionic, whereas atoms in columns II, III, and IV of the periodic table tend to be covalent (C, Ge, Si, Te). The strength of the covalent bond is indicated in Table 4.

The binding of molecular hydrogen (H_2) is a simple example of a covalent bond. The problem is discussed in detail by Pauling and Wilson.[22] The strongest binding (Fig. 13) occurs when the spins of the two electrons are antiparallel. The binding depends on the relative spin orientation not because there are strong magnetic dipole forces between the spins, but because the Pauli principle modifies the distribution of charge according to the spin orientation. This effect is called the **exchange interaction.**

[21] Gallium arsenide has the cubic ZnS crystal structure (Chapter 1). The x-ray structure factor of the (200) reflection depends on the difference of the atomic scattering factors of the Ga and As atoms. If the atoms were present as the ions Ga^- and As^+, the number of electrons would be equal and the (200) structure factor would show only the different distributions of the electrons. If the atoms were present as Ga and As, there would be a difference of two in the number of atomic electrons, so that the structure factor would be larger than for the ionic case. Measurements by J. J. Demarco and R. J. Weiss [Physics Letters **13**, 209 (1964)] indicate qualitatively that the Ga and As atoms are more likely neutral than ionic.

[22] L. Pauling and E. B. Wilson, *Introduction to quantum mechanics*, McGraw-Hill, 1935.

METAL CRYSTALS

Metals are characterized by high electrical conductivity, and a large number of the electrons in a metal must be free to move about, usually one or two per atom. The electrons available to move about are called conduction electrons. In some metals such as the alkali metals the interaction of the ion cores with the conduction electrons makes a large contribution to the binding energy. As in Fig. 1, we may think of an alkali metal crystal as an array of positive ions embedded in a more-or-less uniform sea of negative charge (Chapters 7 to 9). In the transition metals there may be additional binding effects from interactions among the inner electron shells. Transition group elements have incomplete d-electron shells and are characterized by high binding energy (Table 1). In iron and tungsten, for example, the inner electronic shells make a substantial contribution to the binding.

The binding energy of an alkali metal crystal is very considerably less than that of an alkali halide crystal: the bond formed by a quasi-free conduction electron is not very strong. The interatomic distances are relatively large in the alkali metals because the kinetic energy of the conduction electrons is lower at large interatomic distances. This leads to weak binding.

We close this section with a quotation from Wigner and Seitz:[23]

> If one had a great calculating machine, one might apply it to the problem of solving the Schrödinger equation for each metal and obtain thereby the interesting physical quantities, such as the cohesive energy, the lattice constant, and similar parameters. It is not clear, however, that a great deal would be gained by this. Presumably the results would agree with the experimentally determined quantities and nothing vastly new would be learned from the calculation. It would be preferable instead to have a vivid picture of the behavior of the wave functions, a simple description of the essence of the factors which determine cohesion and an understanding of the origins of variation in properties from metal to metal.

HYDROGEN-BONDED CRYSTALS

Because neutral hydrogen has only one electron, it should form a covalent bond with only one other atom. It is known, however, that under certain conditions an atom of hydrogen is attracted by rather strong forces to two atoms, thus forming what is called a **hydrogen bond**[24] between them, with a bond energy of the order of 0.1 ev. It is believed that the hydrogen bond is largely ionic in character, being formed only between the most electronegative atoms, particularly F, O, and N. In the extreme ionic form of the hydrogen bond the hydrogen atom loses its electron to another atom in the molecule; the bare proton forms the hydrogen bond. The small size of the proton per-

[23] E. P. Wigner and F. Seitz, *Solid state physics* 1, 97 (1955).
[24] G. Pimentel and A. McClellan, *Hydrogen bond*, Freeman, 1960.

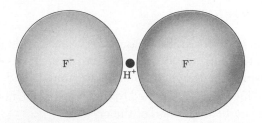

Figure 14

(a) The hydrogen difluoride ion HF_2^- is stabilized by a hydrogen bond. The sketch is of an extreme model of the bond, extreme in the sense that the proton is shown bare of electrons.

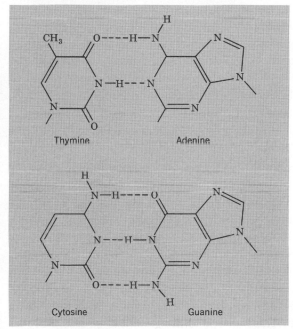

(b) Hydrogen bonding between organic bases as in DNA, after F. H. C. Crick and J. D. Watson.

mits only two nearest-neighbor atoms, because the atoms adjacent to the proton are so close that more than two of them would get in each other's way; thus the hydrogen bond connects only two atoms (Fig. 14a).

The hydrogen bond is an important part of the interaction between H_2O molecules and is responsible together with the electrostatic attraction of the electric dipole moments for the striking physical properties of water and ice.[25] The hydrogen bond restrains protein molecules to their normal geometrical arrangements. It is also responsible for the polymerization of hydrogen fluoride and formic acid, for example. It is important in certain ferroelectric crystals, such as potassium dihydrogen phosphate. It is important also in molecular genetics,[26] by controlling in part the pairing possible between the two strands of a DNA molecule (Fig. 14b).

[25] See L. Pauling, *General chemistry*, Freeman, 1956, pp. 327–331.

[26] F. C. H. Crick and J. D. Watson, Proc. Roy. Soc. (London) **A223**, 80 (1954); see also F. W. Stahl, *Mechanics of inheritance*, Prentice-Hall, 1964; G. Stent, *Molecular biology of bacterial viruses*, Freeman, 1963.

ATOMIC RADII

Distances between atoms in crystals can be measured very accurately by x-ray diffraction methods, often to 1 part in 10^5. Can we say that the observed distance between atoms or ions may be assigned, so much to atom A, and so much to atom B? Can a definite meaning be assigned to the radius of an atom or ion, irrespective of the nature and composition of the crystal?

Strictly, the answer is *no*. The charge distribution around an atom is not limited by a rigid spherical boundary. The size of a sodium atom depends on whether it is free, or in a metal, or in an ionic crystal. The radius of a sodium atom in metallic sodium might be taken as 1.85 Å, which is one-half the nearest-neighbor distance of 3.71 Å, but we would then be hard-pressed to explain the distance Na-F in crystalline sodium fluoride, which is 2.32 Å, leaving only $2.32 - 1.85 = 0.47$ Å for the F^- ion. X-ray and theoretical studies of electron distribution support a larger radius for the F^- ion, more like 1.3 or 1.4 Å. If we had used the value of the atomic radius of Na^+ from Table 6 for ionic crystals, we would have found a more reasonable value for the F^- ion.

But used with care and in the proper context, the concept of atomic radius can be useful and fruitful. The interatomic distance between C atoms in diamond is 1.54 Å; one-half of this is 0.77 Å. In silicon, which has the same crystal structure, one-half the interatomic distance is 1.17 Å. Now SiC crystallizes in two forms, in both of which each atom is surrounded by four atoms of the opposite kind. If we add the C and Si radii just given, we predict 1.94 Å for the length of the C-Si bond, in fair agreement with the 1.89 Å observed for the bond length. This is the kind of agreement (a few percent) which we shall find in using tables of atomic radii.

Tetrahedral Covalent Radii

Pauling[27] has proposed the set of empirical tetrahedral covalent atomic radii given in Table 5 for atoms in crystals with coordination number four, such as the diamond, cubic ZnS, and hexagonal ZnS structures. A large number of observed interatomic distances in appropriate compounds agree closely with the sums of the tetrahedral radii.

Ionic Crystal Radii

In Table 6 we give a set of ionic crystal radii due to Zachariasen. As an example of the use of tables, we consider $BaTiO_3$ (Fig. 12.2), with a measured average lattice constant of 4.004 Å at room temperature. Each

[27] L. Pauling, *The nature of the chemical bond*, Cornell University Press, N.Y., 1960, 3rd ed., Chapters 7, 11, 13. See also Landolt-Börnstein, *Tabellen* 1:4 (1950), p. 521 et seq.; J. C. Slater, J. Chem. Phys. **41**, 3199 (1964).

Table 5   Radii in Å of atoms when in tetrahedral covalent bonds
(After Pauling)

	Be	B	C	N	O	F
	1.06	0.88	0.77	0.70	0.66	0.64
	Mg	Al	Si	P	S	Cl
	1.40	1.26	1.17	1.10	1.04	0.99
Cu	Zn	Ga	Ge	As	Se	Br
1.35	1.31	1.26	1.22	1.18	1.14	1.11
Ag	Cd	In	Sn	Sb	Te	I
1.52	1.48	1.44	1.40	1.36	1.32	1.28
	Hg					
	1.48					

Table 6   Ionic radii in Å, according to Zachariasen
(Unpublished)

The interionic distance D is represented by $D_N = R_C + R_A + \Delta_N$, for ionic crystals, where N is the coordination number of the cation (positive ion), R_C and R_A are the standard radii of the cation and anion, and Δ_N is a correction for coordination number. Room temperature.

(a)

N	$\Delta_N(\text{Å})$	N	$\Delta_N(\text{Å})$	N	$\Delta_N(\text{Å})$
1	-0.50	5	-0.05	9	$+0.11$
2	-0.31	6	0	10	$+0.14$
3	-0.19	7	$+0.04$	11	$+0.17$
4	-0.11	8	$+0.08$	12	$+0.19$

(b) Standard radii in Å for ions with inert gas configurations

Valence										
-2			O	1.46	S	1.90	Se	2.02	Te	2.22	Po	2.30
-1			F	1.33	Cl	1.81	Br	1.96	I	2.19	At	2.27
$+1$	Li	0.68	Na	0.98	K	1.33	Rb	1.48	Cs	1.67	Fr	1.75
$+2$	Be	0.30	Mg	0.65	Ca	0.94	Sr	1.10	Ba	1.29	Ra	1.37
$+3$	B	0.16	Al	0.45	Sc	0.68	Y	0.88	La	1.04	Ac	1.11
$+4$			Si	0.38	Ti	0.60	Zr	0.77	Ce	0.92	Th	0.99
$+5$							Nb	0.67			Pa	0.90
$+6$											U	0.83

Table 7 Empirical ionic radii in Å
(After Pauling)

NH_4^+	1.48	Ti^{++}	0.90	Ti^{+++}	0.76	Ce^{+++}	1.11
Ga^+	1.13	V^{++}	0.88	V^{+++}	0.74	Nd^{+++}	1.08
In^+	1.32	Cr^{++}	0.84	Cr^{+++}	0.69	Sm^{+++}	1.04
Tl^+	1.40	Mn^{++}	0.80	Mn^{+++}	0.66	Gd^{+++}	1.02
O^{--}	1.40	Fe^{++}	0.76	Fe^{+++}	0.64	Dy^{+++}	0.99
F^-	1.36	Co^{++}	0.74	Co^{+++}	0.63	Er^{+++}	0.96
Cl^-	1.81	Ni^{++}	0.72	Ni^{+++}	0.62	Yb^{+++}	0.94
Br^-	1.95	Pd^{++}	0.86				
I^-	2.16						

Ba^{++} ion has twelve nearest O^{--} ions, so that the coordination number is twelve and the correction Δ_{12} of Table 6 applies. If we suppose that the structure is determined by the Ba-O contacts, we have, from Table 6, $D_{12} = 1.29 + 1.46 + 0.19 = 2.94$ Å, or $a = 4.16$ Å; if the Ti-O contact determines the structure, we have $D_6 = 0.60 + 1.46 = 2.06$, or $a = 4.12$ Å. The actual lattice constant is somewhat smaller than the estimates and may perhaps suggest that the bonding is not purely ionic, but is partly covalent. For sodium chloride, probably principally ionic, we have $D_6 = 0.98 + 1.81 = 2.79$, or $a = 5.58$ Å, whereas 5.63 Å is the observed value at room temperature.

Other empirical ionic radii are given in Table 7, after Pauling.

Problems

1. **Ionic radii.** (a) Check the Zachariasen radii (Table 6) against observed lattice constants for CsCl, NaCl, and KBr. (b) Check the tetrahedral radii (Table 5) against CuF, ZnS, and InSb. *Note:* The lattice constants are given in Chapter 1.

2. **Linear ionic crystal.** Consider a line of $2N$ ions of alternating charge $\pm q$ with a repulsive potential energy A/R^n between nearest neighbors. (a) Show that at the equilibrium separation

$$U(R_0) = -\frac{2Nq^2 \log 2}{R_0}\left(1 - \frac{1}{n}\right).$$

(b) Let the crystal be compressed so that $R_0 \rightarrow R_0(1 - \delta)$. Show that the work done in compressing a unit length of the crystal has the leading term $\frac{1}{2}C\delta^2$, where

$$C = \frac{(n - 1)q^2 \log 2}{R_0^2}.$$

Note: We should not expect to obtain this result from the expression for $U(R_0)$, but we must use the complete expression for $U(R)$.

3. *Cubic ZnS structure.* Using λ and ρ from Table 3 and the Madelung constants given in the text, calculate the cohesive energy of KCl in the cubic ZnS structure described in Chapter 1. Compare with the value calculated for KCl in the NaCl structure.

4. *Madelung constant.* Show for the sodium chloride structure that the Madelung constant $\alpha \cong 1.75$. It will be found convenient to set out the enumeration in a systematic form, expressing atomic positions in terms of the integers n_1, n_2, n_3, where $x = n_1 R_0$, $y = n_2 R_0$, $z = n_3 R_0$ give the coordinates relative to Cartesian coordinate axes along the crystal axes. In this notation the distance of the ion at n_1, n_2, n_3 from the origin is $R_0[n_1{}^2 + n_2{}^2 + n_3{}^2]^{1/2}$. We must also know the number of sites at the same distance from the origin. Such sites arise from the same set of numerical values n_1, n_2, n_3, but arranged in all possible orders and with all possible combinations of sign. There are in general six orders and eight combinations of sign, making 48 equivalent positions. If one of the n's is zero, there are 24 equivalent positions. If two n's are equal in magnitude but different from zero, there are 24 equivalent positions. If all three n's are equal in magnitude there are eight equivalent positions, corresponding to the corners of a cube.

5. *Bulk modulus of LiF.* From the experimental values of the cohesive energy and the nearest-neighbor distance, calculate the bulk modulus of LiF. Compare with the observed value.

6. *Hydrogen bonds in ice.* What is the evidence for hydrogen-bonding in ice? (Consult the book by Pauling.)

References

M. Born and K. Huang, *Dynamical theory of crystal lattices*, Oxford, 1954.

L. Pauling, *Nature of the chemical bond*, Cornell University Press, 3rd ed., 1960.

G. Leibfried, in *Encyclo. of physics* 7/1, 1955.

M. P. Tosi, "Cohesion of ionic solids in the Born model," *Solid state physics* 16, 1 (1964).

4

Elastic Constants
and
Elastic Waves

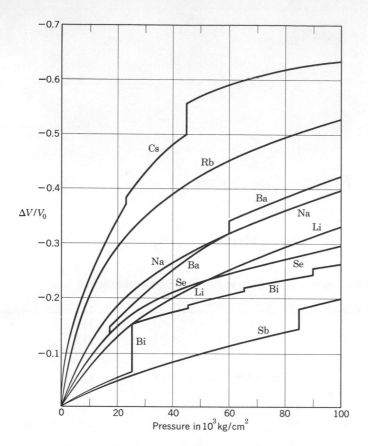

Figure 1 The change of relative volume of a number of substances shown as a function of pressure up to 100,000 kg/cm² (metric atmospheres). The bulk modulus satisfies Hooke's law over a region of pressure in which a part of one of these curves may be represented closely by a straight line, which may mean over perhaps 10^4 atmospheres, or a dilation of -0.05. The vertical breaks mark transformations to another crystal structure and occasionally to another electronic configuration for the ion cores. [After P. W. Bridgman, Endeavour **10**, 68 (1951).]

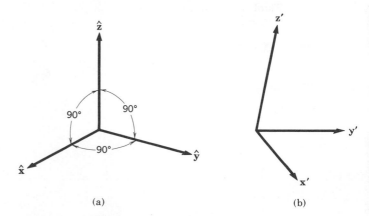

Figure 2 Coordinate axes for the description of the state of strain; the orthogonal unit axes in the unstrained state (a) are deformed in the strained state (b).

This chapter deals with the elastic properties of a crystal viewed as a homogeneous continuous medium rather than as a periodic array of atoms. The continuum approximation is usually valid for elastic waves of wavelengths λ longer than 10^{-6} cm, which means for frequencies below 10^{11} or 10^{12} cps. Higher frequencies are not easily obtainable at present by electronic means; to study higher frequency elastic waves we use the inelastic scattering methods discussed in Chapter 5.

The frequency region for which the continuum approximation is valid is of great interest in solid state physics. Ultrasonic waves are used to measure elastic constants and to study lattice defects, the electronic structure of metals, and superconductivity. There are also numerous technological applications of elastic waves in solids.

Some of the material below looks complicated because of the unavoidable multiplicity of subscripts on the symbols. The basic physical ideas are simple: we use Hooke's law and Newton's second law. **Hooke's law** states that in an elastic solid the strain is directly proportional to the stress. The law applies to small strains only (Fig. 1). We say that we are in the **nonlinear region** when the strains are so large that Hooke's law is no longer satisfied.

ANALYSIS OF ELASTIC STRAINS

We specify the strain in terms of the components e_{xx}, e_{yy}, e_{zz}, e_{xy}, e_{yz}, e_{zx} which are defined below. We treat infinitesimal strains only. We shall not distinguish in our notation between isothermal (constant temperature) and adiabatic (constant entropy) deformations. The small differences between the isothermal and adiabatic elastic constants are not often of importance at room temperature and below.

We imagine that three orthogonal vectors $\hat{x}$, $\hat{y}$, $\hat{z}$ of unit length are embedded securely in the unstrained solid, as shown in Fig. 2. After a small uniform deformation[1] of the solid has taken place the axes are distorted in orientation and in length. The new axes x', y', z' may be written in terms of the old axes:

$$\begin{aligned}
x' &= (1 + \epsilon_{xx})\hat{x} + \epsilon_{xy}\hat{y} + \epsilon_{xz}\hat{z}; \\
y' &= \epsilon_{yx}\hat{x} + (1 + \epsilon_{yy})\hat{y} + \epsilon_{yz}\hat{z}; \\
z' &= \epsilon_{zx}\hat{x} + \epsilon_{zy}\hat{y} + (1 + \epsilon_{zz})\hat{z}.
\end{aligned} \qquad (1)$$

The coefficients $\epsilon_{\alpha\beta}$ define the deformation; they are dimensionless and have values $\ll 1$ if the strain is small. The original axes were of unit length, but the

[1] In a uniform deformation each primitive cell of the crystal is deformed in the same way.

new axes will not necessarily be of unit length. For example,

$$\mathbf{x}' \cdot \mathbf{x}' = 1 + 2\epsilon_{xx} + \epsilon_{xx}^2 + \epsilon_{xy}^2 + \epsilon_{xz}^2,$$

whence $x' \cong 1 + \epsilon_{xx} + \cdots$. The fractional changes of length of the $\hat{\mathbf{x}}$, $\hat{\mathbf{y}}$, and $\hat{\mathbf{z}}$ axes are ϵ_{xx}, ϵ_{yy}, ϵ_{zz}, respectively, to the first order.

What is the effect of the deformation (1) on a point (or atom) originally at $\mathbf{r} = x\hat{\mathbf{x}} + y\hat{\mathbf{y}} + z\hat{\mathbf{z}}$? The origin is taken at some other atom. If the deformation is uniform (Fig. 3a), then after the deformation the point will be at the position[2] $\mathbf{r}' = x\mathbf{x}' + y\mathbf{y}' + z\mathbf{z}'$. The **displacement R** of the deformation is defined by

$$\mathbf{R} \equiv \mathbf{r}' - \mathbf{r} = x(\mathbf{x}' - \hat{\mathbf{x}}) + y(\mathbf{y}' - \hat{\mathbf{y}}) + z(\mathbf{z}' - \hat{\mathbf{z}}), \tag{2}$$

or, from (1),

$$\mathbf{R(r)} \equiv (x\epsilon_{xx} + y\epsilon_{yx} + z\epsilon_{zx})\hat{\mathbf{x}} + (x\epsilon_{xy} + y\epsilon_{yy} + z\epsilon_{zy})\hat{\mathbf{y}}$$
$$+ (x\epsilon_{xz} + y\epsilon_{yz} + z\epsilon_{zz})\hat{\mathbf{z}}. \tag{3}$$

This may be written in a more general form by introducing u, v, w such that the displacement is given by

$$\boxed{\mathbf{R(r)} = u(\mathbf{r})\hat{\mathbf{x}} + v(\mathbf{r})\hat{\mathbf{y}} + w(\mathbf{r})\hat{\mathbf{z}}.} \tag{4}$$

If the deformation is nonuniform as in Fig. 3b we must relate u, v, w to the local strains. We take the origin of $\mathbf{r}$ close to the region of interest; then comparison of (3) and (4) gives, by Taylor series expansion of $\mathbf{R}$ using $\mathbf{R}(0) = 0$,

$$x\epsilon_{xx} \cong x\frac{\partial u}{\partial x}; \quad y\epsilon_{yx} = y\frac{\partial u}{\partial y}; \quad \text{etc.} \tag{5}$$

The derivatives are independent of the origin chosen for $\mathbf{R}$.

It is usual to work with coefficients $e_{\alpha\beta}$ rather than $\epsilon_{\alpha\beta}$. We define the **strain components** e_{xx}, e_{yy}, e_{zz} by the relations

$$\boxed{e_{xx} \equiv \epsilon_{xx} = \frac{\partial u}{\partial x}; \quad e_{yy} \equiv \epsilon_{yy} = \frac{\partial v}{\partial y}; \quad e_{zz} \equiv \epsilon_{zz} = \frac{\partial w}{\partial z},} \tag{6}$$

using (5). The other strain components e_{xy}, e_{yz}, e_{zx} are defined in terms of the changes in angle between the axes: using (1) we may define

$$\boxed{\begin{aligned} e_{xy} &\equiv \mathbf{x}' \cdot \mathbf{y}' \cong \epsilon_{yx} + \epsilon_{xy} = \frac{\partial u}{\partial y} + \frac{\partial v}{\partial x}; \\ e_{yz} &\equiv \mathbf{y}' \cdot \mathbf{z}' \cong \epsilon_{zy} + \epsilon_{yz} = \frac{\partial v}{\partial z} + \frac{\partial w}{\partial y}; \\ e_{zx} &\equiv \mathbf{z}' \cdot \mathbf{x}' \cong \epsilon_{zx} + \epsilon_{xz} = \frac{\partial u}{\partial z} + \frac{\partial w}{\partial x}. \end{aligned}} \tag{7}$$

Uniform strain

Nonuniform strain

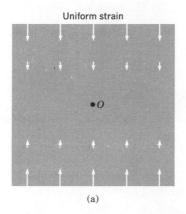 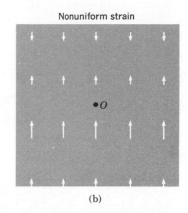

(a)   (b)

Figure 3   (a) Displacement vectors **R** of Eq. (4) in a uniform strain and (b) in a nonuniform strain. The origin is at O. (c) $\mathbf{A} \cdot \mathbf{B} \times \mathbf{C}$ is equal to the volume of the parrallelepiped having edges **A, B, C**. Recall that $\mathbf{B} \times \mathbf{C}$ is a vector perpendicular to the plane of **B** and **C**, and of magnitude equal to the area of the parallelogram having **B, C** as sides.

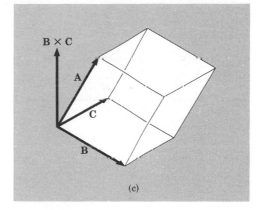

(c)

We may replace the $\cong$ signs by = signs if we neglect terms of order ϵ^2. The six coefficients $e_{\alpha\beta}(=e_{\beta\alpha})$ completely define the strain. The strains as defined are dimensionless.

Dilation

The fractional *increase* of volume associated with a deformation is called the dilation. The dilation is negative for hydrostatic pressure. The unit cube of edges $\hat{\mathbf{x}}, \hat{\mathbf{y}}, \hat{\mathbf{z}}$ has a volume after deformation of

$$V' = \mathbf{x}' \cdot \mathbf{y}' \times \mathbf{z}', \tag{8}$$

by virtue of a well-known result for the volume of a parallelepiped having edges $\mathbf{x}', \mathbf{y}', \mathbf{z}'$ (Fig. 3c). From (1) we have

$$\mathbf{x}' \cdot \mathbf{y}' \times \mathbf{z}' = \begin{vmatrix} 1 + \epsilon_{xx} & \epsilon_{xy} & \epsilon_{xz} \\ \epsilon_{yx} & 1 + \epsilon_{yy} & \epsilon_{yz} \\ \epsilon_{zx} & \epsilon_{zy} & 1 + \epsilon_{zz} \end{vmatrix} \cong 1 + e_{xx} + e_{yy} + e_{zz}. \tag{9}$$

[2] This is obviously correct if we choose the $\hat{\mathbf{x}}$ axis such that $\mathbf{r} = x\hat{\mathbf{x}}$; then $\mathbf{r}' = x\mathbf{x}'$ by definition of $\mathbf{x}'$.

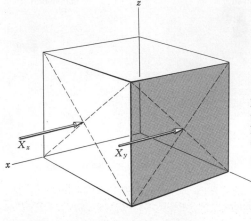

Figure 4 Stress component X_x is a force applied in the x direction to a unit area of a plane whose normal lies in the x direction; X_y is applied in the x direction to a unit area of a plane whose normal lies in the y direction.

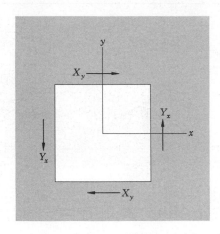

Figure 5 Demonstration that for a body in static equilibrium $Y_x = X_y$. The sum of the forces in the x direction is zero. The sum of the forces in the y direction is also zero. The total force vanishes. The total torque about the origin is also zero if $Y_x = X_y$.

Products of two strain components have been neglected. The dilation δ is then given by

$$\delta \equiv \frac{V' - V}{V} \cong e_{xx} + e_{yy} + e_{zz}. \tag{10}$$

Stress Components

The force acting on a unit area in the solid is defined as the stress. There are nine stress components: X_x, X_y, X_z, Y_x, Y_y, Y_z, Z_x, Z_y, Z_z. The capital letter indicates the direction of the force, and the subscript indicates the normal to the plane to which the force is applied. In Fig. 4 the stress component X_x represents a force applied in the x direction to a unit area of a plane whose normal lies in the x direction; the stress component X_y represents a force applied in the x direction to a unit area of a plane whose normal lies in the y direction. The number of independent stress components is reduced from nine to six by applying to an elementary cube (as in Fig. 5) the condition that the angular acceleration vanish,[3] and hence that the total torque must be zero. It follows that

$$Y_z = Z_y; \quad Z_x = X_z; \quad X_y = Y_x. \tag{11}$$

The six independent stress components may be taken as $X_x, Y_y, Z_z, Y_z, Z_x, X_y$.

Stress components have the dimensions of force per unit area or energy per unit volume. The strain components are ratios of lengths and are dimensionless.

ELASTIC COMPLIANCE AND STIFFNESS CONSTANTS

Hooke's law states that for sufficiently small deformations the strain is directly proportional to the stress, so that the strain components are linear functions of the stress components:

$$
\begin{aligned}
e_{xx} &= S_{11}X_x + S_{12}Y_y + S_{13}Z_z + S_{14}Y_z + S_{15}Z_x + S_{16}X_y; \\
e_{yy} &= S_{21}X_x + S_{22}Y_y + S_{23}Z_z + S_{24}Y_z + S_{25}Z_x + S_{26}X_y; \\
e_{zz} &= S_{31}X_x + S_{32}Y_y + S_{33}Z_z + S_{34}Y_z + S_{35}Z_x + S_{36}X_y; \\
e_{yz} &= S_{41}X_x + S_{42}Y_y + S_{43}Z_z + S_{44}Y_z + S_{45}Z_x + S_{46}X_y; \\
e_{zx} &= S_{51}X_x + S_{52}Y_y + S_{53}Z_z + S_{54}Y_z + S_{55}Z_x + S_{56}X_y; \\
e_{xy} &= S_{61}X_x + S_{62}Y_y + S_{63}Z_z + S_{64}Y_z + S_{65}Z_x + S_{66}X_y.
\end{aligned} \tag{12}
$$

Conversely, the stress components are linear functions of the strain components:

$$
\begin{aligned}
X_x &= C_{11}e_{xx} + C_{12}e_{yy} + C_{13}e_{zz} + C_{14}e_{yz} + C_{15}e_{zx} + C_{16}e_{xy}; \\
Y_y &= C_{21}e_{xx} + C_{22}e_{yy} + C_{23}e_{zz} + C_{24}e_{yz} + C_{25}e_{zx} + C_{26}e_{xy}; \\
Z_z &= C_{31}e_{xx} + C_{32}e_{yy} + C_{33}e_{zz} + C_{34}e_{yz} + C_{35}e_{zx} + C_{36}e_{xy}; \\
Y_z &= C_{41}e_{xx} + C_{42}e_{yy} + C_{43}e_{zz} + C_{44}e_{yz} + C_{45}e_{zx} + C_{46}e_{xy}; \\
Z_x &= C_{51}e_{xx} + C_{52}e_{yy} + C_{53}e_{zz} + C_{54}e_{yz} + C_{55}e_{zx} + C_{56}e_{xy}; \\
X_y &= C_{61}e_{xx} + C_{62}e_{yy} + C_{63}e_{zz} + C_{64}e_{yz} + C_{65}e_{zx} + C_{66}e_{xy}.
\end{aligned} \tag{13}
$$

The quantities $S_{11}, S_{12}, \dots$ are called **elastic compliance constants** or elastic constants; the quantities $C_{11}, C_{12}, \dots$ are called the **elastic stiffness constants** or moduli of elasticity. Other names are also current. The S's have the dimensions of [area]/[force] or [volume]/[energy]. The C's have the dimensions of [force]/[area] or [energy]/[volume].

---

[3] This does not mean we cannot treat problems in which there is an angular acceleration; it just means that we can use the static situation to define the elastic constants.

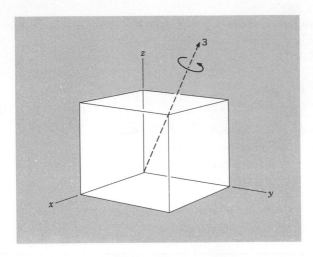

Figure 6 Rotation by $2\pi/3$ about the axis marked 3 changes $x \to y$; $y \to z$; and $z \to x$.

Elastic Energy Density

The 36 constants in (12) or in (13) may be reduced in number by several considerations. The elastic energy density U is a quadratic function of the strains, in the approximation of Hooke's law (recall the expression for the energy of a stretched spring). Thus we may write

$$U = \frac{1}{2} \sum_{\lambda=1}^{6} \sum_{\mu=1}^{6} \tilde{C}_{\lambda\mu} e_\lambda e_\mu, \tag{14}$$

where the indices 1 through 6 are defined as:

$$1 \equiv xx; \quad 2 \equiv yy; \quad 3 \equiv zz; \quad 4 \equiv yz; \quad 5 \equiv zx; \quad 6 \equiv xy. \tag{15}$$

The $\tilde{C}$'s are related to the C's of (13), as we see in (17) below.

The stress components are found from the derivative of U with respect to the associated strain component. This result follows from the definition of potential energy. Consider the stress X_x applied to one face of a unit cube, the opposite face being held at rest:

$$X_x = \frac{\partial U}{\partial e_{xx}} \equiv \frac{\partial U}{\partial e_1} = \tilde{C}_{11} e_1 + \frac{1}{2} \sum_{\beta=2}^{6} (\tilde{C}_{1\beta} + \tilde{C}_{\beta1}) e_\beta. \tag{16}$$

Note that only the combination $\frac{1}{2}(\tilde{C}_{\alpha\beta} + \tilde{C}_{\beta\alpha})$ enters the stress-strain relations. It follows that the elastic stiffness constants are symmetrical:

$$C_{\alpha\beta} = \frac{1}{2}(\tilde{C}_{\alpha\beta} + \tilde{C}_{\beta\alpha}) = C_{\beta\alpha}. \tag{17}$$

Thus the thirty-six elastic stiffness constants are reduced to twenty-one.

Elastic Stiffness Constants of Cubic Crystals

The number of independent elastic stiffness constants is reduced further if the crystal possesses symmetry elements. We now show that in cubic crystals there are only three independent stiffness constants.

We assert that the elastic energy density of a cubic crystal is

$$U = \tfrac{1}{2}C_{11}(e_{xx}^2 + e_{yy}^2 + e_{zz}^2) + \tfrac{1}{2}C_{44}(e_{yz}^2 + e_{zx}^2 + e_{xy}^2)$$
$$+ C_{12}(e_{yy}e_{zz} + e_{zz}e_{xx} + e_{xx}e_{yy}), \quad (18)$$

and that no other quadratic terms occur; that is

$$(e_{xx}e_{xy} + \cdots); \quad (e_{yz}e_{zx} + \cdots); \quad (e_{xx}e_{yz} + \cdots) \qquad (19)$$

do not occur.

The minimum[4] symmetry requirement for a cubic structure is the existence of four three-fold rotation axes. The axes are in the [111] and equivalent directions (Fig. 6). The effect of a rotation of $2\pi/3$ about these four axes is to interchange the x, y, z axes according to the schemes

$$x \to y \to z \to x; \quad -x \to z \to -y \to -x;$$
$$x \to z \to -y \to x; \quad -x \to y \to z \to -x, \qquad (20)$$

according to the axis chosen. Under the first of these schemes, for example,

$$e_{xx}^2 + e_{yy}^2 + e_{zz}^2 \to e_{yy}^2 + e_{zz}^2 + e_{xx}^2,$$

and similarly for the other terms in parentheses in (18). Thus (18) is invariant under the operations considered. But each of the terms exhibited in (19) is odd in one or more indices. A rotation in the set (20) can be found which will change the sign of the term, because $e_{xy} = -e_{x(-y)}$, for example. Thus the terms (19) are not invariant under the required operations.

It remains to verify that the numerical factors in (18) are correct. By (16)

$$\partial U/\partial e_{xx} = X_x = C_{11}e_{xx} + C_{12}(e_{yy} + e_{zz}). \qquad (21)$$

The appearance of $C_{11}e_{xx}$ agrees with (13). On further comparison, we see that

$$C_{12} = C_{13}; \qquad C_{14} = C_{15} = C_{16} = 0. \qquad (22)$$

Further, from (18),

$$\partial U/\partial e_{xy} = X_y = C_{44}e_{xy}; \qquad (23)$$

on comparison with (13) we have

$$C_{61} = C_{62} = C_{63} = C_{64} = C_{65} = 0; \qquad C_{66} = C_{44}. \qquad (24)$$

Thus from (18) we find that the array of values of the elastic stiffness constants is reduced for a cubic crystal to the matrix

[4] See the standard stereographic drawings of the symmetry elements of the cubic point group as given in texts on crystallography; the cubic group with the smallest number of symmetry axes is labeled 23.

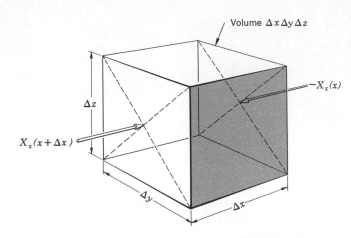

Volume $\Delta x \, \Delta y \, \Delta z$

$-X_x(x)$

Δz

$X_x(x + \Delta x)$

Δy

Δx

Figure 7 Cube of volume $\Delta x \, \Delta y \, \Delta z$ acted on by a stress $-X_x(x)$ on the face at x, and

$$X_x(x + \Delta x) \cong X_x(x) + \frac{\partial X_x}{\partial x} \Delta x \text{ on the parallel}$$

face at $x + \Delta x$. The net force is $\left(\dfrac{\partial X_x}{\partial x} \Delta x\right) \Delta y \, \Delta z$.

Other forces in the x direction arise from the variation across the cube of the stresses X_y and X_z, which are not shown. The net x component of the force on the cube is

$$F_x = \left(\frac{\partial X_x}{\partial x} + \frac{\partial X_y}{\partial y} + \frac{\partial X_z}{\partial z}\right) \Delta x \, \Delta y \, \Delta z.$$

The force equals the mass of the cube times the component of the acceleration in the x direction. The mass is $\rho \, \Delta x \, \Delta y \, \Delta z$ and the acceleration is $\partial^2 u / \partial t^2$.

$$
\begin{array}{c|cccccc}
 & e_{xx} & e_{yy} & e_{zz} & e_{yz} & e_{zx} & e_{xy} \\
\hline
X_x & C_{11} & C_{12} & C_{12} & 0 & 0 & 0 \\
Y_y & C_{12} & C_{11} & C_{12} & 0 & 0 & 0 \\
Z_z & C_{12} & C_{12} & C_{11} & 0 & 0 & 0 \\
Y_z & 0 & 0 & 0 & C_{44} & 0 & 0 \\
Z_x & 0 & 0 & 0 & 0 & C_{44} & 0 \\
X_y & 0 & 0 & 0 & 0 & 0 & C_{44} \\
\end{array}
\tag{25}
$$

For cubic crystals the stiffness and compliance constants are related by

$$C_{44} = 1/S_{44}; \quad C_{11} - C_{12} = (S_{11} - S_{12})^{-1};$$

$$C_{11} + 2C_{12} = (S_{11} + 2S_{12})^{-1}. \tag{26}$$

These relations follow on evaluating the inverse matrix to (25).

Bulk Modulus and Compressibility

Consider the uniform dilation $e_{xx} = e_{yy} = e_{zz} = \frac{1}{3}\delta$. For this deformation the energy density (18) of a cubic crystal is

$$U = \tfrac{1}{6}(C_{11} + 2C_{12})\delta^2. \tag{27}$$

We define the **bulk modulus** B by the relation

then for a cubic crystal
$$U = \tfrac{1}{2}B\delta^2; \tag{28}$$

$$B = \tfrac{1}{3}(C_{11} + 2C_{12}). \tag{29}$$

The **compressibility** K is defined as $K \equiv 1/B$.

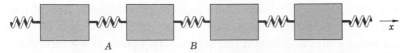

$$A \qquad\qquad B$$

Figure 8 If springs A and B are stretched equally, the block between them experiences no net force. This illustrates the fact that a uniform stress X_x in a solid does not give a net force on a volume element. If the spring at B is stretched more than the spring at A, the block between them will be accelerated by the force $X_x(B) - X_x(A)$.

ELASTIC WAVES IN CUBIC CRYSTALS

By considering as in Fig. 7 the forces acting on an element of volume in the crystal we obtain the equation of motion in the x direction

$$\rho \frac{\partial^2 u}{\partial t^2} = \frac{\partial X_x}{\partial x} + \frac{\partial X_y}{\partial y} + \frac{\partial X_z}{\partial z} ; \tag{30}$$

here ρ is the density and u is the displacement in the x direction. There are similar equations for the y and z directions. From (13) and (25) it follows that for a cubic crystal

$$\rho \frac{\partial^2 u}{\partial t^2} = C_{11} \frac{\partial e_{xx}}{\partial x} + C_{12} \left(\frac{\partial e_{yy}}{\partial x} + \frac{\partial e_{zz}}{\partial x} \right) + C_{44} \left(\frac{\partial e_{xy}}{\partial y} + \frac{\partial e_{zx}}{\partial z} \right) ; \tag{31}$$

here the x, y, z directions are parallel to the cube edges. Using the definitions (6) and (7) of the strain components we have

$$\rho \frac{\partial^2 u}{\partial t^2} = C_{11} \frac{\partial^2 u}{\partial x^2} + C_{44} \left(\frac{\partial^2 u}{\partial y^2} + \frac{\partial^2 u}{\partial z^2} \right) + (C_{12} + C_{44}) \left(\frac{\partial^2 v}{\partial x\, \partial y} + \frac{\partial^2 w}{\partial x\, \partial z} \right),$$
$$\tag{32a}$$

where u, v, w are the components of the displacement $\mathbf{R}$ as defined by (4).

The corresponding equations of motion for $\partial^2 v / \partial t^2$ and $\partial^2 w / \partial t^2$ are found directly from (32a) by symmetry:

$$\rho \frac{\partial^2 v}{\partial t^2} = C_{11} \frac{\partial^2 v}{\partial y^2} + C_{44} \left(\frac{\partial^2 v}{\partial x^2} + \frac{\partial^2 v}{\partial z^2} \right) + (C_{12} + C_{44}) \left(\frac{\partial^2 u}{\partial x\, \partial y} + \frac{\partial^2 w}{\partial y\, \partial z} \right) ;$$
$$\tag{32b}$$

$$\rho \frac{\partial^2 w}{\partial t^2} = C_{11} \frac{\partial^2 w}{\partial z^2} + C_{44} \left(\frac{\partial^2 w}{\partial x^2} + \frac{\partial^2 w}{\partial y^2} \right) + (C_{12} + C_{44}) \left(\frac{\partial^2 u}{\partial x\, \partial z} + \frac{\partial^2 v}{\partial y\, \partial z} \right).$$
$$\tag{32c}$$

We now look for special simple solutions of these equations.

Waves in the [100] Direction

One solution of (32a) is given by a longitudinal wave

$$u = u_0 \exp \left[i(Kx - \omega t) \right], \tag{33}$$

where u is the x component of the particle displacement. Both the wavevector and the particle motion are along the x cube edge. Here $K = 2\pi/\lambda$ is the wavevector and $\omega = 2\pi\nu$ is the angular frequency. If we substitute (33) into (32a) we find

$$\omega^2\rho = C_{11}K^2; \tag{34}$$

thus the velocity of a longitudinal wave in the [100] direction is

$$v_s = \nu\lambda = \omega/K = (C_{11}/\rho)^{1/2}. \tag{35}$$

Consider a transverse or shear wave with the wavevector along the x cube edge and with the particle displacement v in the y direction:

$$v = v_0 \exp[i(Kx - \omega t)] \tag{36}$$

On substitution in (32b) this gives the dispersion relation

$$\omega^2\rho = C_{44}K^2; \tag{37}$$

thus the velocity ω/K of a transverse wave in the [100] direction is

$$v_s = (C_{44}/\rho)^{1/2}. \tag{38}$$

The identical velocity is obtained if the particle displacement is in the z direction. Thus for $\mathbf{K}$ parallel to [100] the two independent shear waves have equal velocities. This is not true for $\mathbf{K}$ in a general direction in the crystal.

Waves in the [110] Direction

There is a special interest in waves which propagate in a face diagonal direction of a cubic crystal, because the three elastic constants can be found simply from the three propagation velocities in this direction.

Consider a shear wave which propagates in the xy plane with particle displacement w in the z direction:

$$w = w_0 \exp[i(K_x x + K_y y - \omega t)], \tag{39}$$

whence (32c) gives

$$\omega^2\rho = C_{44}(K_x^2 + K_y^2) = C_{44}K^2, \tag{40}$$

independent of propagation direction in the plane.

Consider other waves which propagate in the xy plane with particle motion in the xy plane: let

$$u = u_0 \exp[i(K_x x + K_y y - \omega t)]; \qquad v = v_0 \exp[i(K_x x + K_y y - \omega t)]. \tag{41}$$

From (32a) and (32b),

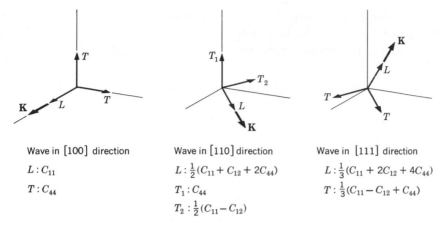

Figure 9 Effective elastic constants for the three modes of elastic waves in the principal propagation directions in cubic crystals. The two transverse modes are degenerate for propagation in the [100] and [111] directions.

$$\omega^2 \rho u = (C_{11}K_x{}^2 + C_{44}K_y{}^2)u + (C_{12} + C_{44})K_x K_y v;$$
$$\omega^2 \rho v = (C_{11}K_y{}^2 + C_{44}K_x{}^2)v + (C_{12} + C_{44})K_x K_y u. \tag{42}$$

This pair of equations has a particularly simple solution for a wave in the [110] direction, for which $K_x = K_y = K/\sqrt{2}$. The condition for a solution is that the determinant of the coefficients of u and v in (42) should equal zero:

$$\begin{vmatrix} -\omega^2\rho + \tfrac{1}{2}(C_{11} + C_{44})K^2 & \tfrac{1}{2}(C_{12} + C_{44})K^2 \\ \tfrac{1}{2}(C_{12} + C_{44})K^2 & -\omega^2\rho + \tfrac{1}{2}(C_{11} + C_{44})K^2 \end{vmatrix} = 0. \tag{43}$$

This equation has the roots

$$\omega^2\rho = \tfrac{1}{2}(C_{11} + C_{12} + 2C_{44})K^2; \qquad \omega^2\rho = \tfrac{1}{2}(C_{11} - C_{12})K^2. \tag{44}$$

The first root describes a longitudinal wave; the second root describes a shear wave. How do we determine the direction of particle displacement? The first root when substituted into the upper equation of (42) gives

$$\tfrac{1}{2}(C_{11} + C_{12} + 2C_{44})K^2 u = \tfrac{1}{2}(C_{11} + C_{44})K^2 u + \tfrac{1}{2}(C_{12} + C_{44})K^2 v, \tag{45}$$

whence the displacement components satisfy $u = v$. Thus the particle displacement is along [110] and parallel to the **K** vector (Fig. 9). The second root of (44) when substituted into the upper equation of (42) gives

$$\tfrac{1}{2}(C_{11} - C_{12})K^2 u = \tfrac{1}{2}(C_{11} + C_{44})K^2 u + \tfrac{1}{2}(C_{12} + C_{44})K^2 v, \tag{46}$$

whence $u = -v$. The particle displacement is along [1$\bar{1}$0] and perpendicular to the **K** vector.

Selected values of the adiabatic elastic stiffness constants of cubic crystals at low temperatures and at room temperature are given in Table 1. Notice the general tendency for the elastic constants to decrease as the temperature is increased. Results for silver are plotted in Fig. 10 and for BaF_2 in Fig. 11.

Table 1   Adiabatic elastic stiffness constants of cubic crystals at low temperature and at room temperature

The values given at $0°K$ were obtained by extrapolation of measurements carried out down to $4°K$. The table was compiled with the assistance of Professor Charles S. Smith.[*]

Crystal	Stiffness constants, in 10^{12} dynes/cm^2			Temperature, °K	Density, gm/cm^3
	C_{11}	C_{12}	C_{44}		
W	5.326	2.049	1.631	0	19.317
	5.233	2.045	1.607	300	–
Ta	2.663	1.582	0.874	0	16.696
	2.609	1.574	0.818	300	–
Cu	1.762	1.249	0.818	0	9.018
	1.684	1.214	0.754	300	–
Ag	1.315	0.973	0.511	0	10.635
	1.240	0.937	0.461	300	–
Au	2.016	1.697	0.454	0	19.488
	1.923	1.631	0.420	300	–
Al	1.143	0.619	0.316	0	2.733
	1.068	0.607	0.282	300	–
K	0.0416	0.0341	0.0286	4	
	0.0370	0.0314	0.0188	295	
Pb	0.555	0.454	0.194	0	11.599
	0.495	0.423	0.149	300	–
Ni	2.612	1.508	1.317	0	8.968
	2.508	1.500	1.235	300	–
Pd	2.341	1.761	0.712	0	12.132
	2.271	1.761	0.717	300	–
V	2.324	1.194	0.460	0	6.051
	2.280	1.187	0.426		–
LiF	1.246	0.424	0.649	0	2.646
	1.112	0.420	0.628	300	–
KCl	0.483	0.054	0.066	4	2.038
	0.403	0.066	0.063	300	–
BaF_2	0.981	0.448	0.254	0	–
	0.891	0.400	0.254	300	4.886

[*]References to the original papers are given in the article by C. Kittel in *Phonons*, R. W. H. Stevenson, ed., Oliver & Boyd, 1966.

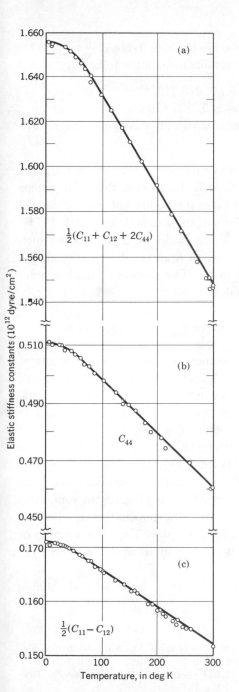

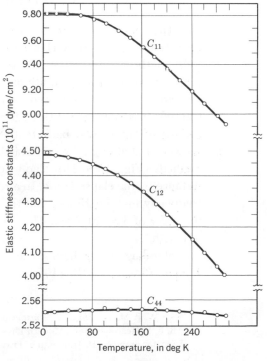

Figure 10 Elastic stiffness constants for silver as a function of temperature, after J. R. Neighbours and G. A. Alers, Phys. Rev. **111**, 707 (1958). The constants plotted are (a): $\frac{1}{2}(C_{11} + C_{12} + 2C_{44})$; (b): C_{44}; (c): $\frac{1}{2}(C_{11} - C_{12})$. These combinations correspond to the three waves in the [110] direction.

Figure 11 The elastic stiffness constants of BaF_2 as a function of temperature, after D. Gerlich, Phys. Rev. **135**, A1331 (1964).

Further values at room temperature alone are given in Table 2.

Useful published tables of elastic constants include the following:

H. B. Huntington, *Solid state physics* **7**, 213 (1958);

R. F. S. Hearmon, Advances in Physics **5**, 323 (1956);

K. S. Aleksandrov and T. V. Ryzhova, Soviet Physics (Crystallography) **6**, 228 (1961).

There are three normal modes of wave motion in a crystal for a given magnitude and direction of the wavevector **K**. In general, the polarizations (directions of particle displacement) of these modes are not exactly parallel or perpendicular to **K**. In the special propagation directions [100], [111], and [110] of a cubic crystal two of the three modes for a given **K** are such that the particle motion is exactly transverse to **K** and in the third mode the motion is exactly longitudinal (parallel to **K**). The analysis is much simpler in these special directions than in general directions.[5]

EXPERIMENTAL DETERMINATION OF ELASTIC CONSTANTS

The classic methods for the measurement of the elastic constants of crystals are described by Hearmon.[6] Since his review the use of the ultrasonic pulse method has become widespread[7] because of its adaptability to a wide range of experimental conditions, although many other methods are valuable and are used. In this method an ultrasonic pulse generated by a quartz[8] transducer is transmitted through the test crystal and reflected from the rear surface of the crystal back to the transducer (Fig. 12). The elapsed time between initiation and receipt of the pulse is measured by standard electronic methods (Figs. 13 to 15). The velocity is obtained by dividing the round-trip distance by the elapsed time. In a representative arrangement the experimental frequency may be 15 mc, and the pulse length 1 μsec. The wavelength is of the order of 3×10^{-2} cm. The crystal specimen may be of the order of 1 cm in length.

Standing wave methods are discussed by D. I. Bolef and M. Menes, J. Appl. Phys. **31**, 1010 (1960).

---

[5] See W. P. Mason, *Physical acoustics and the properties of solids,* Van Nostrand, 1958.

[6] R. F. S. Hearmon, Revs. Modern Phys. **18**, 409 (1946).

[7] See, for example, H. Huntington, Phys. Rev. **72**, 321 (1947); J. K. Galt, Phys. Rev. **73**, 1460 (1948).

[8] A slab may be cut from a quartz crystal in such a way that either a longitudinal or a transverse wave is excited in the slab by the application of an r-f electric field across electrodes evaporated on opposite surfaces. The theory of piezoelectric excitation is discussed briefly in Chapter 13.

**Table 2   Adiabatic elastic stiffness constants
of several cubic crystals
at room temperature or 300°K.**

Most of these data are taken from the compilation by H. B. Huntington; see also D. I. Bolef and M. Menes, J. Appl. Physics, **31**, 1010 (1960).

	Stiffness constants, in 10^{12} dynes/cm^2		
	C_{11}	C_{12}	C_{44}
Diamond	10.76	1.25	5.76
Na	0.073	0.062	0.042
Li	0.135	0.114	0.088
Ge	1.285	0.483	0.680
Si	1.66	0.639	0.796
GaSb	0.885	0.404	0.433
InSb	0.672	0.367	0.302
MgO	2.86	0.87	1.48
NaCl	0.487	0.124	0.126
RbBr	0.317	0.042	0.039
RbI	0.256	0.031	0.029
CsBr	0.300	0.078	0.076
CsI	0.246	0.067	0.062

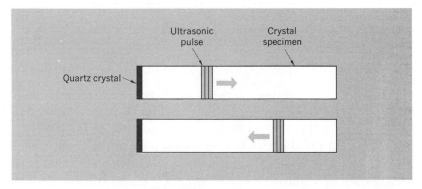

Figure 12   In the ultrasonic pulse method for the determination of elastic wave velocities a pulse of sound is generated by a piezoelectric transducer. The pulse makes successive reflections and is detected each time it reaches the transducer.

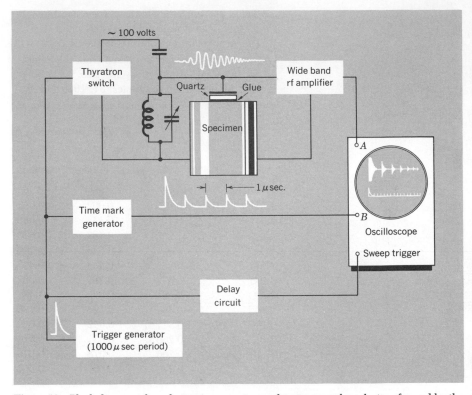

Figure 13 Block diagram of an electronic apparatus used to measure the velocity of sound by the ultrasonic pulse-echo technique. The trigger generator starts the process by closing the thyratron switch; this discharges a condenser through the LC network and imposes the indicated voltage waveform on the quartz transducer glued to the specimen. The waveform becomes a sound pulse which bounces back and forth within the specimen to produce the train of echoes shown on the oscilloscope face. The time mark generator and sweep delay circuit allow the time of arrival of some later echo to be measured accurately. [After G. A. Alers and J. R. Neighbours, J. Phys. Chem. Solids **7**, 58, (1958).]

References to ultrasonic techniques at microwave frequencies are given by E. H. Jacobsen in the book by Bak; see also H. E. Bömmel and K. Dransfeld, Phys. Rev. **117**, 1245 (1960); T. O. Woodruff and H. Ehrenreich, Phys. Rev. **123**, 1553 (1961). The first successful work in the Gcs or 10^9 cps range was done by K. N. Baranskii, Soviet Phys. Doklady **2**, 237 (1957).

The elastic stiffness constants C_{11}, C_{12}, C_{44} of a cubic crystal may be determined from the velocities of three waves, as we have noted. The same crystal orientation can be used for all three waves, but it is necessary to alter the cut and mounting of the quartz crystal transducer in order to excite the desired direction of particle motion in the crystal specimen.

Figure 14 Photograph of a single crystal of aluminum mounted in a spring-loaded holder for making velocity of sound measurements by the ultrasonic pulse-echo technique. The top face of the crystal is a (110) crystal plane on which is glued a quartz transducer with a metal electrode and rf lead in place. (Courtesy of the Scientific Laboratory, Ford Motor Company.)

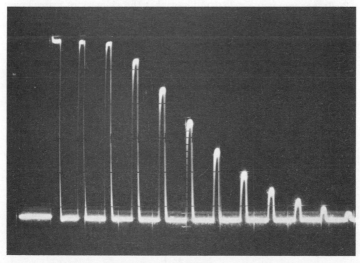

Figure 15 Successive ultrasonic pulse echoes across a crystal. The time interval between successive pulses is measured on the oscilloscope. This interval is the round-trip travel time of the ultrasonic pulse. The attenuation of the wave may be found from the decrease in pulse height of successive pulses, with allowance for losses on reflection at the ends. The voltage across the transducer is directly proportional to the stress in the wave. (Courtesy of H. J. McSkimin.)

Third-Order Elastic Constants

In the region of Hooke's law the elastic energy density is quadratic in the strain components, as in (14). Beyond this region higher order products of strains are needed. The third-order elastic stiffness constants relate the energy to products of three strain components. They are the lowest order constants to enter the description of nonlinear effects (Chapter 6), such as the interaction of phonons and thermal expansion. The third-order constants can be determined from velocity measurements on small amplitude sound waves in statically stressed media. A good account of the definitions of the third-order constants and the theory of their measurement is given by K. Brugger, Phys. Rev. **133**, A1611 (1964); R. N. Thurston and K. Brugger, Phys. Rev. **133**, A1604 (1964).

Problems

1. **Young's modulus and Poisson's ratio.** A cubic crystal is subject to tension in the [100] direction. Find expressions in terms of the elastic stiffnesses for Young's modulus and Poisson's ratio as defined in Fig. 16.
2. **Longitudinal wave velocity.** Show that the velocity of a longitudinal wave in the [111] direction of a cubic crystal is given by $v_s = [\frac{1}{3}(C_{11} + 2C_{12} + 4C_{44})/\rho]^{1/2}$. *Hint:* For such a wave $u = v = w$. Let $u = u_0 e^{iK(x+y+z)/\sqrt{3}} e^{-i\omega t}$, and use Eq. (32a).
3. **Transverse wave velocity.** Show that the velocity of transverse waves in the [111] direction of a cubic crystal is given by $v_s = [\frac{1}{3}(C_{11} - C_{12} + C_{44})/\rho]^{1/2}$. *Hint:* See Problem 2.
4. **Effective shear constant.** Show that the shear constant $\frac{1}{2}(C_{11} - C_{12})$ in a cubic crystal is defined by setting $e_{xx} = -e_{yy} = \frac{1}{2}e$ and all other strains equal to zero, as in Fig. 17. *Hint:* Consider the energy density (18); look for a C' such that $U = \frac{1}{2}C'e^2$.

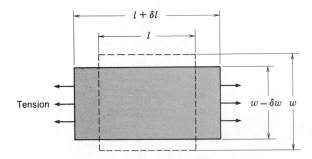

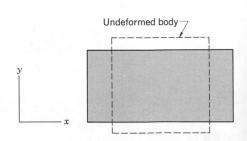

Figure 16 Young's modulus is defined as stress/strain for a tensile stress acting in one direction, with the sides of specimen left free. Poisson's ratio is defined as $\delta w/\delta l$ for this situation.

Figure 17 This deformation is compounded from the two shears $e_{xx} = -e_{yy}$.

5. *Determinantal approach.* It is known[9] that an R-dimensional determinant with all elements equal to unity has roots R and 0, with the R occurring once and the zero occurring $R - 1$ times. (a) Using this result show that if all elements have the value p, then the roots are Rp and 0. (b) Show that if the diagonal elements are q and all other elements are p, then there is one root equal to $(R - 1)p + q$ and $R - 1$ roots equal to $q - p$. (c) Show from the elastic equation (32) for a wave in the [111] direction of a cubic crystal that the determinantal equation which gives ω^2 as a function of K is

$$
\begin{vmatrix}
q - \omega^2\rho & p & p \\
p & q - \omega^2\rho & p \\
p & p & q - \omega^2\rho
\end{vmatrix} = 0,
$$

where $q \equiv \frac{1}{3}K^2(C_{11} + 2C_{44})$ and $p \equiv \frac{1}{3}K^2(C_{12} + C_{44})$. This expresses the condition that three linear homogeneous algebraic equations for the three displacement components u, v, w have a solution. Use the result of part b to find the three roots of ω^2; check with the results given for Problems 2 and 3.

6. *General propagation direction.* (a) By substitution in (32) find the determinantal equation which expresses the condition that the displacement

$$\mathbf{R}(\mathbf{r}) = [u_0\hat{x} + v_0\hat{y} + w_0\hat{z}]\exp[i(\mathbf{K}\cdot\mathbf{r} - \omega t)]$$

be a solution of the elastic wave equations in a cubic crystal. (b) The sum of the roots of a determinantal equation is equal to the sum of the diagonal elements a_{ii}. Show from part (a) that the sum of the squares of the three elastic wave velocities in any direction in a cubic crystal is equal to $(C_{11} + 2C_{44})/\rho$. Recall that $v_s^2 = \omega^2/K^2$.

°7. *Stability criteria.* The criterion that a cubic crystal with one atom in the primitive cell be stable against small homogeneous deformations is that the energy density (18) be positive for all combinations of strain components. What restrictions are thereby imposed on the elastic stiffness constants? (In mathematical language the problem is to find the conditions that a real symmetric quadratic form should be positive definite. The solution is given in books on algebra; see also Korn and Korn, *Mathematical handbook*, McGraw-Hill, 1961, Sec. 13.5–6.) *Ans.* $C_{44} > 0$, $C_{11} > 0$, $C_{11}^2 - C_{12}^2 > 0$, and $C_{11} + 2C_{12} > 0$. For an example of the instability which results when $C_{11} \cong C_{12}$ see L. R. Tesardi et al., Phys. Rev. Letters **15**, 250 (1965).

References

J. F. Nye, *Physical properties of crystals: their representation by tensors and matrices*, Oxford, 1957.
H. B. Huntington, "Elastic constants of crystals," *Solid state physics* **7**, 213 (1958).
A. E. H. Love, *A treatise on the mathematical theory of elasticity*, Dover paperback, 1944.
W. P. Mason, *Physical acoustics and the properties of solids*, Van Nostrand, 1958.
W. P. Mason, ed., *Physical acoustics*, in several volumes, Academic Press, Vol. I, 1964.
C. Zener, *Elasticity and anelasticity of metals*, University of Chicago Press, 1948.
T. A. Bak, ed., *Phonons and phonon interactions*, Benjamin, 1964.

[9] The elements of the determinantal equation are $a_{ij} = 1 - \lambda\delta_{ij}$, where λ is a root; see Appendix E, Eqs. (6) to (10).

5

Phonons
and
Lattice Vibrations

Sign	Name	Field
 $\longrightarrow$	Electron	—
 $\sim\!\!\sim\!\!\sim\!\!\longrightarrow$	Photon	Electromagnetic wave
 $\longrightarrow\!\!\wedge\!\!\wedge\!\!\longrightarrow$	Phonon	Elastic wave
 $\longrightarrow\!\!\dashv\!\vert\!\vdash\!\!\longrightarrow$	Plasmon	Collective electron wave
 $\longrightarrow\!\!\ell\!\ell\!\ell\!\!\longrightarrow$	Magnon	Magnetization wave
–	Polaron	Electron + elastic deformation
–	Exciton	Polarization wave

Figure 1 Some of the important elementary excitations in solids. The signs shown are used in this text.

QUANTIZATION OF LATTICE VIBRATIONS

The energy in a lattice vibration or elastic wave is quantized. The quantum of energy in an elastic wave is called a **phonon,** in analogy with the photon, which is the quantum of energy in an electromagnetic wave (Fig. 1). We first review the story of the photon. Almost all of the concepts, such as the wave-particle duality, which apply to photons apply equally well to phonons. Sound waves in crystals are composed of phonons. Thermal vibrations in crystals are thermally excited phonons, analogous to the thermally excited photons of black-body electromagnetic radiation in an enclosure.

Quantum theory began in 1900 when Max Planck showed that quantization of energy would explain the observed distribution in frequency of the electromagnetic energy radiated by a black body in thermal equilibrium. Planck assumed that the energy of each mode of oscillation of the electromagnetic field in a cavity is equal to an integral multiple of $h\nu$. The energy of one photon is $\epsilon = h\nu$; the energy of n photons in a mode of frequency ν is

$$\epsilon = nh\nu, \tag{1}$$

where n is a positive integer or zero, and the constant h (known now as Planck's constant) has the value 6.6255×10^{-27} erg-sec. We call n the number of photons or number of light quanta in the mode under consideration. We have for convenience omitted the usual zero-point term $\frac{1}{2}h\nu$ from (1); it has no direct effect on the matters we shall consider. It is now more common to write (1) as $\epsilon = n\hbar\omega$, where $\omega \equiv 2\pi\nu$ is the angular frequency and $\hbar \equiv h/2\pi \cong 1.05 \times 10^{-27}$ erg-sec. In theoretical work it is convenient to choose units such that $\hbar \equiv 1$, but we shall not do so in this book.

Let us shine light on a solid. If the energy $\hbar\omega$ of a photon is sufficiently high, when the photon interacts with the solid surface it will cause the emission of an electron. This is the photoelectric effect. Einstein showed that the photoelectric effect provides strong evidence for the quantization of light. When light of frequency ω ejects electrons from a metallic surface, it is observed that the kinetic energy of the ejected electrons is given by $\hbar\omega - I$, where I is the threshold or minimum energy needed to take an electron from the metal to the outside vacuum. The kinetic energy is found to be independent of the intensity of the light beam. No direct analog of the photoelectric experiment has as yet been carried out with phonons. The photoelectric effect does not prove that the photon is a particle, but the effect demonstrates that the electromagnetic field exchanges energy with other systems (here with an electron) in integral units of $\hbar\omega$. We know from innumerable diffraction experiments that the electromagnetic field has many aspects of a wave. What we learn from the photoelectric effect is that the energy in the electromagnetic field is quantized. The same consideration applies to elastic waves.

What is the experimental evidence that the energy of an elastic wave is quantized? The compelling lines of evidence include:

1. The lattice contribution to the heat capacity of solids (Chapter 6) always approaches zero as the temperature approaches zero; this can be explained only if the lattice vibrations are quantized. This was the earliest evidence for phonons.

2. X-rays and neutrons are scattered inelastically by crystals, with energy and momentum changes corresponding to the creation or absorption of one or more phonons. By measuring the recoil of the scattered x-ray or neutron we determine the properties of individual phonons. Such experiments offer the best way of determining the dispersion relations of frequency versus wave-vector for phonons, and provide the strongest evidence for phonons.

PHONON MOMENTUM

A phonon of wavevector **K** interacts with other particles and fields as if[1] it had a momentum $\hbar\mathbf{K}$. A phonon on a lattice does not really have momentum; we show in Problem 5 that only the $\mathbf{K} = 0$ or uniform mode phonon carries physical momentum. But for most practical purposes a phonon acts as if its momentum were $\hbar\mathbf{K}$. Sometimes $\hbar\mathbf{K}$ is called the **crystal momentum**. There exist momentum conservation laws in crystals in the sense of selection rules for allowed transitions between quantum states: these selection rules involve $\hbar\mathbf{K}$. That is why $\hbar\mathbf{K}$ is of physical importance.

In Chapter 2 we saw that the elastic scattering (Bragg diffraction) of an x-ray photon by a crystal is governed by the wavevector conservation law

$$\mathbf{k'} = \mathbf{k} + \mathbf{G}, \tag{2}$$

where **G** is a vector in the reciprocal lattice; **k** is the wavevector of the incident photon; and **k'** is the wavevector of the scattered photon. (In the reflection process (2) the crystal as a whole will recoil with momentum $-\hbar\mathbf{G}$, but this is rarely considered explicitly.)

---

[1] For a discussion of this delicate point, see G. Leibfried in *Encyclo. of physics* **VII**/1, 104 (1955); G. Süssman, Z. Naturf. **11a**, 1 (1956); G. Beck, Anals. Acad. Brasil. Ci. **26**, 64 (1954). The reason that phonons on a lattice do not carry momentum is that a phonon coordinate except for $\mathbf{K} = 0$ involves *relative* coordinates of the atoms. Thus in an H_2 molecule the internuclear vibrational coordinate $\mathbf{r}_1 - \mathbf{r}_2$ is a relative coordinate and does not carry linear momentum; the center of mass coordinate $\frac{1}{2}(\mathbf{r}_1 + \mathbf{r}_2)$ corresponds to the uniform mode and can carry linear momentum.

If the scattering of the photon is inelastic, with the creation of a phonon of wavevector $\mathbf{K}$, then the wavevector conservation law becomes[2]

$$\mathbf{k'} + \mathbf{K} = \mathbf{k} + \mathbf{G}. \qquad (3)$$

If a phonon $\mathbf{K}$ is absorbed in the process, we have instead the relation

$$\mathbf{k'} = \mathbf{k} + \mathbf{K} + \mathbf{G}. \qquad (4)$$

Relations (4) and (3) are natural extensions of (2).

INELASTIC SCATTERING OF PHOTONS BY LONG WAVELENGTH PHONONS

Consider a photon of frequency $\nu = \omega/2\pi$ which propagates in a crystal. If the crystal is viewed as a continuum of refractive index n, then the wavevector of the photon is determined by the relation

$$\omega = ck/n \qquad \text{or} \qquad \lambda\nu = c/n, \qquad (5)$$

where c is the velocity of light. The momentum of the photon is

$$\mathbf{p} = \hbar\mathbf{k}. \qquad (6)$$

Let a photon in this beam interact with a phonon beam or sound wave in the crystal. The photon can be scattered by the sound wave. The interaction may occur because the elastic strain field of the sound wave changes the local concentration of atoms and therefore the refractive index of the crystal. Thus the sound wave modulates the optical properties of the medium. Reciprocally, the electric field of the light wave sets up a periodic mechanical strain in the medium, and thus modulates the elastic properties of the medium.

In a crystal a photon can create or absorb a phonon. The photon will be scattered in the process; its wavevector will change from $\mathbf{k}$ to $\mathbf{k'}$ and its frequency from ω to ω'. Suppose that a phonon is created with a wavevector $\mathbf{K}$

---

[2] We can exhibit by an example the mathematics involved in the different selection rules for a lattice and for a continuum. Suppose two phonons $\mathbf{K}_1$, $\mathbf{K}_2$ interact through third-order anharmonic terms in the elastic energy as discussed in Chapter 6 to create a third phonon $\mathbf{K}_3$. The probability of the collision will involve the product of the three phonon wave amplitudes, summed over all lattice sites:

$$\sum_n \exp\left[i(\mathbf{K}_3 - \mathbf{K}_1 - \mathbf{K}_2) \cdot \mathbf{r}_n\right].$$

By the argument of (2.19–31) this sum in the limit of a large number of lattice sites approaches zero unless $\mathbf{K}_3 = \mathbf{K}_1 + \mathbf{K}_2$ or unless $\mathbf{K}_3 = \mathbf{K}_1 + \mathbf{K}_2 + \mathbf{G}$. In a continuum the matrix element in the same problem involves

$$\int d^3x \exp\left[i(\mathbf{K}_3 - \mathbf{K}_1 - \mathbf{K}_2) \cdot \mathbf{r}\right] = (2\pi)^3\delta(\mathbf{K}_3 - \mathbf{K}_1 - \mathbf{K}_2),$$

where δ is the Dirac delta function; in the continuum no G enters.

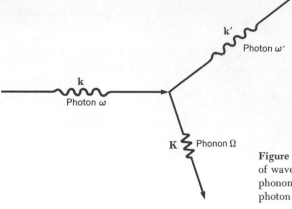

Figure 2 Inelastic scattering of a photon of wavevector **k**, with the production of a phonon of wavevector **K**. The scattered photon has wavevector **k**′.

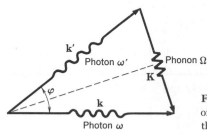

Figure 3 Momentum balance diagram for the process of Fig. 2. If $k = k'$, the triangle is isosceles. The base of the triangle is $K = 2k \sin \frac{1}{2}\varphi$.

and angular frequency Ω. The kinematics of the collision event (Fig. 2) are simple. By conservation of energy

$$\hbar\omega = \hbar\omega' + \hbar\Omega. \tag{7}$$

By conservation of wavevector

$$\hbar\mathbf{k} = \hbar\mathbf{k}' + \hbar\mathbf{K}, \tag{8}$$

where for simplicity we do not include in (8) the possibility (3) that the scattering may be combined with a Bragg diffraction involving a reciprocal lattice vector of the crystal lattice. If the velocity of sound v_s is constant, we have $\Omega = v_s K$, because $\lambda\Omega/2\pi = v_s$.

Now a phonon can carry off only a small part of the energy of the incident photon: The velocity of sound v_s is very much less than the velocity of light c. For a phonon wavevector K comparable in magnitude to the photon wavevector k, it follows that $ck \gg v_s K$. Now $\omega = ck$ and $\Omega = v_s K$; thus $\omega \gg \Omega$. It follows from (7) that $\omega' \cong \omega$ and $k' \cong k$.

If $k' \cong k$, we see from Fig. 3 that

$$K \cong 2k \sin \tfrac{1}{2}\varphi, \tag{9}$$

or, using $k = \omega n/c$ from (5),

$$v_s K \cong \frac{2v_s \omega n}{c} \sin \tfrac{1}{2}\varphi. \tag{10}$$

Because $\Omega = v_s K$, the phonons produced when photons are scattered inelastically at an angle φ from the incident direction will be of frequency

$$\Omega \cong (2v_s \omega n/c) \sin \tfrac{1}{2}\varphi, \tag{11}$$

where n is the refractive index of the crystal.

EXAMPLE: *Generation of Phonons.* The maximum phonon frequency generated by scattering of visible light of vacuum wavelength $\lambda = 4000$ Å is, for $v_s \approx 5 \times 10^5$ cm/sec and $n \approx 1.5$,

$$\Omega \approx 2(5 \times 10^5)(2\pi)(1.5)/(4 \times 10^{-5}) \approx 2 \times 10^{11} \text{ sec}^{-1}, \tag{12}$$

using (11) with $\sin \tfrac{1}{2}\varphi = 1$. At this frequency $K = \Omega/v_s \approx 4 \times 10^5$ cm^{-1}. The fractional change in the frequency of the light on scattering is 5×10^{-5}.

The scattering of visible light from an intense laser source has been used[3] to generate phonons in the microwave frequency range in quartz and in sapphire. The photon frequency shifts observed are in close agreement with the shifts calculated from Eq. (11), using values of the velocity of sound measured at lower frequencies by ultrasonic methods.

The scattering of light by phonons in solids and liquids is known as **Brillouin scattering**.[4] The spectrum after scattering of monochromatic light incident on water is shown in Fig. 4. The excitation of microwave phonons in crystals has been detected by the diffraction of light.[5]

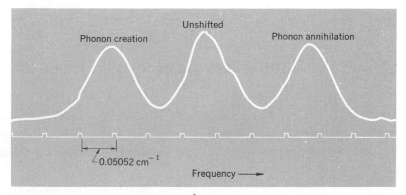

Figure 4 Spectrum of light at 6328 Å scattered at right angles in water at room temperature. The unshifted central peak at the laser frequency is due largely to Tyndall scattering from tiny suspended particles in the water. The line width is due to the slit width of the spectrograph. The spectrum was swept out on the recorder in 5 minutes. The phonon frequency was determined from this trace to be $(4.33 \pm 0.02) \times 10^9$ cps. The velocity is calculated from Eq. (18) to be $(1.457 \pm 0.010) \times 10^5$ cm/sec. [After G. B. Benedek et al., J. Opt. Soc. Amer. **54**, 1284 (1964).]

[3] See R. Y. Chiao, C. H. Townes, and B. P. Stoicheff, Phys. Rev. Letters **12**, 592 (1964).

[4] L. Brillouin, Ann. phy. **17**, 88 (1922); a review of the Raman effect in crystals is given by R. Loudon, Adv. in Physics **13**, 424–482 (1964).

[5] K. N. Baranskii, Soviet Phys. Doklady **2**, 237 (1957); see also Fig. 1 of H. E. Bömmel and K. Dransfeld, Phys. Rev. Letters **1**, 234 (1958).

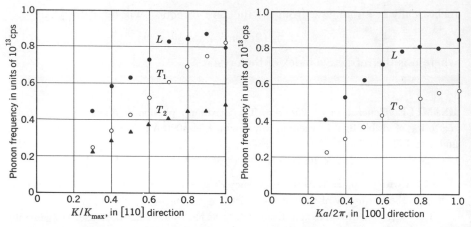

Figure 5 Dispersion curves determined by the inelastic scattering of x-rays for phonons propagating along the [110] axis in aluminum. The longitudinal wave is shown by solid circles; the transverse wave T_1 for which the particle motion is parallel to the [001] axis is shown by open circles; and the transverse wave T_2 parallel to the [$\bar{1}$10] axis is shown by solid triangles. [After C. B. Walker, Phys. Rev. **103**, 547 (1956).]

Figure 6 Dispersion curves for elastic waves propagating along the [100] axis in aluminum, as observed by inelastic scattering of x-rays. The longitudinal and transverse waves are shown, respectively, by the solid and open circles. (After C. B. Walker.)

INELASTIC SCATTERING OF X-RAYS BY PHONONS

One method of studying the phonon spectrum of solids is by the inelastic scattering of x-rays. The principles described above can be applied to the inelastic or diffuse scattering of x-ray photons in processes in which one phonon is created or absorbed. Results obtained by Walker for aluminum are plotted in Figs. 5 and 6.

In such experiments we want to find the phonon frequency as a function of the phonon wavevector **K**. The wavevector is determined by application of the general condition (10) or (11) for conservation of wavevector. Unfortunately, it is difficult to determine directly the small frequency shift of the scattered x-ray beam. In neutron scattering experiments the energy shift can usually be measured directly, which is an advantage.

INELASTIC SCATTERING OF NEUTRONS BY PHONONS

A neutron sees the crystal lattice chiefly by interaction with the nuclei of the atoms. The kinematics of the scattering of a neutron beam by a crystal lattice are described by the general wavevector conservation relation (3) or (4):

$$\mathbf{k} = \mathbf{k}' + \mathbf{G} \pm \mathbf{K}, \tag{13}$$

and by the requirement of conservation of energy. Here $\mathbf{K}$ is the wavevector of the phonon created ($+$) or absorbed ($-$) in the process, and $\mathbf{G}$ is any reciprocal lattice vector.

The kinetic energy of the incident neutron is $p^2/2M_n$, where M_n is the mass of the neutron. The momentum $\mathbf{p}$ is given by $\hbar\mathbf{k}$, where $\mathbf{k}$ is the wavevector of the neutron. Thus $\hbar^2 k^2/2M_n$ is the kinetic energy of the incident neutron. If $\mathbf{k}'$ is the wavevector of the scattered neutron, the energy of the scattered neutron is $\hbar^2 k'^2/2M_n$. The statement of conservation of energy is

$$\frac{\hbar^2 k^2}{2M_n} = \frac{\hbar^2 k'^2}{2M_n} \pm \hbar\omega_{\mathbf{K}}, \tag{14}$$

where $\hbar\omega_{\mathbf{K}}$ is the energy of the phonon created ($+$) or absorbed ($-$) in the process.

To determine the dispersion relation[6] using (13) and (14) it is necessary in the experiment to find the energy gain or loss of the scattered neutrons as a function of the scattering direction $\mathbf{k} - \mathbf{k}'$.

An example of an accurate determination of phonon spectra in a metal is shown by Fig. 7a for sodium. In Fig. 7b phonon spectra are given for an ionic crystal, potassium bromide.

Under favorable conditions neutron scattering is the ideal method for the determination of phonon spectra. The method is not applicable when the absorption of neutrons by the nuclei of the crystal is high. In some circumstances it is possible to obtain important data on phonon lifetimes from the angular width of the scattered neutron beam. The spectrometer used at Chalk River, one of the centers of research in this field, is shown in Figs. 8 and 9.

[6] A geometrical construction to illustrate the kinematics of inelastic neutron scattering is given on p. 377 of *QTS*. An excellent review of inelastic neutron scattering is given by B. N. Brockhouse, S. Hautecler, and H. Stiller, in Strumane et al., ed., *Interaction of radiation with solids*, North-Holland, 1963.

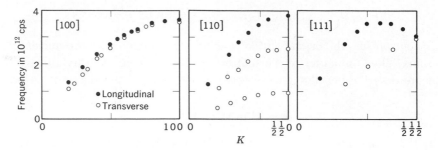

Figure 7a   The dispersion curves of sodium for phonons propagating in the [001], [110], and [111] directions at 90°K as determined by inelastic scattering of neutrons. [Woods, Brockhouse, March and Bowers, Proc. Phys. Soc. London **79**, pt. 2, 440 (1962).]

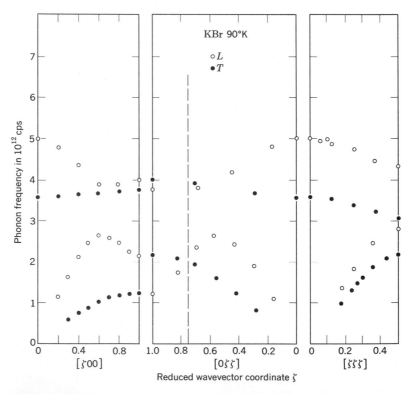

Figure 7b   Dispersion curves for the optical and acoustic branches of the phonon spectrum of potassium bromide at 90°K, after A. D. B. Woods, B. N. Brockhouse, R. A. Cowley, and W. Cochran, Phys. Rev. **131**, 1025 (1963). The data can be fitted very well by a simple model called the shell model, discussed by A. D. B. Woods, W. Cochran, and B. N. Brockhouse, Phys. Rev. **119**, 980 (1960); B. J. Dick and A. W. Overhauser, Phys. Rev. **112**, 90 (1958); J. E. Hanlon and A. W. Lawson, Phys. Rev. **113**, 472 (1959).

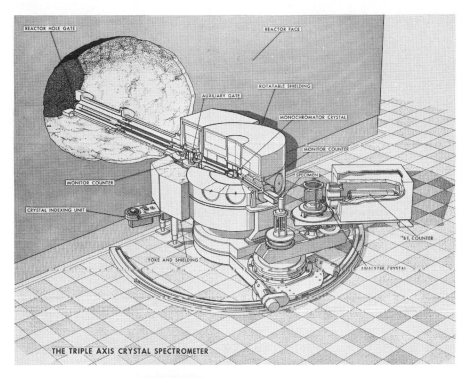

THE TRIPLE AXIS CRYSTAL SPECTROMETER

Figure 8 (*above*) Cutaway drawing of the Brockhouse triple-axis crystal spectrometer, as in Fig. 9.

Figure 9 (*right*)   Triple-axis crystal spectrometer at the high flux reactor at the Chalk River Nuclear Laboratories of Atomic Energy of Canada Limited. The spectrometer was developed by Dr. B. N. Brockhouse and colleagues to carry out studies of phonons in crystals using the inelastic scattering of neutrons.

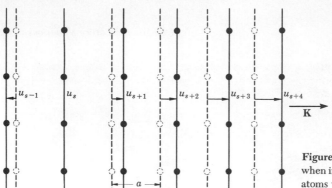

Figure 10 (Dashed lines) planes of atoms when in equilibrium. (Solid lines) planes of atoms when displaced as for a longitudinal wave.

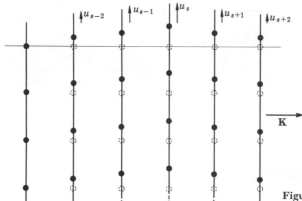

Figure 11 Planes of atoms as displaced during passage of a transverse wave.

VIBRATIONS OF MONATOMIC LATTICES

We now extend the discussion of the elastic vibrations of crystals to the short wavelength range, where the wavelength of the lattice wave is comparable with the lattice constant of the crystal. The periodicity of the crystal structure has important consequences for elastic waves just as for x-rays.

To simplify the problem we consider elastic waves propagating in directions such that the wave polarizations are purely transverse or purely longitudinal.[7] (We consider only crystals for which the primitive basis contains only one atom.) In a cubic crystal these are the 100, 111, and 110 directions. When a wave propagates along one of these directions, entire planes of atoms in the crystal move in phase. The motion is parallel to the propagation direction if the wave is longitudinal and perpendicular to the propagation direction if the wave is transverse. We can learn a great deal about the forces which connect different planes of atoms from the relation between frequency ω and wavevector $\mathbf{K}$ for these special modes of propagation.

If planes of atoms are displaced as a whole parallel or perpendicular to the wavevector $\mathbf{K}$ during the passage of a wave, we can describe by a single coordinate u_s the displacement of the plane s from equilibrium. The problem is

[7] In general directions of propagation the polarizations are not purely longitudinal or transverse.

then one-dimensional. We suppose for the present that all planes of atoms are identical. We consider one polarization direction, either longitudinal or transverse. Figure 10 shows the particle displacement for a longitudinal wave, Fig. 11 for a transverse wave.

We assume that the force on the plane labeled s as caused by the displacement of the plane labeled $s + p$ is proportional to the difference of their displacements, so that the total force on plane s is given by

$$F_s = \sum_p C_p(u_{s+p} - u_s). \tag{15}$$

This expression is linear in the displacements and is of the form of Hooke's law. The constant C_p is the force constant between planes removed from each other by p. The C_p's will be different for longitudinal and transverse waves. It is convenient to regard F and C_p as defined for one atom of the plane, so that F_s is the force on one atom in the plane s. The equation of motion of the plane s is

$$M\frac{d^2u_s}{dt^2} = \sum_p C_p(u_{s+p} - u_s), \tag{16}$$

where M is the mass of an atom. In the summation p runs over all positive and negative integers.

We look for solutions to (16) of the form of a traveling wave:

$$u_{s+p} = u(0)e^{i(s+p)Ka - i\omega t}, \tag{17}$$

where a is the spacing[8] between planes and K is the wavevector. Then (16) reduces to

$$-\omega^2 Mu(0)e^{i(sKa - \omega t)} = \sum_p C_p(e^{i(s+p)Ka} - e^{isKa})u(0)e^{-i\omega t}. \tag{18}$$

We may cancel $u(0)e^{isKa}e^{-i\omega t}$ from both sides, so that

$$\omega^2 M = -\sum_p C_p(e^{ipKa} - 1). \tag{19}$$

As the primitive basis contains only one atom it follows from the translational symmetry that $C_p = C_{-p}$, and we may regroup (19) as

$$\omega^2 M = -\sum_{p>0} C_p(e^{ipKa} + e^{-ipKa} - 2). \tag{20}$$

Using the identity $2\cos pKa \equiv e^{ipKa} + e^{-ipKa}$ we have the dispersion relation

$$\boxed{\omega^2 = \frac{2}{M}\sum_{p>0} C_p(1 - \cos pKa).} \tag{21}$$

If there are interactions only among nearest-neighbor planes, then (21) reduces to

$$\omega^2 = (2C_1/M)(1 - \cos Ka). \tag{22}$$

[8] The value of the interplanar spacing a for a given lattice will depend on the direction of **K**.

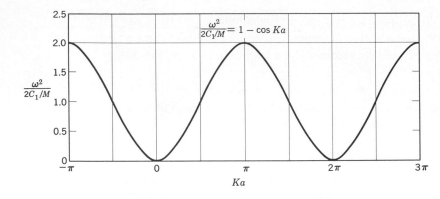

Figure 12 Plot of ω^2 versus K for lattice with interactions only between nearest neighbor planes. The interplanar force constant is C_1 and the interplanar spacing is a.

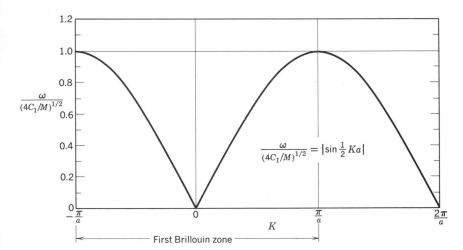

Figure 13 Plot of ω versus K for model of Fig. 12. The region of $K \ll 1/a$ or $\lambda \gg a$ corresponds to the continuum approximation; here ω is directly proportional to K.

By a trigonometric identity this may be written as

$$\omega^2 = (4C_1/M)\,\sin^2 \tfrac{1}{2}Ka; \qquad \omega = (4C_1/M)^{1/2}\,|\sin \tfrac{1}{2}Ka|. \qquad (23)$$

We arrange the sign of the square root so that the angular frequency ω is always positive for a stable lattice. We have plotted ω^2 versus Ka in Fig. 12 and ω versus Ka in Fig. 13. Both curves are periodic functions of K, with period $2\pi/a$.

First Brillouin Zone

What range of K is physically significant for phonons? From (17) the ratio of the displacements of two successive planes is given by

$$\frac{u_{s+p+1}}{u_{s+p}} = \frac{u(0)\,\exp\{i[(s+p+1)Ka - \omega t]\}}{u(0)\,\exp\{i[(s+p)Ka - \omega t]\}} = e^{iKa}. \qquad (24)$$

A range of 2π for Ka covers all independent values of e^{iKa}. We want both positive and negative values of K because waves can propagate to the right or to the left. Thus the range of independent values of K can be specified by[9]

$$-\pi \leq Ka \leq \pi, \quad \text{or} \quad -\frac{\pi}{a} \leq K \leq \frac{\pi}{a}. \tag{25}$$

This range of values of K is referred to as the **first Brillouin zone** of the linear lattice, as defined in Chapter 2. The extreme values of K in this zone are

$$K_{\max} = \pm\frac{\pi}{a}, \tag{26}$$

where $K_{\max}$ may be of the order of 10^8 cm^{-1}.

Suppose we use in (17) values of K outside of the first Brillouin zone? Such values merely reproduce lattice motions already described by values of K within the limits $\pm\pi/a$. We show that we may treat a value of K outside of these limits by subtracting the appropriate integral multiple of $2\pi/a$ which will give a wavevector inside these limits.

Suppose K lies outside the first zone, but $K' \equiv K - 2\pi n/a$ lies within the first zone, where n is an integer. Then the displacement ratio (24) becomes

$$u_{s+p+1}/u_{s+p} = e^{iKa} \equiv e^{2\pi ni}e^{i(Ka-2\pi n)} \equiv e^{iK'a}, \tag{27}$$

because $e^{i2\pi n} = 1$. Thus the displacement can always be described by a wavevector value lying within the first zone. Note that $2\pi n/a$ is a reciprocal lattice vector.

At the boundaries $K_{\max} = \pm\pi/a$ of the Brillouin zone the solution $u_s = u(0) \exp[i(sKa - \omega t)]$ does not represent a traveling wave, but a standing wave:[10] at the zone boundaries $sK_{\max}a = \pm s\pi$, whence

$$u_s = u(0)e^{\pm is\pi}e^{-i\omega t} = u(0) \, e^{-i\omega t} \cos s\pi. \tag{28}$$

This is a standing wave. For this wave alternate atoms move in opposite phases, because $\cos s\pi = \pm 1$ according to whether s is an even or an odd integer. This situation is equivalent to Bragg reflection of x-rays: when the Bragg condition is satisfied a traveling wave cannot propagate in a lattice, but through successive reflections back and forth a standing wave is set up. The critical value $K_{\max} = \pm\pi/a$ found here satisfies the Bragg condition $2d \sin \theta = n\lambda$: we have $\theta = \frac{1}{2}\pi$, $d = a$, $K = 2\pi/\lambda$, $n = 1$, so that $\lambda = 2a$. With x-rays it is possible to have n equal to other integers besides unity because the amplitude of the wave has a meaning in the space between atoms, but the displacement amplitude of an elastic wave has a meaning only at the atoms themselves.

Group Velocity

The velocity of a wave packet is the group velocity, given from physical optics as $v_g = \partial\omega/\partial K$. It is the velocity of energy transmission in the medium.

---

[9] Note that this represents a real difference from the behavior of an elastic continuum. In the continuum limit $a \to 0$ and $K_{\max} \to \pm\infty$.

[10] We shall find this property in Chapter 9 for conduction electron wavefunctions at the zone boundaries.

146

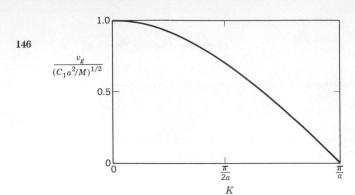

Figure 14 Group velocity v versus K, for model of Fig. 12. At the zone boundary the group velocity is zero. The range of K of laboratory-produced ultrasonic waves is too limited at present to be visible at the left of the graph.

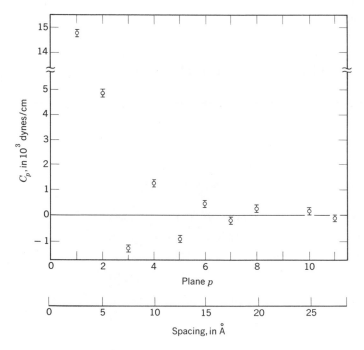

Figure 15 The interplanar force constants for longitudinal waves in the [100] direction in lead at 100°K, after Brockhouse et al., Phys. Rev. **128**, 1099 (1962). The horizontal axis gives the distance of the plane from the reference plane.

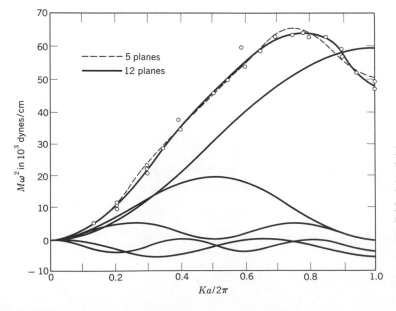

Figure 16 Values of $M\omega^2$ for the longitudinal branch in the [100] direction in Pb, plotted against the reduced wavevector. The fitted curves with twelve planes (good fit) and with five planes are shown. The first five Fourier components are also plotted.

For the dispersion relation (23) the group velocity (Fig. 14) is

$$v_g = (C_1 a^2 / M)^{1/2} \cos \tfrac{1}{2} Ka. \tag{29}$$

If $K = \pm \pi / a$ the argument of the cosine is $\pm \pi / 2$, so that the group velocity is zero at the edge of the zone. This is what we expect from a standing wave! The same result applies for the general dispersion relation (21).

Long Wavelength or Continuum Limit

For $pKa \ll 1$ we have $\cos pKa \cong 1 - \tfrac{1}{2}(pKa)^2$, and the dispersion relation (21) becomes

$$\omega^2 = K^2 \left(\frac{a^2}{M} \right) \sum_{p>0} p^2 C_p. \tag{30}$$

But from Chapter 4 we know that $\omega^2 = K^2 \times$ (elastic stiffness/density). The p^2 term in the summation in (30) will tend to make long-range force components play an important role in determining the macroscopic elastic constants. Can you understand this physically for a uniform deformation?

Derivation of Force Constants from Experimental Dispersion Relation

In many metals the effective forces may be of quite long range. Effects have been found which connect planes of atoms separated by as many as twenty planes.[11] It is quite simple to make a statement about the range of the forces if we know the dispersion relation for ω.

We solve for the C_p by multiplying both sides of (21) by $\cos rKa$, where r is an integer, and integrating over the range of independent values of K:

$$M \int_{-\pi/a}^{\pi/a} dK \, \omega_K^2 \cos rKa = 2 \sum_{p>0} C_p \int_{-\pi/a}^{\pi/a} dK (1 - \cos pKa) \cos rKa$$

$$= -2\pi C_r / a. \tag{31a}$$

Thus

$$C_p = -(Ma/2\pi) \int_{-\pi/a}^{\pi/a} dK \, \omega_K^2 \cos pKa. \tag{31b}$$

This important result[12] expresses the force constant from the pth plane of atoms in terms of the Fourier cosine transform of ω^2 as a function of K. It holds only for monatomic lattices.

---

[11] J. M. Rowe, B. N. Brockhouse, and E. C. Svensson, Phys. Rev. Letters **14**, 554 (1965).

[12] The result (31b) is due to A. J. E. Foreman and W. M. Lomer, Proc. Phys. Soc. (London) **B70**, 1143 (1957). The application to the observed dispersion relations of lead (Figs. 15 and 16) is considered by Brockhouse et al., Phys. Rev. **128**, 1099 (1962). The origin of the long-range forces observed in several metals is discussed by W. A. Harrison, Phys. Rev. **129**, 2512 (1963) and by S. H. Koenig, Phys. Rev. **135**, A1693 (1964). The first treatment along these lines was given for sodium by T. Toya in 1958.

148

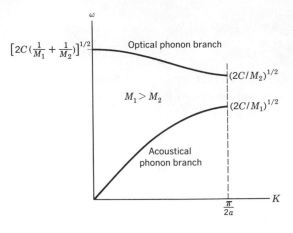

$$\left[2C\left(\frac{1}{M_1}+\frac{1}{M_2}\right)\right]^{1/2}$$

Optical phonon branch

$(2C/M_2)^{1/2}$

$M_1 > M_2$

$(2C/M_1)^{1/2}$

Acoustical phonon branch

$\dfrac{\pi}{2a}$

Figure 17 (*left*) Optical and acoustical phonon branches of the dispersion relation for a diatomic linear lattice, showing the limiting frequencies at $K = 0$ and $K = K_{\max} = \pi/2a$. The lattice constant is $2a$.

Figure 18 (*below*) Transverse optical and transverse acoustical waves in a diatomic linear lattice, illustrated by the particle displacements for the two modes at the same wavelength.

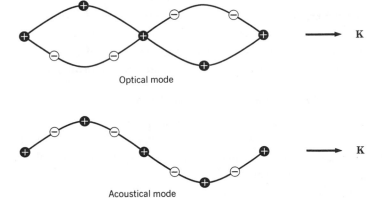

Optical mode

K

Acoustical mode

K

LATTICE WITH TWO ATOMS PER PRIMITIVE CELL

With crystals having more than one atom per primitive cell the vibrational spectrum shows new features. We consider two atoms per primitive cell, as in the NaCl structure or the diamond structure. For each polarization mode in a given propagation direction the dispersion relation ω versus K develops two branches, known as the **acoustical** and **optical branches,** with phonons named to suit. We have longitudinal LA and transverse acoustical TA phonons, and longitudinal LO and transverse optical TO phonons.

We consider a cubic crystal (Fig. 17) where atoms of mass M_1 lie on the odd-numbered planes and atoms of mass M_2 lie on the even-numbered planes. (It is not essential that the masses be different; the subscripts 1 and 2 refer to the two atoms of the basis, even if the atoms are identical. The force constants could be different, as in Problem 6.) Let the planes be a distance a apart, so that $2a$ is the repeat distance. We now consider only waves which propagate in a symmetry direction, such as [111] in NaCl or [100] in CsCl, for which a single plane contains only a single type of ion.

The equations of motion are, under the assumption that each plane interacts only with its nearest-neighbor planes and that the force constants are identical between all pairs of nearest-neighbor planes,

$$M_1 \frac{d^2 u_{2s+1}}{dt^2} = C(u_{2s+2} + u_{2s} - 2u_{2s+1});$$

$$M_2 \frac{d^2 u_{2s}}{dt^2} = C(u_{2s+1} + u_{2s-1} - 2u_{2s}). \tag{32}$$

We look for solutions having the form of traveling waves, but with different amplitudes ξ and η on the odd- and even-numbered planes:

$$u_{2s+1} = \xi \, e^{i[(2s+1)Ka - \omega t]}; \qquad u_{2s} = \eta \, e^{i(2sKa - \omega t)}. \tag{33}$$

On substitution of (33) in (32) we have

$$-\omega^2 M_1 \xi = C\eta(e^{iKa} + e^{-iKa}) - 2C\xi;$$

$$-\omega^2 M_2 \eta = C\xi(e^{iKa} + e^{-iKa}) - 2C\eta. \tag{34}$$

We write $2 \cos Ka$ for $e^{iKa} + e^{-iKa}$. The set (34) of homogeneous linear equations in the two unknowns ξ, η has a nontrivial solution only if the determinant of the coefficients of ξ and η vanishes:

$$\begin{vmatrix} 2C - M_1\omega^2 & -2C \cos Ka \\ -2C \cos Ka & 2C - M_2\omega^2 \end{vmatrix} = 0, \tag{35}$$

or

$$\omega^2 = C\left(\frac{1}{M_1} + \frac{1}{M_2}\right) \pm C\left[\left(\frac{1}{M_1} + \frac{1}{M_2}\right)^2 - \frac{4 \sin^2 Ka}{M_1 M_2}\right]^{1/2}. \tag{36}$$

For small K the two roots of (36) are

$$\omega^2 \cong 2C\left(\frac{1}{M_1} + \frac{1}{M_2}\right) \qquad \text{(optical branch);} \tag{37}$$

$$\omega^2 \cong \frac{2C}{M_1 + M_2} K^2 a^2 \qquad \text{(acoustical branch).} \tag{38}$$

The range of the first Brillouin zone is $-\pi/2a \leq K \leq \pi/2a$, where $2a$ is the repeat distance of the lattice. At $K_{\max} = \pm\pi/2a$ the roots are

$$\omega^2 = 2C/M_1; \qquad \omega^2 = 2C/M_2. \tag{39}$$

The variation of ω with K described by (36) is shown in Fig. 17 for $M_1 > M_2$.

The particle displacement in the TA and TO branches is shown in Fig. 18. For the optical branch at $K = 0$ we find, from (34) and (37),

$$\xi/\eta = -M_2/M_1. \tag{40}$$

The atoms vibrate against each other, but their center of mass is fixed. If the two atoms carry opposite charges we may excite a motion of this type with the electric field of a light wave,[13] so that the branch is called the optical branch.[14]

If a photon is absorbed by the crystal with the creation of a single phonon,[15] then by wavevector conservation $\mathbf{k}_{photon} = \mathbf{K}_{phonon}$. The photon wavevectors at the relevant frequencies ($\sim 10^{13}$ cps) are of the order of 10^3 cm^{-1}, whereas phonon wavevectors run up to 10^8 cm^{-1}. Thus the phonons excited have small wavevectors.

Figure 17 shows that wavelike solutions do not exist for frequencies between $(2C/M_1)^{1/2}$ and $(2C/M_2)^{1/2}$. This is a characteristic feature of elastic waves in diatomic lattices. There is a **frequency gap** at the boundary $K_{max} = \pm\pi/2a$ of the first Brillouin zone. If we look for solutions in the gap with ω real, then the wavevector K will be complex, so that the wave is damped in space. The same effect is demonstrated for photons in Appendix A. An excellent discussion of wave propagation in a diatomic lattice is given in the book by Brillouin.

Another solution besides (40) for the amplitude ratio at small K is $\xi = \eta$; the atoms (and their center of mass) move together, as in long wavelength acoustical vibrations; hence the term acoustical branch. If there are p atoms in the primitive cell, there will be $3p$ branches to the phonon dispersion relation: 3 acoustical branches and $3p - 3$ optical branches.

OPTICAL PROPERTIES IN THE INFRARED

We consider the response of a diatomic crystal of ions $\pm e$ to infrared photons. In the long wavelength limit the equations of motion in an electric field $E_l e^{-i\omega t}$ are, on adding a force term $\pm eE_l$ to (34),

$$-\omega^2 M_1 \xi = 2C(\eta - \xi) + eE_l; \qquad -\omega^2 M_2 \eta = -2C(\eta - \xi) - eE_l. \quad (41)$$

Here E_l is the amplitude of the electric field intensity at the ion and $\pm e$ is the ionic charge. Thus

$$\xi = \frac{(e/M_1)E_l}{\omega_T^2 - \omega^2}; \qquad \eta = \frac{-(e/M_2)E_l}{\omega_T^2 - \omega^2}; \qquad (42)$$

where

$$\omega_T^2 = 2C\left(\frac{1}{M_1} + \frac{1}{M_2}\right) = \frac{2C}{\mu} \qquad (43)$$

is the $K = 0$ limit (37) of the optical branch. Here μ denotes the reduced mass of an ion pair. Equations (42) exhibit a resonance at $\omega = \omega_T$. The positive and negative ions are displaced with opposite signs because their charges

---

[13] Effects of the magnetic field of the light wave are weaker because the magnetic force on a charge involves v/c, where v is the velocity of an ion in the lattice.

[14] Absorption frequencies in the optical branch lie in the infrared portion of the spectrum.

[15] This process is different from that considered earlier in which the photon is scattered by creating or absorbing a phonon.

are opposite. Our solution has been derived explicitly for a transverse electromagnetic wave with $\mathbf{E} \perp \mathbf{k}$, so that ω_T refers to a transverse optical phonon.

The dielectric polarization $\mathbf{P}$ is defined as the dipole moment per unit volume. If there are N positive and N negative ions per unit volume, then the contribution to the polarization from the ionic displacements is

$$P \text{ (ionic)} = Ne(\xi - \eta) = \frac{Ne^2/\mu}{\omega_T^2 - \omega^2} E_l. \tag{44}$$

We show in detail in Chapter 12 that this leads to a frequency-dependent dielectric constant of the form

$$\epsilon(\omega) = \epsilon(\infty) + \frac{S}{\omega_T^2 - \omega^2}, \tag{45}$$

where $\epsilon(\infty)$ denotes the core electron contribution (Chapter 12) to the dielectric constant at optical frequencies much higher than ω_T; the constant S is of the order of magnitude of $4\pi Ne^2/\mu$.

An important and surprising property of the dielectric constant (45) is that electromagnetic waves in an infinite crystal will not propagate in a forbidden frequency region defined by

$$\omega_T^2 < \omega^2 < \omega_T^2 + S/\epsilon(\infty) \equiv \omega_L^2. \tag{46}$$

Between these two frequencies (Fig. 19) the dielectric constant (45) is negative, the refractive index $n = \epsilon^{1/2}$ is imaginary, and *wavelike solutions of the wave equation do not exist*. This forbidden frequency gap is different from Bragg reflection and has nothing to do with the periodicity of the lattice. The upper bound of the forbidden band of frequencies in (46) is denoted by ω_L; it is the root of

$$\epsilon(\omega_L) = 0. \tag{47}$$

Observe from (45) that $\epsilon(0) = \epsilon(\infty) + S/\omega_T^2$, so that

$$\frac{\epsilon(0)}{\epsilon(\infty)} = 1 + \frac{S}{\epsilon(\infty)\omega_T^2}, \tag{48}$$

or, using (46),

$$\boxed{\frac{\epsilon(0)}{\epsilon(\infty)} = \frac{\omega_L^2}{\omega_T^2}.} \tag{49}$$

This is known as the **Lyddane-Sachs-Teller relation.**[16] The extension to complex lattices has been treated by several workers; a relatively simple derivation

[16] The frequency ω_L defined by (46) is *also* the longitudinal optical phonon frequency for small K, as is shown in detail at the end of Chapter 12. We can establish the connection quite generally, as follows. The Maxwell equation div $\mathbf{D} = 0$ or ϵ div $\mathbf{E} = 0$ has two types of roots: one for div $\mathbf{E} = 0$ can always be satisfied if the wavevector $\mathbf{K}$ is perpendicular to $\mathbf{E}$, as in a transverse mode; the other type arises as in (47) when $\epsilon = 0$, which allows $\mathbf{D} = 0$ as in a longitudinal optical mode.

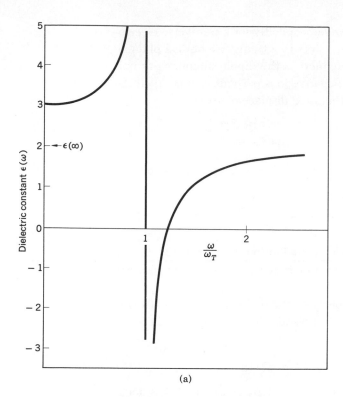

Figure 19a Plot of $\epsilon(\omega) = \epsilon(\infty) + S/(\omega_T{}^2 - \omega^2)$ for $\epsilon(\infty) = 2$ and $S/\omega_T{}^2 = 1$. The dielectric constant is negative between $\omega = \omega_T$ and $\omega = (3/2)^{1/2}\omega_T$; that is, between the zero of $1/\epsilon(\omega)$ and the zero of $\epsilon(\omega)$.

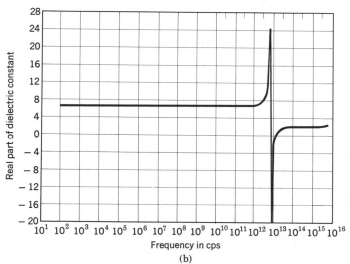

Figure 19b Dielectric constant (real part) of SrF_2 as measured over a wide frequency range, exhibiting the decrease of the ionic polarizability at high frequencies. (Courtesy of A. von Hippel.)

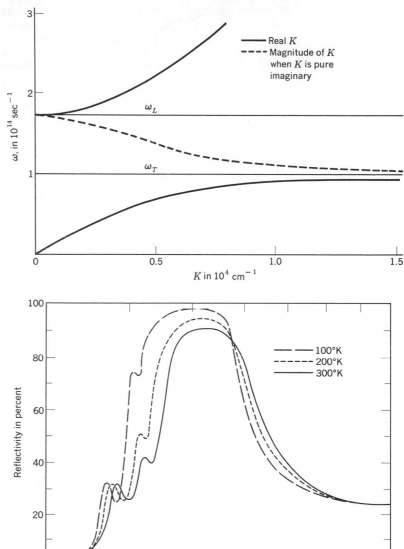

Figure 20 Coupled modes of photons and transverse optical phonons in an ionic crystal. The broken line corresponds to absorption.

Figure 21 Reflectivity of a thick crystal of NaCl at several temperatures, versus wavelength. The nominal values of ω_L and ω_T at room temperature correspond to wavelengths of 38 and 61 microns, respectively. [After A. Mitsuishi et al., J. Opt. Soc. Am. **52**, 14 (1962).]

of the generalized relation is given by A. S. Barker, Jr., Phys. Rev. **136**, 1290 (1964).

In Fig. 20 we show the solutions of the dispersion relation $\omega^2 = c^2 k^2/\epsilon(\omega)$ for electromagnetic waves in matter. There are two branches, with a forbidden frequency gap between ω_T and ω_L. Undamped electromagnetic waves with frequencies within the gap cannot propagate in an infinite crystal. The reflectivity of a crystal surface is expected to be high in this frequency region, as in Fig. 21. For films of thickness less than a wavelength the situation is

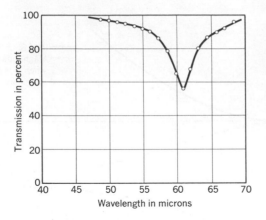

Figure 23 (*below*)   Reflectance versus wavelength of a LiF film backed by silver, for radiation incident near 30°. The longitudinal optical phonon absorbs strongly the radiation polarized (p) in the plane normal to the film, but absorbs hardly at all the radiation polarized (s) parallel to the film. (After Berreman.)

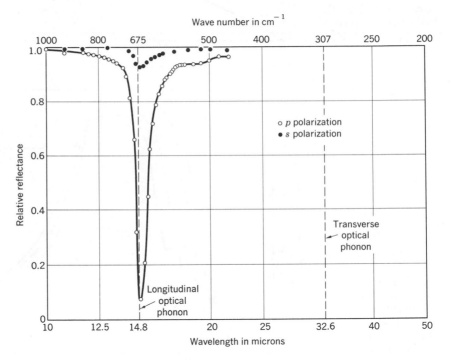

changed: it can be shown that radiation will propagate through the film with absorption at normal incidence only near the frequency ω_T, as in Fig. 22. D. W. Berreman, Phys. Rev. **130**, 2193 (1963), has shown that the frequency ω_L of longitudinal optical phonons can be observed in thin films by reflection at non-normal incidence, as in Fig. 23.

The wavelength corresponding to ω_T is known as the residual ray or, from the German, *Reststrahl* wavelength. The dispersive aspect of the optical properties of ionic crystals is applied in prisms in infrared spectroscopy. The

Figure 24 Infrared absorption of crystals. In the plot the absorption constant is the quantity α in the expression $I(x) = I_0 10^{-\alpha x}$ for the intensity. (After G. Joos.)

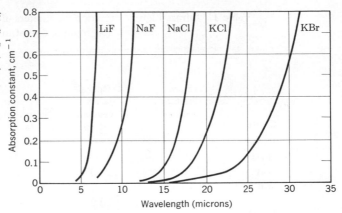

Figure 25 Wavelength dependence of the index of refraction of crystals of LiF and NaF. [After H. W. Hohls, Ann. Physik **29**, 433 (1937).]

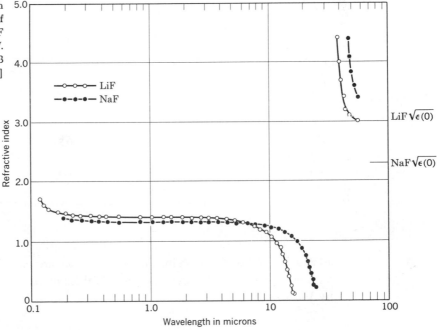

absorption coefficients and refractive indices of a number of crystals in the infrared are shown in Figs. 24 and 25. Large single crystals are produced commercially for use in prisms, and also for use as windows and lens elements. For some purposes it is desired to have ω_T at as low frequency as possible: then the masses of the constituent atoms should be as heavy as practical. A mixed thallium bromide–thallium iodide crystal known as KRS-5 is widely used because of the heavy masses of the atoms.

Experimental values of $\epsilon(0)$, $\epsilon(\infty)$, and ω_T are given in Table 1, largely

Table 1   Infrared lattice vibration parameters of NaCl and CsCl type crystals
(At room temperature)

Crystal	Static dielectric constant $\epsilon(0)$	Optical dielectric constant $\epsilon(\infty)$	ω_T in 10^{13} sec^{-1}, experimental	ω_L in 10^{13} sec^{-1}, calculated from three preceding columns by LST relation
LiH	12.9	3.6	11.	21.
LiF	8.9	1.9	5.8	12.
LiCl	12.0	2.7	3.6	7.5
LiBr	13.2	3.2	3.0	6.1
NaF	5.1	1.7	4.5	7.8
NaCl	5.9	2.25	3.1	5.0
NaBr	6.4	2.6	2.5	3.9
KF	5.5	1.5	3.6	6.1
KCl	4.85	2.1	2.7	4.0
KI	5.1	2.7	1.9	2.6
RbF	6.5	1.9	2.9	5.4
RbI	5.5	2.6	1.4	1.9
CsCl	7.2	2.6	1.9	3.1
CsI	5.65	3.0	1.2	1.6
TlCl	31.9	5.1	1.2	3.0
TlBr	29.8	5.4	0.81	1.9
AgCl	12.3	4.0	1.9	3.4
AgBr	13.1	4.6	1.5	2.5
MgO	9.8	2.95	7.5	14.

after a review by E. Burstein. The values of ω_L are calculated from the other data using the LST relation, Eq. (49). Values of ω_T at 4°K have been given by Jones et al.[17]

LOCAL PHONON MODES

The phonon spectrum in a crystal is modified by lattice defects and impurity atoms. Consider the substitution of a light ion for a heavy ion, such as an H$^-$ ion substituted for a Cl$^-$ ion in a KCl crystal (Fig. 26). This impurity is called a U-center. Physical insight suggests that there is a high frequency mode of motion in which the light H$^-$ ion moves back and forth in the heavy cage of K$^+$ ions by which it is surrounded. This mode has an

[17] G. O. Jones et al., Proc. Roy. Soc. (London) **A261**, 10 (1961).

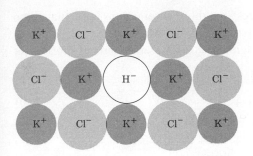

Figure 26 An H⁻ ion substituted for a Cl⁻ ion in a crystal of KCl; such an impurity center is known as a U-center. High frequency local phonon modes are associated with the H⁻ ions.

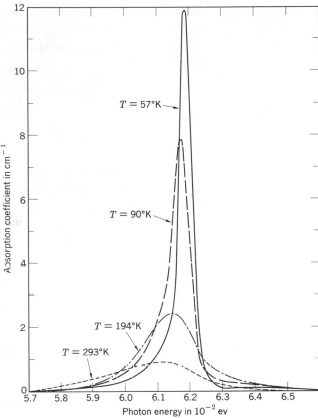

Figure 27 Infrared absorption by H⁻ ions in KCl at several temperatures. The concentration of H⁻ ions in 3×10^{17} per cm³. The photon energy at the center of the line corresponds to a wavelength of about 21 microns. [After G. Schaefer, J. Phys. Chem. Solids **12**, 233 (1960).]

electric dipole moment. The crystal lattice near the H⁻ ion will be deformed slightly during the motion, but the amplitude of the deformation should decrease rapidly with the distance from the H⁻ ion. Such a vibration is called a **localized phonon**. The earliest theoretical studies of localized phonons were by Lifshitz.[18]

Experiments on optical absorption due to localized phonons associated with H⁻ ions in alkali halides have been carried out by Schaefer, whose results for KCl are given in Fig. 27. For additional references to relevant experiments, see A. J. Sievers, Phys. Rev. Letters **13**, 310 (1964). Local phonons have also been observed by neutron scattering.

The simplest local phonon problem is that of a linear lattice of atoms all of mass M, except for one atom of mass $M' < M$. We shall show that one of the normal modes of the lattice is localized around the light atom, and the corresponding frequency is raised above the upper limit $\omega_{\max}$ of the unper-

[18] Full references to the theoretical literature are found in Chap. V of A. A. Maradudin, E. W. Montroll, and G. H. Weiss, *Theory of lattice dynamics in the harmonic approximation*, Academic Press, 1963.

turbed lattice. We assume only nearest-neighbor interactions, and that these are the same between M' and M as between M and M.

Let the light atom be at the origin, $s = 0$. The equations of motion for the lattice are:

$$M' \frac{d^2 u_0}{dt^2} = C(u_1 + u_{-1} - 2u_0); \tag{50}$$

$$M \frac{d^2 u_1}{dt^2} = C(u_2 + u_0 - 2u_1); \quad \text{etc.} \tag{51}$$

We look for a solution which is exponentially damped as we go away from $s = 0$, and which in the limit $M' \to M$ approaches the form of the highest frequency normal mode of the unperturbed lattice. The solution at the zone boundary for the unperturbed lattice is given by (28): $u_s = u(0) \cos s\pi\, e^{-i\omega t} \equiv u(0)(-1)^s e^{-i\omega t}$. For the perturbed lattice let us try

$$u_s = u_0(-1)^s e^{-i\omega t} e^{-|s|/\alpha}, \tag{52}$$

where α is to be determined. On substitution in (51) we find

$$\omega^2 = (C/M)(2 + e^{-\alpha} + e^{\alpha}), \tag{53}$$

while on substitution in (50) we find

$$\omega^2 = (C/M')(2 + 2e^{-\alpha}). \tag{54}$$

Equations (53) and (54) are consistent if $e^{\alpha} = (2M - M')/M'$, whence

$$\omega^2 = \omega_{\max}{}^2 \cdot \frac{M^2}{2MM' - M'^2}, \tag{55}$$

where $\omega_{\max} = (4C/M)^{1/2}$ is the cutoff frequency [see (23)] of the unperturbed lattice, for which $M = M'$. If $M' \ll M$, then (55) reduces to $\omega^2 = \omega_{\max}{}^2(M/2M')$.

Problems

1. **Vibrations of square lattice.** We consider transverse vibrations of a planar square lattice of rows and columns of identical atoms, and let $u_{l,m}$ denote the displacement normal to the plane of the lattice of the atom in the lth column and mth row (Fig. 28). The mass of each atom is M, and C is the force constant for nearest neighbor atoms.
   (a) Show that the equation of motion is

   $$M(d^2 u_{lm}/dt^2) = C[(u_{l+1,m} + u_{l-1,m} - 2u_{lm}) + (u_{l,m+1} + u_{l,m-1} - 2u_{lm})]$$

   (b) Assume solutions of the form

   $$u_{lm} = u(0)e^{i(lK_x a + mK_y a - \omega t)},$$

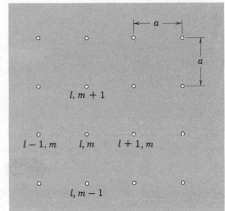

Figure 28 Square array of lattice constant a. The displacements considered are normal to the plane of the lattice.

where a is the spacing between nearest-neighbor atoms. Show that the equation of motion is satisfied if

$$\omega^2 M = 2C(2 - \cos K_x a - \cos K_y a).$$

This is the dispersion relation for the problem.

(c) Show that the region of **K** space for which independent solutions exist may be taken as a square of side $2\pi/a$.   This is the first Brillouin zone of the square lattice. Sketch ω versus K for $K = K_x$ with $K_y = 0$, and for $K_x = K_y$.

(d) For $Ka \ll 1$, show that

$$\omega = (Ca^2/M)^{1/2}(K_x{}^2 + K_y{}^2)^{1/2} = (Ca^2/M)^{1/2}K.$$

2. *Monatomic linear lattice.* Consider a longitudinal wave

$$u_s = u(0) \cos (\omega t - sKa)$$

which propagates in a monatomic linear lattice of atoms of mass M, spacing a, and nearest-neighbor interaction C.

(a) Show that the total energy of the wave is

$$E = \tfrac{1}{2}M \sum_s (du_s/dt)^2 + \tfrac{1}{2}C \sum_s (u_s - u_{s+1})^2,$$

where s runs over all atoms.

(b) By substitution of u_s in this expression, show that the time-average total energy per atom is

$$\tfrac{1}{4}M\omega^2 u^2(0) + \tfrac{1}{2}C(1 - \cos Ka)u^2(0) = \tfrac{1}{2}M\omega^2 u^2(0),$$

where in the last step we have used the dispersion relation (22) for this problem.

3. *Continuum wave equation.* Show that for long wavelengths the equation of motion (16) reduces to the continuum elastic wave equation

$$\frac{\partial^2 u}{\partial t^2} = v^2 \frac{\partial^2 u}{\partial x^2},$$

where v is the velocity of sound.

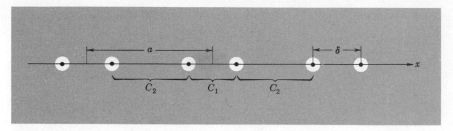

Figure 29 A linear lattice of atoms of equal mass; the primitive basis consists of two atoms separated by δ. The lattice constant is a. Two force constants are shown.

4. **Optical phonons.** For optical phonons with $K = 0$ the relative displacement of adjacent ions on a diatomic lattice is given by $\xi - \eta$, in the notation of (33). Estimate the root-mean-square magnitude of $\xi - \eta$ in Å for 1 cm^3 of KCl, with 100 phonons excited in this mode.

5. **Momentum of phonon.** (a) Show from (17) that the linear momentum of a crystal in which a wave of wavevector K is excited is

$$\mathbf{p} = -i\omega M N^2 \mathbf{u}(0) e^{-i\omega t} \sum_{r=0}^{N-1} e^{irKa},$$

where the crystal consists of N planes each of N^2 atoms of mass M.

(b) Show that for $K = 0$ the momentum is $-i\omega M N^3 \mathbf{u}(0) e^{-i\omega t}$; show that $K = 0$ corresponds to a uniform translation of the lattice as a whole.

(c) For $K \neq 0$, show that the summation in part (a) is equal to

$$\frac{1 - e^{iNKa}}{1 - e^{iKa}}.$$

(d) Let us apply the periodic boundary condition $u_r = u_{r+N}$. Show that this restricts K to values such that $\exp(iNKa) = 1$. Using the result of part (c), we see that $\mathbf{p} = 0$ except for $K = 0$. Thus a phonon really carries zero momentum, except for $K = 0$.

6. **Basis of two identical atoms.** Determine and sketch the longitudinal phonon acoustical and optical spectrum of a linear lattice of primitive lattice constant a, having a basis of two identical atoms of mass M at equilibrium separation $\delta < \frac{1}{2}a$. Both atoms of the basis are on the line. The force constant is C_1 between the atoms of the basis, and C_2 between one atom of the basis and the nearer of the two atoms belonging to the nearest basis (Fig. 29). Note: the structure is not entirely unlike a hydrocarbon chain with alternate single and double bonds: $-C=C-C=C-C=$.

7. **Basis of two unlike atoms.** For the problem treated by (32) to (39), find the amplitude ratios ξ/η for the two branches at $K_{\max} = \pi/2a$. Show that at this value of K one lattice remains at rest while the other lattice moves.

References

A. A. Maradudin, E. W. Montroll, and G. H. Weiss, "Theory of lattice dynamics in the harmonic approximation," *Solid state physics*, Supp. 3 (1963).

S. S. Mitra, "Vibrational spectra of solids," *Solid state physics* 13, 1–80 (1962).

W. Cochran, "Lattice vibrations," Repts. Prog. Phys. 26, 1 (1963).

M. Born and K. Huang, *Dynamical theory of crystal lattices*, Oxford, 1954.

L. Brillouin, *Wave propagation in periodic structures*, Dover, 1953.

T. A. Bak, ed., *Phonons and phonon interactions*, Benjamin, 1964.

R. F. Wallis, ed., *Lattice dynamics* (Copenhagen conference 1963), Pergamon, 1965.

P. W. Kruse, L. D. McGlauchlin, and R. B. McQuistan, *Elements of infrared technology*, Wiley, 1962.

D. E. McCarthy, "Reflection and transmission of infrared materials: 1, Spectra from 2–50 microns; 2, Bibliography," Applied Optics 2, 591, 596 (1963).

G. Leibfried, "Gittertheorie der mechanischen and thermischen Eigenschaften der Kristalle," *Encyclo. of physics* 7/1, 104–324 (1955).

R. W. H. Stevenson, ed., *Phonons* (Aberdeen 1965 summer school), Oliver and Boyd, 1966.

6

Thermal Properties of Insulators

We discuss the Einstein and Debye approximations to the heat capacity associated with the lattice vibrations of crystals; the features of more exact calculations are indicated. We then consider effects of anharmonic lattice interactions, including thermal expansion, the Grüneisen relation, and the thermal conductivity of insulators. The thermal properties of metals are considered in Chapter 7, of superconductors in Chapter 11, and the thermal properties particular to magnetic materials are considered in Chapters 14 and 15.

LATTICE HEAT CAPACITY

By heat capacity we shall usually mean the heat capacity at constant volume, which is more fundamental than the heat capacity at constant pressure, which is what the experiments determine.[1] The heat capacity at constant volume is defined as

$$C_V \equiv T \left(\frac{\partial S}{\partial T} \right)_V = \left(\frac{\partial E}{\partial T} \right)_V, \tag{1}$$

where S is the entropy, E the internal energy, and T the temperature.

The experimental facts about the heat capacity of representative inorganic solids are these:

1. In the room-temperature range the value of the heat capacity of nearly all solids is close to $3Nk_B$, where N is the number of atoms in the specimen and k_B is the Boltzmann constant, 1.38×10^{-16} erg/deg. For one mole (6.03×10^{23}) of atoms, C_V is of the order of 2.5×10^8 ergs/mole-deg or 25 joules/mole-deg or 6 cal/mole-deg.

2. At lower temperatures the heat capacity drops markedly and approaches zero as T^3 in insulators and as T in metals. If the metal becomes a superconductor, the drop is even faster. Metals are discussed starting with Chapter 7.

3. In magnetic solids (Chapter 15) there is a large contribution to the heat capacity near the temperature at which the magnetic moments become ordered.[2] Below 0.1°K the ordering of nuclear moments may give very large heat capacities.

[1] A simple thermodynamic relation connects C_V and C_p:

$$C_p - C_V = 9\alpha^2 BVT,$$

where α is the temperature coefficient of linear expansion, V the volume, and B the bulk modulus. If $\alpha \approx 10^{-5}$ per deg K, $V \approx 10$ cm^3/mole, $B \approx 10^{11}$ ergs/cm^3, $T \approx 300°$K, we have $C_p - C_V \approx 3 \times 10^5$ ergs/mole-deg K. A representative value of C_V for a monatomic solid at room temperature is 10^9 ergs/mole-deg K. The fractional difference between C_p and C_V is relatively small and often may be neglected, particularly below room temperature.

[2] A change in the degree of order means a change in the entropy and thus a contribution to the heat capacity.

The first and second points are illustrated by Fig. 1 for silicon and germanium. For tables of heat capacities, see Section 4e of the *American Institute of Physics Handbook*, McGraw-Hill (1963), 2nd ed., and also the *National Bureau of Standards Monograph 21* (1960).

The normal modes of vibration of a lattice are independent if Hooke's law is applicable. Thus the energy of a lattice mode depends only on its frequency ω and phonon occupancy n, and is independent of the occupancy of the other lattice modes. In thermal equilibrium at temperature T the occupancy is given by the Planck or Bose-Einstein distribution

$$\langle n \rangle = \frac{1}{e^{\hbar\omega/k_B T} - 1},\tag{2}$$

where the $\langle \cdots \rangle$ denotes the average in thermal equilibrium and k_B is the Boltzmann constant. A graph of this function is given in Fig. 2.

REVIEW: *Bose-Einstein distribution.*[3] Consider a set of identical harmonic oscillators in thermal equilibrium. The ratio of the number of oscillators in their $(n + 1)$st quantum state of excitation to the number in the nth quantum state is

$$N_{n+1}/N_n = e^{-\beta\hbar\omega}, \qquad (\beta = 1/k_B T),\tag{3}$$

according to the Boltzmann factor. Thus the fraction of the total number of oscillators in the nth quantum state is

$$\frac{N_n}{\sum\limits_{s=0}^{\infty} N_s} = \frac{e^{-n\beta\hbar\omega}}{\sum\limits_{s=0}^{\infty} e^{-s\beta\hbar\omega}}.\tag{4}$$

From (4) we see that the average excitation quantum number of an oscillator is

$$\langle n \rangle = \frac{\sum\limits_{s} s e^{-s\beta\hbar\omega}}{\sum\limits_{s} e^{s\beta\hbar\omega}}.\tag{5}$$

The summation in the denominator of (5) is of the form,

$$\sum_s x^s = \frac{1}{1-x},\tag{6}$$

with $x = \exp(-\beta\hbar\omega)$. The numerator is of the form

$$\sum_s s x^s = x\frac{d}{dx}\sum_s x^s = \frac{x}{(1-x)^2}.\tag{7}$$

Thus we may rewrite (5) in the form of the Bose-Einstein distribution:

$$\langle n \rangle = \frac{x}{1-x} = \frac{1}{e^{\beta\hbar\omega} - 1}.\tag{8}$$

[3] For an elementary introduction to statistical mechanics, see the first 125 pages of C. Kittel, *Elementary statistical physics*, Wiley, 1958.

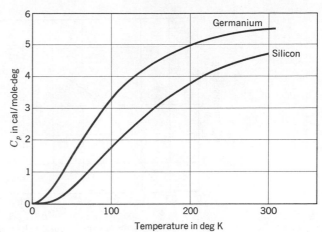

Figure 1 Heat capacity of silicon and germanium. Note the decrease at low temperatures.

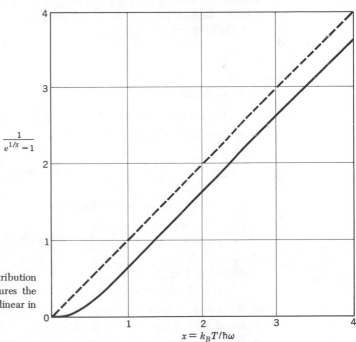

Figure 2 Plot of Bose-Einstein distribution function. Note that at high temperatures the occupancy of a state is approximately linear in the temperature.

We remarked in Fig. 2 that

$$\langle n \rangle \cong k_B T / \hbar \omega \tag{9}$$

if $\hbar \omega < k_B T$, because

$$e^{\beta \hbar \omega} \cong 1 + \beta \hbar \omega + \cdots. \tag{10}$$

When (9) is satisfied we say that the occupation is classical in the sense that each oscillator has energy $\langle n \rangle \hbar \omega \approx k_B T$. This is roughly satisfied even for $\hbar \omega / k_B T \sim 1$. At low temperatures $\hbar \omega / k_B T \gg 1$ and we have

$$\langle n \rangle \cong e^{-\beta \hbar \omega}. \tag{11}$$

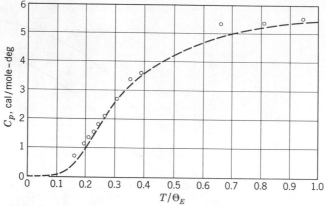

Figure 3 Comparison of experimental values of the heat capacity of diamond with values calculated on the Einstein model, using the characteristic temperature $\Theta_E = \hbar\omega/k_B = 1320°\text{K}$. [After A. Einstein, Ann. Physik **22**, 180 (1907).]

Einstein Model

The average energy of an oscillator of frequency ω is $\langle n \rangle \hbar\omega$. For N oscillators, all having the same resonance frequency, the energy E is

$$E = N\langle n \rangle \hbar\omega = \frac{N\hbar\omega}{e^{\beta\hbar\omega} - 1}. \tag{12}$$

The heat capacity of the oscillators is

$$C_V = \left(\frac{\partial E}{\partial T}\right)_V = Nk_B(\beta\hbar\omega)^2 \frac{e^{\beta\hbar\omega}}{(e^{\beta\hbar\omega} - 1)^2}, \tag{13}$$

as plotted in Fig. 3.

This is the result of the Einstein model for the contribution of N oscillators of the same resonance frequency to the heat capacity of a solid. If N is replaced by $3N$ because each of N atoms has three degrees of freedom, the high-temperature limit of (13) becomes $3Nk_B$, the Dulong and Petit value. At low temperatures (13) decreases as in Fig. 2 but gives $C_V \propto e^{-\beta\hbar\omega}$, whereas the experimental lattice contribution is known to be $C_V \propto T^3$, which can be accounted for by the Debye model discussed later. The limitation of the Einstein model is that all the elastic waves in a solid do not have the same frequency. (At the time Einstein wanted to show[4] that mechanical oscillators should be quantized just as Planck had quantized radiation oscillators. Einstein's example was a quick demonstration of why the heat capacity of solids dropped to zero as $T \to 0$. But the Einstein model is often used to approximate part of the phonon spectrum, particularly optical phonons.)

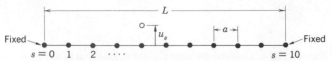

Figure 4   Elastic line of $N + 1$ atoms, with $N = 10$, for boundary conditions that the end atoms $s = 0$ and $s = 10$ are fixed. The particle displacements in the normal modes for either longitudinal or transverse displacements are of the form $u_s \propto \sin sKa$. This form is automatically zero at the atom at the end $s = 0$, and we choose K to make the displacement zero at the other end, $s = 10$.

Enumeration of Normal Modes

The energy in thermal equilibrium of a collection of oscillators of different frequencies ω_K is

$$E - \sum_K \langle n_K \rangle \hbar \omega_K, \tag{14}$$

where each $\langle n_K \rangle$ is related to ω_K by the Bose-Einstein distribution. It is often convenient to replace the summation in (14) by an integral. Suppose that the crystal has $\mathfrak{D}(\omega)\, d\omega$ modes of vibration in the frequency range ω to $\omega + d\omega$. Then the energy is

$$E = \int d\omega\, \mathfrak{D}(\omega) \langle n(\omega, T) \rangle \hbar \omega; \tag{15}$$

the heat capacity is found from this by differentiation of $n(\omega, T)$ with respect to temperature. The central problem is to find $\mathfrak{D}(\omega)$, the density of states per unit frequency range.

Density of States in One Dimension

Let us first consider the elastic problem for a one-dimensional line (Fig. 4) of length L carrying $N + 1$ particles at separation a. We suppose that the particles $s = 0$ and $s = N$ at the ends of the line are held fixed. Each normal mode is a standing wave:

$$u_s = u(0)e^{-i\omega_K t} \sin sKa, \tag{16}$$

where ω_K is related to K by the appropriate dispersion relation, such as (5.21).

[4] See the historical note by M. J. Klein, Physics Today, p. 38 (Jan. 1965).

$$K \longrightarrow$$

Figure 5 The boundary condition $\sin sKa = 0$ for $s = 10$ can be satisfied by choosing $K = \pi/10a$, $2\pi/10a, \ldots, 10\pi/10a$, where $10a$ is the length L of the line. The present figure is in K space. The dots are not atoms but are the allowed values of K. Of the $N + 1$ particles on the line, only $N - 1$ are allowed to move, and their most general motion can be expressed in terms of the $N - 1$ allowed values of K. This quantization of K has nothing to do with quantum mechanics but follows classically from the boundary conditions that the end atoms be fixed. (There are three types of polarization possible for each K value: two transverse, in which the particles move up and down in the plane of the page or in and out of the plane, and one longitudinal, in which the motion is parallel to the line of atoms.)

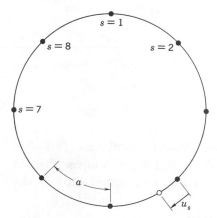

Figure 6 Consider N particles constrained to remain on a circular ring. The particles can oscillate if connected by elastic springs. In a normal mode the displacement u_s of atoms s will be of the form $\sin sKa$ or $\cos sKa$: these are independent modes. By the geometrical periodicity of the ring the boundary condition is that $u_{N+s} = u_s$ for all s, so that the NKa must be an integral multiple of 2π. For $N = 8$ the allowed independent values of K are 0, $2\pi/8a$, $4\pi/8a$, $6\pi/8a$, and $8\pi/8a$. The value $K = 0$ has a meaning only for the cosine form, because $\sin s0a = 0$. The value $8\pi/8a$ also has a meaning only for the cosine form, because $\sin (s8\pi a/8a) = \sin s\pi = 0$. The three other values of K are allowed for both the sine and cosine modes, giving a total of eight allowed modes for the eight particles. Thus the *periodic* boundary condition leads to one allowed mode per particle, exactly as for the fixed-end boundary condition of Fig. 4. If we had taken the modes in the complex form $\exp (isKa)$, the periodic boundary condition would lead to the eight modes with $K = 0$, $\pm 2\pi/Na$, $\pm 4\pi/Na$, $\pm 6\pi/Na$, and $8\pi/Na$, as in Eq. (20).

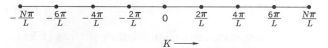

$$K \longrightarrow$$

Figure 7 Allowed values of wavevector K for periodic boundary conditions applied to a linear lattice of periodicity $N = 8$ atoms on a line of length L. The $K = 0$ solution is the uniform mode. The special points $\pm N\pi/L$ represent only a *single* solution; thus there are eight allowed modes, with displacements of the sth atom described by 1, $e^{\pm i\pi s/4}$, $e^{\pm i\pi s/2}$, $e^{\pm i3\pi s/4}$, $e^{i\pi s}$.

Here K is restricted by the fixed-end boundary conditions to the values

$$K = \pi/L, \qquad 2\pi/L, \qquad 3\pi/L, \ldots, \qquad N\pi/L, \tag{17}$$

as in Fig. 5. The argument for terminating the enumeration at $N\pi/L$ ($=\pi/a$) was discussed in (5.28).

The solution for $K = \pi/L$ has

$$u_s \propto \sin(s\pi a/L) \tag{18a}$$

and vanishes for $s = 0$ and $s = N$ as required. The solution for $K = N\pi/L = \pi/a = K_{\max}$ has

$$u_s \propto \sin s\pi; \tag{18b}$$

this permits no motion of any atom, because $\sin s\pi$ vanishes at each atom. Thus there are $N - 1$ allowed independent values of K in (17). This number is equal to the number of particles allowed to move. Each allowed value of K is associated with a solution of the form (16).

The number of modes per unit range of K is denoted by $w(K)$ and is called the density of states in K space. For the one-dimensional line of lattice constant a there is one mode for each interval $\Delta K = \pi/L$, so that

$$w(K) = \begin{cases} L/\pi & \text{for } K \le \dfrac{\pi}{a}; \\ 0 & \text{for } K > \dfrac{\pi}{a}. \end{cases} \tag{19}$$

There is another device for enumerating states which is often used and which is equally valid. We consider the medium as unbounded, but require that the solutions be periodic over a large distance L, so that $u(sa) = u(sa + L)$. The method of **periodic boundary conditions** (Figs. 6 and 7) does not change the physics of the problem in any essential respect for a large system. Then in the running wave solution $u_s = u(0) \exp[i(sKa - \omega_K t)]$ the allowed values of K are

$$K = 0, \qquad \pm 2\pi/L, \qquad \pm 4\pi/L, \qquad \pm 6\pi/L, \ldots, \qquad N\pi/L. \tag{20}$$

This method of enumeration gives the same number of states (one per mobile atom) as given by (18), but we have now both plus and minus values of K, with the interval $\Delta K = 2\pi/L$ between successive values of K. For periodic boundary conditions

$$w(K) = \begin{cases} L/2\pi & \text{for } -\dfrac{\pi}{a} \le K \le \dfrac{\pi}{a}; \\ 0 & \text{otherwise.} \end{cases} \tag{21}$$

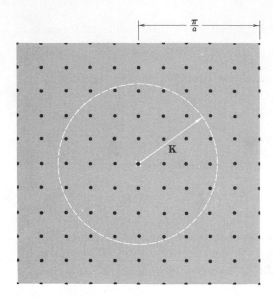

Figure 8 Allowed values in Fourier space of the phonon wavevector **K** for a square lattice of lattice constant a, with periodic boundary conditions applied over a square of side $L = 10a$. The uniform mode is marked with a cross. There is one allowed value of **K** per area element $(2\pi/10a)^2 = (2\pi/L)^2$, so that within the circle of area πK^2 the smoothed number of allowed points is $\pi K^2 (L/2\pi)^2$.

If for convenience in counting we restrict K to positive values we regain (19) for $w(K)$. The situation in a two-dimensional lattice is portrayed in Fig. 8.

We need to know $\mathfrak{D}(\omega)$, the number of states per unit frequency range. In terms of $w(K)$, the number of states $\mathfrak{D}(\omega)\,d\omega$ in $d\omega$ at ω is given by

$$\mathfrak{D}(\omega)\,d\omega = w(K)\frac{dK}{d\omega}\,d\omega = \frac{w(K)}{d\omega/dK}\,d\omega. \tag{22}$$

We can obtain the group velocity $d\omega/dK$ from the dispersion relation; the quantity $w(K)$ is given by (19). There is a singularity in $\mathfrak{D}(\omega)$ whenever the dispersion relation $\omega(K)$ is horizontal.

In the continuum or Debye approximation $\omega = vK$, so that $d\omega/dK = v$, the constant velocity of sound. In one dimension we have from (19) and (22) that

$$\mathfrak{D}(\omega) = \frac{L}{\pi v} \tag{23}$$

for $\omega \leq v\pi/a$ and $\mathfrak{D}(\omega) = 0$ otherwise. The spectrum is cut off at $\omega_D = v\pi/a$ in order to give the correct value N for the total number of modes. The result (23) is the density of states for each polarization type. If there are three modes of different polarizations for each K value, then (23) is to be summed over the three polarizations, using the appropriate values of the velocity of sound v for each polarization.

For N Einstein oscillators at frequency ω_E we have $\mathfrak{D}(\omega) = N\delta(\omega - \omega_E)$, where δ is the Dirac delta function.

The dispersion relation for a monatomic line of atoms with nearest-neighbor interactions is necessarily of the form of Eq. (5.23) for interacting

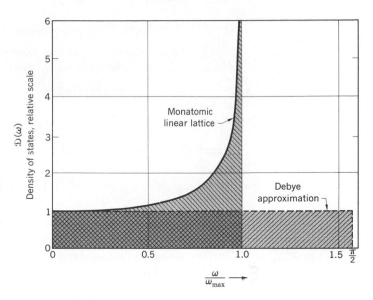

Figure 9 Density of phonon states $\mathfrak{D}(\omega)$ for monatomic line of atoms with nearest-neighbor interactions, after Eq. (27), as compared with the density of states in the Debye or continuum approximation calculated from Eq. (23) for the same velocity of sound in the limit of low frequencies. Note that the lattice model has a singularity which is absent in the Debye approximation. The Debye spectrum must be cut off at $\omega_D = \pi\omega_{max}/2$ if the total number of states is to be equal to the number of atoms. We could approximate the exact $\mathfrak{D}(\omega)$ by a combination of Debye and Einstein distributions.

parallel layers:

$$\omega = \omega_m|\sin \tfrac{1}{2}Ka|, \tag{24}$$

where a is the spacing and ω_m is the maximum frequency. We may solve this for K as a function of ω:

$$K = \frac{2}{a} \sin^{-1} \frac{\omega}{\omega_m}, \tag{25}$$

whence

$$\frac{dK}{d\omega} = \frac{2}{a} \cdot \frac{1}{(\omega_m^2 - \omega^2)^{1/2}}. \tag{26}$$

From (22) the density of states is

$$\mathfrak{D}(\omega) = \frac{L}{\pi} \cdot \frac{dK}{d\omega} = \frac{2L}{\pi a} \cdot \frac{1}{(\omega_m^2 - \omega^2)^{1/2}}, \tag{27}$$

as plotted in Fig. 9. The singularity in the density of states results from the zero of $d\omega/dK$ at $K = \pi/a$.

The dispersion relation for a diatomic linear lattice is given by Eq. (5.36) under the assumption of nearest-neighbor interactions. The density of states in the acoustical branch will be somewhat similar to (27); in the optical branch of the linear lattice the density of states has singularities at the upper and lower limiting frequencies. If the mass of one of the ions is much less than that of the other ion, we see from (5.36) that the frequency in the optical branch is approximately independent of the wavevector. Thus $d\omega/dK$ is nearly zero, and the density of states in the optical branch may be approximated by a delta function at the appropriate frequency. This is an example of the Einstein model.

Density of States in Three Dimensions

We apply periodic boundary conditions over N^3 atoms within a cube of side L, so that $\mathbf{K}$ is determined by the condition

$$e^{i(K_x x + K_y y + K_z z)} \equiv e^{i[K_x(x+L) + K_y(y+L) + K_z(z+L)]}, \tag{28}$$

whence

$$K_x, \, K_y, \, K_z = 0; \quad \pm 2\pi/L; \quad \pm 4\pi/L; \quad \ldots; \quad N\pi/L. \tag{29}$$

Therefore there is one allowed value of $\mathbf{K}$ per volume $(2\pi/L)^3$ in $\mathbf{K}$ space, or

$$w(\mathbf{K}) = \left(\frac{L}{2\pi}\right)^3 \tag{30}$$

allowed values of $\mathbf{K}$ per unit volume of $\mathbf{K}$ space, for each polarization.

We want to find in three dimensions an expression for $\mathfrak{D}(\omega)$, the density of states per unit frequency range. The number of states of frequency between ω and $\omega + d\omega$ is

$$\mathfrak{D}(\omega) \, d\omega = \int_{\text{shell}} d^3 K \, w(\mathbf{K}) = \left(\frac{L}{2\pi}\right)^3 \int_{\text{shell}} d^3 K, \tag{31}$$

where the integral is extended over the volume of the shell in $\mathbf{K}$ space for which the frequency lies between ω and $\omega + d\omega$. Let dS_ω denote an element of area in $\mathbf{K}$ space on the surface for which the frequency is constant and equal to ω, as in Fig. 10. The element of volume in $\mathbf{K}$ space between the constant frequency surfaces at ω and $\omega + d\omega$ is thus a cylinder of base dS_ω and of height $dK_\perp$, where

$$d\omega = |d\mathbf{K} \cdot \nabla_{\mathbf{K}} \omega| = |\nabla_{\mathbf{K}} \omega| \, dK_\perp. \tag{32}$$

Thus (31) may be written as

$$\mathfrak{D}(\omega) \, d\omega = \left(\frac{L}{2\pi}\right)^3 \int dS_\omega \, dK_\perp = \left(\frac{L}{2\pi}\right)^3 \left(\int \frac{dS_\omega}{|\nabla_{\mathbf{K}} \omega|}\right) d\omega. \tag{33}$$

On dividing both sides by $d\omega$ we have

$$\boxed{\mathfrak{D}(\omega) = \left(\frac{L}{2\pi}\right)^3 \int \frac{dS_\omega}{v_g},} \tag{34}$$

where $v_g = |\nabla_{\mathbf{K}} \omega|$ is the magnitude of group velocity. The integral is to be taken over the surface of constant frequency ω.

In the continuum or Debye approximation $v_g = v$, a constant, and

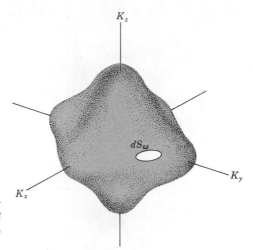

Figure 10 Element of area dS_ω on a constant frequency surface in **K** space. The volume between two surfaces of constant frequency at ω and $\omega + d\omega$ is equal to $\int dS_\omega \, d\omega / |\nabla_{\mathbf{K}} \omega|$.

$\omega = vK$, whence

$$\int \frac{dS_\omega}{v_g} = \frac{1}{v} \int dS_\omega = \frac{4\pi K^2}{v} = \frac{4\pi \omega^2}{v^3} \tag{35}$$

and

$$\mathfrak{D}(\omega) = \frac{\omega^2 L^3}{2\pi^2 v^3}, \qquad \omega < \omega_D, \tag{36}$$

for each polarization type. For N atoms the total number of states of each polarization type is N, so that the cutoff frequency ω_D is determined by

$$N = \int_0^{\omega_D} d\omega \cdot \frac{\omega^2 L^3}{2\pi^2 v^3} = \frac{\omega_D^3 L^3}{6\pi^2 v^3}. \tag{37}$$

This corresponds to a cutoff $K_D = \omega_D/v$ in **K** space, with

$$K_D = \frac{(6\pi^2 N)^{1/3}}{L} \tag{38}$$

as the radius of the allowed sphere in **K** space.

Thus in the Debye approximation we not only replace the actual density of states by the density of states (36) which follows from the linear dispersion relation $\omega = vK$, but we also replace the correct region of integration in

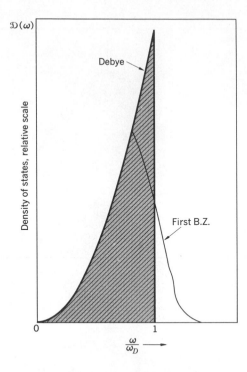

$\mathfrak{D}(\omega)$

Density of states, relative scale

Debye

First B.Z.

0   1

$\dfrac{\omega}{\omega_D}$ ⟶

Figure 11   Density of states $\mathfrak{D}(\omega)$ versus ω, with assumed constant phonon velocity, for integration in **K** space over the Debye sphere (shaded area) and over the first Brillouin zone of a monatomic simple cubic lattice. (Courtesy of C. Fong.)

K space, which is a Brillouin zone, by a spherical region. The density of states given by (36) for the Debye approximation is plotted in Fig. 11, along with the density of states for the correct region of integration for a simple cubic lattice, still with the assumption of constant velocity of sound. If $v = 5 \times 10^5$ cm/sec and $N/L^3 = 10^{23}$ atoms/cm³, then

$$\omega_D \simeq 1 \times 10^{14} \text{ sec}^{-1}$$

and

$$K_D \simeq 2 \times 10^8 \text{ cm}^{-1} \tag{39}$$

The distribution function $\mathfrak{D}(\omega)$ may also be calculated from experimental or from realistic theoretical dispersion relations. The labor involved may be appreciable, and the problem is often handled with the aid of electronic computers. We need to find ω over a very fine mesh grid in **K** space, and we then construct a histogram giving the number of points lying in small equal intervals of ω values. Calculations for aluminum are shown in Figs. 12 and 13.

The distribution functions for actual lattices have singularities known as **Van Hove singularities.**[5] These arise from critical points where the group velocity v_g in (34) is zero. An elementary discussion is given by Wannier.[6] Equation (27) is an example of a Van Hove singularity in a linear lattice.

[5] L. Van Hove, Phys. Rev. **89**, 1189 (1953); see also H. P. Rosenstock, Phys. Rev. **97**, 290 (1955); J. C. Phillips, Phys. Rev. **104**, 1263 (1956).

[6] G. H. Wannier, *Elements of solid state theory*, Cambridge University Press, 1959.

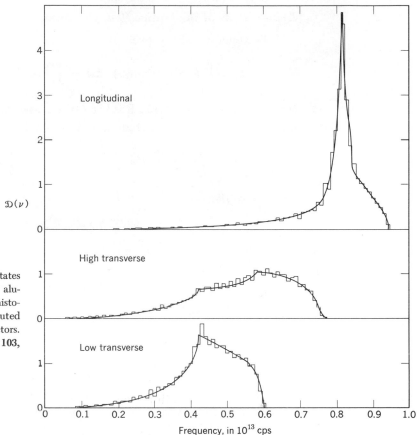

$\mathfrak{D}(\nu)$

Longitudinal

High transverse

Low transverse

Frequency, in 10^{13} cps

Figure 12 Phonon density of states $\mathfrak{D}(\nu)$ for the three branches of aluminum; here $\nu = \omega/2\pi$. The histograms are obtained from computed frequencies for 2791 wavevectors. [After C. B. Walker, Phys. Rev. **103**, 547 (1956).]

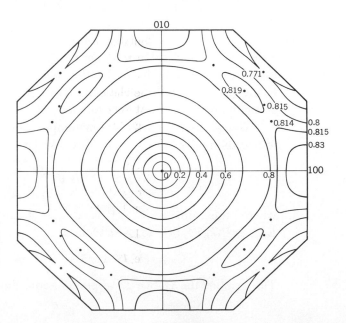

010

0.771
0.819
0.815
0.814
0.8
0.815
0.83
100

0 0.2 0.4 0.6 0.8

Figure 13 Surfaces of constant frequency in aluminum, for longitudinal phonons. The section shown is the (100) plane of the reciprocal lattice. (After C. B. Walker.)

Debye Model of the Lattice Heat Capacity

The energy (15) is given by

$$E = \int d\omega \, \mathfrak{D}(\omega) \cdot n(\omega) \cdot \hbar\omega = \int_0^{\omega_D} d\omega \left(\frac{\omega^2 L^3}{2\pi^2 v^3}\right)\left(\frac{\hbar\omega}{e^{\beta\hbar\omega} - 1}\right), \quad (40)$$

for each polarization type. For brevity we assume that the phonon velocity is independent of the polarization, so we multiply (40) by the factor 3 to obtain

$$E = \frac{3L^3\hbar}{2\pi^2 v^3} \int_0^{\omega_D} d\omega \, \frac{\omega^3}{e^{\beta\hbar\omega} - 1} = \frac{3L^3 k^4 T^4}{2\pi^2 v^3 \hbar^3} \int_0^{x_D} dx \, \frac{x^3}{e^x - 1}, \quad (41)$$

where $x \equiv \beta\hbar\omega \equiv \hbar\omega/k_B T$ and

$$x_D \equiv \hbar\omega_D/k_B T \equiv \Theta/T. \quad (42)$$

This defines the **Debye temperature** Θ in terms of ω_D defined by (37). We may express Θ as

$$\Theta = (\hbar v/k_B L)(6\pi^2 N)^{1/3}, \quad (43)$$

so that (41) becomes

$$E = 9Nk_B T\left(\frac{T}{\Theta}\right)^3 \int_0^{x_D} dx \, \frac{x^3}{e^x - 1}, \quad (44)$$

where N is the number of atoms in the specimen and $x_D = \Theta/T$.

The heat capacity is found most easily by differentiating the middle expression of (41) with respect to temperature. Then

$$C_V = \frac{3L^3\hbar^2}{2\pi^2 v^3 k_B T^2} \int_0^{\omega_D} d\omega \, \frac{\omega^4 \, e^{\beta\hbar\omega}}{(e^{\beta\hbar\omega} - 1)^2} = 9Nk_B \left(\frac{T}{\Theta}\right)^3 \int_0^{x_D} dx \, \frac{x^4 e^x}{(e^x - 1)^2}. \quad (45)$$

Tables have been calculated for E, C_V, and other quantities on the Debye theory and are given in the Landolt-Börnstein tables and also in the Jahnke-Emde-Lösch tables. The heat capacity is plotted in Fig. 14. At $T \gg \Theta$ the heat capacity approaches the classical value of $3Nk_B$.

Debye T^3 Law. At very low temperatures we may approximate (44) by letting the upper limit go to infinity. We have

$$\int_0^\infty dx \, \frac{x^3}{e^x - 1} = \int_0^\infty dx \, x^3 \sum_{s=1}^\infty e^{-sx} = 6\sum_1^\infty \frac{1}{s^4} = \frac{\pi^4}{15}, \quad (46)$$

where the sum over s^{-4} is to be found in standard tables. Thus $E \cong 3\pi^4 Nk_B T^4/5\Theta^3$ for $T \ll \Theta$, and

$$C_V \cong (12\pi^4 Nk_B/5)(T/\Theta)^3 = 234Nk_B(T/\Theta)^3. \quad (47)$$

This exhibits the Debye T^3 approximation. For sufficiently low temperatures

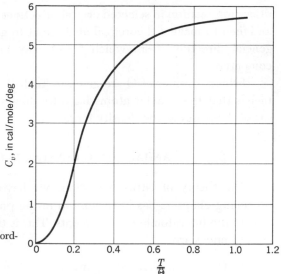

Figure 14 Heat capacity of a solid, according to the Debye approximation.

the Debye approximation should be quite good, as here only long wavelength acoustic modes are excited. These are just the modes which may be treated as in an elastic continuum with macroscopic elastic constants. The energy of short wavelength modes is too high to allow these to be populated at low temperatures, according to (11).

We can understand the T^3 region by a simple argument. Only those lattice modes having $\hbar\omega \leq k_B T$ will be excited to any appreciable extent at a low temperature T. The excitation of these modes will be approximately classical with an energy close to $k_B T$, according to Eq. (9) and Fig. 2. The volume in **K** space occupied by the excited modes is of the order of $(K/K_D)^3$ or $(T/\Theta)^3$ of the total volume in **K** space, so that there are of the order of $N(T/\Theta)^3$ excited modes, each having energy $k_B T$. The internal energy is $\sim Nk_B T(T/\Theta)^3$, and the heat capacity is $\sim Nk_B(T/\Theta)^3$. The large numerical factor, 234, in (47) may be traced to the inclusion in accordance with convention of the factor $(6\pi^2)^{1/3}$ in the definition of Θ in (43).

Methods for the determination of a suitable average sound velocity to be used in calculating Θ have been given by Blackman.[7] For actual lattices the temperatures at which the T^3 approximation holds are quite low. It may be necessary to be below $T = \Theta/50$ to get reasonably pure T^3 behavior. The heat capacity is, however, relatively insensitive to changes in the density of states.

The best practical way to obtain the density of states is to measure the

---

[7] M. Blackman, Repts. Prog. Phys. **8**, 11 (1941); for a comparison of the Debye Θ determined from elastic constants and from calorimetry, see G. A. Alers and J. R. Neighbours, Rev. Mod. Phys. **31**, 675 (1959).

dispersion relation in selected crystal directions by inelastic neutron scattering and then to make a theoretical analytic fit to give the dispersion relation in a general direction, from which $\mathcal{D}(\omega)$ may be calculated by an electronic computer.

Selected values of Θ are given in Table 1. Note for example in the alkali metals that the heavier atoms have the lowest Θ's, because the velocity of sound decreases as the density increases.

ANHARMONIC CRYSTAL INTERACTIONS

The theory of lattice vibrations we have discussed in this and in the preceding chapters has been limited in the potential energy to terms quadratic in the interatomic displacements. This is the harmonic theory; among its consequences are:

1. There is no thermal expansion.
2. Adiabatic and isothermal elastic constants are equal.
3. The elastic constants are independent of pressure and temperature.
4. The heat capacity becomes constant at high temperatures $T > \Theta$.
5. Two lattice waves do not interact; a single wave does not decay or change form with time.

In real crystals none of these consequences is satisfied accurately. The deviations may be attributed to the neglect of anharmonic (higher than quadratic) terms in the interatomic displacements. We shall discuss only some of the simpler aspects of anharmonic effects; for further details consult the references at the end of the chapter.

Table 1   Representative values of the Debye Θ
(Compiled by N. Phillips)

Substance	°K	Substance	°K
Li	335	Al	428
Na	156	Ga	325
K	91.1	In	111.0
Rb	55.5	Tl	78.5
Cs	39.5	Sn	199
Cu	343	Ti	428
Ag	226.2	Zr	292
Au	162.4	Hf	252
Cd	209	Nb	275
Hg	71.9		

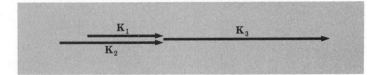

Figure 15 Colinear interaction of two longitudinal phonons to produce a third longitudinal phonon. In the nondispersive region of the phonon spectrum it is possible to satisfy simultaneously with this arrangement the energy and wavevector conservation relations $\omega_1 + \omega_2 = \omega_3$ and $\mathbf{K}_1 + \mathbf{K}_2 = \mathbf{K}_3$. In the Shiren experiment, power conversions up to 70 percent were observed over an interaction path of 2 cm, for input power levels $\sim$0.5 watts/cm^2.

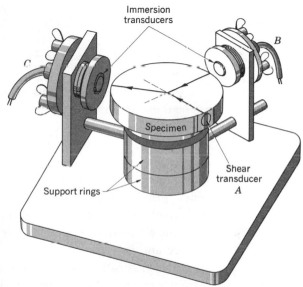

Figure 16 Ultrasonic experiment on three-phonon interactions. In a typical experiment the transducer A generates a 10-Mc shear wave which interacts near the center of the disc-shaped specimen with a 15-Mc longitudinal wave generated by B, to produce by their interaction a 25-Mc longitudinal wave detected by the transducer C: $L(15) + T(10) \rightarrow L(25)$. The wavevectors satisfy $\mathbf{K}_{15} + \mathbf{K}_{10} = \mathbf{K}_{25}$. The angle φ is easily calculated from this equation and the wave velocities. The whole apparatus is immersed in a suitable fluid to provide coupling between the immersion transducers and the specimen. (After Rollins, Taylor, and Todd.)

Beautiful demonstrations of anharmonic effects are the experiments on the interaction of two phonons to produce a third phonon at a frequency $\omega_3 = \omega_1 + \omega_2$. Shiren[8] describes an experiment in which a beam of longitudinal phonons of frequency 9.20 Gc/sec interacts in an MgO crystal with a parallel beam of longitudinal phonons at 9.18 Gc/sec. The interaction of the two beams (Fig. 15) produced a third beam of longitudinal phonons at $9.20 + 9.18 = 18.38$ Gc/sec.

Rollins[9] et al. carried out the elegant experiment pictured in Fig. 16. Two narrow ultrasonic beams are allowed to interact near the center of a large circular disk. They verified that a third beam is generated at the volume

[8] N. S. Shiren, Phys. Rev. Letters **11**, 3 (1963).

[9] F. R. Rollins, Jr., L. H. Taylor, and P. H. Todd, Jr., Phys. Rev. **136**, A597 (1964).

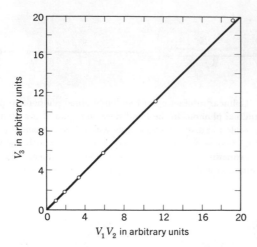

Figure 17 The displacement amplitude of the generated beam should be proportional to the product of the amplitudes of the two primary beams. This curve (due to Rollins et al.) shows the experimental linear relationship between $(V_1 V_2)$ and V_3 where V_1 and V_2 are the voltages applied to the two primary transducers and V_3 is the transducer voltage produced by the interaction wave.

of interaction only when energy and wavevector are conserved between the three beams.

The three-phonon processes are caused by cubic terms in the lattice potential energy. A typical term might be

$$U \text{ (cubic)} = A e_{xx} e_{yy} e_{zz}, \tag{48}$$

where the e's are strain components and A is a constant. The A's have the same dimensions as the elastic stiffness constants in Chapter 4, but may have values perhaps an order of magnitude larger than the C's. The physics of the phonon interaction can be stated simply: the presence of one phonon causes a periodic elastic strain which (through the anharmonic interaction) modulates in space and time the elastic constant of the crystal. A second phonon perceives the modulation of the elastic constant and is thereupon scattered, just as from a moving three-dimensional grating. In the absence of anharmonic terms the acoustic modulation does not occur.

Equation of State of Solids

We can make considerable progress in the phenomenological description of nonlinear interactions in cubic crystals by introducing a single empirical parameter. We examine here the consequences of the assumption that the frequency of a lattice vibration of specified wavevector depends on the volume —this is a nonlinear effect. We shall assume that $V d\omega_K / \omega_K dV$ is a constant.

Consider the free energy $F = E - TS$, from which $dF = -p \, dV - S \, dT$ and

$$p = -(\partial F / \partial V)_T; \qquad S = -(\partial F / \partial T)_V. \tag{49}$$

Then

$$E = F + TS = F - T(\partial F / \partial T)_V. \tag{50}$$

We make the approximate separation

$$F = E_0(V) + F_D(T,V); \qquad E = E_0(V) + E_D(T,V), \qquad (51)$$

where $E_0(V)$ is the internal energy at $0°K$ and F_D is the contribution in the Debye approximation of the lattice vibrations to the free energy. In the harmonic or linear model F_D is independent of the volume but depends only on the number of atoms. One effect of anharmonic interactions is to make F_D dependent on V; we suppose that this dependence is adequately described by specifying the dependence of the Debye temperature Θ on V. Thus

$$p = -(\partial E_0/\partial V) - (\partial F_D/\partial\Theta)(\partial\Theta/\partial V). \qquad (52)$$

In the Debye approximation the internal energy E_D in (44) due to lattice vibrations involves T times a function of Θ/T. By substitution in (50) we see that F_D must be of the same form:

$$F_D = Tf(\Theta/T). \qquad (53)$$

Then

$$\partial F_D/\partial\Theta = f' = F_D/\Theta. \qquad (54)$$

Thus from (52) we have the Debye equation of state,

$$p = -(\partial E_0/\partial V) - (E_D/\Theta)(\partial\Theta/\partial V) = -(\partial E_0/\partial V) + \gamma E_D/V, \qquad (55)$$

where

$$\boxed{\gamma \equiv -d(\log\Theta)/d(\log V) = -(V/\Theta)(d\Theta/dV)} \qquad (56)$$

is known as the **Grüneisen constant.** If ω_K is an eigenfrequency of the solid, we may define a Grüneisen constant for this mode by $\gamma_K \equiv -d(\log\omega_K)/d(\log V)$. In discussing anharmonic effects in solids, it is always useful to try to express the results in terms of γ. For some effects it is necessary to consider the dependence of γ_K on **K**.

Grüneisen Relation

On differentiating (55) we have

$$(\partial p/\partial T)_V = \gamma C_V/V. \qquad (57)$$

Now the linear expansion coefficient α is one-third of the volume expansion coefficient, so that

$$\alpha = \frac{1}{3V}\left(\frac{\partial V}{\partial T}\right)_p = -\frac{1}{3V}\cdot\frac{(\partial p/\partial T)_V}{(\partial p/\partial V)_T} = \frac{1}{3B}\left(\frac{\partial p}{\partial T}\right)_V = \frac{\gamma C_V}{3BV}, \qquad (58)$$

where B is the bulk modulus, (3.11). The Grüneisen relation

$$\alpha = \gamma C_V/3BV \qquad (59)$$

Table 2 Values of the Grüneisen γ

Substance	Grüneisen	Slater	Substance	Grüneisen	Slater
Na	1.25	1.50	Ag	2.40	2.2
K	1.34	2.32	Pt	2.54	3.0
Al	2.17	0.94	NaCl	1.63	1.52
Mn	2.42	5.5	KF	1.45	1.93
Fe	1.6	1.4	KCl	1.60	1.26
Co	1.87	1.8	KBr	1.68	1.29
Ni	1.88	1.9	KI	1.63	1.21
Cu	1.96	1.63			

connecting the linear expansion coefficient with the heat capacity is satisfied experimentally for cubic crystals, taking γ as independent of temperature.

In Table 2 we give a comparison of γ deduced from the Grüneisen relation (59) with γ deduced by Slater[10] (with a correction suggested by Dugdale and MacDonald) from measurements of the change of compressibility with pressure. The agreement is fairly good.

Thermal Expansion

We may understand the origin of thermal expansion by considering for a classical oscillator the effect of anharmonic terms in the potential energy of the mean separation of a pair of atoms at a temperature T. We take the potential energy of the atoms at a displacement x from their equilibrium separation at $0°K$ as

$$U(x) = cx^2 - gx^3 - fx^4, \tag{60}$$

with c, g, and f all positive. The term in x^3 represents the asymmetry of the mutual repulsion of the atoms and the term in x^4 represents the softening of the vibration at large amplitudes. The minimum of (60) at $x = 0$ is not an absolute minimum, but for small oscillations the form is an adequate representation of an interatomic potential, such as Fig. 3.5.

We calculate the average displacement by using the Boltzmann distribution function, which weights the possible values of x according to their thermodynamic probability:

$$\langle x \rangle = \frac{\int_{-\infty}^{\infty} dx\, x e^{-\beta U(x)}}{\int_{-\infty}^{\infty} dx\, e^{-\beta U(x)}}, \tag{61}$$

with $\beta \equiv 1/k_B T$. For displacements such that the anharmonic terms in the

---

[10] J. C. Slater, Phys. Rev. **57**, 744 (1940); *Introduction to chemical physics*, McGraw-Hill, 1939, pp. 393, 451; J. S. Dugdale and D. K. C. MacDonald, Phys. Rev. **89**, 832 (1953).

Table 3   Coefficients of linear thermal expansion
near room temperature.[*]

$$\alpha = \frac{1}{\ell}\frac{\partial \ell}{\partial T}$$

Substance	$\alpha \times 10^6$, per deg K	Substance	$\alpha \times 10^6$, per deg K
Li	45	Fe	11.7
Na	71	Ni	12.5
K	83	Cr	7.5
Cs	97	Mo	5.2
Cu	17.0	Ta	6.6
Ag	18.9	W	4.6
Au	13.9	Ir	6.5
Ca	22.5	Pd	11.6
Al	23.6	Pt	8.9
Pb	28.8		

[*]See W. B. Pearson, *A handbook of lattice spacings and structures of metals and alloys*, Pergamon, 1958. For data at low temperature, see K. Andres, Phys. kondens. Materie **2**, 294 (1964).

energy are small in comparison with $k_B T$, we may expand the integrands in (61) as

$$\int dx\, x e^{-\beta U} \cong \int dx\, e^{-\beta c x^2}(x + \beta g x^4 + \beta f x^5) = (3\pi^{1/2}/4)\,(g/c^{5/2})\beta^{-3/2}; \quad (62)$$

$$\int dx\, e^{-\beta U} \cong \int dx\, e^{-\beta c x^2} = (\pi/\beta c)^{1/2}, \quad (63)$$

whence

$$\langle x \rangle = (3g/4c^2)k_B T \quad (64)$$

in the classical region.[11] Several values of the linear expansion coefficient are given in Table 3.

THERMAL CONDUCTIVITY

The thermal conductivity coefficient K of a solid is most easily defined with respect to the steady-state flow of heat down a long rod with a temperature gradient dT/dx:

$$Q = K\, dT/dx, \quad (65)$$

where Q is the flux of thermal energy (energy transmitted across unit area

[11] Compare with the discussion of the anharmonic oscillator on pp. 227–229 of the *Berkeley physics course*, Vol. I., McGraw-Hill (1964).

per unit time); K is often expressed in units of cal/cm-sec-deg or watts/cm-deg. To convert to watts/cm-deg, multiply K in cal/cm-sec-deg by 4.186.

The form of the equation (65) which defines the conductivity implies that the process of thermal energy transfer is a random process. The energy does not simply enter one end of the specimen and proceed directly in a straight path to the other end, but rather the energy diffuses through the specimen, suffering frequent collisions. If the energy were propagated directly through the specimen without deflection, then the expression for the thermal flux would not depend on the temperature gradient, but only on the difference in temperature ΔT between the ends of the specimen, regardless of the length of the specimen. It is the random nature of the conductivity process that brings the temperature gradient into the expression for the thermal flux.

From the kinetic theory of gases we find below in a certain approximation the following expression for the thermal conductivity:

$$K = \tfrac{1}{3}Cv\ell, \tag{66}$$

where C is the heat capacity per unit volume, v is the average particle velocity, and ℓ is the mean free path of a particle between collisions. This result is derived below. It was applied first by Debye to describe thermal conductivity in dielectric solids, with C as the heat capacity of the phonons, v the phonon velocity, and ℓ the phonon mean free path. Several representative values of the mean free path are given in Table 4.

We give first the elementary kinetic theory which leads to (66). The flux of particles in the $\hat{x}$ direction is $\tfrac{1}{2}n\langle|v_x|\rangle$, where n is the concentration of molecules; in equilibrium there is a flux of equal magnitude in the opposite direction. The $\langle\cdots\rangle$ denote average value. If c is the heat capacity of a particle, then in moving from a region at local temperature $T + \Delta T$ to a region at local temperature T a particle will give up energy $c\,\Delta T$. Now ΔT between the ends of a free path of the particle is given by

$$\Delta T = \frac{dT}{dx}\,v_x\tau, \tag{67}$$

where τ is the average time between collisions.

The net flux of energy (from both senses of the particle flux) is therefore

$$Q = n\langle v_x^2\rangle\,c\tau\frac{dT}{dx} = \tfrac{1}{3}n\langle v^2\rangle\,c\tau\frac{dT}{dx}. \tag{68}$$

If, as for phonons, v is constant, we may write (68) as

$$Q = \tfrac{1}{3}Cv\ell\frac{dT}{dx}, \tag{69}$$

with $\ell \equiv v\tau$ and $C \equiv nc$. Thus $K = \tfrac{1}{3}Cv\ell$.

Table 4   Phonon mean free path values
[Calculated from (66), taking $v = 5 \times 10^5$ cm/sec as a representative sound velocity.
The ℓ's obtained in this way refer to umklapp processes defined by (72)].

Crystal	T, °C	C, cal/cm³-deg	K, cal/cm-deg-sec	ℓ, in Å
Quartz°	0	0.48	0.03	40
	−190	0.13	0.12	540
NaCl	0	0.45	0.17	23
	−190	0.24	0.064	100

°Parallel to optic axis.

Lattice Thermal Resistivity

The phonon mean free path ℓ is determined principally by two processes, geometrical scattering and scattering by other phonons. If the forces between atoms were purely harmonic, there would be no mechanism for collisions between different phonons, and the mean free path would be limited solely by collisions of a phonon with the crystal boundary, and by lattice imperfections. There are situations where these effects are dominant. With anharmonic lattice interactions such as (48) there is a coupling between different phonons which limits the value of the mean free path. The phonons are no longer exact normal modes of the system. We consider first the thermal resistivity from lattice interactions.

The theory of the effect of anharmonic coupling on thermal resistivity is a complicated problem. An approximate calculation has been given by Debye,[12] and Peierls[13] has considered the problem in great detail. They both show that ℓ is proportional to $1/T$ at high temperatures, in agreement with many experiments. We can understand this dependence in terms of the number of phonons with which a given phonon can interact: at high temperature the total number of excited phonons is proportional to T, according to (9). The mean free path of a given phonon should be inversely proportional to the number of phonons with which it can collide, whence $\ell \propto 1/T$.

To establish a thermal conductivity there must exist mechanisms in the crystal whereby the distribution of phonons may be brought locally into

[12] P. Debye, "Zustandsgleichung und Quantenhypothese mit einem Anhang über Wärmeleitung." In *Vortrage über die kinetische Theorie der Materie und der Elektrizität*, von M. Planck et al. (Mathematische Vorlesungen an der Universität Göttingen: VI.) Leipzig, Teubner, 1914, pp. 19–60.

[13] R. Peierls, Ann. Physik 3, 1055 (1929); see also C. Herring, Phys. Rev. 95, 954 (1954); J. Callaway, Phys. Rev. 113, 1046 (1959); R. E. Nettleton, Phys. Rev. 132, 2032 (1963); and the reviews cited at the end of the chapter. The Callaway and Nettleton papers contribute to an understanding of the combined effects of lattice and impurity scattering; see also M. G. Holland, Phys. Rev. 132, 2461 (1963); P. Erdös, Phys. Rev. 138, A1200 (1965).

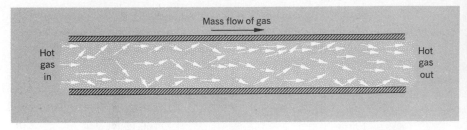

Figure 18a Flow of gas molecules down a long open tube with frictionless walls. Elastic collision processes among the gas molecules do not change the momentum or energy flux of the gas because in each collision the velocity of the center of mass of the colliding particles and their energy remain unchanged. Thus energy is transported from left to right without being driven by a temperature gradient. Therefore the thermal resistivity is zero and the thermal conductivity is infinite.

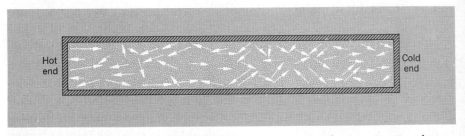

Figure 18b The usual definition of thermal conductivity in a gas refers to a situation where no mass flow is permitted. Here the tube is closed at both ends, preventing the escape or entrance of molecules. With a temperature gradient the colliding pairs with above-average center of mass velocities will tend to be directed to the right; those with below-average velocities will tend to be directed to the left. A slight concentration gradient, high on the right, will be set up to enable the net mass transport to be zero while allowing a net energy transport from the hot to the cold end.

thermal equilibrium. Without such mechanisms we may not speak of the phonons at one end of the crystal as being in thermal equilibrium at a temperature T_2 and those at the other end in equilibrium at T_1. It is not sufficient for thermal conductivity to have only a way of limiting the mean free path, but there must also be a way of establishing a true equilibrium distribution of phonons.

Phonon collisions with a static imperfection or a crystal boundary will not by themselves establish thermal equilibrium, because such collisions do not change the energy of individual phonons: the frequency ω_2 of the scattered phonon is equal to the frequency ω_1 of the incident phonon.

It is rather remarkable also that a three-phonon collision process

$$\mathbf{K}_1 + \mathbf{K}_2 = \mathbf{K}_3 \tag{70}$$

will not establish equilibrium, but for a subtle reason: the total momentum of the phonon gas is not changed by such a collision. An equilibrium distribu-

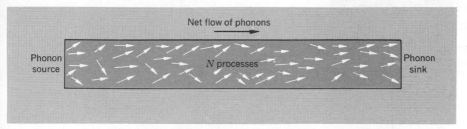

Figure 18c In a crystal we may arrange to create phonons chiefly at one end, as by illuminating the left end with a lamp. From that end there will be a net flux of phonons toward the right end of the crystal. If only N processes ($\mathbf{K}_1 + \mathbf{K}_2 = \mathbf{K}_3$) occur, the phonon flux is unchanged in momentum on collision and some phonon flux will persist down the length of the crystal. On arrival of phonons at the right end we can arrange in principle to convert most of their energy to radiation, thereby creating a sink for the phonons. Just as in (a) the thermal resistivity is zero.

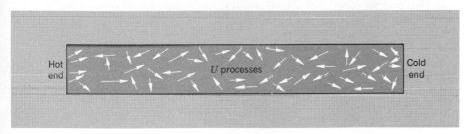

Figure 18d In U processes ($\mathbf{K}_1 + \mathbf{K}_2 = \mathbf{K}_3 + \mathbf{G}$, as in Fig. 19b) there is a large net change in phonon momentum in each collision event. An initial net phonon flux will rapidly decay as we move to the right. The ends may act as sources and sinks. Net energy transport under a temperature gradient occurs somewhat as in (b).

tion of phonons at a temperature T can move down the crystal with a drift velocity which is not disturbed by three-phonon collisions[14] of the form (70). For in such collisions the phonon momentum

$$\mathbf{J} = \sum_{K} \mathbf{K} n_{\mathbf{K}} \tag{71}$$

is conserved, because on collision the change in $\mathbf{J}$ is $\mathbf{K}_3 - \mathbf{K}_2 - \mathbf{K}_1 = 0$. Here $n_{\mathbf{K}}$ is the number of phonons having wavevector $\mathbf{K}$. For a distribution with $\mathbf{J} \neq 0$, collisions such as (70) are incapable of establishing complete thermal equilibrium because they leave $\mathbf{J}$ unchanged. If we start a distribution of hot phonons down a rod with $\mathbf{J} \neq 0$, the distribution will propagate down the rod with $\mathbf{J}$ unchanged. Therefore there is no thermal resistance.

The problem as illustrated in Fig. 18 is like that of the collisions between molecules of a gas in a straight tube with frictionless walls.

[14] See R. E. Peierls, *Quantum theory of solids*, Oxford, 1955, pp. 41–45. The same result holds for collision processes with any number of phonons.

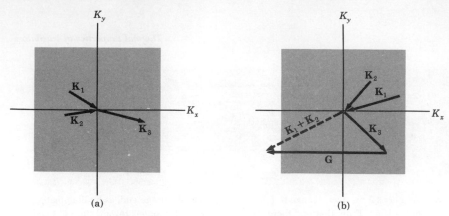

Figure 19 (a) Normal $\mathbf{K}_1 + \mathbf{K}_2 = \mathbf{K}_3$ and (b) umklapp $\mathbf{K}_1 + \mathbf{K}_2 = \mathbf{K}_3 + \mathbf{G}$ phonon collision processes in a two-dimensional square lattice. The square in each figure represents the first Brillouin zone in the phonon $\mathbf{K}$ space; this zone contains all the possible independent values of the phonon wavevector. Vectors $\mathbf{K}$ which have arrowheads at the center of the zone represent phonons absorbed in the collision process; those with arrowheads away from the center of the zone represent phonons emitted in the collision. The reciprocal lattice vector $\mathbf{G}$ as shown is of length $2\pi/a$, where a is the lattice constant of the crystal lattice, and is parallel to the K_x axis. For all processes, N or U, energy is conserved, so that $\omega_1 + \omega_2 = \omega_3$.

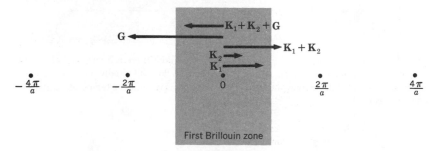

Figure 20 Central reciprocal lattice points for monatomic linear crystal of lattice constant a. A typical umklapp process is shown: here a phonon of wavevector $\mathbf{K}_1$ collides with a phonon of wavevector $\mathbf{K}_2$. The sum $\mathbf{K}_1 + \mathbf{K}_2$ lies outside the first Brillouin zone of the reciprocal lattice, but by the argument of Eq. (5.43) such a $\mathbf{K}$ value is always equivalent to a wavevector $\mathbf{K}_1 + \mathbf{K}_2 + \mathbf{G}$ inside the first zone, where $\mathbf{G}$ is a suitable reciprocal lattice vector. For the process shown $G = -2\pi/a$. For the thermal conductivity there is a difference between processes in which $\mathbf{K}_1 + \mathbf{K}_2$ lies inside the first Brillouin zone and those in which $\mathbf{K}_1 + \mathbf{K}_2$ lies outside and has to be brought back by adding a suitable $\mathbf{G}$.

Umklapp Processes

Peierls pointed out that the important three-phonon processes for thermal conductivity are not of the form $\mathbf{K}_1 + \mathbf{K}_2 + \mathbf{K}_3$, as in (70), but are of the form

$$\mathbf{K}_1 + \mathbf{K}_2 = \mathbf{K}_3 + \mathbf{G}, \tag{72}$$

where $\mathbf{G}$ is a reciprocal lattice vector (Fig. 19). We recall that $\mathbf{G}$ may occur in all momentum conservation laws in crystal lattices. We have already encountered in Chapters 2 and 5 examples of wave interaction processes in crystals for which the total wavevector change need not be zero, but may be a reciprocal lattice vector. Such processes are always possible in periodic lattices, but in a continuum model $\mathbf{G}$ is always zero.

Processes or collisions in which $\mathbf{G} \neq 0$ are called **umklapp processes,** after the German for "flipping over." This term refers to the circumstance (as in Fig. 19b) that a collision of two phonons both having a negative K_x can by umklapp give after collision a phonon with a positive K_x. Umklapp processes are also called U processes. Collisions in which $\mathbf{G} = 0$ are called **normal processes** or N processes. A typical umklapp process is shown in Fig. 20 for a linear lattice.

At high temperatures $(T > \Theta)$ all phonons are excited because $k_B T > \hbar\omega_{max}$. A substantial proportion of all phonon collisions will then be U processes, with the attendant high momentum change in the collision. We can estimate the thermal resistivity without particular distinction between N and U processes; by the earlier argument about nonlinear effects we expect to find a lattice thermal resistivity $\propto T$.

The energy of phonons $\mathbf{K}_1$, $\mathbf{K}_2$ suitable for umklapp to occur is of the order of $k_B\Theta/2$, because each of the phonons 1 and 2 must have wavevectors of the order of $G/2$ in order for the collision (72) to be possible. (If both phonons have low K, and therefore low energy, there is no way to get from their collision a phonon of wavevector comparable to $\frac{1}{2}G$. The umklapp process must conserve energy, just as for the normal process.) At low temperatures the number of suitable phonons of the high energy $k_B\Theta/2$ required may be expected to vary roughly as $e^{-\Theta/2T}$, according to the Boltzmann factor. The exponential form is in good agreement with experiment. In summary, the phonon mean free path which enters (66) is the mean free path for umklapp collisions between phonons and not for all collisions between phonons.

Imperfections

Geometrical effects may also be important in limiting the mean free path. We must consider scattering by crystal boundaries, the distribution of isotopic masses in natural chemical elements, chemical impurities, lattice imperfections, and amorphous structures.

When at low temperatures the mean free path ℓ becomes comparable with the width of the test specimen, the value of ℓ is limited by the width, and the thermal conductivity becomes a function of the dimensions of the specimen. This effect was discovered by de Haas and Biermasz,[15] and the explanation was suggested by Peierls and worked out by Casimir;[16] results of

[15] W. J. de Haas and T. Biermasz, Physica **2**, 673 (1935); **4**, 752 (1937); **5**, 47, 320, 619 (1938); see also R. Berman, Proc. Roy. Soc. (London) **A208**, 90 (1951).

[16] H. B. G. Casimir, Physica **5**, 495 (1938); R. E. B. Makinson, Proc. Cambridge Phil. Soc. **34**, 474 (1938).

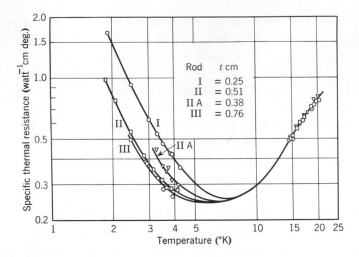

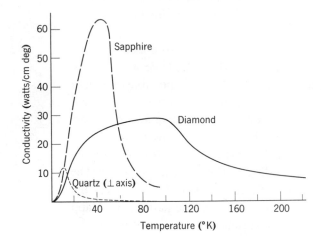

Figure 21 Thermal resistivity of a single crystal of potassium chloride as measured by Biermasz and de Haas. Below 5°K the resistivity is a function of the crystal thickness t, because the phonon mean free path is determined by the crystal dimensions. The increase in thermal resistivity at low temperatures is caused by the decrease in lattice heat capacity; the increase in resistivity above 10°K is caused by the exponential onset of umklapp processes.

Figure 22 Thermal conductivities of quartz, synthetic sapphire, and diamond. (Berman, Simon, and Wilks.)

measurements on potassium chloride crystals are given in Fig. 21. The abrupt decrease in thermal conductivity of pure crystals at low temperatures is caused by the size effect. At low temperatures the umklapp process becomes ineffective in limiting the thermal conductivity, and the size effect becomes dominant as shown also in Fig. 22. One would expect then that the phonon mean free path would be constant and of the order of the diameter D of the specimen, so that

$$K \approx CvD. \qquad (73)$$

The only temperature-dependent term on the right is C, the heat capacity, which varies as T^3 at low temperatures. We may therefore expect the thermal conductivity to vary as T^3 at low temperatures. The size effect enters when-

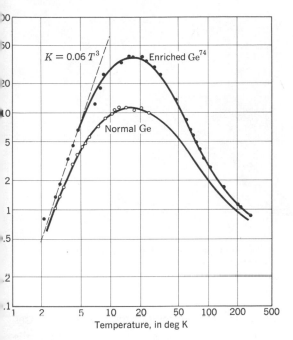

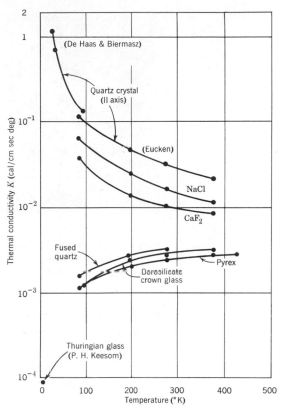

Figure 23 Isotope effect on thermal conduction in germanium, amounting to a factor of three at the conductivity maximum. The enriched specimen is 96 percent Ge^{74}; natural germanium is 20 percent Ge^{70}, 27 percent Ge^{72}, 8 percent Ge^{73}, 37 percent Ge^{74}, and 8 percent Ge^{76}. Below 5°K the enriched specimen has $K = 0.060\ T^3$, which agrees well with Casimir's theory for thermal resistance caused by boundary scattering. The conductivity data lead to a boundary-scattering mean free path of 1.80 mm, as compared with 1.57 mm calculated from the area of the cross-section. [After T. H. Geballe and G. W. Hull, *Phys. Rev.* **110**, 773 (1958).]

Figure 24 Temperature dependence of the thermal conductivity of various crystals and glasses.

ever the phonon mean free path becomes comparable with the diameter of the specimen.

In an otherwise perfect crystal the distribution of isotopes of the chemical elements often provides an important mechanism for phonon scattering. (The random distribution of isotopes disturbs the periodicity of the lattice as seen by an elastic wave.) In some substances the importance of scattering of phonons by isotopes is comparable to scattering by other phonons, even at room temperature.[17] Results for germanium are shown in Fig. 23.

In glasses the thermal conductivity (Fig. 24) decreases as the temperature is lowered, even at room temperature. The values of the thermal conduc-

[17] See J. M. Ziman, *Electrons and phonons*, Oxford, 1960, Sec. 8.6.

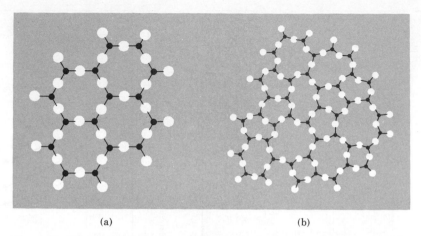

(a)   (b)

Figure 25 Schematic two-dimensional analogs, after Zachariasen, illustrating the differ-ence between: (a) the regularly repeating structure of a crystal and (b) the random net-work of a glass. The solid circles are oxygen atoms.

tivity at room temperature run about an order of magnitude lower for glasses than for crystals. The mean free path in quartz glass at room temperature is 8 Å, which is of the order of magnitude of the dimensions of a silicon dioxide tetrahedron (7 Å). A glass such as fused quartz is made up of a random, but continuous, network[18] (Fig. 25) of silicon-oxygen bonds. The effective crys-tallite size is only of the order of a single tetrahedron of the structure. We expect that (except at low temperatures, where the phonon wavelengths are so long that the structure looks uniform) the phonon mean free path will be constant, limited by the crystallite size, and the decline in the conductivity as the temperature is lowered may be attributed to the decline in the heat capacity.

Dielectric crystals may have thermal conductivities as high as metals. Synthetic sapphire (Al_2O_3) has one of the highest values of the conductivity: nearly 200 watts/cm-deg at 30°K. Glasses have values as low as 5×10^{-4} watt/cm-deg at 2°K, and Berman[19] has suggested the conductivity of micro-crystalline graphite at 1°K may be 10^{-5} watt/cm-deg. The maximum of the thermal conductivity in sapphire is greater than the maximum of 50 watts/cm-deg in copper.[20] The electronic contribution to the thermal conductivity of metals is treated in Chapter 7.

[18] W. H. Zachariasen, J. Am. Chem. Soc. **54**, 3841 (1932); B. E. Warren, J. Appl. Phys. **8**, 645 (1937); **13**, 602 (1942); E. U. Condon, "Physics of the glassy state," Am. J. Phys. **22**, 43, 132, 224, 310 (1954).

[19] R. Berman, Phys. Rev. **76**, 315 (1949).

[20] R. Berman and D. K. C. MacDonald, Proc. Roy. Soc. (London) **A211**, 122 (1952).

Problems

1. *Heat capacity of one-dimensional lattice.* Show that the heat capacity of a monatomic lattice in one dimension in the Debye approximation is proportional to T/Θ for low temperatures $T \ll \Theta$, where Θ is the effective Debye temperature in one dimension defined as $\Theta = \hbar\omega_m/k_B = \hbar\pi v_0/k_B a$; here k_B is the Boltzmann constant and a the interatomic separation.

2. *Energy and partition function.* Show that the expression for the average energy of a system may be written as

$$\langle E \rangle = k_B T^2 \frac{d \log Z}{dT},$$

where the partition function Z is defined for a classical one-dimensional system by

$$Z = \iint dp\, dx \exp\left[-E(p,x)/k_B T\right];$$

here p is the momentum.

3. *Heat capacity of anharmonic oscillator.* Using the anharmonic potential $U(x) = cx^2 - gx^3 - fx^4$, show that the approximate heat capacity of the classical anharmonic oscillator is

$$C \cong k_B \left[1 + \left(\frac{3f}{2c^2} + \frac{15g^2}{8c^3}\right)k_B T\right].$$

Note: $\log(1 + \delta) \cong \delta - \frac{1}{2}\delta^2$ for $\delta \ll 1$; the calculation is shorter if the partition function (Problem 2) is employed. We assume that the oscillations about $x = 0$ are small so that $c\langle x^2 \rangle$ is dominant in U.

4. *Three-phonon interactions.* Consider a crystal for which $\omega_L = v_L K$ and $\omega_T = v_T K$, where v_L, v_T are independent of $\mathbf{K}$. The subscripts L, T denote longitudinal and transverse. If $v_L > v_T$, show that the normal three-phonon process $T + L \leftrightarrow T$ cannot satisfy conservation of energy and wavevector.

References

A. A. Maradudin, E. W. Montroll, and G. H. Weiss, "Theory of lattice dynamics in the harmonic approximation," *Solid state physics*, Supp. **3**, 1963.

G. Leibfried and W. Ludwig, "Theory of anharmonic effects in crystals," *Solid state physics* **12**, 276–444 (1961).

THERMAL CONDUCTIVITY

P. G. Klemens, "Thermal conductivity and lattice vibration modes," *Solid state physics* **7**, 1–98 (1958); see also *Encyclo. of physics* **14**, 198 (1956).

K. Mendelssohn and H. M. Rosenberg, "Thermal conductivity of metals at low temperatures," *Solid state physics* **12**, 223–274 (1961).

H. M. Rosenberg, *Low temperature solid state physics*, Oxford, 1963, Chap. 3.

J. M. Ziman, *Electrons and phonons*, Oxford, 1960, Chap. 8.

7
Free Electron
Fermi Gas I

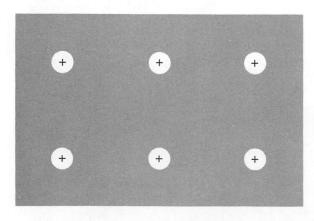

Figure 1 Schematic model of a crystal of sodium metal. The atomic cores are Na$^+$ ions; they are immersed in a sea of conduction electrons. The conduction electrons are derived from the 3s valence electrons of the free atoms. The atomic cores contain ten electrons in the configuration 1s^2 2s^2 2p^6. In an alkali metal the atomic cores occupy a relatively small part ($\sim$10 percent) of the total volume of the crystal, but in a noble metal (Cu, Ag, Au) the atomic cores are relatively larger and may be in contact with each other. The common crystal structure at room temperature is bcc for the alkali metals and fcc for the noble metals.

We can understand a number of important physical properties of metals, particularly the simple metals, in terms of the free electron model. According to this model the most weakly bound electrons of the constituent atoms move about freely through the volume of the metal. The valence electrons of the atoms become the conductors of electricity in the metal and are called *conduction electrons*. The forces between the conduction electrons and the ion cores are neglected in the free electron approximation: all calculations proceed as if the conduction electrons were free to move everywhere within the specimen. The total energy is all kinetic energy; the potential energy is neglected.

Even in metals for which the free electron model works well, the actual charge distribution of the conduction electrons is known to reflect the strong electrostatic potential of the ion cores. The usefulness of the free electron model depends essentially upon the kinetic properties of the conduction electrons. A later chapter is concerned with the effects of the conduction electron interaction with the lattice.

The simple metals are the alkali metals (lithium, sodium, potassium, cesium, and rubidium) and, sometimes, the noble metals (copper, silver, and gold). All metals show some free electron aspects, but electrons in metals formed from monovalent elements act most nearly free.

Conduction electrons in a simple metal arise from the valence electrons of the constituent atoms. In a sodium atom the valence electron is in a $3s$ state; in the metal this electron becomes a conduction electron, roving throughout the crystal. A monovalent crystal which contains N atoms will have N conduction electrons and N positive ion cores. The ten electrons of the Na^+ ion core fill the $1s$, the $2s$, and the $2p$ states in the free ion; the distribution of core electrons is essentially the same in the metal as in the free ion.

The ion cores fill only about 15 percent of the volume of a sodium crystal, as in Fig. 1. The radius of the free Na^+ ion (Table 3.6) is 0.98 Å, whereas one-half of the nearest neighbor distance of the metal (Table 1.4) is 1.85 Å.

The interpretation of metallic properties in terms of free electrons was developed long before the invention of quantum mechanics. The classical theory had several conspicuous successes and several remarkable failures. The successes include the derivation of the form of Ohm's law, which connects the electric current with the electric field, and the derivation of the relation between the electrical conductivity and the thermal conductivity. The classical theory completely fails to explain the heat capacity and the paramagnetic susceptibility of the conduction electrons.

There is a further difficulty: using the classical theory we cannot understand the occurrence of long electronic mean free paths. From many types of

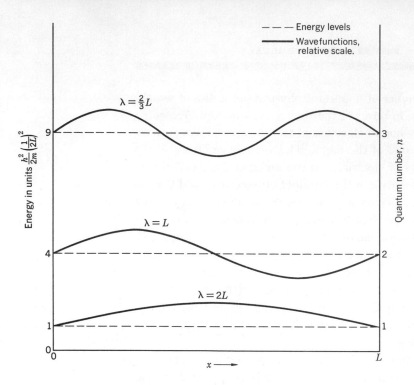

Energy in units $\frac{h^2}{2m}\left(\frac{1}{2L}\right)^2$

Quantum number, n

$\lambda = \frac{2}{3}L$

$\lambda = L$

$\lambda = 2L$

— — — Energy levels
——— Wavefunctions, relative scale.

Figure 2 First three energy levels and wavefunctions of a free electron of mass m confined to a line of length L. The energy levels are labeled according to the quantum number n which gives the number of half-wavelengths in the wavefunction. The wavelengths are indicated on the wavefunctions. The energy ϵ_n of the level of quantum number n is equal to $(h^2/2m)(n/2L)^2$.

experiments it is abundantly clear that a conduction electron in a metal can move freely in a straight path over many atomic distances, undeflected by collisions with other conduction electrons or by collisions with the atom cores. In a very pure specimen at low temperatures the mean free path may be as long as 10^8 or 10^9 interatomic spacings (more than 1 cm), vastly longer than we would expect from the known areas of atoms. We must ask why condensed matter is so transparent to conduction electrons. The conduction electrons act in this respect as a gas of noninteracting particles.

There are two parts to the answer to our question: (a) A conduction electron is not deflected by ion cores arranged on a *periodic* lattice because matter waves propagate freely in a periodic structure. We showed free propagation of x-rays in periodic lattices in Chapter 2; we discuss electron waves in lattices in Chapter 9. (b) A conduction electron is scattered only infrequently by other conduction electrons. This property is a consequence of the Pauli exclusion principle. By a **free electron Fermi gas** we shall mean a gas of free and noninteracting electrons which are subject to the Pauli principle.

ENERGY LEVELS AND DENSITY OF STATES IN ONE DIMENSION

We first discuss the behavior of a free electron gas in one dimension, taking account of quantum theory and of the Pauli principle. Consider an electron of mass m confined to a line of length L by infinite barriers at the ends of the line (Fig. 2). The wavefunction $\psi_n(x)$ of the electron is described by the Schrödinger equation $\mathcal{H}\psi = \epsilon\psi$; with the neglect of potential energy we

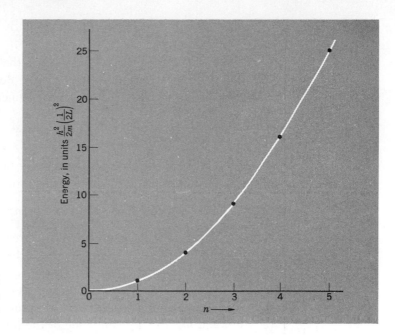

Figure 3 The energy is a quadratic function of the quantum number n, for the free electron confined to a line.

have $\mathcal{H} = p^2/2m$, where p is the momentum. Then

$$-\frac{\hbar^2}{2m}\frac{d^2\psi_n}{dx^2} = \epsilon_n\psi_n, \tag{1}$$

where ϵ_n is the energy of the electron in the state n. The boundary conditions are

$$\psi_n(0) = 0; \qquad \psi_n(L) = 0, \tag{2}$$

as imposed by the infinite potential energy barrier at the ends of the line. The boundary conditions are automatically satisfied if the wavefunction is sine-like with an integral number n of half-wavelengths between 0 and L:

$$\psi_n \propto \sin\left(\frac{2\pi}{\lambda_n}x\right); \qquad \tfrac{1}{2}n\lambda_n = L. \tag{3}$$

Thus

$$\psi_n = A\sin\left(\frac{n\pi}{L}x\right), \tag{4}$$

where A is a constant. We see that (4) is a solution of the Schrödinger equation, because

$$\frac{d\psi_n}{dx} = A\left(\frac{n\pi}{L}\right)\cos\left(\frac{n\pi}{L}x\right); \qquad \frac{d^2\psi_n}{dx^2} = -A\left(\frac{n\pi}{L}\right)^2\sin\left(\frac{n\pi}{L}x\right),$$

whence the energy eigenvalue ϵ_n is given by

$$\epsilon_n = \frac{\hbar^2}{2m}\left(\frac{n\pi}{L}\right)^2 = \frac{h^2}{2m}\left(\frac{n}{2L}\right)^2. \tag{5}$$

for one dimension. The energy is a quadratic function of the quantum number n, as shown in Fig. 3.

201

We must choose the constant A in (4) so that there is unit probability of finding the electron somewhere on the line. Because $\psi^*(x)\psi(x)\,dx$ is the probability that the electron is in the line segment dx at x, we require that

$$\int_0^L dx\,\psi_n^*(x)\psi_n(x) = 1. \tag{6}$$

The probability the electron is somewhere on the line is unity. The integral of $\sin^2$ over the interval L is $\frac{1}{2}L$, so that the normalized wavefunction is

$$\psi_n(x) = (2/L)^{1/2}\sin\,(n\pi x/L). \tag{7}$$

Suppose we want to accommodate N electrons on the line. The elementary statement of the **Pauli exclusion principle** is that *no two electrons can have all their quantum numbers identical.* That is, each quantum state can be occupied by at most one electron. This applies to atoms, molecules, or solids. In a solid the quantum numbers of an electron in the conduction electron states are n and m_s: For a given value of the integer n in (7) there are two possible orientations of an electron spin, say, along the $+\hat{z}$ or the $-\hat{z}$ direction. We have the quantum numbers n and m_s, where n is any positive integer and $m_s = \pm\frac{1}{2}$, according to the spin orientation. Each energy level[1] labeled by the quantum number n can accommodate two electrons, one with its spin up and one with its spin down. If there are eight electrons, then in the ground state of the system the levels with $n = 1, 2, 3$, and 4 are filled and the levels of higher n are empty.

Let n_F denote the topmost filled energy level, where we start filling the levels from the bottom $(n = 1)$ and continue filling the higher levels with electrons until all N electrons are accommodated. It is convenient to suppose that N is an even number; then the condition

$$2n_F = N \tag{8}$$

determines n_F. The **Fermi energy** ϵ_F is defined as the energy of the topmost filled level. By (5) with $n = n_F$ we have

$$\epsilon_F = \frac{h^2}{2m}\left(\frac{n_F}{2L}\right)^2 = \frac{h^2}{2m}\left(\frac{N}{4L}\right)^2. \tag{9}$$

As a practical example, suppose that $N/L = 0.4$ electrons per angstrom $= 4 \times 10^7$ cm^{-1}. Then (9) gives

$$\epsilon_F \approx \frac{(7 \times 10^{-27})^2}{2 \times 10^{-27}}\,(10^7)^2 \approx 2 \times 10^{-12}\ \mathrm{erg} \approx 1\ \mathrm{ev}. \tag{10}$$

---

[1] Different **energy levels** are defined as having different energies, but more than one **quantum state** may have the same energy. The number of states with the same energy is called the **degeneracy** of the energy level.

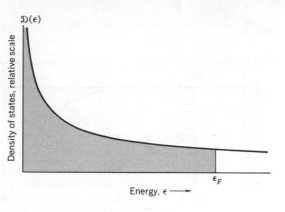

$\mathfrak{D}(\epsilon)$

Energy, $\epsilon \longrightarrow$

Density of states, relative scale

ϵ_F

Figure 4 Density of electronic states versus energy, for one-dimensional line. This may be compared with Fig. 7 for three dimensions. At absolute zero all states are filled up to the Fermi energy ϵ_F. The Fermi energy at absolute zero is determined by the condition that all N electrons of the system be accommodated in states below or at the Fermi energy.

Thus to accommodate 4×10^7 electrons per cm of line the kinetic energy of the uppermost electron must be of the order of 1 ev.

The total energy E_0 of N electrons in the lowest energy state of the entire system is found by summing the individual energies ϵ_n between $n = 1$ and $n_F = \frac{1}{2}N$, where the $\frac{1}{2}$ arises from the spin degeneracy. Thus

$$E_0 = 2 \sum_{n=1}^{N/2} \epsilon_n = 2 \cdot \frac{h^2}{2m} \left(\frac{1}{2L}\right)^2 \sum_{n=1}^{N/2} n^2, \tag{11}$$

taking account of the two electrons in each level. The sum has the value

$$\sum_{n=1}^{s} n^2 = \frac{1}{6}s(2s^2 + 3s + 1) \cong \frac{1}{3}s^3, \tag{12}$$

for $s \gg 1$. Thus the total ground-state energy of the N-electron system is

$$E_0 \cong \frac{h^2}{3m} \left(\frac{1}{2L}\right)^2 \left(\frac{N}{2}\right)^3 = \frac{1}{3}N\epsilon_F, \tag{13}$$

using (9) for ϵ_F. For the one-dimensional problem the average kinetic energy in the ground state is one-third of the Fermi energy.

The **density of states** $\mathfrak{D}(\epsilon)$ is defined as the number of electronic states per unit energy range; compare with Chapter 6 for phonons. On taking differentials in (5) we have for free electrons

$$d\epsilon = \frac{h^2}{m} \left(\frac{n}{2L}\right) \frac{dn}{L}. \tag{14}$$

Now $dn/d\epsilon$ gives the number of energy levels per unit energy. There are two quantum states for each energy level, one of spin up and one of spin down, so that the density of states of a free electron gas in one dimension is

$$\mathfrak{D}(\epsilon) = 2\frac{dn}{d\epsilon} = \frac{8L^2 m}{h^2} \cdot \frac{1}{n} = 4L \left(\frac{m}{2\epsilon}\right)^{1/2} \frac{1}{h}. \tag{15}$$

We have used (5) to express n in terms of ϵ. The result (15) is plotted in Fig. 4.

In Fig. 4 we indicate for the ground state of the system of N electrons

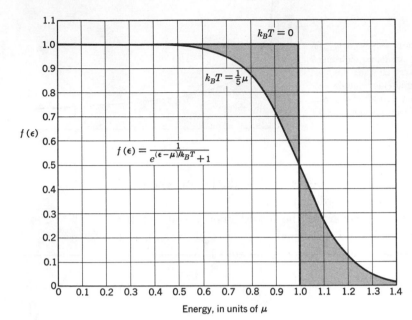

Figure 5a Plot of the Fermi-Dirac distribution function $f(\epsilon)$ versus ϵ/μ, for zero temperature and for a temperature $k_B T = \frac{1}{5}\mu$. The value of $f(\epsilon)$ gives the fraction of levels at a given energy which are occupied when the system is in thermal equilibrium. When the system is heated from absolute zero, electrons are transferred from the shaded region at $\epsilon/\mu < 1$ to the shaded region at $\epsilon/\mu > 1$. For a metal μ might correspond to $50{,}000°\mathrm{K}$.

In the figure:

$$f(\epsilon) = \frac{1}{e^{(\epsilon - \mu)/k_B T} + 1}$$

$k_B T = 0$

$k_B T = \frac{1}{5}\mu$

$f(\epsilon)$

Energy, in units of μ

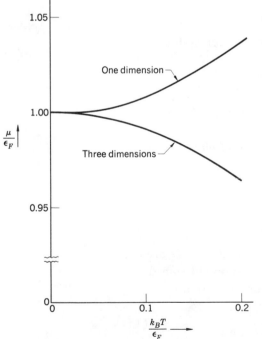

Figure 5b Variation with temperature of the chemical potential μ, for free electron Fermi gases in one and three dimensions. In common metals $k_B T/\epsilon_F \approx 0.01$ at room temperature, so that μ is closely equal to ϵ_F.

One dimension

Three dimensions

$\dfrac{\mu}{\epsilon_F}$

$\dfrac{k_B T}{\epsilon_F}$

the energy range in which all levels are filled with electrons. The filled levels extend from 0 to ϵ_F, the Fermi energy; levels above ϵ_F are empty.

EFFECT OF TEMPERATURE ON THE FERMI-DIRAC DISTRIBUTION FUNCTION

The ground state is the state of the system at absolute zero. What happens as the temperature is increased? This is a standard problem in elementary statistical mechanics and the solution (Appendix C) is given by the Fermi-Dirac distribution function. The kinetic energy of the electron gas increases as the temperature is increased: some energy levels are occupied which were vacant at absolute zero, and some levels are vacant which were occupied at absolute zero.

The situation is illustrated by Fig. 5a, where the plotted curves are of the function

$$f(\epsilon) = \frac{1}{e^{(\epsilon-\mu)/k_B T} + 1}. \tag{16}$$

This is the **Fermi-Dirac distribution function**: it gives the probability that a state at energy ϵ will be occupied in an ideal electron gas in thermal equilibrium. (The probability that a state is occupied by an electron is the average number of electrons in the state.)

The quantity μ is a function of the temperature; μ is to be chosen for the particular problem in such a way that the total number of particles in the system comes out correctly—that is, equal[2] to N. At absolute zero $\mu = \epsilon_F$, because in the limit $T \rightarrow 0$ the function $f(\epsilon)$ changes discontinuously from the value 1 (filled) to the value 0 (empty) at $\epsilon = \epsilon_F = \mu$. *At all temperatures* $f(\epsilon)$ *is equal to* $\frac{1}{2}$ *when* $\epsilon = \mu$, for then the denominator of (16) has the value 2. The quantity μ is called the **chemical potential**,[3] and we see that at absolute zero the chemical potential is equal to the Fermi energy. At low temperatures μ is close to ϵ_F in value, as in Fig. 5b. The Fermi energy was defined as the topmost filled energy state at absolute zero.

The high energy tail of the distribution is that part for which $\epsilon - \mu \gg k_B T$; here the exponential term is dominant in the denominator of (16), so that $f(\epsilon) \cong e^{(\mu-\epsilon)/k_B T}$. Note that this is essentially the Boltzmann distribution.

---

[2] If the energy levels are ϵ_i, then we must have $\sum_i f(\epsilon_i) = N$ at all temperatures. In integral form $\int_0^\infty d\epsilon\, f(\epsilon)\, \mathfrak{D}(\epsilon) = N$.

[3] Sometimes (particularly in semiconductor problems), the chemical potential is called the **Fermi level**.

FREE ELECTRON GAS IN THREE DIMENSIONS

The free-particle Schrödinger equation in three dimensions is

$$-\frac{\hbar^2}{2m}\left(\frac{\partial^2}{\partial x^2} + \frac{\partial^2}{\partial y^2} + \frac{\partial^2}{\partial z^2}\right)\psi_k(\mathbf{r}) = \epsilon_k\psi_k(\mathbf{r}). \qquad (17)$$

If the electrons are confined to a cube of edge L, the analog to the normalized wavefunction (7) is

$$\psi_r(\mathbf{r}) = (8/L^3)^{1/2} \sin\,(\pi n_x x/L)\,\sin\,(\pi n_y y/L)\,\sin\,(\pi n_z z/L), \qquad (18)$$

where n_x, n_y, n_z are positive integers. This is a standing wave. The factor $(8/L^3)^{1/2}$ gives the correct normalization over the volume $V = L^3$ of the cube:

$$\frac{8}{L^3} \int_V dx\,dy\,dz \sin^2\,(\pi n_x x/L)\,\sin^2\,(\pi n_y y/L)\,\sin^2\,(\pi n_z z/L) = 1. \qquad (19)$$

It is convenient to introduce wavefunctions which satisfy periodic boundary conditions, as we did for phonons in Chapter (6). We now require the wavefunctions to be periodic in x, y, z with period L. Thus

$$\psi(x + L, y, z) = \psi(x, y, z), \qquad (20)$$

and similarly for the y and z coordinates. Wavefunctions satisfying the free-particle Schrödinger equation (17), the normalization condition over the volume $V = L^3$, and the periodicity condition (20) are of the traveling plane waveform

$$\boxed{\psi_k(\mathbf{r}) = (1/V)^{1/2}e^{i\mathbf{k}\cdot\mathbf{r}},} \qquad (21)$$

provided that the components of the wavevector $\mathbf{k}$ satisfy

$$k_x = 0; \quad \pm\frac{2\pi}{L}; \quad \pm\frac{4\pi}{L}; \quad \cdots, \qquad (22)$$

and similarly for k_y and k_z. That is, any component of $\mathbf{k}$ is of the form $2n\pi/L$, where n is a positive or negative integer. The components of $\mathbf{k}$ are the quantum numbers of the problem, along with the quantum number m_s for the spin direction. We confirm that these values of k_x satisfy (20), for

$$\exp\,[ik_x(x + L)] = \exp\,[i2n\pi(x + L)/L] =$$
$$\exp\,(i2n\pi x/L)\,\exp\,(i2n\pi) = \exp\,(i2n\pi x/L) = \exp\,(ik_x x). \qquad (23)$$

The normalization condition is satisfied by (21) because

$$\frac{1}{V} \int_V dx\,dy\,dz\,e^{-i\mathbf{k}\cdot\mathbf{r}}e^{i\mathbf{k}\cdot\mathbf{r}} = 1. \qquad (24)$$

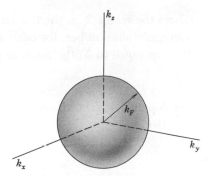

Figure 6 In the ground state of a system of N free electrons the occupied states of the system fill a sphere of radius k_F, where $\epsilon_F = \hbar^2 k_F^2/2m$ is the energy of an electron having a wavevector k_F on the surface of a sphere.

On substituting (21) in (17) we have

$$\epsilon_{\mathbf{k}} = \frac{\hbar^2}{2m} k^2 = \frac{\hbar^2}{2m} (k_x^2 + k_y^2 + k_z^2) \tag{25}$$

for the energy eigenvalue $\epsilon_{\mathbf{k}}$ of the state with wavevector $\mathbf{k}$; here $\epsilon_{\mathbf{k}}=0$ for $\mathbf{k}= 0$. The magnitude of the wavevector is related to the wavelength λ by

$$k = 2\pi/\lambda. \tag{26}$$

The linear momentum $\mathbf{p}$ may be represented in quantum mechanics by the operator $\mathbf{p} = -i\hbar\nabla$, whence for the state (21)

$$\mathbf{p}\psi_{\mathbf{k}}(\mathbf{r}) = -i\hbar\nabla\psi_{\mathbf{k}}(\mathbf{r}) = \hbar\mathbf{k}\psi_{\mathbf{k}}(\mathbf{r}), \tag{27}$$

so that the plane wave $\psi_{\mathbf{k}}$ is an eigenfunction of the linear momentum with the eigenvalue $\hbar\mathbf{k}$. The particle velocity in the state $\mathbf{k}$ is given by

$$m\mathbf{v} = \hbar\mathbf{k}. \tag{28}$$

In the ground state of a system of N free electrons the occupied states may be represented as points inside a sphere in $\mathbf{k}$ space. The energy at the surface of the sphere is the Fermi energy; the wavevectors at the Fermi surface have a magnitude k_F such that (Fig. 6)

$$\epsilon_F = \frac{\hbar^2}{2m} k_F^2. \tag{29}$$

From the conditions (22) we see that there is one allowed wavevector—that is, one distinct triplet of quantum numbers k_x, k_y, k_z—for the volume element $(2\pi/L)^3$ of $\mathbf{k}$ space. Thus in the sphere of volume $4\pi k_F^3/3$ the total allowed number of states is

$$2 \cdot \frac{4\pi k_F^3/3}{(2\pi/L)^3} = \frac{V}{3\pi^2} k_F^3 = N, \tag{30}$$

where the factor 2 on the left comes from the two allowed values of m_s, the spin quantum number, for each allowed value of $\mathbf{k}$. We have set the number of states equal to N, the number of electrons. Then

$$k_F = (3\pi^2 N/V)^{1/3};$$ (31)

this depends only on the particle concentration and not on the mass.

Using (29),

$$\boxed{\epsilon_F = \frac{\hbar^2}{2m}(3\pi^2 N/V)^{2/3}.}$$ (32)

This relates the Fermi energy to the electron concentration N/V and the mass m. The electron velocity v_F at the Fermi surface is

$$v_F = \hbar k_F/m = (\hbar/m)(3\pi^2 N/V)^{1/3},$$ (33)

where $\hbar/m \cong 1.16$ cm^2/sec. Calculated values of k_F, v_F, and ϵ_F are given in Table 1 for monovalent metals; also given are values of the quantity T_F which is defined as ϵ_F/k_B. (The quantity T_F has nothing to do with the temperature of the electron gas!)

We now give an expression valid in three dimensions for the number of states per unit energy range, $\mathfrak{D}(\epsilon)$. By direct analogy with the argument of Eq. (6.34) we have the general result

$$\mathfrak{D}(\epsilon) = \frac{2V}{(2\pi)^3}\int\frac{dS_\epsilon}{|\mathrm{grad}_\mathbf{k}\,\epsilon|},$$ (34)

where the factor of 2 arises from the two spin orientations; V is the volume of the specimen; and dS_ϵ is the element of area in $\mathbf{k}$ space of the surface of

Table 1   Calculated Fermi surface parameters for free electrons

	Electron concentration N/V, per cm^3	Wavevector k_F, in cm^{-1}	Velocity v_F, in cm/sec	Energy ϵ_F, in ev	Temperature $T_F = \epsilon_F/k_B$, in deg K
Li	4.6×10^{22}	1.1×10^8	1.3×10^8	4.7	5.5×10^4
Na	2.5	0.90	1.1	3.1	3.7
K	1.34	0.73	0.85	2.1	2.4
Rb	1.08	0.68	0.79	1.8	2.1
Cs	0.86	0.63	0.73	1.5	1.8
Cu	8.50	1.35	1.56	7.0	8.2
Ag	5.76	1.19	1.38	5.5	6.4
Au	5.90	1.20	1.39	5.5	6.4

constant energy ϵ. For free electrons $|\text{grad}_k \epsilon| = \hbar^2 k/m$ from (25), and the surface of constant energy ϵ is spherical with area

$$S_\epsilon = 4\pi k^2. \tag{35}$$

Thus the density of states for free electrons is

$$\mathfrak{D}(\epsilon) = \frac{2V}{(2\pi)^3} \cdot \frac{4\pi k^2}{\hbar^2 k/m} = \frac{V}{\pi^2} \cdot \frac{mk}{\hbar^2} \tag{36}$$

or

$$\boxed{\mathfrak{D}(\epsilon) = \frac{V}{2\pi^2} \cdot \left(\frac{2m}{\hbar^2}\right)^{3/2} \cdot \epsilon^{1/2}.} \tag{37}$$

This is plotted in Fig. 7. The dashed curve in the figure is a plot for some finite temperature of the density of *filled* states as given by the product $f(\epsilon)\mathfrak{D}(\epsilon)$ of the Fermi-Dirac distribution function times the density of states.

HEAT CAPACITY OF THE ELECTRON GAS

The question which caused the greatest difficulty in the early development of the electron theory of metals concerns the heat capacity of the conduction electrons. Classical statistical mechanics predicts that a free point particle should have a heat capacity of $\frac{3}{2}k_B$, where k_B is the Boltzmann constant. If N atoms give one valence electron each to the electron gas, and the electrons are freely mobile, then the electronic contribution to the heat capacity should be $\frac{3}{2}Nk_B$. But experimentally the electronic contribution at room temperature is usually not more than 0.01 of this value. This discrepancy distracted the early workers, such as Lorentz: how could the electrons participate in electrical conduction processes as if they were mobile, while not contributing to the heat capacity? The question was answered only upon the discovery of the Pauli exclusion principle.

In Fig. 7 we see that on heating from absolute zero not every electron gains an energy $\sim k_B T$ as expected classically, but only those electrons in states within an energy range $k_B T$ of the Fermi level are excited thermally; these electrons gain an energy which is itself of the order of $k_B T$, as in the figure.

This drastic modification of the thermal properties of the conduction electrons gives an immediate qualitative solution to the problem of the heat capacity of the conduction electron gas. If N is the total number of electrons, only a fraction of the order of T/T_F can be excited thermally at temperature T, because only these lie within an energy range of the order of $k_B T$ of the top of the energy distribution. Each of these NT/T_F electrons has a thermal energy of the order of $k_B T$, and so the total electronic thermal energy E_{el} is

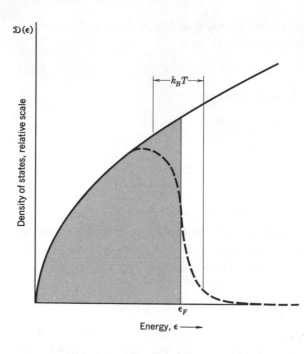

Figure 7 Density of single-particle states as a function of energy, for a free electron gas in three dimensions. The dashed curve represents the density $f(\epsilon, T)\mathfrak{D}(\epsilon)$ of *filled* states at a finite temperature, but such that $k_B T$ is small in comparison with ϵ_F. The shaded area represents the filled states at absolute zero.

of the order of

$$E_{el} \approx \frac{NT}{T_F} k_B T.$$

The electronic heat capacity is given by

$$C_{el} = \frac{\partial E_{el}}{\partial T} \approx N k_B \cdot \frac{T}{T_F} \tag{38}$$

and is directly proportional to T, in agreement with the experimental results as discussed in the following section. At room temperature C_{el} in (38) is smaller than the classical value $\frac{3}{2}N k_B$ by a factor of the order of 0.01 or less, if we take $T_F \sim 5 \times 10^4$ deg, as in Table 1.

We now derive a quantitative expression for the electronic heat capacity valid at low temperatures $k_B T \ll \epsilon_F$. The change E_{el} in the total energy of the system of N electrons on heating from 0 to T is

$$E_{el}(T) = \int_{\epsilon_F}^{\infty} d\epsilon \, (\epsilon - \epsilon_F) f(\epsilon) \mathfrak{D}(\epsilon) + \int_0^{\epsilon_F} d\epsilon \, (\epsilon_F - \epsilon)[1 - f(\epsilon)]\mathfrak{D}(\epsilon), \tag{39}$$

where the first integral gives the energy needed to take electrons from ϵ_F to the states $\epsilon > \epsilon_F$ and the second integral gives the energy needed to take electrons to ϵ_F from states below. Here f is the Fermi-Dirac function (16). The factor $[1 - f(\epsilon)]$ in the second integral gives the probability that an electron has been removed from a state at ϵ lying below ϵ_F.

The electronic heat capacity is

$$C_{el} = \frac{\partial E_{el}}{\partial T} = \int_0^\infty d\epsilon \, (\epsilon - \epsilon_F) \frac{\partial f}{\partial T} \mathcal{D}(\epsilon). \tag{40}$$

At the low temperatures $(k_B T/\epsilon_F < 0.01)$ of interest the derivative $\partial f/\partial T$ is large only at energies near ϵ_F, so that we may take $\mathcal{D}(\epsilon)$ evaluated at ϵ_F outside of the integrand:

$$C_{el} \cong \mathcal{D}(\epsilon_F) \int_0^\infty d\epsilon \, (\epsilon - \epsilon_F) \frac{\partial f}{\partial T}. \tag{41}$$

Examination[4] of Fig. 5b suggests that to the first order in T we may in the expression (16) for f replace the chemical potential μ by the constant Fermi energy ϵ_F as defined by $\epsilon_F \equiv \mu(0)$. Then

$$\frac{\partial f}{\partial T} = \frac{\epsilon - \epsilon_F}{k_B T^2} \cdot \frac{e^{(\epsilon - \epsilon_F)/k_B T}}{[e^{(\epsilon - \epsilon_F)/k_B T} + 1]^2}, \tag{42}$$

and, setting

$$x \equiv (\epsilon - \epsilon_F)/k_B T, \tag{43}$$

it follows from (41) that

$$C_{el} = \mathcal{D}(\epsilon_F)(k_B^2 T) \int_{-\epsilon_F/k_B T}^\infty dx \, x^2 \frac{e^x}{(e^x + 1)^2}. \tag{44}$$

Because the factor e^x in the integrand is negligible at $x = -\epsilon_F/k_B T$, we may safely replace the lower limit by $-\infty$. The integral becomes[5]

$$\int_{-\infty}^\infty dx \, x^2 \frac{e^x}{(e^x + 1)^2} = \frac{\pi^2}{3}, \tag{45}$$

or

$$\boxed{C_{el} = \tfrac{1}{3}\pi^2 \mathcal{D}(\epsilon_F) k_B^2 T.} \tag{46}$$

From (32) and (37) we have for a free electron gas:

$$\mathcal{D}(\epsilon_F) = \frac{3N}{2\epsilon_F} = \frac{3N}{2k_B T_F}, \tag{47}$$

with $k_B T_F \equiv \epsilon_F$. The spin degeneracy has been included in (47). Thus

$$C_{el} = \tfrac{1}{2}\pi^2 N k_B \cdot \frac{k_B T}{\epsilon_F} = \tfrac{1}{2}\pi^2 N k_B \cdot \frac{T}{T_F}, \tag{48}$$

in agreement with the qualitative result (38).

[4] The present derivation was suggested by J. Twidell, private communication.

[5] See, for example, integral 313.11b of the Gröbner and Hofreiter tables, Vol. 2; note that the integrand is an even function of x.

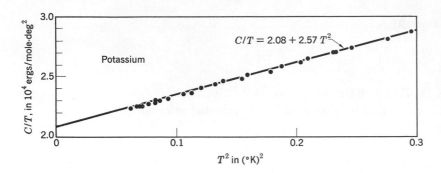

Figure 8 Experimental heat capacity values for potassium, plotted as C/T versus T^2. The solid points were determined with an adiabatic demagnetization cryostat. [After W. H. Lien and N. E. Phillips, Phys. Rev. **133**, A1370 (1964).]

Experimental Heat Capacity of Metals

At temperatures much below the Debye temperature and very much below the Fermi temperature, the heat capacity of metals at constant volume may be written as the sum of electronic and lattice contributions:

$$C = \gamma T + AT^3, \tag{49}$$

where γ and A are constants characteristic of the material and are given by (46) and (6.47). The electronic term is linear in T and is dominant at sufficiently low temperatures. It is convenient to exhibit the experimental values

Table 2 Experimental electronic heat capacities of metals
(Courtesy of N. Phillips)
(The values of γ are in millijoules mole^{-1} deg^{-2}, which is 10^4 ergs mole^{-1} deg^{-2})

Metal	γ, in mJ/mole-deg^2	Metal	γ, in mJ/mole-deg^2
Li	1.63	Sn	1.78
Na	1.38	Pb	2.98
K	2.08	Ti	3.35
Rb	2.41	Zr	2.80
Cs	3.20	Hf	2.16
Cu	0.695	V	9.26
Ag	0.646	Nb	7.79
Au	0.729	Cr	1.40
		γ-Mn	9.20
Zn	0.64	Fe	4.98
Cd	0.688	Co	4.73
Hg	1.79	Ni	7.02
Al	1.35		
Ga	0.596		
In	1.69		
Tl	1.47		

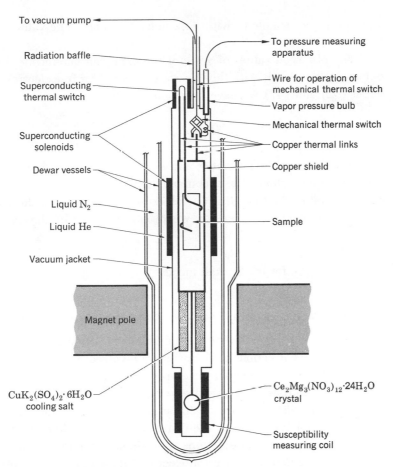

To vacuum pump

Radiation baffle

Superconducting thermal switch

Superconducting solenoids

Dewar vessels

Liquid N_2

Liquid He

Vacuum jacket

Magnet pole

$CuK_2(SO_4)_2 \cdot 6H_2O$ cooling salt

To pressure measuring apparatus

Wire for operation of mechanical thermal switch

Vapor pressure bulb

Mechanical thermal switch

Copper thermal links

Copper shield

Sample

$Ce_2Mg_3(NO_3)_{12} \cdot 24H_2O$ crystal

Susceptibility measuring coil

Figure 9 Apparatus for heat capacity measurements between 0.05 and 1°K. The mechanical thermal switch is used to cool the sample and paramagnetic salts to 1°K by evaporation of liquid He. Temperatures below 1°K are produced by adiabatic demagnetization (Chapter 14) of $CuK_2(SO_4)_2 \cdot 6H_2O$, and determined from the magnetic susceptibility of $Ce_2Mg_3(NO_3)_{12} \cdot 24H_2O$, which follows a Curie law at these temperatures. Thermal contact between the sample and the paramagnetic salts is made through the superconducting thermal switch, a Pb wire that can be made either normal (good heat conductor) or superconducting (poor heat conductor) by adjustment of the current in the surrounding superconducting solenoid. A resistance thermometer, which is calibrated against the magnetic thermometer, and a resistance heater are attached directly to the sample. (Courtesy of N. Phillips.)

of C as a plot of C/T versus T^2:

$$C/T = \gamma + AT^2, \tag{50}$$

for then the points should lie on a straight line with slope A and intercept γ. Such a plot for potassium is shown in Fig. 8. The apparatus used for these measurements is shown in Fig. 9.

Observed values of γ are given in Table 2; values of the Debye Θ derived from observed values of A were given in Table 6.1. The values given for γ are believed to be reliable to within perhaps 2 percent. The values refer to one mole.

The observed values of γ are of the expected magnitude, but often do not agree very closely with the value γ_f calculated for free electrons of mass m. From (32) and (47) we have, per mole,

$$\gamma_f = \tfrac{1}{3}\pi^2 \mathfrak{D}(\epsilon_F) k_B{}^2 = \frac{\pi^2 k_B{}^2 m N_0}{\hbar^2 (3\pi^2 N/V)^{2/3}}, \tag{51}$$

where N_0 is Avogadro's number and N/V is the number of conduction electrons per unit volume. It is common practice to express the ratio of the experimental to the free electron values of γ as a ratio of a **thermal effective mass** m_{th}^* to the electron mass m, where m_{th}^* is defined by the relation

$$\gamma_{\exp}/\gamma_f \equiv m_{th}^*/m. \tag{52}$$

Values of $\gamma_{\exp}/\gamma_f$ for three alkali metals[6] are given below:

	K	Rb	Cs
$\gamma_{\exp}/\gamma_f$	1.25	1.26	1.43

The theoretical explanation of these numbers is not entirely clear at present. Three separate corrections to the mass are involved: from the periodic potential of the lattice as discussed in Chapters 9 and 10, from interactions of the conduction electrons among themselves, and from interactions of the conduction electrons with phonons. Calculations[7] carried out for Na, Al, and Pb suggest that for these metals the contribution to the thermal effective mass from electron-phonon interactions may dominate those from the periodic lattice potential and from electron-electron interactions. The electron-phonon coupling tends to increase the effective mass of the electron: as the electron moves, a local distortion of the ions of the lattice moves with it. The calculated values of the mass increase from this source are:

	Na	Al	Pb
$\left(\dfrac{\delta m}{m}\right)_{el\text{-}ph}$	0.18	0.49	1.05

[6] W. H. Lien and N. E. Phillips, Phys. Rev. **133**, A1370 (1964).

[7] N. W. Ashcroft and J. W. Wilkins, Physics Letters **14**, 285 (1965).

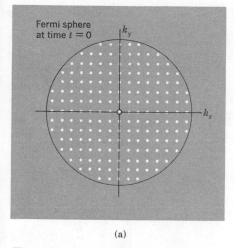
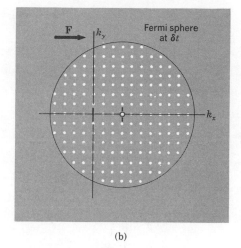

(a)   (b)

Figure 10   (a) The Fermi sphere encloses the occupied electron states in k space in the ground state of the electron gas. The net momentum is zero, because for every occupied state **k** there is an occupied state at −**k**. (b) Under the influence of a constant force **F** acting for a time interval δt every state has its **k** vector increased by $\delta k = F\delta t/\hbar$. This is equivalent to a displacement of the whole Fermi sphere by δk. The total momentum is $N\hbar\delta k$, if there are N electrons present. The application of the force increases the energy of the system by $N(\hbar\delta k)^2/2m$.

ELECTRICAL CONDUCTIVITY AND OHM'S LAW

The momentum of a free electron is related to the wavevector by (27):

$$\mathbf{p} = \hbar\mathbf{k}, \tag{53}$$

In an electric field **E** the force **F** on the electron[8] is −e**E**, so that Newton's second law of motion becomes

$$\mathbf{F} = \frac{d\mathbf{p}}{dt} = \hbar\frac{d\mathbf{k}}{dt} = -e\mathbf{E}. \tag{54}$$

In the absence of collisions the Fermi sphere (Fig. 10) in k space is displaced uniformly by an applied electric field: If the field is applied at time $t = 0$ to an electron gas which fills the Fermi sphere centered at the origin of k space, then at a later time δt, the sphere will be displaced to a new center at

$$\delta\mathbf{k} = \mathbf{F} \cdot \delta t/\hbar. \tag{55}$$

Because of collisions of electrons with impurities, lattice imperfections, and phonons, the displaced sphere may be maintained in a steady state in an electric field. The effects of the collisions on the distribution after the applied

---

[8] The charge on the proton is written as e.

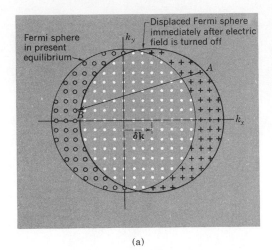
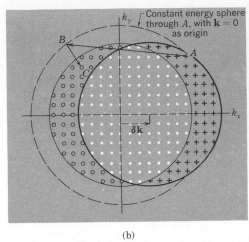

(a)   (b)

Figure 11 (a) When the applied force is turned off, collision processes tend to return the system to the ground state. We need to transfer electrons from those filled states marked with crosses ($+$) to those empty states marked with circles ($\circ$). An electron at A can make a transition to an empty state, say B, by the emission of a phonon of suitable wavevector and frequency. (b) Elastic scattering of an electron at A by a static imperfection or impurity can carry the electron to any point such as B which lies on the sphere of constant energy ϵ_A. Elastic scattering will reduce the total momentum to zero by redistributing the occupied states ($+$), but phonon processes such as $B \to C$ are needed to return the distribution to the ground state.

field is switched off are shown in Fig. 11. If collision time is τ, the displacement of the Fermi sphere in the steady state is

$$\delta \mathbf{k} = \mathbf{F}\tau/\hbar. \tag{56}$$

This displacement gives every electron an incremental momentum $\hbar\,\delta\mathbf{k} = \mathbf{F}\tau$ and an incremental velocity

$$\delta\mathbf{v} = \mathbf{F}\tau/m = -e\mathbf{E}\tau/m. \tag{57}$$

If there are n electrons of charge $q = -e$ per unit volume, the electric current density is

$$\mathbf{j} = nq\,\delta\mathbf{v} = ne^2\tau\mathbf{E}/m, \tag{58}$$

using (57). This is in the form of Ohm's law. The electrical conductivity σ is defined by $\mathbf{j} = \sigma\mathbf{E}$, so that

$$\sigma = ne^2\tau/m. \tag{59}$$

The electrical resistivity ρ is defined as the reciprocal of the conductivity, so that

$$\rho = 1/\sigma = m/ne^2\tau. \tag{60}$$

It is easy to understand the result (59) for the conductivity. We expect the charge transported to be proportional to the charge density ne; the factor

e/m enters because the acceleration in a given electric field is proportional to e and inversely proportional to the mass m; and the time τ describes the free time during which the field acts on the carrier (We suppose that the next collision removes all memory of the drift velocity.)

It is instructive to use (59) and the observed conductivity to estimate the order of magnitude of the relaxation time τ. We consider copper at room temperature. The handbook value of the conductivity σ is 6×10^5 (ohm-cm)$^{-1}$. This value is in practical units. To convert to esu we must multiply by $(10)^{-1}(3 \times 10^{10})(300) = 9 \times 10^{11}$. The factor $(10)^{-1}$ converts current to absolute amperes, and the factor 3×10^{10} converts to statamperes. The factor 300 is involved in the conversion of volts/cm to statvolts/cm.

$$\frac{\sigma(\text{esu})}{\sigma(\text{practical})} = \frac{j(\text{esu})}{j(\text{practical})} \frac{E(\text{practical})}{E(\text{esu})} = (3 \times 10^9)(300). \quad (61)$$

In these conversions we have taken the value of the velocity of light to be 3×10^{10} cm/sec. For Cu at room temperature $\sigma(\text{esu}) \cong (6 \times 10^5)(9 \times 10^{11}) \cong 5 \times 10^{17}$ sec^{-1}, where in esu the conductivity has the dimensions of a frequency.

In the metal each atom of copper contributes one valence electron to the conduction band, according to all evidence. The concentration n of conduction electrons is the number of copper atoms per unit volume, or the Avogadro number divided by the molar volume. The molar volume is the molecular weight divided by the density, or $63.5/8.94 = 7.1$ cm^3 for copper. Hence $n = 6.02 \times 10^{23}/7.1 = 8.5 \times 10^{22}$ cm^{-3}, and

$$\tau = \sigma m/ne^2 \approx (5 \times 10^{17})(9 \times 10^{-28})/(9 \times 10^{22})(5 \times 10^{-10})^2$$
$$\approx 2 \times 10^{-14} \text{ sec.}$$

It is possible to obtain crystals of copper so pure that their conductivity at liquid helium temperatures (4°K) is nearly 10^5 times that at room temperature; for these conditions $\tau \approx 2 \times 10^{-9}$ sec at 4°K.

The mean free path ℓ of a conduction electron is defined as

$$\ell = v_F \tau, \quad (62)$$

where v_F is the velocity at the Fermi surface. We see from Fig. 11 that all collisions involve only electrons near the Fermi surface. From Table 1 we have $v_F = 1.56 \times 10^8$ cm/sec for Cu; thus the mean free path is

$$\ell(300°K) \approx 3 \times 10^{-6} \text{ cm}; \qquad \ell(4°K) \approx 0.3 \text{ cm.}$$

It is of interest to measure the mean free path directly, for such an experiment offers a rough check on value of the concentration n of conduction electrons. In one experiment, Reynolds and Stilwell[9] (Fig. 12) measured

[9] F. W. Reynolds and G. R. Stilwell, Phys. Rev. **88**, 418 (1952).

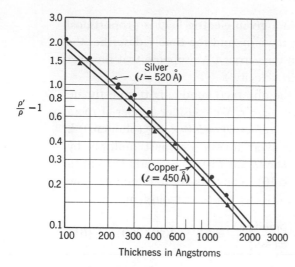

Figure 12 Experimental resistivity of Cu and Ag films at room temperature, with curves calculated from theory to obtain approximate values of mean free paths. Here ρ' is the resistivity in the film; ρ is the bulk resistivity. (After Reynolds and Stilwell.)

the resistivity of good films of copper and silver as a function of the thickness of the film. The resistivity has two contributions, one from collisions in the bulk of the material and another from diffuse scattering of the electrons at the surface of the film. In thick specimens the bulk scattering is dominant; in thin films the surface scattering is dominant. The theory of the combined scattering has been worked out by K. Fuchs[10] and is in good agreement with the observations if the bulk mean free path is taken to be 450 Å in copper. This is in satisfactory agreement with our rough estimate. The results of more careful calculations of ℓ from the bulk resistivity at room temperature give $\ell(\mathrm{Cu}) = 420$ Å and $\ell(\mathrm{Ag}) = 570$ Å. The agreement with Fig. 12 supports the model of the Fermi gas of conduction electrons.

Experimental Electrical Resistivity of Metals

The electrical resistivity of most metals is dominated at room temperature ($300°K$) by collisions of the conduction electrons with lattice phonons and at liquid helium temperature ($4°K$) by collisions with impurity atoms and mechanical imperfections in the lattice (Fig. 13).

The resistivity of a metal containing impurity atoms may usually be written in the form

$$\rho = \rho_L + \rho_i, \qquad (63)$$

where ρ_L is the resistivity caused by thermal motion of the lattice, and ρ_i is the resistivity caused by scattering of the electron waves by impurity atoms which disturb the periodicity of the lattice. If the concentration of impurity atoms is small, ρ_i is found to be independent of temperature; this statement is known as **Matthiessen's rule**. The **residual resistivity** is the extrapolated

[10] K. Fuchs, Proc. Cambridge Phil. Soc. **34**, 100 (1938).

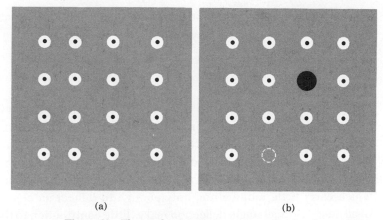

(a)   (b)

Figure 13 Electrical resistivity in most metals arises from collisions of electrons with irregularities in the lattice, as in (a) by phonons and in (b) by impurities and vacant lattice sites.

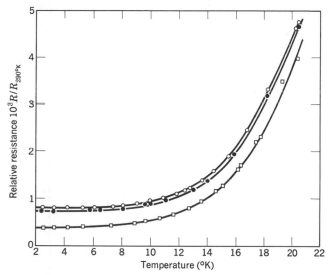

Figure 14 Resistance of sodium below 20°K, as measured on three specimens by MacDonald and Mendelssohn, Proc. Roy. Soc. (London) **A202**, 103 (1950).

resistivity at $0°K$ and is equivalent to ρ_i, because ρ_L vanishes as $T \rightarrow 0$. Measurements on sodium in Fig. 14 show that the residual resistance may vary from specimen to specimen, whereas the resistivity caused by thermal motion is independent of the specimen. The **resistivity ratio** of a specimen is usually defined as the ratio of its resistivity at room temperature to its resistivity at liquid helium temperature. In exceptional specimens the ratio may be as high as 10^4 or even 10^5; in certain alloys the ratio may be of the order of 2.

The lattice or phonon contribution to the electrical resistivity depends on temperature in simple metals essentially as

$$\rho_L \propto T \qquad \text{for } T \gg \Theta;$$
$$\rho_L \propto T^5 \qquad \text{for } T \ll \Theta.$$

The direct proportionality to T at high temperatures follows because the probability of scattering of an electron is proportional to the number of phonons. (At high temperatures the number of phonons is a measure of the mean square local strain.) At low temperatures the number of phonons varies as T^3, and the excited phonon spectrum consists of long wavelength phonons which carry little momentum, only enough to deflect an electron through a small angle. A small-angle deflection makes little contribution to the resistivity.[11]

It has been found by Grüneisen that the observed temperature dependence of the resistivity is described quite well at all temperatures by the semi-empirical formula $\rho \propto TG(\Theta/T)$, where

$$G(x) = x^{-4} \int_0^x \frac{s^5 \, ds}{(e^s - 1)(1 - e^{-s})} \tag{64}$$

The formula gives proportionality to T for $T \gg \Theta$ and to T^5 for $T \ll \Theta$, as required by theory. Figure 15 shows that the Grüneisen relation (64) works quite well for the metals indicated there; at quite low temperatures, however, departures from the T^5 law are usually observed. Reference to detailed theoretical calculations of the conductivity of metals are given in the review by Bardeen.[12]

THERMAL CONDUCTIVITY OF METALS

In Chapter 6 we found an expression

$$K = \tfrac{1}{3}Cv\ell \tag{65}$$

for the thermal conductivity by particles of velocity v, heat capacity C per unit volume, and mean free path ℓ. For a Fermi gas using (48) for the heat capacity, and with $\epsilon_F = \tfrac{1}{2}mv_F^2$:

$$K_{el} = \frac{\pi^2}{3} \cdot \frac{nk_B^2 T}{mv_F^2} \cdot v_F \cdot \ell = \frac{\pi^2 nk_B^2 T\tau}{3m}. \tag{66}$$

Here $\ell = v_F\tau$, and n is the electron concentration.

Do the electrons or the phonons carry the greater part of the heat current

---

[11] For a more accurate explanation of the T^5 region, see J. Ziman, *Electrons and phonons*, p. 365.

[12] J. Bardeen, J. Appl. Phys. **11**, 88 (1940).

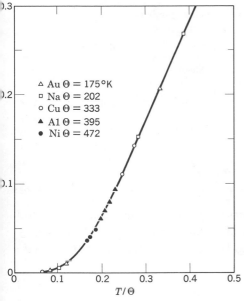

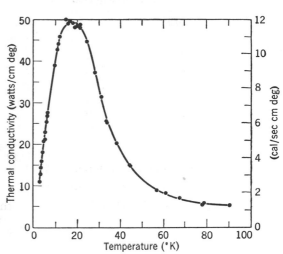

Figure 15 Theoretical (Grüneisen) temperature variation of electrical resistance, and experimental values of various metals. (After Bardeen.)

Figure 16 The thermal conductivity of copper, after Berman and MacDonald.

in a metal? At room temperature normal pure metals tend to have values of the thermal conductivity one or two orders of magnitude higher than for dielectric solids, so that under these conditions the electrons must carry almost all the heat current. Some values of the thermal conductivity K near room temperature in cal/cm-sec-deg follow:

Al	Cu	Na	Ag	NaCl	KCl	Chrome alum
0.54	0.94	0.33	1.00	0.017	0.017	0.0045

In pure metals the electronic contribution is dominant at all temperatures. In impure metals or in disordered alloys the phonon contribution may be comparable with the electronic contribution.

Measurements on copper are shown in Fig. 16. Experimental curves for many metals at low temperatures are given by H. M. Rosenberg, Phil. Trans. Roy. Soc. (London) **A247,** 441–497 (1955), and R. L. Powell and W. A. Blanpied, "Thermal conductivities of metals and alloys at low temperatures," National Bureau of Standards Circular 556.

Ratio of Thermal to Electrical Conductivity

The **Wiedemann-Franz law** states that for metals at not too low temperatures the ratio of the thermal conductivity to the electrical conductivity was directly proportional to the temperature, with the value of constant of pro-

Table 3   Experimental Lorenz numbers

Metal	$L \times 10^8$ watt-ohms/deg^2 0°C	100°C	Metal	$L \times 10^8$ watt-ohms/deg^2 0°C	100°C
Ag	2.31	2.37	Pb	2.47	2.56
Au	2.35	2.40	Pt	2.51	2.60
Cd	2.42	2.43	Sn	2.52	2.49
Cu	2.23	2.33	W	3.04	3.20
Ir	2.49	2.49	Zn	2.31	2.33
Mo	2.61	2.79			

portionality independent of the particular metal. This result was most important in the history of the theory of metals, for it supported the picture of an electron gas. It can be explained by using (59) for σ and (66) for K:

$$\frac{K}{\sigma} = \frac{\pi^2 k_B{}^2 T n \tau / 3m}{ne^2\tau/m} = \frac{\pi^2}{3}\left(\frac{k_B}{e}\right)^2 T. \tag{67}$$

The **Lorenz number** L is defined as

$$L \equiv K/\sigma T, \tag{68}$$

and according to (67) should have the value

$$L = \frac{\pi^2}{3}\left(\frac{k_B}{e}\right)^2 = 2.72 \times 10^{-13} \text{ esu/deg}^2 = 2.45 \times 10^{-8} \text{ watt-ohm/deg}^2, \tag{69}$$

This remarkable result involves neither n nor m. It does not involve τ if the relaxation times are identical for electrical and thermal processes. Experimental values of L at 0°C and at 100°C as given in Table 3 are in good agreement with (69).

At low temperatures ($T \ll \Theta$) the value of L tends to decrease; for pure copper[13] near 15°K the value of L is an order of magnitude smaller than (69). The reason is attributed to a difference in the types of collisions involved in determining K and σ. For different thermal and electrical relaxation times we have

$$L = \frac{\pi^2}{3}\left(\frac{k_B}{e}\right)^2 \frac{\tau_{th}}{\tau_{el}}. \tag{70}$$

The ratio of relaxation times in (70) decreases at low temperatures, although the ratio may be of the order of unity at room temperature.

[13] R. Berman and D. K. C. MacDonald, Proc. Roy. Soc. (London) **A209**, 368 (1951); **A211**, 122 (1952).

Problems

1. **Particle in a box.** (a) Using the boundary condition $\psi = 0$ on the surface of a cube of side L, find all the wavefunctions for the first three distinct energy levels. (b) Give an expression for the energy of each level. (c) What is the degeneracy of each level? That is, what is the number of independent wavefunctions having the same energy? (Omit the electron spin from the enumeration.)

2. **Kinetic energy of electron gas.** Show that the kinetic energy of a three-dimensional gas of N free electrons at $0°K$ is

$$E_0 = \tfrac{3}{5}N\epsilon_F.$$

[The result for a one-dimensional gas is given in Eq. (13).]

3. **Pressure and bulk modulus of an electron gas.** (a) Derive a relation connecting the pressure and volume of an electron gas at $0°K$. *Hint:* Use the result of Problem 2 and the relation between ϵ_F and electron concentration. The result may be written as $P = \tfrac{2}{3}(E_0/V)$. (b) Show that the bulk modulus $B = -V(\partial P/\partial V)$ of an electron gas at $0°K$ is $B = \tfrac{5}{3}P = 10E_0/9V$. (c) Estimate for lithium, using Table 1, the value of the electron gas contribution to B and compare it with the experimental bulk modulus, using Table 4.2 and Eq. (1.29).

4. **Nonlinear conductivity region.** (a) Using the relaxation time for electrons in Cu at room temperature, estimate the magnitude of the electric field intensity required to make the field-induced shift δk in the Fermi sphere equal to 0.01 of the wavevector k_F at the Fermi surface. (b) What is the current density at this electric field? (For stronger fields we might expect nonlinear effects to modify the form of Ohm's law. Such effects are of little importance in normal metals, but they can be important in semiconductors where they are known as "hot electron" effects.)

5. **Chemical potential.** Find an exact transcendental equation for the chemical potential $\mu(T)$ of a Fermi gas in two dimensions. *Note:* The density of states of a free electron gas in two dimensions is independent of energy: $\mathcal{D}(\epsilon) = m/\pi\hbar^2$ per unit area of specimen.

References

H. M. Rosenberg, *Low temperature solid state physics*, Oxford, 1963, Chaps. 4 and 5.
J. M. Ziman, *Electrons and phonons*, Oxford, 1960, Chap. 9.

8

Free Electron Fermi Gas II

In this chapter we complete the treatment of the most important properties of the free electron gas. Our object is to get a good physical feeling for the behavior of free electrons before we go on in Chapter 9 to treat the modifications introduced by interactions of the conduction electrons with the crystal lattice.

ELECTRICAL CONDUCTIVITY AT HIGH FREQUENCIES

By combining the arguments of (7.54) to (7.56) we may describe the displacement of the Fermi sphere in $\mathbf{k}$ space by an applied force $\mathbf{F}$:

$$\hbar\left(\frac{d}{dt} + \frac{1}{\tau}\right)\delta\mathbf{k} = \mathbf{F}, \tag{1}$$

where τ is the collision time or relaxation time. In the steady state $\delta\mathbf{k} = $ constant, so that (1) reduces to $\delta\mathbf{k} = \mathbf{F}\tau/\hbar$, which is just (7.56). In the absence of collisions $\tau \to \infty$, and we retrieve (7.54). In terms of the incremental velocity $\delta\mathbf{v}$ related to $\delta\mathbf{k}$ by[1] $m\,\delta\mathbf{v} \equiv \hbar\,\delta\mathbf{k}$, we may rewrite (1) as

$$m\left(\frac{d}{dt} + \frac{1}{\tau}\right)\delta\mathbf{v}(t) = \mathbf{F}, \tag{2}$$

which is the equation of motion for the average or drift velocity of a gas with collision time τ.

The force on an electron in an alternating electric field is

$$\mathbf{F} = -e\mathbf{E}e^{-i\omega t}. \tag{3}$$

If we look for a solution of (2) of the form $\delta\mathbf{v}(t) = \delta\mathbf{v}\,e^{-i\omega t}$ we find

$$m\left(-i\omega + \frac{1}{\tau}\right)\delta\mathbf{v} = -e\mathbf{E}, \tag{4}$$

or

$$\delta\mathbf{v} = -\frac{e\tau/m}{1 - i\omega\tau}\,\mathbf{E}. \tag{5}$$

The current density is

$$\mathbf{j} = nq\,\delta\mathbf{v} = \frac{ne^2\tau}{m(1 - i\omega\tau)}\,\mathbf{E}, \tag{6}$$

---

[1] This follows from the de Broglie relation $mv = \hbar k$.

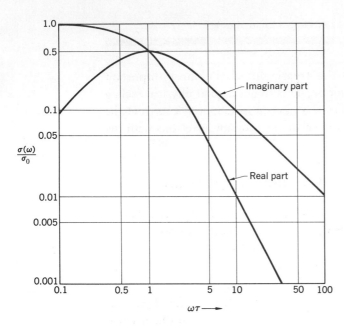

Figure 1 Log-log plot of real and imaginary parts of the conductivity as a function of $\omega\tau$, where ω is the angular frequency and τ is the relaxation time. Here σ_0 is the dc conductivity.

where n is the electron concentration and $q = -e$ is the charge on the electron. The electrical conductivity is

$$\sigma(\omega) = \frac{ne^2\tau}{m(1 - i\omega\tau)} = \sigma_0 \cdot \frac{1 + i\omega\tau}{1 + (\omega\tau)^2}, \tag{7}$$

as plotted in Fig. 1; here $\sigma_0 = ne^2\tau/m$ is the dc conductivity (7.59).

At high frequencies such that $\omega\tau \gg 1$ we have

$$\sigma(\omega) \cong \sigma_0 \left(\frac{1}{(\omega\tau)^2} + \frac{i}{\omega\tau}\right) = \frac{ne^2}{m\omega^2\tau} + i\frac{ne^2}{m\omega}; \tag{8}$$

here the imaginary term is dominant and is independent of τ.

When the imaginary term in $\sigma(\omega)$ is dominant it may be convenient to express the result as a complex dielectric constant rather than as a complex conductivity. If $\delta\mathbf{r}$ is the spatial displacement of an electron, then $\mathbf{P} = -ne\delta\mathbf{r}$ is the polarization, defined in Chapter 12 as the dipole moment/volume. We rewrite (2) as

$$m\left(\frac{d^2}{dt^2} + \frac{1}{\tau}\frac{d}{dt}\right)\delta\mathbf{r} = -e\mathbf{E}, \tag{9}$$

or

$$m(-\omega^2 - i\omega/\tau)\,\delta\mathbf{r} = -e\mathbf{E}; \qquad \mathbf{P} = -\frac{ne^2/m}{\omega^2 + i\omega/\tau}\,\mathbf{E}. \tag{10}$$

Now the dielectric constant $\epsilon \equiv 1 + 4\pi P/E$, so that

$$\boxed{\epsilon(\omega) = 1 - \frac{4\pi ne^2/m}{\omega^2 + i\omega/\tau}.} \tag{11}$$

This is the dielectric constant of a free electron gas.

For $\tau \to \infty$ the dielectric constant is positive and real if

$$\omega^2 > 4\pi n e^2/m. \tag{12}$$

Electromagnetic waves cannot propagate in a medium with a negative dielectric constant because the wavevector is imaginary[2] and the wave decays exponentially. Waves incident on such a medium are totally reflected. An electron gas acts as a high-pass filter: the gas is transparent when the frequency is high enough to satisfy the inequality (12). We denote the **cutoff frequency** ω_p by

$$\omega_p \equiv (4\pi n e^2/m)^{1/2}. \tag{13}$$

We see that $\epsilon(\omega_p) = 0$.

The cutoff frequency is also called the **plasma frequency** for reasons discussed below. The associated wavelength (in vacuum) is $\lambda_p \equiv 2\pi c/\omega_p$. Values of ω_p and $\lambda_p \equiv 2\pi c/\omega_p$ for electron concentrations of interest in solids are given below. A wave will propagate in the medium only if its free space wavelength is less than λ_p. (A magnetic field may alter the situation drastically.)

n in electrons/cm^3	10^{22}	10^{18}	10^{14}	10^{10}
ω_p in sec^{-1}	5.7×10^{15}	5.7×10^{13}	5.7×10^{11}	5.7×10^9
λ_p	3300 Å	33 μ	0.33 cm	33 cm

Transparency of Alkali Metals in the Ultraviolet

One consequence of the preceding discussion of the dielectric constant is that the alkali metals should be transparent to ultraviolet light. The effect was discovered by Wood[3] and explained by Zener.[4] A comparison of calculated and observed cutoff wavelengths is given in Table 1.

Table 1   Ultraviolet transmission of alkalis, in Å
(A metal film is transparent for $\lambda < \lambda_p$)

	Li	Na	K	Rb	Cs
λ_p, calculated, mass m	1550	2090	2870	3220	3620
λ_p, observed	1550	2100	3150	3400	–

[2] The dispersion relation for an electromagnetic wave was shown in Chapter 5 to be $\omega^2\epsilon(\omega) = c^2k^2$; if ϵ is negative then k must be imaginary.

[3] R. W. Wood, Phys. Rev. **44**, 353 (1933); R. W. Wood and C. Lukens, Phys. Rev. **54**, 332 (1938); H. E. Ives and H. B. Briggs, J. Opt. Soc. Am. **26**, 238 (1936); **27**, 181 (1937). For a review of the optical properties of metals, see M. P. Givens, *Solid state physics* **6**, 313 (1958).

[4] C. Zener, Nature **132**, 968 (1933).

Anomalous Skin Effect

The standard calculation of the **skin depth** for the penetration of rf radiation into a thick plane slab of metal proceeds from the Maxwell equations in the form

$$\text{curl } \mathbf{H} = \frac{4\pi}{c}\sigma\mathbf{E}; \qquad \text{curl } \mathbf{E} = -\frac{1}{c}\frac{\partial \mathbf{H}}{\partial t}. \qquad (14)$$

We have assumed that the frequency is low enough ($\omega \ll \sigma$) to neglect the $\partial\mathbf{D}/\partial t$ term in the first Maxwell equation; we have also assumed that the material is nonmagnetic, so that $\mathbf{B} \equiv \mathbf{H}$. From (14) we have

$$\nabla^2\mathbf{E} = \frac{4\pi\sigma}{c^2}\frac{\partial\mathbf{E}}{\partial t}. \qquad (15)$$

If $\mathbf{E} = \hat{\mathbf{x}}E_0 e^{-i\omega t}e^{ikz}$, then (15) yields

$$k^2 = i(4\pi\sigma\omega/c^2); \qquad k = (1+i)(2\pi\sigma\omega/c^2)^{1/2}, \qquad (16)$$

using the root $\sqrt{i} = (1+i)/\sqrt{2}$. The spatial variation of $\mathbf{E}$ inside the metal is, for σ real,

$$E_x \propto e^{-z/\delta_0}e^{iz/\delta_0}; \qquad \delta_0 \equiv \left(\frac{c^2}{2\pi\sigma\omega}\right)^{1/2}, \qquad (17)$$

where δ_0 defines the **classical skin depth**. If the conductivity σ is not real in the frequency region of interest we define δ_0 as the reciprocal of the imaginary part of k in (16).

Values of the classical skin depth calculated for copper at room temperature for several wavelengths are given in Table 2. In the calculations we used the dc conductivity $\sigma_0 \cong 5 \times 10^{17}$ sec^{-1} for which $\tau \cong 2 \times 10^{-14}$ sec, as estimated in Chapter 7. (At $\lambda = 10^{-4}$ cm we see that $\omega\tau \gg 1$, so that σ is complex and it is really not correct to use the dc conductivity.)

The calculation of the classical skin effect is based on the implicit assumption that the mean free path of the conduction electrons is short in comparison with the skin depth: we calculate the current density $\mathbf{j}(\mathbf{r})$ as a function of the *local* value $\mathbf{E}(\mathbf{r})$ of the electric field, as in $\mathbf{j}(\mathbf{r}) = \sigma\mathbf{E}(\mathbf{r})$. This is legitimate only if the electric field does not vary rapidly in space over the distance of the electron mean free path. In reasonably pure metals this is not true at liquid helium temperatures, even at microwave frequencies. Quick numerical

Table 2   Classical skin depth δ_0 in Cu at 300°K
($\sigma_0 = 5 \times 10^{17}$ sec^{-1}; $\tau \cong 2 \times 10^{-14}$ sec)

Wavelength λ, cm	1	10^{-2}	10^{-4}
Angular frequency ω, sec^{-1}	1.9×10^{11}	1.9×10^{13}	1.9×10^{15}
$\omega\tau$	4×10^{-3}	4×10^{-1}	40
δ_0 in Å	4000	400	40

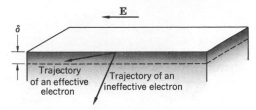

Figure 2 The electrons which are accelerated most effectively by the rf electric field are those which complete their free path within the skin depth. The proportion of effective electrons is of the order of δ/ℓ, where δ is the skin depth and ℓ is the mean free path.

estimates lead to mean free paths perhaps 10^4 longer than the classical skin depth. We are therefore faced with a nonlocal problem, an entirely new kind of conductivity problem. Now it is no longer adequate to use a conductivity $\sigma(\omega)$; in a complete theory[5] we need the conductivity $\sigma(\omega, \mathbf{k})$ as a function of ω and the wavevector $\mathbf{k}$.

The region in which $\ell \gtrsim \delta_0$ is known as the region of the **anomalous skin effect**. If $\ell \gg \delta_0$ we have the extreme anomalous skin effect, for which a qualitative description has been given by Pippard. Those electrons contribute most to the current which spend their entire mean free path in the skin depth (Fig. 2). The concentration n_{eff} of "effective" electrons in the extreme anomalous limit is of the order of

$$n_{\text{eff}} \approx (\delta/\ell)n \qquad (18)$$

where n is the total electron concentration, δ is the actual skin depth, and ℓ is the mean free path. The effective conductivity (for $\omega\tau \ll 1$) is arrived at by replacing n by n_{eff} in free conductivity:

$$\sigma_{\text{eff}} \approx \frac{\delta}{\ell}\sigma_0 = \frac{\delta}{\ell}\frac{ne^2\tau}{m} = \frac{\delta}{\ell}\cdot\frac{ne^2\ell}{mv_F} = \frac{ne^2\delta}{mv_F}. \qquad (19)$$

It is remarkable that σ_{eff} is independent of the mean free path in this limit.

It is plausible to expect the actual skin depth in the extreme anomalous region to be given by the obvious extension of (17):

$$\delta \approx \left(\frac{c^2}{2\pi\sigma_{\text{eff}}\omega}\right)^{1/2} \approx \left(\frac{c^2 mv_F}{2\pi ne^2\delta\,\omega}\right)^{1/2}, \qquad (20)$$

whence

$$\delta \approx \left(\frac{c^2 mv_F}{2\pi ne^2\omega}\right)^{1/3}, \qquad (21)$$

independent of ℓ. A determination of the skin depth in the extreme anomalous limit enables us to measure the electron velocity at the Fermi surface.

[5] G. E. H. Reuter and E. H. Sondheimer, Proc. Roy. Soc. (London) **A195**, 336 (1948); see also *QTS*, Chap. 16.

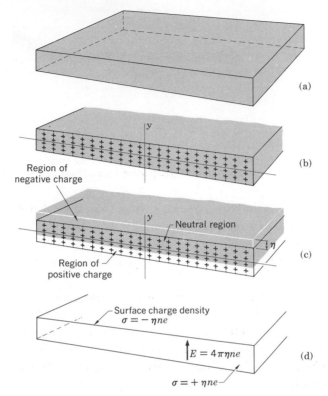

Figure 3 In (a) is shown a thin slab or film of a metal. A cross-section is shown in (b), with the positive ion cores indicated by $+$ signs and the electron sea indicated by the gray background. The slab is electrically neutral. In (c) the negative charge has been displaced upward uniformly by a small distance η, shown exaggerated in the figure. As shown in (d), this displacement establishes a surface charge density $-\eta ne$ on the upper surface of the slab and $+\eta ne$ on the lower surface, where n is the electron concentration. An electric field $E = 4\pi\eta ne$ is produced inside the slab. This field tends to restore the electron sea to its equilibrium position (b).

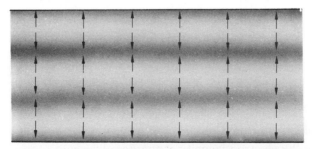

Figure 4 A plasma oscillation of finite wavelength. The arrows indicate the direction of displacement of the electrons.

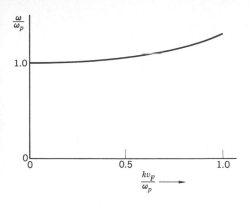

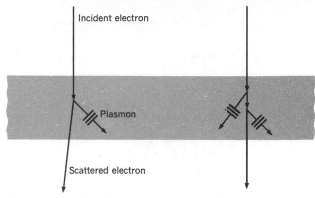

Figure 5 Theoretical plasmon dispersion relation, ω versus k. Here ω_p is the plasmon frequency for $k \to 0$ and v_F is the electron velocity at the Fermi surface.

Figure 6 Creation of a plasmon in a metal film by inelastic scattering of an electron. The incident electron typically has an energy 1 to 10 kev; the plasmon energy may be of the order of 10 ev. An event is also shown in which two plasmons are created.

PLASMONS

A plasma oscillation is a collective longitudinal excitation of an electron gas. A **plasmon** is a quantized plasma oscillation. The excitation is most simply described by consideration of a uniform displacement of an electron gas in a thin metallic slab (Fig. 3). The electron gas is moved as a whole with respect to the positive ion background. A displacement of amplitude η creates an electric field $E = 4\pi ne\eta$ which acts as a restoring force. The equation of motion of a unit volume of the electron gas is

$$nm \frac{d^2\eta}{dt^2} = -neE = -4\pi n^2 e^2 \eta, \tag{22}$$

or

$$\frac{d^2\eta}{dt^2} + \omega_p{}^2\eta = 0; \qquad \omega_p = \left(\frac{4\pi ne^2}{m} \right)^{1/2}. \tag{23}$$

This is the equation of motion of a simple harmonic oscillator of frequency ω_p, called the **plasma frequency**. The expression for ω_p is identical with (13), which arose in quite a different connection. The theoretical discussion of plasmon excitations in metals is due largely to Bohm and Pines.

A plasma oscillation of small wavevector (Fig. 4) will have approximately the frequency (23). It turns out[6] that the wavevector dependence of the plasmon dispersion relation is given by

$$\omega \cong \omega_p \left(1 + \frac{3k^2 v_F{}^2}{10\omega_p{}^2} + \cdots \right), \tag{24}$$

as plotted in Fig. 5.

It is possible to excite a plasmon by passing an electron through a thin metallic film (Fig. 6) or by reflecting an electron from the film. The Coulomb field of the electron couples with the electrostatic field fluctuations of the plasma oscillations. The reflected or transmitted electron will show an energy

[6] D. Pines, *Elementary excitations in solids*, Benjamin, 1963, Chap. 3.

233

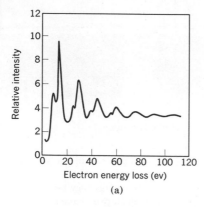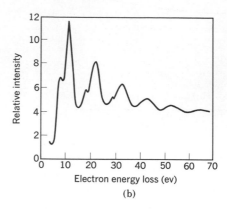

Figure 7 Energy loss spectra for electrons reflected from films of (a) aluminum and (b) magnesium, for primary electron energies of 2020 ev. The twelve loss peaks observed in Al are made up of combinations of 10.3 and 15.3 ev losses, where the 10.3 ev loss is due to surface plasmons (see Prob. 6) and the 15.3 ev loss is due to volume plasmons, as described by Eq. (23). The ten loss peaks observed in Mg are made up of combinations of 7.1 ev surface plasmons and 10.6 ev volume plasmons. [After C. J. Powell and J. B. Swan, Phys. Rev. **115**, 869 (1959); **116**, 81 (1959).]

Table 3 Volume plasmon energies in metals

Metal	Observed $\hbar\omega_p$ in ev	Calculated $\hbar\omega_p$ in ev		Reference
		Free electron, Eq. (23)	Corrected for core polarization	
Li	7.12	8.02	7.96	a
Na	5.71	5.95	5.58	a
	5.85			b
K	3.72	4.29	3.86	a
	3.87			c
Mg	10.6	10.9		d
Al	15.3	15.8		e

a. C. Kunz, Physics Letters **15**, 312 (1965).

b. J. B. Swan, Phys. Rev. **135**, A1467 (1964).

c. J. L. Robins and F. E. Best, Proc. Phys. Soc. (London) **79**, 110 (1962).

d. C. J. Powell and J. B. Swan, Phys. Rev. **116**, 81 (1959).

e. C. J. Powell and J. B. Swan, Phys. Rev. **115**, 869 (1959). This paper contains abundant references to the earlier experimental literature.

loss equal to integral multiples of the plasmon energy. Experimental energy loss spectra for Al and Mg are shown in Fig. 7. A comparison of observed and calculated values of plasmon energies is given in Table 3; references to further data are given in citations (c) and (e). It is even possible to excite plasmons in dielectric films. Photons from the decay[7] of plasma oscillations in metal films following excitation by electron bombardment have been detected.

A plasma oscillation may be viewed as a kind of longitudinal optical phonon in which the electron gas plays the part of the negative ions. Because a gas has no shear elastic modulus we may take the transverse phonon frequency to be zero. Then (5.46) reduces to

$$\omega_L{}^2 = 4\pi n e^2/m = \omega_p{}^2. \tag{25}$$

In (25) we use the electron mass m because the reduced mass

$$\frac{1}{\mu} = \frac{1}{m} + \frac{1}{M} \simeq \frac{1}{m} \tag{26}$$

Electrostatic Screening

If we immerse a point test charge q at rest in a metal, the electron concentration near the test charge will be perturbed in such a way that the electric field of the charge is essentially canceled by the induced disturbance in the electron concentration. We say that the test charge is screened by the electron gas. There is a **screening length** within which the screening tends to be ineffective and outside which the screening becomes progressively more complete.

We give now an approximate treatment of the static screening problem. The Poisson equation of electrostatics is

$$\nabla^2\varphi = -4\pi[\rho(\mathbf{r}) - \rho_0] = 4\pi e[n(\mathbf{r}) - n_0], \tag{27}$$

where $\varphi(\mathbf{r})$ is the electrostatic potential; $[\rho(\mathbf{r}) - \rho_0]$ is the deviation from uniform charge density; and $[n(\mathbf{r}) - n_0]$ is the deviation from uniform electron concentration. We now make the Thomas-Fermi approximation: we assume that $n(\mathbf{r})$ is related to the maximum electronic kinetic energy by an extension of (7.32):[8]

$$\epsilon_F + e\varphi(\mathbf{r}) = \frac{\hbar^2}{2m} [3\pi^2 n(\mathbf{r})]^{2/3}, \tag{28}$$

[7] R. A. Ferrell, Phys. Rev. **111**, 1214 (1958); E. T. Arakawa, R. J. Herickhoff, and R. D. Birkhoff, Phys. Rev. Letters **12**, 319 (1964).

[8] This is a crucial step. It says that if we know the maximum kinetic energy of a Fermi gas in the ground state, then we also know the electron concentration. The assumption is good only for potentials which vary slowly in comparison with an electron wavelength.

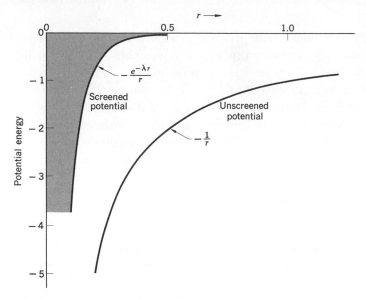

Figure 8a Comparison of screened and unscreened Coulomb potentials for a unit positive charge embedded in a Fermi gas of electrons. The screening charge density has the same form as the screened potential, as we see from (31). The screening length $1/\lambda$ has been taken as equal to unity.

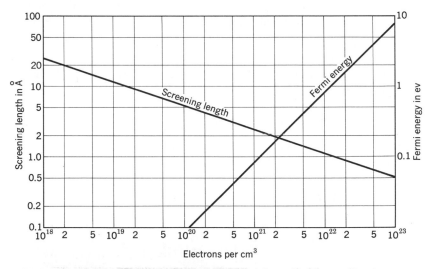

Figure 8b Log-log plot of the screening length $1/\lambda$ on the Thomas-Fermi model as a function of electron concentration, from Eq. (31). The Fermi energy is also plotted from Eq. (7.32).

where ϵ_F is a constant defined by $\epsilon_F = (\hbar^2/2m)(3\pi^2 n_0)^{2/3}$. We write (28) as

$$n(\mathbf{r}) = \frac{1}{3\pi^2}\left(\frac{2m}{\hbar^2}\right)^{3/2}[\epsilon_F + e\varphi(\mathbf{r})]^{3/2} \cong \frac{1}{3\pi^2}\left(\frac{2m}{\hbar^2}\right)^{3/2}\epsilon_F{}^{3/2}\left[1 + \frac{3e\varphi(\mathbf{r})}{2\epsilon_F}\right]$$

$$= n_0 + \tfrac{3}{2}n_0\frac{e\varphi(\mathbf{r})}{\epsilon_F}. \qquad (29)$$

This expression states that the chemical potential $\mu(\mathbf{r}) = \epsilon_F + e\varphi(\mathbf{r})$ is constant in equilibrium for each region over which $\varphi(\mathbf{r})$ is nearly constant.

Thus (27) becomes

$$\nabla^2\varphi = \lambda^2\varphi, \qquad (30)$$

where

$$\lambda \equiv (6\pi n_0 e^2/\epsilon_F)^{1/2}. \qquad (31)$$

The order of magnitude of λ is ω_p/v_F, where ω_p is given by (23) and v_F is the Fermi velocity.

We look for a potential with spherical symmetry which is a solution of

$$\left(\frac{d^2}{dr^2} + \frac{2}{r}\frac{d}{dr}\right)\varphi(r) = \lambda^2\varphi(r). \qquad (32)$$

The desired solution is

$$\boxed{\varphi(r) = \frac{qe^{-\lambda r}}{r},} \qquad (33)$$

for

$$\frac{d\varphi}{dr} = -\frac{qe^{-\lambda r}}{r}\left(\lambda + \frac{1}{r}\right); \qquad \frac{d^2\varphi}{dr^2} = \frac{qe^{-\lambda r}}{r}\left(\lambda^2 + \frac{2\lambda}{r} + \frac{2}{r^2}\right). \qquad (34)$$

Equation (33) is called the **screened Coulomb potential**; the **screening length** is defined to be $1/\lambda$ (Fig. 8a). For copper with $n_0 = 8.5 \times 10^{22}$ electrons/cm^3 we have $1/\lambda = 0.55$ Å. The screening length is plotted in Fig. 8b as a function of electron concentration. Improved calculations of screening effects are discussed in *QTS*, Chap. 6.

Electron-Electron Collisions

The interaction of an electron with a charged impurity atom or electron has a range of the order of $1/\lambda$. From numerical calculations one finds the effective cross-section with screening for collisions between electrons to be of the order of 10^{-15} cm² or 10 Å² in typical metals. The effect of screening is greatly to reduce the scattering cross-section in electron-electron collisions below the value expected from the Rutherford scattering equation for the unscreened Coulomb potential.

But the Fermi-Dirac distribution is the most important factor in reducing electron-electron scattering in metals. Figure 9 shows a typical collision between two electrons. For such a collision to occur in a Fermi sea it is necessary that initially there be electrons in the states k_1 and k_2 and initially the states k_3 and k_4 must be vacant. Otherwise the scattered electrons cannot be received in the states for which they were intended according to the kinematics of the particular collision process.

In the energy shell of width $k_B T$ about the Fermi energy ϵ_F there is a reasonable probability of finding filled and vacant states of comparable energies, as in Fig. 10a. A substantial proportion of the collisions between electrons in this shell will be allowed by the Pauli exclusion principle. Collisions of an electron in this shell with an electron deeper in the Fermi sea (Fig. 10b) are unlikely: the kinematics of energy conservation would require one or both of the final states to be in a region of the Fermi sea which is always entirely filled.

The energy shell contains roughly the fraction $k_B T/\epsilon_F$ of the total number of electrons. As *both* initial electrons must lie in or near this shell, the rate at which electron-electron collisions take place is reduced below the classical value by the square of this, which is $(k_B T/\epsilon_F)^2$, whence

$$\sigma(el\text{-}el) \approx \left(\frac{k_B T}{\epsilon_F}\right)^2 \sigma_0, \tag{35}$$

where σ_0 is the cross-section for the screened Coulomb interaction, or $\sim 10^{-15}$ cm².

At room temperature in a typical metal $k_B T/\epsilon_F$ is $\sim 10^{-2}$, so that $\sigma \sim 10^{-4}\sigma_0 \sim 10^{-19}$ cm². The mean free path for electron-electron collisions is therefore of the order

$$\ell_{el-el} \approx \frac{1}{n\sigma} \sim 10^{-4} \text{ cm} \tag{36}$$

at room temperature. This is longer than the mean free path due to electron-phonon collisions at room temperature by at least a factor of 10, so that collisions with phonons are dominant. At low temperatures collisions with the boundaries of the specimen provide the dominant scattering mechanism. At

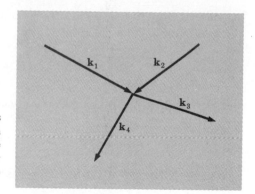

Figure 9 A collision between two electrons of wavevector k_1 and k_2. After the collision the particles have wavevector k_3 and k_4. The Pauli exclusion principle allows collisions only to final states k_3, k_4 which were vacant before the collision.

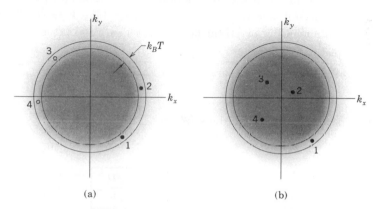

Figure 10 In (a) the electrons in initial states 1 and 2 collide. If the states 3 and 4 are initially vacant, the electrons 1 and 2 can occupy 3 and 4 after the collision. Energy and momentum are conserved. In (b) the electrons in initial states 1 and 2 have no vacant final states available which will allow energy to be conserved in the collision. States such as 3 and 4 would conserve energy and momentum, but they are already filled with other electrons.

helium temperatures $\ell_{el-el} \sim 1$ cm. We have thus explained one of the central problems of the theory of metals: the electrons move through macroscopic distances without colliding with each other.

MOTION IN MAGNETIC FIELDS

At the beginning of this chapter we considered the equation of motion for the displacement δk of a Fermi sphere of particles acted on by a force F:

$$\hbar \left(\frac{d}{dt} + \frac{1}{\tau} \right) \delta k = F. \tag{37}$$

Consider now the motion of the system in a uniform magnetic field **H**. The Lorentz force on an electron[9] is

$$\mathbf{F} = -e\left(\mathbf{E} + \frac{1}{c}\mathbf{v} \times \mathbf{H}\right). \tag{38}$$

If $m\,\delta\mathbf{v} = \hbar\,\delta\mathbf{k}$, then the equation of motion is

$$m\left(\frac{d}{dt} + \frac{1}{\tau}\right)\delta\mathbf{v} = -e\left(\mathbf{E} + \frac{1}{c}\delta\mathbf{v} \times \mathbf{H}\right), \tag{39}$$

We have written $\delta\mathbf{v}$ in the force term as the average of $\mathbf{v}$ over the Fermi sphere.

Cyclotron Frequency

Consider first the free motion of the system, with **H** parallel to the z axis. For convenience we let $\tau \to \infty$; and we take $\mathbf{E} = 0$. The equations could equally well be solved for finite τ; the condition for a well-defined resonance is that $\omega_c\tau > 1$, where ω_c is defined by (42) below. Now (39) becomes

$$m\frac{d}{dt}\delta v_x = -\frac{eH}{c}\delta v_y; \qquad m\frac{d}{dt}\delta v_y = \frac{eH}{c}\delta v_x. \tag{40}$$

These equations have the solution

$$\delta v_x = v_0\cos\omega_c t; \qquad \delta v_y = v_0\sin\omega_c t, \tag{41}$$

where

$$\boxed{\omega_c \equiv \frac{eH}{mc}.} \tag{42}$$

This is the **cyclotron frequency** for a free electron. Numerically, as in Fig. 11,

$$f_c\,(\text{Mcs}) \cong 2.80\,H\,(\text{gauss}), \tag{43}$$

with $f_c \equiv \omega_c/2\pi$. The constant v_0 in (41) is not the Fermi velocity, but is the magnitude of whatever initial velocity $\delta\mathbf{v}$ is given to the Fermi sea.

Static Magnetoconductivity

An important situation is the following: let a static electric field **E** lie in the xy plane and **H** along the z axis. Then, for electrons,

$$m\left(\frac{d}{dt} + \frac{1}{\tau}\right)\delta v_x = -e\left(E_x + \frac{H}{c}\delta v_y\right);$$
$$m\left(\frac{d}{dt} + \frac{1}{\tau}\right)\delta v_y = -e\left(E_y - \frac{H}{c}\delta v_x\right). \tag{44}$$

[9] To conform with the solid state literature we write **H** whenever $\mathbf{H} \equiv \mathbf{B}$. In a ferromagnet $\mathbf{B} \neq \mathbf{H}$; it is known that in a ferromagnet one should write **B** in (38) and in all results derived from it.

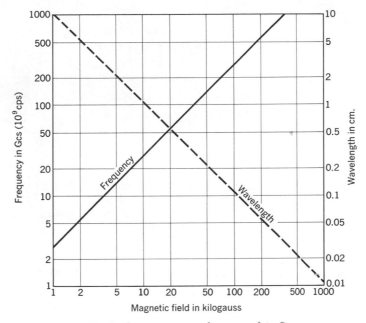

Figure 11 Cyclotron resonance frequency f_c in Gcs versus magnetic field in kG, for free electron. Also plotted is the free space electromagnetic wavelength λ_c for cyclotron resonance versus magnetic field. (The frequency and wavelength scales are drawn independently of each other.)

In the steady state the time derivatives are zero, so that (44) reduces to

$$\delta v_x = -\frac{e\tau}{m}E_x - \omega_c\tau\,\delta v_y; \qquad \delta v_y = -\frac{e\tau}{m}E_y + \omega_c\tau\,\delta v_x. \qquad (45)$$

On solving for δv_x and δv_y we have

$$\delta v_x = -\frac{e\tau/m}{1+(\omega_c\tau)^2}(E_x - \omega_c\tau E_y);$$

$$\delta v_y = -\frac{e\tau/m}{1+(\omega_c\tau)^2}(E_y + \omega_c\tau E_x). \qquad (46)$$

The components of the electric current density are, with $\sigma_0 \equiv ne^2\tau/m$,

$$j_x = \sigma_{xx}E_x + \sigma_{xy}E_y = \frac{\sigma_0}{1+(\omega_c\tau)^2}(E_x - \omega_c\tau E_y); \qquad (47)$$

$$j_y = \sigma_{yx}E_x + \sigma_{yy}E_y = \frac{\sigma_0}{1+(\omega_c\tau)^2}(\omega_c\tau E_x + E_y).$$

The z component of the current is not affected by a magnetic field in the z

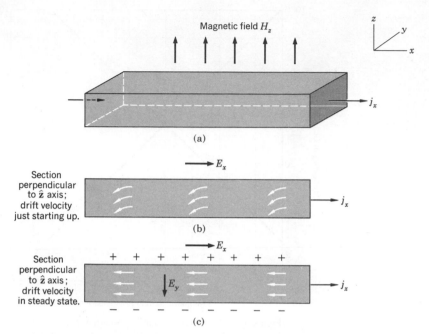

Magnetic field H_z

(a)

Section perpendicular to $\hat{z}$ axis; drift velocity just starting up.

E_x

j_x

(b)

Section perpendicular to $\hat{z}$ axis; drift velocity in steady state.

E_x

E_y

j_x

(c)

Figure 12 The standard geometry for the Hall effect: a rod-shaped specimen of rectangular cross-section is placed in a magnetic field H_z, as in (a). An electric field E_x applied across the end electrodes causes an electric current density j_x to flow down the rod. The drift velocity of the electrons immediately after the electric field is applied is shown in (b). The deflection in the $-y$ direction is caused by the magnetic field. Electrons accumulate on one face of the rod and a positive ion excess is established on the opposite face until, as in (c), the transverse electric field (Hall field) just cancels the force due to the magnetic field.

direction, so that $j_z = \sigma_0 \, E_z$. The current density can be written in matrix form as

$$
\begin{pmatrix} j_x \\ j_y \\ j_z \end{pmatrix} = \frac{\sigma_0}{1 + (\omega_c \tau)^2} \begin{pmatrix} 1 & -\omega_c \tau & 0 \\ \omega_c \tau & 1 & 0 \\ 0 & 0 & 1 + (\omega_c \tau)^2 \end{pmatrix} \begin{pmatrix} E_x \\ E_y \\ E_z \end{pmatrix}. \tag{48}
$$

We see from (47) that the diagonal components σ_{xx} and σ_{yy} of the magnetoconductivity tensor decrease monotonically as the magnetic field (or ω_c) is increased. The magnitude of the off-diagonal components σ_{xy} and σ_{yx} at first increase and later decrease as H is increased. However, to find the electrical resistivity in a magnetic field we must specify the experimental geometry (see Problem 4).

Hall Effect

Consider a rod-shaped specimen in a longitudinal electric field E_x and a transverse magnetic field, as in Fig. 12. If current cannot flow out of the rod in the y direction we must have $j_y = 0$. From (47) this is possible only if there is a transverse electric field E_y of magnitude

$$E_y = -\omega_c \tau \, E_x = -\frac{eH\tau}{mc} E_x. \qquad (49)$$

We can measure this transverse electric field. It is known as the **Hall field.** The quantity

$$\boxed{R_H = \frac{E_y}{j_x H}} \qquad (50)$$

is called the **Hall constant.** It has the value, from (47) and (49),

$$R_H = -\frac{eH\tau E_x/mc}{ne^2\tau E_x H/m} = -\frac{1}{nec}, \qquad (51)$$

and is negative for free electrons. The lower the carrier concentration, the greater the magnitude of the Hall constant. Measuring R_H is a way of measuring the carrier concentration.

The simple result $R_H = -1/nec$ follows from the assumption that all relaxation times are equal, independent of the velocity of the electron. A numerical factor of order unity enters if the relaxation time is a function of the velocity. The expression (51) becomes somewhat more complicated if both electrons and holes contribute to the conductivity, as considered in a problem at the end of Chapter 10.

Observed values of the Hall constant for several metals are compared in Table 4 with values calculated directly from the concentration of valence electrons. For the monovalent metals the agreement between observed and calculated values is quite satisfactory. But the sign of the effect in beryllium, cadmium, and tungsten is opposite to that predicted for electrons. This

Table 4   Comparison of observed Hall constants with those calculated on free electron theory
(After Ziman; here n is the concentration of *atoms*)

Metal	Observed value of $R_H \cdot nec$	Metal	Observed value of $R_H \cdot nec$
Li	−1.3	Au	−0.7
Na	−0.9	Be	+5.0
K	−0.9	Mg	−0.7
Rb	−1.0	Ca	−0.7
Cs	−1.1	Cd	+0.5
Cu	−0.8	Al	−0.4
Ag	−0.8	W	+1.2

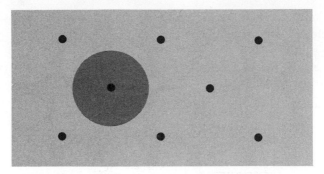

Figure 13 Most of the cohesive energy of *jellium* is due to the attractive potential energy of a point positive charge embedded in a sphere uniformly filled with electrons. The entire arrangement is neutral.

situation represented a famous unsolved problem until clarified by band theory (Chapter 9). We shall see that according to band theory vacant states near the top of an otherwise filled electron energy band behave as if endowed with a positive charge. States of this character give rise to the positive Hall constants.

In Gaussian units the order of magnitude of R_H for a simple metal such as potassium is

$$R_H \sim -\frac{1}{(10^{22})(5 \times 10^{-10})(3 \times 10^{10})} \sim -1 \times 10^{-23} \text{ esu.}$$

To convert R_H in esu to v-cm/amp-gauss, we multiply by $(300)(3 \times 10^9) = 9 \times 10^{11}$, so that $R_H \sim -1 \times 10^{-11}$ v-cm/amp-gauss.

COHESIVE ENERGY AND INTERATOMIC SPACING OF AN IDEALIZED METAL

In Chapter 3 we avoided discussion of the cohesive energy of metals. The cohesion of an idealized metal which we shall call **jellium** arises from the Coulomb energy of point positive charges arranged on a lattice and imbedded in a uniform sea of conduction electrons (Fig. 13). To a close approximation the Coulomb energy of jellium is obtained by calculating the energy of a positive point charge e interacting electrostatically with a negative charge $-e$ distributed uniformly throughout a sphere of volume equal to the atomic volume. The repulsive part of the energy is given by the kinetic energy of the electron gas.

The total electrostatic energy of interaction U_C of a point positive charge e with the charge $-e$ uniformly distributed throughout a sphere of radius r_s is easily calculated. The net charge inside a sphere of radius $r < r_s$ is

$$q(r) = e - e(r/r_s)^3. \tag{52}$$

The electrostatic potential is $\varphi(r) = q(r)/r$; the electrostatic potential energy of an electron shell of thickness dr located at r is

$$dU_C = (4\pi r^2 \rho \, dr)e[1 - (r/r_s)^3]/r, \tag{53}$$

where $\rho = -e/(4\pi r_s^3/3)$ is the charge density in the electron shell. Thus the Coulomb energy per atom is

$$U_C = \int_0^{r_s} dU_C = -\frac{e^2}{r_s}\left(\frac{3}{2} - \frac{3}{5}\right) = -\frac{9e^2}{10r_s}. \tag{54}$$

The average kinetic energy of the Fermi gas is given by the result of Problem 7.2:

$$U_F = \frac{3}{5}\epsilon_F = \frac{3}{5}\cdot\frac{\hbar^2}{2m}(3\pi^2 n)^{2/3}, \tag{55}$$

where n is the electron concentration. Now $n(4\pi r_s^3/3) = 1$ by the definition of r_s, so that

$$U_F = \frac{3}{10}\left(\frac{9\pi}{4}\right)^{2/3}\frac{\hbar^2}{m}\cdot\frac{1}{r_s^2}. \tag{56}$$

Thus the total energy per atom is

$$U(r_s) = U_C + U_F = -\frac{9e^2}{10r_s} + \frac{3}{10}\left(\frac{9\pi}{4}\right)^{2/3}\frac{\hbar^2}{mr_s^2}. \tag{57}$$

The equilibrium value of r_s is given by

$$\frac{dU}{dr_s} = 0 = \frac{9e^2}{10r_s^2} - \frac{6}{10}\left(\frac{9\pi}{4}\right)^{2/3}\frac{\hbar^2}{mr_s^3}, \tag{58}$$

or

$$r_s = \frac{2}{3}\left(\frac{9\pi}{4}\right)^{2/3}\frac{\hbar^2}{e^2 m} \cong 2.45\, a_H \cong 1.30\text{ Å}, \tag{59}$$

where $a_H \equiv \hbar^2/e^2 m$ is the Bohr radius of hydrogen. This is not a bad estimate for r_s. The equilibrium value of the energy is found on substituting (59) in (57):

$$U_0 = -\frac{9e^2}{20r_s} = -0.37\text{ rydberg} \approx -5\text{ ev}, \tag{60}$$

per atom. To obtain the cohesive energy we should compare U_0 with the ionization energy of a jellium atom, but at this stage our naive model is being pushed too far. It is useful, however, to calculate the velocity of sound for jellium, and this is the subject of Problem 5.

THERMIONIC EMISSION

In the early days of the electron theory of metals it was known experimentally that the velocity distribution of the electrons evaporated from a hot metal filament was Maxwellian, just as if the electrons within the metal themselves had a Maxwellian (classical) distribution of velocities. But we know that the electrons in a metal have a Fermi-Dirac distribution. The electrons which come *out* of a metal are those in the high-energy tail of the equilibrium distribution which have an energy greater than the chemical potential μ by the amount of the **work function** ϕ defined by Fig. 14. The value of ϕ may be several electron volts, at least one or two orders of magnitude larger than the value of $k_B T$. Under these conditions $\epsilon - \mu \gg k_B T$ for the evaporated electrons. The Fermi-Dirac distribution function in this region is of the form

$$f(\epsilon) \cong e^{(\mu-\epsilon)/k_B T}. \tag{61}$$

If ϵ_1 is the energy of an electron referred to the vacuum level ϵ_0, then $\epsilon = \epsilon_0 + \epsilon_1$ and (61) becomes

$$f(\epsilon_1) \cong \exp\left[(\mu - \epsilon_0)/k_B T\right] \exp\left(-\epsilon_1/k_B T\right)$$
$$= \exp\left(-\phi/k_B T\right) \exp\left(-\epsilon_1/k_B T\right), \tag{62}$$

so that the distribution of ϵ_1 is like the Boltzmann (classical) distribution: there is no way of telling only from measurements on the emitted electrons that the electrons in the metal obey the Fermi-Dirac distribution.

We now calculate the saturation electron current density evaporated from a metal. Let ϵ_0 be the work necessary to remove to infinity an electron from the *lowest* conduction electron state in the metal. If the electron is taken from the level of the chemical potential, the work done is

$$\phi = \epsilon_0 - \mu. \tag{63}$$

The rate at which electrons in the metal in the momentum range between $\mathbf{p}$ and $\mathbf{p} + d\mathbf{p}$ strike a unit area of the surface is

$$v_x n(\mathbf{p}) \, d\mathbf{p} = \frac{\partial \epsilon}{\partial p_x} n(\mathbf{p}) \, d\mathbf{p} = n(\mathbf{p}) \, d\epsilon \, dp_y \, dp_z \tag{64}$$

where ϵ is the kinetic energy. Here $n(\mathbf{p})$ is the number of electrons per unit volume of phase space, and is given in terms of the Fermi-Dirac distribution function f by

$$n(\mathbf{p}) = (2/h^3)f, \tag{65}$$

by the arguments of Chapter 7. The electronic charge $-e$ times the rate at which electrons having $p_x^2/2m > \phi + \mu$ strike unit area of the surface will be the emission current density j, apart from possible quantum reflection effects which we neglect. Then

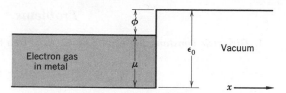

Figure 14   Model for calculation of thermionic emission. The work function is ϕ and the chemical potential is μ.

$$j = \frac{2e}{h^3} \int_{-\infty}^{\infty} \int_{-\infty}^{\infty} \int_{\varphi+\mu}^{\infty} dp_y \, dp_z \, d\epsilon \cdot \frac{1}{\exp\left[(\epsilon - \mu)/k_B T\right] + 1}$$

$$= \frac{2k_B T e}{h^3} \int_{-\infty}^{\infty} \int_{-\infty}^{\infty} dp_y \, dp_z \, \log\left[1 + e^{-\theta}\right], \tag{66}$$

where
$$\theta = [\phi + (p_y{}^2 + p_z{}^2)/2m]/k_B T.$$

Ordinarily $\theta \gg 1$; then we may expand the logarithm and retain only the first term:

$$j = \frac{2k_B T e}{h^3} e^{-\phi/k_B T} \iint dp_y \, dp_z \, e^{-(p_y{}^2 + p_z{}^2)/2mk_B T} = 4\pi m e (k_B T)^2 h^{-3} e^{-\phi/k_B T}. \tag{67}$$

This is the Richardson-Dushman equation. We may write it in the form

$$j = AT^2 e^{-\phi/k_B T}, \tag{68}$$

where

$$A = 4\pi m e k_B{}^2 h^{-3} = 120 \text{ amp/cm}^2\text{-deg}^2. \tag{69}$$

Experimental values of A and ϕ are given in Table 5. The values are sensitive to surface conditions, particularly to surface films and nonuniform surfaces.[10]

Table 5   Representative thermionic emission data

Metal	A, in amp/cm²-deg²	φ, in ev
W	~75	4.5
Ta	55	4.2
Ni	30	4.6
Ag	–	4.8
Cs	160	1.8
Pt	32	5.3
Ba on W	1.5	1.56
Cs on W	3.2	1.36
Cr	48	4.60

[10] C. Herring and M. H. Nichols, Revs. Modern Phys. **21**, 185 (1949).

Problems

1. **Dielectric constant and conductivity.** (a) From the Maxwell equation

$$\text{curl } \mathbf{H} = \frac{4\pi}{c}\,\sigma\mathbf{E} + \frac{1}{c}\frac{\partial \mathbf{D}}{\partial t},$$

with $\mathbf{D} = \epsilon\mathbf{E}$, show that for time dependence $e^{-i\omega t}$ we can describe the properties of the medium by the generalized conductivity

$$\tilde{\sigma}(\omega) = \sigma(\omega) - i\omega\epsilon(\omega)/4\pi$$

or by the generalized dielectric constant

$$\tilde{\epsilon}(\omega) = \epsilon(\omega) + i4\pi\sigma(\omega)/\omega.$$

That is, we can replace the right-hand side of the Maxwell equation by either $\dfrac{4\pi}{c}\,\tilde{\sigma}(\omega)\mathbf{E}$ or $\dfrac{\tilde{\epsilon}(\omega)}{c}\dfrac{\partial \mathbf{E}}{\partial t}$. (b) Show that Eq. (7) is consistent with Eq. (11).

2. **Hagen-Rubens relation for infrared reflectivity of metals.** The complex refractive index $n + i\kappa$ of a metal for $\omega\tau \ll 1$ is given by

$$\epsilon \equiv (n + i\kappa)^2 = 1 + 4\pi i\sigma_0/\omega,$$

where σ_0 is the conductivity for static fields. (a) Using the relation

$$R = \frac{(n - 1)^2 + \kappa^2}{(n + 1)^2 + \kappa^2}$$

for the reflection coefficient at normal incidence, show that

$$R \cong 1 - (2\omega/\pi\sigma_0)^{1/2}.$$

This is the Hagen-Rubens relation. (b) Estimate τ for sodium at room temperature, using the observed conductivity. *Note:* For a discussion of experiments on Al see H. E. Bennett, M. Silver, and E. J. Ashley, J. Opt. Soc. Am. **53**, 1089 (1963).

3. **Refractive index for x-rays.** Estimate the dielectric constant and refractive index of metallic Na for x-rays of energy 10 kev. Neglect the ionization energy of the electrons in comparison with the photon energy: thus *all* the electrons of Na are to be treated as free electrons in this experiment. Assume that the relaxation time τ is infinite.

4. **Magnetoresistance.** The transverse magnetoresistivity of a solid is defined as E_x/j_x for the standard geometry of Fig. 12. Show that (47) leads to $j_x = \sigma_0 E_x$, because $j_y = 0$ for this geometry. Thus the resistivity is independent of the magnetic field, whereas experiments generally show a resistivity which increases as the magnetic field is increased. This defect of our model is caused in part by the unrealistic assumption that all electrons have the identical relaxation time τ, independent of the electron velocity.

5. **Bulk modulus of jellium.** (a) Show from (57) and (59) that the bulk modulus of jellium is $B = 3e^2/40\pi r_s^4$ at the equilibrium value of r_s. (b) Then show that the velocity of a longitudinal sound wave in jellium is given by

$$v_L^2 = \frac{m}{15M} v_F^2,$$

where M is the atomic mass and v_F the Fermi velocity. (c) Estimate v_L for lithium and compare with the experimental values in Chapter 4.

°6. **Surface plasmons.** Consider a semi-infinite plasma on the positive side of the plane $z = 0$. A solution of Laplace's equation $\nabla^2\varphi = 0$ in the plasma is

$$\varphi_i(x,z) = A \cos kx\, e^{-kz},$$

whence $E_{zi} = kA \cos kx\, e^{-kz}$; $E_{xi} = kA \sin kx\, e^{-kz}$. (a) Show that in the vacuum

$$\varphi_0(x,z) = A \cos kx\, e^{kz}$$

for $z < 0$ satisfies the boundary condition that the tangential component of **E** be continuous at the boundary; i.e., find E_{xo}. (b) Note that $\mathbf{D}_i = \epsilon(\omega)\mathbf{E}_i$; $\mathbf{D}_o = \mathbf{E}_o$. Show that the boundary condition that the normal component of **D** be continuous at the boundary requires that $\epsilon(\omega) = -1$, whence from (11) we have

$$\omega_s^2 = \tfrac{1}{2}\omega_p^2$$

for the frequency ω_s of a surface plasma oscillation. Refs.: R. H. Ritchie, Phys. Rev. **106**, 874 (1957); E. A. Stern and R. A. Ferrell, Phys. Rev. **120**, 130 (1960).

7. **Debye-Hückel screening.** The arguments leading to (29) for $n(\mathbf{r}) - n_0$ in the text were based upon the Fermi distribution. What is the corresponding screening length in one dimension if the electrons obey the classical Boltzmann distribution?

References

PLASMONS

D. Pines, *Solid state physics* 1, 367 (1955).
H. Raether, "Solid state excitations by electrons; plasma oscillations and single electron transitions," *Ergebnisse der exacten Naturwissenschaften* 38, 84 (1965).
M. P. Givens, "Optical properties of metals," *Solid state physics* 6, 313 (1958).
F. Stern, "Elementary theory of the optical properties of metals," *Solid state physics* 15, 300 (1963).

9

Energy Bands

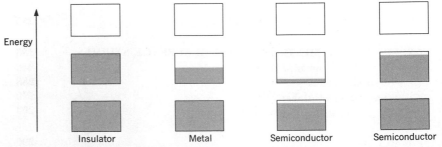

Figure 1 Schematic electron occupancy of allowed energy bands for an insulator, metal, and two semiconductors. The vertical extent of the boxes indicates the allowed energy regions; the shaded areas indicate the regions filled with electrons.

This chapter is not the easiest one in the book,[1] but it is the most important. Here we find all the important new concepts associated with the quantum theory of solids: energy bands, band gaps, Fermi surfaces, effective masses, and holes. An account is given of some of the central experiments used to determine the shape of the **Fermi surface,** which is defined as the surface of constant energy ϵ_F in $\mathbf{k}$ space.

The free electron model of metals developed in the preceding chapters gave us considerable insight into several of the electronic properties of metals, yet there are other electronic properties of solids for which the free electron model gives us no help. The model cannot help us understand why some chemical elements crystallize to form good conductors of electricity and others to form insulators; still others form semiconductors, with electrical properties varying markedly with temperature. Yet the distinction between the resistivity values of normal metallic conductors and insulators is striking: the resistivity of a pure metal at low temperatures may be of the order of 10^{-10} ohm-cm, and the resistivity of a good insulator may be as high as 10^{22} ohm-cm. E. M. McMillan has remarked that this observed range of 10^{32} in resistivity may be the widest range of any common physical property of solids.

Every solid contains electrons; the important question for electrical conductivity is under what circumstances does a proportion of the electrons respond to an applied electric field as if partly free. We shall see how to answer this question: electrons in crystals are arranged in energy bands (Fig. 1) separated by regions in energy for which no electron energy states are allowed; such forbidden regions are called **energy gaps** or **band gaps.** If the number of electrons in a crystal is such that the allowed energy bands are either filled or empty, then no electrons can move in an electric field and the crystal will behave as an insulator. If one or more bands are partly filled, say 10 to 90 percent filled, the crystal will act as a metal. If all bands are entirely filled, except for one or two bands which are slightly filled or slightly empty, we say that the crystal is a semiconductor or, sometimes, a semimetal.[2]

To understand the difference between insulators and conductors we must extend the free electron model to take account of the periodic lattice of the solid. The most important new property which emerges is the possibility of a band gap. We shall encounter other quite remarkable properties possessed by

---

[1] For a semipopular account see J. Ziman, *Electrons in metals—a short guide to the Fermi surface,* Taylor & Francis, London, 1963.

[2] In a **semimetal** one or two bands are slightly filled or slightly empty even at absolute zero, but a **semiconductor** at absolute zero becomes an insulator.

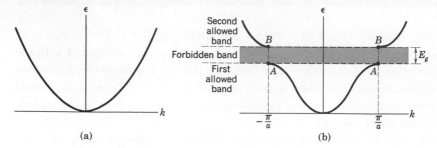

Figure 2 (a) Plot of energy ϵ versus wavevector k for a free electron. (b) Plot of energy versus wavevector for an electron in a monatomic linear lattice of lattice constant a. The energy gap E_g shown is associated with the first Bragg reflection at $k = \pm\pi/a$; other gaps are found at $\pm n\pi/a$, for integral values of n.

electrons in crystals: they respond to applied electric or magnetic fields as if the electrons were endowed with an effective mass m^*, which may be larger or smaller than the free electron mass, or may even be negative. Further, there are situations as in the Hall effect where it is appropriate to attribute to some of the charge carriers in crystals a positive charge e; we denote such carriers as holes, in contrast to electrons which behave with their normal negative charge $-e$.

On the free electron model the allowed energy values are distributed continuously from zero to infinity. We saw in Eq. (7.25) that

$$\epsilon_{\mathbf{k}} = \frac{\hbar^2}{2m}\,(k_x{}^2 + k_y{}^2 + k_z{}^2), \tag{1}$$

where, for periodic boundary conditions over a cube of side L,

$$k_x, k_y, k_z = 0; \qquad \pm\frac{2\pi}{L}; \ \pm\frac{4\pi}{L}; \ \cdots, \tag{2}$$

as in (7.22). The free electron wavefunctions are of the form

$$\psi_{\mathbf{k}}(\mathbf{r}) = (1/V)^{1/2}e^{i\mathbf{k}\cdot\mathbf{r}}, \tag{3}$$

as in (7.21); they represent running waves and carry momentum $\mathbf{p} = \hbar\mathbf{k}$.

We saw in Chapter 2 in discussing x-ray and neutron propagation that Bragg reflection is a characteristic feature of wave propagation in crystals. Bragg reflection occurs also for electron waves in crystals and leads to energy gaps.[3] That is, there may arise substantial regions of energy in which wave-like solutions of the Schrödinger equation do not exist, as in Fig. 2. These energy gaps are of decisive significance in determining whether a solid is an insulator or a conductor.

[3] An energy gap for an electron is directly analogous to the frequency gap for x-rays exhibited in Fig. A.1.

NEARLY FREE ELECTRON MODEL

In many situations the band structure of a crystal can be accounted for by the nearly free electron model for which the band electrons are treated as perturbed only weakly by the periodic potential of the ion cores. Often the gross overall aspects of the band structure and the intricate detail of the observed Fermi surfaces can be explained on this model; we shall also point out some situations where it is not applicable. But this model answers almost all the qualitative questions about the behavior of electrons in metals.

Let us understand physically the reason for forbidden bands, considering first the simple problem of a linear lattice of lattice constant a. The low energy portions of the band structure are shown qualitatively in Fig. 2, in (a) for entirely free electrons and in (b) for electrons which are nearly free, but with an energy gap at $k = \pm\pi/a$. The Bragg condition $(\mathbf{k} + \mathbf{G})^2 = k^2$ for diffraction of a wave of wavevector $\mathbf{k}$ becomes in one dimension

$$k = \pm\tfrac{1}{2}G = \pm n\pi/a, \tag{4}$$

where $G = \pm 2n\pi/a$ is a reciprocal lattice vector and n is an integer. The first reflections and the first energy gap occur at $k = \pm\pi/a$. Other energy gaps occur for the other values of the integer n in (4).

The reflection at $k = \pm\pi/a$ arises because the wave reflected from one atom in the linear lattice interferes constructively with the wave reflected from a nearest-neighbor atom. The difference in phase between the two reflected waves is just $\pm 2\pi$ for these two values of k. The region in k space between $-\pi/a$ and π/a is called the **first Brillouin zone** of this lattice, as in Chapter 2.

At $k = \pm\pi/a$ the wavefunctions are not the traveling waves $e^{i\pi x/a}$ and $e^{-i\pi x/a}$ of the free electron model. We shall show that the solutions at these particular k values are made up *equally* of waves traveling to the right and to the left: the solutions are standing waves. We first give a plausibility argument. When the Bragg condition is satisfied a wave traveling in one direction is soon Bragg-reflected and then travels in the opposite direction. Each subsequent Bragg reflection reverses the direction of travel again. The only time-independent situation is formed by standing waves. We can form two different standing waves from the traveling waves $e^{i\pi x/a}$ and $e^{-i\pi x/a}$:

$$
\begin{aligned}
\psi(+) &\propto (e^{i\pi x/a} + e^{-i\pi x/a}) = 2\cos(\pi x/a); \\
\psi(-) &\propto (e^{i\pi x/a} - e^{-i\pi x/a}) = 2i\sin(\pi x/a).
\end{aligned}
\tag{5}
$$

The standing waves are labeled $(+)$ or $(-)$ according to whether they are even or odd when $-x$ is substituted for x. Symmetry excludes other forms.

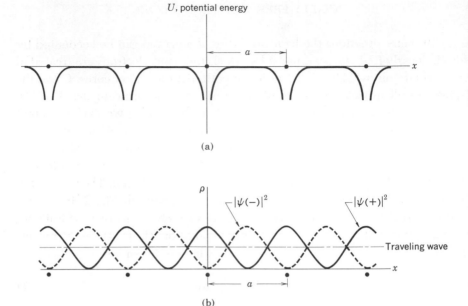

Figure 3 (a) Variation of potential energy of a conduction electron in the field of the ion cores of a linear lattice. (b) Distribution of probability density ρ in the lattice for $|\psi(-)|^2 \propto \sin^2\pi x/a$; $|\psi(+)|^2 \propto \cos^2\pi x/a$; and for a traveling wave. The wavefunction $\psi(+)$ piles up electronic charge on the cores of the positive ions, thereby lowering the potential energy in comparison with the average potential energy seen by a traveling wave. The wavefunction $\psi(-)$ piles up charge in the region between the ions and removes it from the ion cores, thereby raising the potential energy in comparison with that seen by a traveling wave.

Origin of the Energy Gap

The two standing waves $\psi(+)$ and $\psi(-)$ correspond in a lattice to different values of the energy: We recall that in quantum mechanics the probability density ρ of a particle is $|\psi|^2$. For a pure traveling wave $\psi \propto e^{ikx}$, so that $\rho \propto e^{-ikx}e^{ikx} = 1$, a constant. But ρ is not constant for linear combinations of plane waves. Consider the linear combination $\psi(+)$ in (5): for $\psi(+)$ we have $\rho \propto \cos^2(\pi x/a)$. Figure 3a indicates schematically the variation of the electrostatic potential energy of a conduction electron in the field of the positive ion cores of a monatomic linear lattice. The ion cores bear a positive charge, as in forming the metal each has lost one or more valence electrons. The potential energy of an electron in the field of a positive ion is negative. In (b) we sketch the distribution of electron density corresponding to the standing waves $\psi(+)$, $\psi(-)$, and to a traveling wave.

The traveling wave e^{ikx} distributes electrons uniformly over the line; the standing wave $\psi(-) \propto \sin \pi x/a$ distributes electrons preferentially midway[4] between ion cores; and the standing wave $\psi(+) \propto \cos \pi x/a$ distributes elec-

---

[4] The origin of x is at the center of an ion.

trons preferentially on the ion cores, where the potential energy is lowest. On calculating average values of the potential energy over the three charge distributions, we expect to find the potential energy of $\psi(+)$ lower than that of a traveling wave, whereas the potential energy of $\psi(-)$ is higher than that of a traveling wave. If the potential energies of $\psi(-)$ and $\psi(+)$ differ by an amount E_g, we have an energy gap of width E_g between the two solutions at $k = \pi/a$, in Fig. 2 or between the two solutions at $k = -\pi/a$. The wavefunction at points A in Fig. 2 will be $\psi(+)$, and the wavefunction above the energy gap at points B will be $\psi(-)$.

WAVE EQUATION OF ELECTRON IN A PERIODIC POTENTIAL

We considered above the approximate form we expect the solution of the Schrödinger equation to have if the wavevector is at a zone boundary in wavevector space. We now treat in detail the wave equation and its solution.

Let $U(x)$ denote the potential energy of an electron in a linear lattice of lattice constant a. We know that the potential energy is invariant under a crystal lattice translation:

$$U(x) = U(x + a). \tag{6}$$

By the result of Problem 2.6 we may expand $U(x)$ as a Fourier series summed over all reciprocal lattice vectors G:

$$U(x) = \sum_G U_G e^{iGx}. \tag{7}$$

The wave equation of an electron in the crystal is $\mathcal{H}\psi = \epsilon\psi$, where $\mathcal{H}$ is the hamiltonian and ϵ the energy eigenvalue. Explicitly,

$$\left(\frac{1}{2m}p^2 + U(x)\right)\psi(x) = \left(\frac{1}{2m}p^2 + \sum_G U_G e^{iGx}\right)\psi(x) = \epsilon\psi(x), \tag{8}$$

using (7). The momentum operator p is represented by $-i\hbar\, d/dx$. Equation (8) is written in the one-electron approximation: it is assumed that the electron moves in the potential of the ion cores and in the average potential of the other electrons.

The wavefunction $\psi(x)$ may be expressed as a Fourier series[5] summed over all values of the wavevector permitted by the boundary conditions, so that

$$\psi(x) = \sum_K C(K) e^{iKx}. \tag{9}$$

Our problem is to determine the values of the C's, or at least of the largest C's.

[5] This analysis parallels that of Appendix A for electromagnetic waves in a crystal. Notice that we do not assume $\psi(x)$ is periodic in the lattice translation a. Appendix D gives another approach to the energy band problem.

We substitute (9) in (8). For the separate terms we have

$$\frac{1}{2m}p^2\psi(x) = \frac{1}{2m}\left(-i\hbar\frac{d}{dx}\right)^2\psi(x) = -\frac{\hbar^2}{2m}\frac{d^2\psi}{dx^2} = \frac{\hbar^2}{2m}\sum_K K^2 C(K)e^{iKx}$$

and

$$\left(\sum_G U_G e^{iGx}\right)\psi(x) = \sum_G\sum_K U_G C(K)e^{i(K+G)x} = \sum_{K'}\sum_G U_G C(K' - G)e^{iK'x},$$

where K' has been written for $K + G$. But K' is only a dummy index which is summed over, and we may just as well write the last double summation as $\sum_K\sum_G U_G C(K - G)e^{iKx}$. Thus the wave equation (8) becomes

$$\sum_K\left\{\frac{\hbar^2}{2m}K^2 C(K) + \sum_G U_G C(K - G)\right\}e^{iKx} = \epsilon\sum_K C(K)e^{iKx}. \tag{10}$$

This equation is satisfied for every K if the coefficients of e^{iKx} on both sides of the equation are equal:

$$\frac{\hbar^2}{2m}K^2 C(K) + \sum_G U_G C(K - G) = \epsilon C(K). \tag{11}$$

Writing

$$\lambda_K \equiv \hbar^2 K^2/2m \tag{12}$$

we have

$$\boxed{(\lambda_K - \epsilon)C(K) + \sum_G U_G C(K - G) = 0.} \tag{13}$$

This is a very useful way of writing the wave equation (8). It appears unfamiliar only because a set of algebraic equations has emerged in place of the usual differential equation. The differential equation is hard to handle in a physical or instructive way when the potential energy is a periodic function.

Equation (13) connects the Fourier coefficient $C(K)$ with every other Fourier coefficient C for which the wavevector differs from K by a reciprocal lattice vector. In principle an infinite number of coefficients are connected by (13), and we can obtain an infinite number of independent equations of the same form by subtracting any reciprocal lattice vector from K in (13). Thus if we subtract a particular G' from K, we have

$$(\lambda_{K-G'} - \epsilon)C(K - G') + \sum_G U_G C(K - G' - G) = 0. \tag{14}$$

In this way we can generate an infinite set of linear homogeneous algebraic equations. In practice we can often approximate successfully with two or perhaps four equations! We would then solve the determinant of the four equations in the four C's for the four roots ϵ which are the energy eigenvalues. With these roots we can then determine the values of the C's.

Bloch Functions

We can derive starting from (13) an exceedingly important and useful result about the form of the eigenfunctions ψ. First we need a method of labeling any particular ψ: Let us pick *any* wavevector which appears in the sum (9) and call it k; this will be the label. It does not matter that the choice is not unique.

We observe from (13) that a continuous distribution of Fourier coefficients $C(K)$ is not involved in a given ψ_k, but *only those of the form $C(k - G)$ enter into ψ_k*, where G is any reciprocal lattice vector. The allowed K's in the wavefunction (9) are of the form $k - G$. Once we have picked the label k, then the set of wavevectors which appear in the Fourier expansion of ψ_k is determined: Equation (9) reduces to a sum over reciprocal lattice vectors:

$$\psi_k(x) = \sum_G C(k - G)e^{i(k-G)x}. \tag{15}$$

This may be rewritten as

$$\psi_k(x) = \left(\sum_G C(k - G)e^{-iGx}\right)e^{ikx} = e^{ikx}u_k(x), \tag{16}$$

with

$$u_k(x) \equiv \sum_G C(k - G)e^{-iGx}. \tag{17}$$

Because $u_k(x)$ is a Fourier series over the reciprocal lattice vectors, it is invariant[6] under a crystal lattice translation T, so that

$$u_k(x) = u_k(x + T). \tag{18}$$

The result (16) is an example of the **Bloch theorem** which states that *the eigenfunctions of the wave equation for a periodic potential are of the form*

$$\boxed{\psi_{\mathbf{k}}(\mathbf{r}) = e^{i\mathbf{k}\cdot\mathbf{r}}u_{\mathbf{k}}(\mathbf{r}),} \tag{19}$$

where $u_{\mathbf{k}}(\mathbf{r})$ is periodic in the crystal lattice. The subscript $\mathbf{k}$ indicates that the function $u_{\mathbf{k}}(\mathbf{r})$ depends on $\mathbf{k}$. A function of the form (19) is known as a **Bloch function.** All one-electron wavefunctions in an ideal crystal are of the Bloch form.

---

[6] Verify this by evaluating $u_k(x + a)$. Because $\exp(iGa) = 1$ it follows that $u_k(x + a) = u_k(x)$, thereby establishing the periodicity of u_k.

Crystal Momentum of an Electron

What is the significance of the **k** which we used to label the Bloch function? It has several properties:

(a) Under a crystal lattice translation which carries **r** to **r** + **T** we have

$$\psi_{\mathbf{k}}(\mathbf{r} + \mathbf{T}) = e^{i\mathbf{k}\cdot\mathbf{T}}e^{i\mathbf{k}\cdot\mathbf{r}}u_{\mathbf{k}}(\mathbf{r} + \mathbf{T}) = e^{i\mathbf{k}\cdot\mathbf{T}}\psi_{\mathbf{k}}(\mathbf{r}), \tag{20}$$

because $u_{\mathbf{k}}(\mathbf{r} + \mathbf{T}) = u_{\mathbf{k}}(\mathbf{r})$ by (18). Thus $e^{i\mathbf{k}\cdot\mathbf{T}}$ is the phase factor[7] by which a Bloch function is multiplied when we make a crystal lattice translation **T**.

(b) If the lattice potential vanishes, Eq. (13) reduces to $(\lambda_{\mathbf{k}} - \epsilon)C(\mathbf{k}) = 0$, so that all $C(\mathbf{k} - \mathbf{G})$ are zero except $C(\mathbf{k})$, and thus $u_{\mathbf{k}}(\mathbf{r})$ is constant. We have

$$\psi_{\mathbf{k}}(\mathbf{r}) = e^{i\mathbf{k}\cdot\mathbf{r}}, \tag{21}$$

just as for a free electron. (This assumes we have had the foresight to pick the "right" **k** as the label; for many purposes other choices of **k**, as we shall see, are more convenient.)

(c) The value of **k** enters into the conservation laws for collision processes of electrons in crystals. For this reason **k** is called the **crystal momentum** of the electron. When an electron **k** collides with a phonon of wavevector **K**, the selection rule is

$$\mathbf{k} + \mathbf{K} = \mathbf{k}' + \mathbf{G}, \tag{22}$$

if the phonon is absorbed in the collision. The electron has been scattered from a state **k** to a state **k**'; and **G** is any reciprocal lattice vector.[8]

Reduced Zone Scheme

It is possible and often convenient to select the wavevector index **k** of the Bloch function so that it always lies within the first Brillouin zone. This procedure is known as the **reduced zone scheme**. If we encounter a Bloch function written as

$$\psi_{\mathbf{k}'}(\mathbf{r}) = e^{i\mathbf{k}'\cdot\mathbf{r}}u_{\mathbf{k}'}(\mathbf{r}), \tag{23}$$

with **k**' outside the first zone, as in Fig. 4, we may always find a suitable

---

[7] We may also say that exp $(i\mathbf{k}\cdot\mathbf{T})$ is the eigenvalue of the crystal translation operation $\mathfrak{T}$, and $\psi_{\mathbf{k}}$ is the eigenvector. That is, $\mathfrak{T}\psi_{\mathbf{k}}(x) = \psi_{\mathbf{k}}(x + \mathbf{T}) = $ exp $(i\mathbf{k}\cdot\mathbf{T})\psi_{\mathbf{k}}(x)$, so that **k** is a suitable label for the eigenvalue. Here we have used the Bloch theorem.

[8] The probability of the collision involves a matrix element roughly of the form

$$\int d^3x\,\psi_{\mathbf{k}'}^*(\mathbf{r})\,\exp\,(i\mathbf{K}\cdot\mathbf{r})\,\psi_{\mathbf{k}}(\mathbf{r}) = \int d^3x\,u_{\mathbf{k}'}^*(\mathbf{r})u_{\mathbf{k}}(\mathbf{r})\,\exp\,[i(\mathbf{k} + \mathbf{K} - \mathbf{k}')\cdot\mathbf{r}].$$

The product $u_{\mathbf{k}'}^*u_{\mathbf{k}}$ is periodic in the crystal lattice and can be expressed as a Fourier series in the **G**'s. The integral vanishes unless $\mathbf{k} + \mathbf{K} - \mathbf{k}' = $ a reciprocal lattice vector **G**, because the integral over all space of the function exp $(i\mathbf{Q}\cdot\mathbf{r})$ vanishes unless $\mathbf{Q} = 0$. The presence of **G** takes care of the arbitrariness in the assignment of **k** and **k**'.

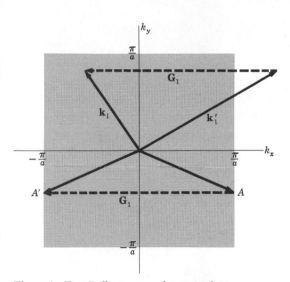

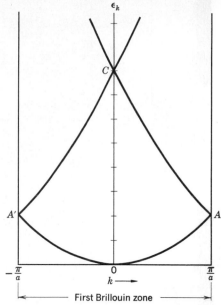

Figure 4 First Brillouin zone of a square lattice of side a. The wavevector $\mathbf{k_1'}$ can be carried into the first zone by forming $\mathbf{k_1'} + \mathbf{G_1}$. The wavevector at a point A on the zone boundary is carried by $\mathbf{G_1}$ to the point A' on the opposite boundary of the same zone. Shall we count both A and A' as lying in the first zone? We count them as *one* identical point in the zone.

Figure 5 Energy-wavevector relation $\epsilon_k = \hbar^2 k^2/2m$ for free electrons as drawn in the reduced zone scheme. This construction often gives a useful idea of the overall appearance of the band structure of a crystal. The branch AC if reflected in the vertical line at $k = \pi/a$ gives the usual free electron curve for ϵ_k versus k for positive k. The branch $A'C$ if reflected in $k = -\pi/a$ gives the usual curve for negative k. A crystal potential $U(x)$ will introduce band gaps at the edges of the zone (as at A and A') and at the center of the zone (as at C), but the overall width and gross features of the band structure are often indicated properly by the "free electron bands" in the reduced zone scheme.

reciprocal lattice vector $\mathbf{G}'$ such that

$$\mathbf{k} = \mathbf{k}' - \mathbf{G}' \tag{24}$$

lies within the first Brillouin zone. Then (23) may be written as

$$\psi_{\mathbf{k}'}(\mathbf{r}) = e^{i\mathbf{k}'\cdot\mathbf{r}} u_{\mathbf{k}'}(\mathbf{r}) = e^{i\mathbf{k}\cdot\mathbf{r}}(e^{i\mathbf{G}'\cdot\mathbf{r}} u_{\mathbf{k}'}(\mathbf{r})) \equiv e^{i\mathbf{k}\cdot\mathbf{r}} u_{\mathbf{k}}(\mathbf{r}) = \psi_{\mathbf{k}}(\mathbf{r}), \tag{25a}$$

where we have defined

$$u_{\mathbf{k}}(\mathbf{r}) \equiv e^{i\mathbf{G}'\cdot\mathbf{r}} u_{\mathbf{k}'}(\mathbf{r}). \tag{25b}$$

Both $e^{i\mathbf{G}'\cdot\mathbf{r}}$ and $u_{\mathbf{k}'}(\mathbf{r})$ are periodic in the crystal lattice, so $u_{\mathbf{k}}(\mathbf{r})$ is also, whence $\psi_{\mathbf{k}}(\mathbf{r})$ is of the Bloch form. Even with free electrons it may be useful to work in the reduced zone scheme, as in Fig. 5. It follows also that any energy $\epsilon_{\mathbf{k}'}$ for $\mathbf{k}'$ outside the first zone is equal to an $\epsilon_{\mathbf{k}}$ in the first zone, where $\mathbf{k}$ is related to $\mathbf{k}'$ by (24). Thus we need solve for the energy only in the first Brillouin zone, for each band.

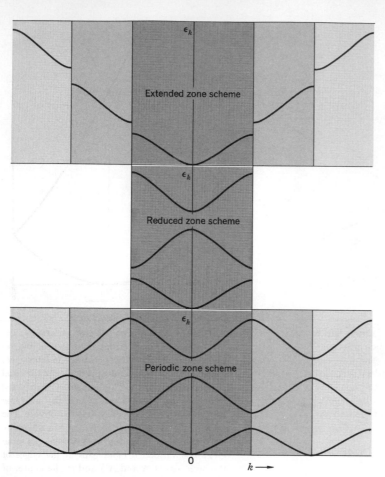

ϵ_k

Extended zone scheme

ϵ_k

Reduced zone scheme

ϵ_k

Periodic zone scheme

0    $k \longrightarrow$

Figure 6 Three energy bands of a linear lattice plotted in the extended (Brillouin), reduced, and periodic zone schemes.

Periodic Zone Scheme

Sometimes it is helpful to repeat the first Brillouin zone[9] periodically through all of **k** space. If we can translate the contents of other zones into the first zone, then we can translate the first zone into any or every other zone. That is, we can view ϵ_k as periodic in the reciprocal lattice:

$$\epsilon_k = \epsilon_{k+G}. \tag{26}$$

Here ϵ_{k+G} is understood to refer to the same energy band as ϵ_k. This construction is known as the periodic or repeated zone scheme. The scheme is helpful in exhibiting the connectivity of electron orbits in a magnetic field.

There are three different zone schemes which can be useful—the **extended** or Brillouin zone scheme, the **reduced** zone scheme, and the **periodic** zone scheme. These are displayed in Fig. 6. The periodic zone scheme is used below in Figs. 15c, 24, and 32.

APPROXIMATE SOLUTION NEAR A ZONE BOUNDARY

We are now equipped to understand the occurrence of band gaps and light effective masses, and the role of holes as charge carriers. Let us suppose

[9] Or whatever zone we have mapped into the first Brillouin zone.

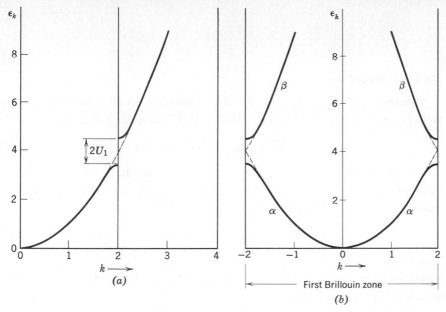

Figure 7 (a) Plot in the extended zone scheme of ϵ_k versus k, in units such that $G_1 = 4$; $U_1 = 0.5$; $u/u = 2$; and $\hbar^2/2m = 1$. (b) The band structure of (a) plotted in the reduced zone scheme, in which all k's are in the first Brillouin zone. The dashed portions are for free electrons. Two energy bands are shown, labeled by α and β.

that in a one-dimensional problem the values of the potential energy Fourier components U_G are small in comparison with the kinetic energy $\lambda_k = \hbar^2 k^2/2m$ of a free electron.

For k at the zone boundary at $\frac{1}{2}G_1$ we note that $(k - G_1)^2 = k^2$ and λ_k defined by (12) satisfies

$$\lambda_{k-G_1} = \lambda_k. \tag{27}$$

Near the zone boundary we need an approximation in which we retain in (13) and (14) two terms, those in C_k and C_{k-G_1}:

$$(\lambda_k - \epsilon_k)C(k) + U_{G_1}C(k - G_1) = 0; \tag{28a}$$

$$(\lambda_{k-G_1} - \epsilon_k)C(k - G_1) + U_{-G_1}C(k) = 0. \tag{28b}$$

Notice that U_{-G_1} appears in (28b). For convenience we take $U(x)$ in (7) as an even function of x, so that $U_G = U_{-G}$. Let us denote U_{G_1} and U_{-G_1} by U_1.

Equations (28a) and (28b) have a solution if

$$\begin{vmatrix} \lambda_k - \epsilon_k & U_1 \\ U_1 & \lambda_{k-G_1} - \epsilon_k \end{vmatrix} = 0 \tag{29}$$

or

$$\epsilon_k^2 - \epsilon_k(\lambda_{k-G_1} + \lambda_k) + \lambda_{k-G_1}\lambda_k - U_1^2 = 0. \tag{30}$$

There are two roots for ϵ_k:

$$\epsilon_k = \frac{1}{2}(\lambda_{k-G_1} + \lambda_k) \pm [\frac{1}{4}(\lambda_{k-G_1} - \lambda_k)^2 + U_1^2]^{1/2}. \tag{31}$$

The roots are plotted in Fig. 7. We now consider several limiting cases of (31).

On Zone Boundary

Here $k = \frac{1}{2}G_1$ and $\lambda_{k-G_1} = \lambda_k$. It is convenient to introduce the notation ϵ_1 and λ_1 for the values of ϵ and λ at $k = \frac{1}{2}G_1$. Then (31) reduces to

$$\epsilon_1(+) = \lambda_1 + U_1; \qquad \epsilon_1(-) = \lambda_1 - U_1. \tag{32}$$

The roots of ϵ at the boundary are separated by an energy gap $2|U_1|$. From (28) we see that the root marked $(+)$ has $C(\frac{1}{2}G_1) = C(-\frac{1}{2}G_1)$ and the root marked $(-)$ has $C(\frac{1}{2}G_1) = -C(-\frac{1}{2}G_1)$. We have

$$\psi_{G_1/2}{}^{(\pm)}(x) \propto \exp{(i\tfrac{1}{2}G_1x)} \pm \exp{(-i\tfrac{1}{2}G_1x)}, \tag{33}$$

These results agree with Eq. (5): the two solutions for ψ at $\frac{1}{2}G_1$ are standing waves and are even and odd under change of sign of x. If the potential U_1 is negative, the even solution has the lower energy.

Near Zone Boundary

It is convenient to define the quantity δ by

$$k = \tfrac{1}{2}G_1 - \delta. \tag{34}$$

Thus the wavevector δ measures the difference of k from the zone boundary. Then (31) becomes

$$\begin{aligned}
\epsilon_k &= (\hbar^2/2m)(\tfrac{1}{4}G_1{}^2 + \delta^2) \pm [4\lambda_1(\hbar^2\delta^2/2m) + U_1{}^2]^{1/2} \\
&\cong (\hbar^2/2m)(\tfrac{1}{4}G_1{}^2 + \delta^2) \pm U_1[1 + 2(\lambda_1/U_1{}^2)(\hbar^2\delta^2/2m)],
\end{aligned} \tag{35}$$

so long as $\hbar^2 G_1/2m \ll |U_1|$. Using (32) for ϵ_1 $(\pm)$ we may write (35) as

$$\epsilon_k(+) = \epsilon_1(+) + (\hbar^2\delta^2/2m)[1 + 2(\lambda_1/U_1)]; \tag{36}$$

$$\epsilon_k(-) = \epsilon_1(-) + (\hbar^2\delta^2/2m)[1 - 2(\lambda_1/U_1)]. \tag{37}$$

Note the quadratic dependence of the energy on the wavevector δ. For U_1 negative as in (44) below, the solution $\epsilon_k(-)$ corresponds to the upper of the two bands.

NUMBER OF STATES IN A BAND

Consider a linear crystal constructed of primitive cells of length a. We make the crystal finite by applying periodic boundary conditions to the wavefunctions over the length $L = Na$ of the crystal, where N is the number of primitive cells. The allowed values of the electron wavevector k in the first Brillouin zone are given by (2):

$$k = 0; \quad \pm\frac{2\pi}{L}; \quad \pm\frac{4\pi}{L}; \quad \cdots; \quad \frac{N\pi}{L}. \tag{38}$$

We have cut the series off at $N\pi/L \equiv \pi/a$, for this is the boundary of the zone. The point $-N\pi/L - -\pi/a$ is not to be counted as an independent point because it is connected by a reciprocal lattice vector with π/a. The total number of points given in (38) is exactly N. We see that *each primitive cell contributes exactly one independent value of* k *to each energy band.*[10] This result carries over into three dimensions.

With account taken of the two spin orientations, *there are* 2N *independent states in each energy band.* If there is a single atom of valence one in each primitive cell, the band will be half-filled with electrons.

If each atom contributes two valence electrons to the band, the band will be exactly filled (at absolute zero). If there are two atoms of valence one in each primitive cell, the band will also be exactly filled.

[10] An energy band, such as α or β in Fig. 7, is the line or surface which runs between the boundaries of one Brillouin zone.

Metals and Insulators

If the valence electrons exactly fill one or more bands, the crystal will be an insulator. An external electric field will not cause the flow of current.[11] If a full band is separated by an energy gap from the next higher band, there is no way to change the total crystal momentum of the electrons. Every accessible state is filled; nothing changes when the field is applied. (This is unlike the situation for free electrons pictured in Fig. 7.10.)

Another way of seeing what happens is by the force equation (50) below:

$$\hbar \, d\mathbf{k}/dt = \mathbf{F}. \qquad (39)$$

Under the action of a constant force the wavevector of an electron will increase continuously with time. But when $\mathbf{k}(t)$ reaches the boundary of the zone the wavevector will be umklapped (Fig. 8) to the opposite boundary. The motion will then start all over again, but there has been no net acceleration when averaged over all states of the band.[12]

A crystal can be an insulator only if the number of valence electrons in a primitive cell of the crystal is an even integer. (An exception must be made sometimes for electrons in tightly bound inner shells which cannot be treated by band theory.) Given an even number of valence electrons per primitive cell, it is necessary to consider whether or not the bands overlap in energy. If the bands overlap, then instead of one filled band giving an insulator, we can have two or more partly filled bands giving a metal.

The alkali metals and the noble metals have one valence electron per primitive cell, so they have to be metals. The alkaline earth metals have two valence electrons per primitive cell; they could be insulators, but the bands overlap in energy as in Fig. 9b, thereby giving metals, but not very good metals. Diamond, silicon, and germanium each have eight valence electrons per primitive cell; the bands do not overlap, so that the pure crystals are insulators at absolute zero. (There are two atoms of valence four in a primitive cell.)

---

[11] We suppose that the electric field is not strong enough to disrupt the electronic structure, as in the Zener effect (see J. M. Ziman, *Principles of the theory of solids,* Cambridge University Press, 1964, sec. 6.8).

[12] According to this argument it would appear that there is no net current even if the band is not entirely filled. Strictly, this is true in absence of collision processes. But because of collision processes the high energy states in the conduction band of a metal are occupied less often than are the low energy states, and the electrical conductivity can be calculated as in Chapters 7 and 8.

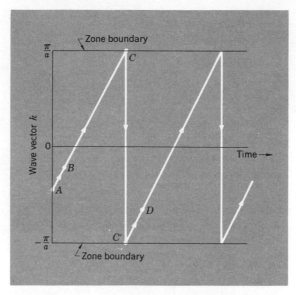

Figure 8   Motion in k space of the value of the wavevector of an electron in a linear crystal in an external electric field, with all collision processes neglected. An electron with wavevector initially at A will be accelerated by the field to B and then to C at the zone boundary. But C is equivalent by a reciprocal lattice vector to C' at the opposite boundary of the zone. After a further interval the electron will reach D from C', and the process will repeat itself.

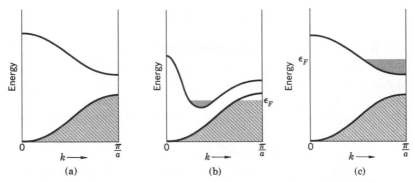

Figure 9   Occupied states and band structures giving (a) an insulator, (b) a metal because of band overlap, and (c) a metal because of electron concentration.

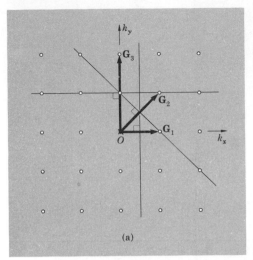
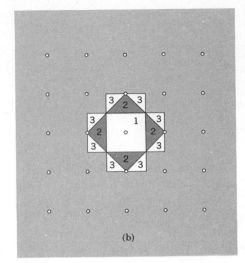

Figure 10 (a) Construction in **k** space of the first three Brillouin zones of a square lattice. The three shortest forms of the reciprocal lattice vectors are indicated as G_1, G_2, and G_3. The lines drawn are the perpendicular bisectors of these **G**'s. (b) On constructing all lines equivalent by symmetry to the three lines in (a) we obtain the regions in **k** space which form the first three Brillouin zones. The numbers denote the zone to which the regions belong; the numbers here are ordered according to the length of the vector **G** involved in the construction of the outer boundary of the region.

CONSTRUCTION OF FERMI SURFACES

With metals we are particularly concerned with the shape of the Fermi surface, the surface of constant energy ϵ_F in **k** space. The electronic properties of the metal are largely determined by the shape of the Fermi surface because the current is due to changes in the occupancy of states near the Fermi surface. Often the shape as determined experimentally may appear to be intricate, yet it may have a very simple interpretation in terms of a free or nearly free electron gas viewed in the reduced zone scheme.

In Fig. 5 we plotted ϵ versus k for free electrons in one dimension in the reduced zone scheme. It is useful to extend the analysis to two and three dimensions, as in Fig. 10. The Bragg equation (2.49) for the zone boundaries is $2\mathbf{k} \cdot \mathbf{G} + G^2 = 0$. This is satisfied if **k** terminates on the plane normal to **G** at the midpoint of **G**. The first Brillouin zone of the square lattice is obtained as the area enclosed by the perpendicular bisectors of G_1 and the three reciprocal vectors equivalent by symmetry to G_1 in Fig. 10a. If the lattice constant is a, the four reciprocal lattice vectors needed in the construction of the first zone are $\pm(2\pi/a)\hat{\mathbf{k}}_x$ and $\pm(2\pi/a)\hat{\mathbf{k}}_y$.

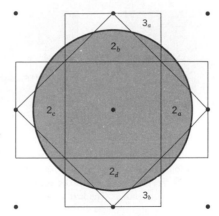

Figure 11   The circle is a surface of constant energy for free electrons; it is the Fermi surface for some value of the electron concentration. The labels within the sections of the second zone refer to Fig. 12, and within the third zone to Fig. 13.

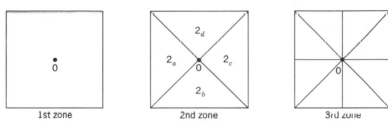

Figure 12   Mapping of the first, second, and third Brillouin zones or energy bands in the reduced zone scheme. The sections of the second zone in Fig. 11 are put together into a square by translation through an appropriate reciprocal lattice vector. A different **G** is needed for each piece of a zone.

The second zone is constructed from G_2 and the three vectors equivalent to it by symmetry, and similarly for the third zone. The pieces of the second and third zones are drawn in Fig. 10b. To determine the boundaries of some zones we have to draw lines to sets of several nonequivalent reciprocal lattice points. Thus the boundaries of section 3_a of the third zone are formed from the perpendicular bisectors of three **G**'s, namely, $(4\pi/a)\hat{\mathbf{k}}_x$; $(2\pi/a)\hat{\mathbf{k}}_y$; and $(2\pi/a)(\hat{\mathbf{k}}_x + \hat{\mathbf{k}}_y)$.

The free electron Fermi surface for an arbitrary electron concentration is shown in Fig. 11. It is inconvenient to have sections of the Fermi surface which belong to the same zone, such as the second zone, appear so detached from one another. The detachment can be repaired by a transformation to the reduced zone scheme, discussed in Eqs. (23) to (26). We take from Fig. 11 the triangle labeled 2_a and move it by a reciprocal lattice vector, in this instance by $\mathbf{G} = -(2\pi/a)\hat{\mathbf{k}}_x$, such that the triangle reappears in the area of the first Brillouin zone (Fig. 12). Other reciprocal lattice vectors will shift the triangles 2_b, 2_c, 2_d to the first zone, thereby completing the mapping of

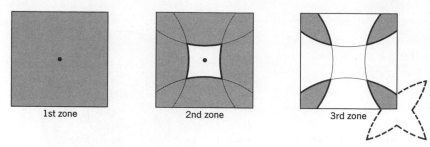

Figure 13 The free electron Fermi surface of Fig. 11, as viewed in the reduced zone scheme. The shaded areas represent occupied electron states. Parts of the Fermi surface fall in the second, third, and fourth zones. The fourth zone is not shown. The first zone is shown entirely occupied.

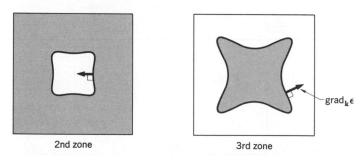

Figure 14 Qualitative impression of the effect of a weak periodic crystal potential on the Fermi surface of Fig. 13. At one point on each Fermi surface we have shown the vector $\mathrm{grad}_k\ \epsilon$. In the second zone the energy increases toward the interior of the figure, and in the third zone the energy increases toward the exterior. The shaded regions are filled with electrons and are lower in energy than the unshaded regions. We shall see that a Fermi surface like that of the third zone is electronlike, whereas one like that of the second zone is holelike.

the second zone into the reduced zone scheme. The Fermi surface falling in the second zone is now connected, as shown in Fig. 13.

A third zone has been assembled into a square in Fig. 13, but the parts of the Fermi surface falling in the third zone still appear disconnected. Translations from Fig. 11 by other reciprocal lattice vectors will assemble[13] the sections of the Fermi surface in the third zone into the connected rosette shown at the lower right-hand corner of Fig. 13. For example, starting from Fig. 11, section 3_a has been dropped by $-(2\pi/a)\hat{\mathbf{k}}_y$ and section 3_b has been left in place.

How do we go from Fermi surfaces for free electrons to Fermi surfaces for nearly free electrons? (a) The interaction of the electron with the periodic potential of the crystal causes energy gaps to appear at the zone boundaries. (b) Almost always the Fermi surface will intersect zone boundaries perpendicularly. (c) The crystal potential will also act to round out sharp corners in the free electron Fermi surfaces. Without making a detailed calculation as we did earlier for one dimension we cannot make quantitative statements, but qualitatively we expect the Fermi surfaces of the second and third zones of Fig. 13 to be changed in the direction of those of Fig. 14. Even such freehand impressions of Fermi surfaces are quite useful.

---

[13] This and other complicated Fermi surface constructions for free electrons are most easily carried out by a procedure due to W. A. Harrison; see *QTS*, pp. 258–259.

ELECTRONS, HOLES, AND OPEN ORBITS

The motion of an electron in a constant magnetic field $\mathbf{H}$ is given by the equation of motion

$$\hbar\frac{d\mathbf{k}}{dt} = -\frac{e}{c}\mathbf{v} \times \mathbf{H}. \tag{40}$$

This was derived for free electrons in Chapter 8; it is derived for the general case in (50) below. Further, the group velocity is given by $\hbar\mathbf{v} = \mathrm{grad}_\mathbf{k}\,\epsilon$, so that (40) becomes

$$\frac{d\mathbf{k}}{dt} = -\frac{e}{\hbar^2 c}\nabla_\mathbf{k}\epsilon \times \mathbf{H}. \tag{41}$$

We see from this vector cross-product that in a magnetic field an electron moves in $\mathbf{k}$ space normal to the direction of $\nabla_\mathbf{k}\epsilon$; that is, *the electron moves on a surface of constant energy.* Further, the motion in $\mathbf{k}$ space is in a plane normal to the direction of $\mathbf{H}$. The value of the projection k_H of $\mathbf{k}$ on $\mathbf{H}$ is constant during the motion.

Therefore in a magnetic field an electron at the Fermi surface[14] will follow an orbit given by the intersection of the Fermi surface with a plane $\perp \mathbf{H}$ at an arbitrary value of k_H. In two-dimensional problems we always consider $\mathbf{H}$ to be perpendicular to the plane of the lattice; then k_H is necessarily zero.

Three types of orbits in a magnetic field are shown in Fig. 15. The closed orbits of (a) and (b) are traversed in opposite senses. Because particles of opposite charge circulate in a magnetic field in opposite senses it is natural to say that one orbit is **electronlike** and the other orbit is **holelike.** In (c) the orbit is not closed: the particle on reaching the zone boundary at A is instantly umklapped back to B, where B is equivalent to B' because they are connected by a reciprocal lattice vector. Such an orbit is called an **open orbit.** Open orbits have an important effect on the magnetoresistance.[15]

Vacant states near the top of an otherwise filled band give rise to holelike orbits, as in Fig. 16. Electrons in holelike orbits move in a magnetic field as if endowed with a positive charge. Thus holes give positive Hall constants, thereby resolving the problem of positive Hall constants discussed in Chapter 8.

[14] Here and in Fig. 15 we discuss the motion of electrons at the Fermi surface, but we could as well discuss the motion on any surface of constant energy. Most experiments when analyzed in detail involve only the properties of orbits on the Fermi surface because the *changes* in the occupancy of states in $\mathbf{k}$ space occur at the Fermi surface.

[15] *QTS*, Chap. 12.

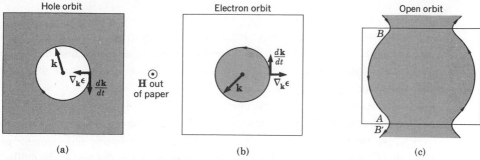

Hole orbit   Electron orbit   Open orbit

(a)   (b)   (c)

Figure 15 Motion in a magnetic field of the wavevector of an electron on the Fermi surface, in (a) and (b) for Fermi surfaces topologically equivalent to those of Fig. 14. In (a) the wavevector moves around the orbit in a clockwise direction; in (b) the wavevector moves around the orbit in a counterclockwise direction. The direction in (b) is what we expect for a free electron of charge $-e$: the smaller **k** values have the lower energy, so that the filled electron states lie inside the Fermi surface. We call the orbit in (b) **electronlike.** The sense of the motion in a magnetic field is opposite in (a) to that in (b), so that we refer to the orbit in (a) as **holelike.** A hole moves as a particle of positive charge e. In (c) for a rectangular zone we show the motion on an open orbit. This is topologically intermediate between a hole orbit and an electron orbit. For clarity the open orbit is shown with a suggestion of a periodic zone scheme.

Figure 16 Vacant states near the top of a filled band in a two-dimensional crystal. This figure is equivalent to Fig. 15a.

Holes

The existence of holes is one of the most interesting features of the band theory of solids. It is also a feature of practical importance, because the operation of transistors depends directly on the coexistence of holes and electrons within semiconducting crystals.

Vacant states in a band are commonly called hole states, but this is a rather loose definition. The simplest case to discuss is that of a single (or a few) vacant states near the top of an otherwise filled energy band. The concept of a hole *orbit* is also well-defined even if there are more vacant states than filled states in the band, but the topological nature (hole or electron) of the orbit may depend on the direction of the applied magnetic field.

It has been established (see Chapter 10) by means of cyclotron resonance experiments with circularly polarized radiation on semiconductors that holes and electrons rotate in opposite senses in a magnetic field, as one would expect for charges of opposite sign. The radiation is absorbed by electrons for one sense of circular polarization and by holes for the opposite sense.

Consider the motion of a hole in an applied electric field, as in Fig. 17. Initially the band is filled except for the single vacant state F at the top of the band. An electric field E_x is now applied in the $+x$ direction. The motion of the electrons in the band is governed by the usual equation

$$\hbar \, dk_x/dt = -eE_x; \tag{42}$$

each electron changes its k_x value at the same time. We see that Δk_x is negative in the figure. The vacancy initially at state F is displaced first to state E and subsequently to state D. That is, the hole moves along with the electrons in the direction of decreasing k_x.

For the portion of the energy surface to the left of F the slope $d\epsilon/dk_x$ is positive. The group velocity is $v_g = \hbar^{-1} \, d\epsilon/dk_x$, so that the velocity of the hole increases in the direction of the electric field. This fact alone would be compatible with the assignment to the hole of either a positive charge and positive mass, or negative charge and negative mass. Below we show that only the positive possibility is correct. We have to establish the connection between the direction of the charge flow and the direction of hole flow.

The total wavevector and total velocity of the electrons in a filled band is zero: $\Sigma \mathbf{k} = 0$ and $\sum_{\mathbf{k}} \mathbf{v}(\mathbf{k}) = 0$. If the band is filled, all pairs of states $\mathbf{k}$ and $-\mathbf{k}$ are necessarily filled and the total wavevector is zero. The electrons in states $\mathbf{k}$ and $-\mathbf{k}$ have equal but opposite velocities, so that their contribution to the total velocity cancels. These results hold even for crystals of low symmetry. The result $\Sigma \mathbf{k} = 0$ follows from the geometrical definition of a Brillouin zone. The result $\Sigma \mathbf{v}(\mathbf{k}) = 0$ follows on using $v_x = \partial \epsilon / \partial k_x$ and carrying out the integral $\int dk_x (\partial \epsilon / \partial k_x)$, which vanishes for a filled band.

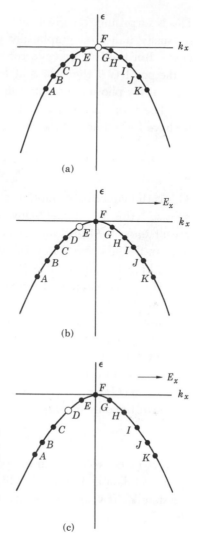

Figure 17   (a) At $t = 0$ all states are filled except F at the top of the band; the velocity v_x is zero at F because $d\epsilon/dk_x = 0$. (b) An electric field E_x is applied in the $+x$ direction. The force on the electrons is in the $-k_x$ direction and all electrons make transitions together in the $-k_x$ direction, moving the hole to the state E. (c) After a further interval the electrons move farther along in k space and the hole is now at D.

Even for a filled band every electron changes its **k** value at a rate given by $\hbar \, d\mathbf{k}/dt = \mathbf{F}$, as derived in (50) below. The electrons are not blocked on reaching the zone boundary, for on reaching it they are umklapped back to the opposite boundary.

If the band is filled except for a missing electron in the state E (Fig. 17b), we say that there is a hole in the state E. The "physical properties of the hole" follow from those of the totality of electrons in the band. If the electron is missing from a state $\mathbf{k}_e$, the total wavevector of the system is $-\mathbf{k}_e$, so that the wavevector to be attributed to the hole is

$$\mathbf{k}_h = -\mathbf{k}_e. \tag{43a}$$

This is surprising: the electron is missing from $\mathbf{k}_e$ and the position of the hole is usually indicated graphically as situated at $\mathbf{k}_e$, as we have done in the figure. But the true wavevector of the hole is $-\mathbf{k}_e$, which is the wavevector of the point G if the hole is at E. The true wavevector enters into selection rules, as for photon absorption in Figure 10.4a.

The force law $\mathbf{F}_e = \hbar\, d\mathbf{k}_e/dt$ holds for an electron. Because $\mathbf{k}_h = -\mathbf{k}_e$ we have for a hole $-\hbar\, d\mathbf{k}_h/dt = \mathbf{F}_e$, or

$$-\mathbf{F}_e = -\hbar\frac{d\mathbf{k}_e}{dt} = \hbar\frac{d\mathbf{k}_h}{dt} = e\left(\mathbf{E} + \frac{1}{c}\mathbf{v}_e \times \mathbf{H}\right). \tag{43b}$$

This is the equation of motion of a particle of *positive* charge, provided that $\mathbf{v}_e = \mathbf{v}_h$ (this we prove below). The point to grasp is that although the vacant state in Fig. 17 moves along from $E \to D \to C \ldots$ just like the electrons in neighboring states, the state of the corresponding unpaired electron moves backward from $G \to H \to I \ldots$ in k space.

The determination of the velocity $\mathbf{v}_h$ of the hole is perhaps a little tricky. Consider the motion in an electric field. From (43b) we must assign the hole a positive charge. The velocity must then be assigned so that the electric current comes out correctly. The contribution of an electron in state E of Fig. 17 to the total velocity is $\mathbf{v}(E)$. It is given by $\mathbf{v}_e = \hbar^{-1}\,\nabla_{\mathbf{k}}\,\epsilon(\mathbf{k})$ evaluated at E. An electron in the state G with $\mathbf{k}(G) = -\mathbf{k}(E)$ has an equal but opposite velocity: $\mathbf{v}(G) = -\mathbf{v}(E)$. If an electron is missing from E, then the current is that of the only unpaired electron, that at G:

$$\mathbf{j} = -e\mathbf{v}(G) = (-e)[-\mathbf{v}(E)] = e\mathbf{v}(E). \tag{43c}$$

Thus to be consistent with the positive charge of a hole, the velocity of a hole must be taken as that of the missing electron. The electron is missing from the state $\mathbf{k}_e$. If $\mathbf{v}_e$ is the velocity which an electron would have in the state $\mathbf{k}_e$, then

$$\mathbf{v}_h = \mathbf{v}_e = \hbar^{-1}\,\nabla_{\mathbf{k}_e}\epsilon(\mathbf{k}_e). \tag{43d}$$

Here as before the symbol $\epsilon(\mathbf{k}_e)$ denotes the energy of an electron in the state $\mathbf{k}_e$. For convenience we may take the zero of energy at the top of the filled or nearly filled band. The hole created by the removal of an electron from $\mathbf{k}_e$ may be assigned the energy

$$\epsilon_h = -\epsilon_e(\mathbf{k}_e) \equiv -\epsilon(\mathbf{k}_e). \tag{43e}$$

If the band is symmetric with $\epsilon(\mathbf{k}) = \epsilon(-\mathbf{k})$ we may interpret ϵ_h as $\epsilon_h(\mathbf{k}_h)$. The energy of the hole is opposite in sign to the energy of the missing electron—it takes more work to remove an electron from a low energy state than from a higher state. For a symmetric band we have from (43a) and (43e) that

$$\mathbf{v}_h = \hbar^{-1} \, \nabla_{\mathbf{k}_h} \epsilon_h(\mathbf{k}_h). \tag{43d'}$$

From (43b) and (43d) we have

$$\hbar \frac{d\mathbf{k}_h}{dt} = e\left(\mathbf{E} + \frac{1}{c} \mathbf{v}_h \times \mathbf{H}\right) = \mathbf{F}_h, \tag{43f}$$

where $\mathbf{v}_h$ may be found from (43d) or (43d').

The effective mass (see following section) of the hole is opposite in sign to that of the missing electron: The effective mass of the electron in the state $\mathbf{k}_e$ (where it has velocity $\mathbf{v}_e$) is defined by $m_e \, d\mathbf{v}_e/dt = -e\mathbf{E}$; the effective mass of a hole is defined by $m_h \, d\mathbf{v}_h/dt = e\mathbf{E}$, but we have seen from (43d) that $\mathbf{v}_e = \mathbf{v}_h$, so that $d\mathbf{v}_e/dt = d\mathbf{v}_h/dt$ and

$$m_h = -m_e. \tag{43g}$$

There is a real difference between the behavior of a *single* hole near the top of an otherwise filled band and a *single* electron near the top of an otherwise empty band. The single electron has negative charge and, by the argument of the following section, the effective mass of an electron near the top of a band is negative. The hole in a similar position in the band acts as if it had positive charge and positive mass. Thus the ratio of charge to mass is the same for the single electron as for the corresponding single hole. It follows that the electron and hole will be accelerated in the same direction by an electric field, but the field will do work on the hole whereas the electron does work on the field. The particles will circulate in the same sense in a static magnetic field. We can tell them apart by effects such as electric conductivity which depend on the ratio (charge)^2/mass. The conductivity of the hole will be positive, leading to power absorption by the specimen in an electric field. The conductivity of the isolated electron in a negative mass state will be negative,[16] leading to power emission (rather than absorption) by the specimen in an electric field. The electron is unstable in such a state. Notice that electrons at high ϵ_k tend to sink to lower energies in approaching equilibrium, whereas holes at low ϵ_k tend to float to higher energies.

EFFECTIVE MASS OF ELECTRONS IN CRYSTALS

Going back to (37) and to Fig. 7 we see that an electron in a state near the bottom of the second band (band β) has an energy of the form

$$\epsilon(\delta) = \epsilon_1(-) + \hbar^2 \, \delta^2/2m^*, \tag{44}$$

[16] See H. Kroemer, Phys. Rev. **109**, 1856 (1955); C. Kittel, Proc. Nat. Acad. Sci. **45**, 744 (1959).

where δ is the wavevector as measured from the zone boundary and

$$m^* \equiv m/[1 - 2\lambda_1/U_1]; \tag{45}$$

λ_1 is defined above (32); U_1 is taken such that $U(x) = U_1 \cos G_1 x$. We take U_1 as negative in order to give an attractive potential at $x = 0$, in line with the example discussed following (15).

The form of (44) suggests that an electron in a crystal may behave as if it had a mass different from the free electron mass. There are crystals in which the effective mass of the carriers is much larger or much smaller than m; the effective mass may be anisotropic, and it may even be negative. Effective masses less than $0.01\ m$ have been observed. The crystal does not weigh any less if m^* is smaller than m, nor is Newton's second law violated for the crystal *taken as a whole*. The important point is that an electron in a periodic potential is accelerated relative to the lattice in an applied electric or magnetic field as if its mass were equal to an effective mass which we now define.

We look first at the motion of a wave packet in a linear crystal in an applied electric field E. Suppose that the wave packet is made up of states near a particular k value in a single band. We repeat from a general viewpoint an argument given for dk/dt in Chapter 7 for free electrons. We have already used the result (50) in the discussion of (40).

We assume the general expression for the group velocity $v_g = d\omega/dk$, a familiar result in wave optics. The frequency associated with a wavefunction of energy ϵ is given by $\omega = \epsilon/\hbar$, and so

$$v_g = \hbar^{-1} \frac{d\epsilon}{dk}. \tag{46}$$

The work $\delta\epsilon$ done on the electron by the electric field E in the time interval δt is

$$\delta\epsilon = -eEv_g\, \delta t. \tag{47}$$

We observe that

$$\delta\epsilon = \frac{d\epsilon}{dk}\, \delta k = \hbar v_g\, \delta k, \tag{48}$$

using (46). Thus on comparing (47) with (48) we have

$$\delta k = -(eE/\hbar)\, \delta t, \tag{49}$$

whence $\hbar \, dk/dt = -eE$, or

$$\hbar \frac{d\mathbf{k}}{dt} = \mathbf{F}.$$ (50)

This is an important relation: In a crystal $\hbar \, d\mathbf{k}/dt$ is equal to the external force on the electron. In free space $d(m\mathbf{v})/dt$ is equal to the force. We have not overthrown Newton's second law of motion: the electron in the crystal is subject to forces from the crystal lattice as well as from external sources. If we choose to express the motion of the electron in terms of the external force alone, it is not surprising that the resulting equation of motion is not simply $\mathbf{F} = m\mathbf{a}$. Perhaps it is more surprising that any good at all comes out of an approach involving only external forces.

From (46)

$$\frac{dv_g}{dt} = \hbar^{-1} \frac{d^2\epsilon}{dk \, dt} = \hbar^{-1} \left(\frac{d^2\epsilon}{dk^2} \frac{dk}{dt} \right).$$ (51)

Using (50) for dk/dt, we have

$$\frac{dv_g}{dt} = \frac{d^2\epsilon}{dk^2} \frac{F}{\hbar^2}; \qquad \frac{\hbar^2}{d^2\epsilon/dk^2} \frac{dv_g}{dt} = F.$$ (52)

It is evident that $\hbar^2/(d^2\epsilon/dk^2)$ plays the role of a mass. We call this quantity the **effective mass** m^*:

$$m^* = \frac{\hbar^2}{d^2\epsilon/dk^2}.$$ (53)

If the energy is a quadratic function of k we may write $\epsilon = (\hbar^2/2m^*)k^2$.

It is easy to generalize (53) to take account of an anisotropic energy surface. We find for the components of the effective mass tensor

$$\left(\frac{m}{m^*} \right)_{ij} = \frac{m}{\hbar^2} \frac{d^2\epsilon_{\mathbf{k}}}{dk_i \, dk_j},$$ (54)

where i, j are Cartesian coordinates. By (52) it is $(1/m^*)_{ij}$ which enters naturally into the equations of motion; note that this quantity is not in general the same as $1/(m^*)_{ij}$.

Physical Basis of the Effective Mass

How can an electron of mass m when put into a crystal respond to applied fields as if the mass were m^*? It is helpful to think of the process of Bragg reflection of electron waves in a lattice.

Consider the familiar weak binding approximation for which the band structure was shown in Fig. 7. Near the bottom of the lower band the state is represented quite adequately by a plane wave exp (ikx); the component exp $[i(k - G_1)x]$ is small and increases only slowly as k is increased, and in this region $m^* \cong m$. An increase in the reflected component exp $[i(k - G_1)x]$ represents momentum transfer between the lattice and the electron. Near the boundary the reflected component is quite large; at the boundary it becomes equal in amplitude to exp (ikx), at which point the eigenfunctions are standing waves, rather than running waves.

It is not surprising to find negative values for m^* just below a zone boundary. A negative[17] effective mass means that on going from state k to state $k + \Delta k$ the momentum transfer from the lattice to the electron is opposite to and larger than the momentum transfer from the applied force to the electron. Although k is increased by Δk by the applied electric field, the consequent Bragg reflection results in an overall decrease in the forward momentum of the electron, so that the effective mass may be described as being negative.

---

[17] A *single electron* in an energy band may have positive or negative effective mass: the states of positive effective mass occur near the bottom of a band because positive effective mass means that the band has upward curvature ($\partial^2 \epsilon / \partial k^2$ is positive). States of negative effective mass occur near the top of the band.

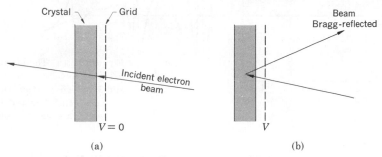

Figure 18   Explanation of light effective masses which occur near a Brillouin zone boundary. In (a) the energy of the electron beam incident on a thin crystal is slightly too low or too high to satisfy the condition for Bragg reflection and the beam is transmitted through the crystal. The application of a small voltage across the grid may, as in (b), cause the Bragg condition to be satisfied, and the electron beam will then be reflected from the appropriate set of crystal planes. We see that a small change in the energy of the electron beam has caused a very large change in the momentum of the beam; this situation corresponds to a light effective mass. The effective mass may be positive or negative in this experiment, according to whether the initial energy is above or below the Bragg energy. The crystal itself experiences the usual classical recoil when an electron is reflected.

As we proceed in the second band away from the boundary, the amplitude of $\exp[i(k - G_1)x]$ decreases and m^* assumes a small positive value. Here the increase in electron velocity resulting from a given impulse is larger than that which a free electron would experience. The lattice makes up the difference through the recoil it experiences when the amplitude of $\exp[i(k - G_1)x]$ is diminished. A pictorial discussion of this argument is given in Fig. 18.

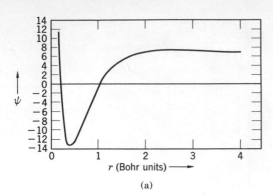

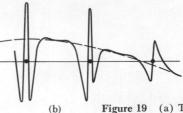

(b)

Figure 19 (a) The lowest wavefunction $u_0(\mathbf{r})$ of metallic sodium, after Wigner and Seitz. The unit of length is 0.529×10^{-8} cm. (b) Schematic wavefunction in sodium for a finite value of $\mathbf{k}$.

(a)

WAVEFUNCTIONS FOR ZERO WAVEVECTOR

It may appear to the reader that there is an inconsistency between the complicated form of the electron wavefunctions in free atoms and the usefulness of a nearly free electron model of the overall band structure. We now show that it is possible over most of a band for the energy to depend on the wavevector in approximately the same way as for a free electron. At the same time the wavefunction may be quite unlike a plane wave, but may pile up charge on the positive ion cores much as in the isolated atom.

The wave equation satisfied by the Bloch function (19) is

$$\left(\frac{1}{2m}p^2 + U(\mathbf{r})\right)e^{i\mathbf{k}\cdot\mathbf{r}}u_{\mathbf{k}}(\mathbf{r}) = \epsilon_{\mathbf{k}}e^{i\mathbf{k}\cdot\mathbf{r}}u_{\mathbf{k}}(\mathbf{r}). \tag{55}$$

With $\mathbf{p} \equiv -i\hbar$ grad,

$$\mathbf{p}e^{i\mathbf{k}\cdot\mathbf{r}}u_{\mathbf{k}}(\mathbf{r}) = \hbar\mathbf{k}e^{i\mathbf{k}\cdot\mathbf{r}}u_{\mathbf{k}}(\mathbf{r}) + e^{i\mathbf{k}\cdot\mathbf{r}}\mathbf{p}u_{\mathbf{k}}(\mathbf{r});$$

$$p^2e^{i\mathbf{k}\cdot\mathbf{r}}u_{\mathbf{k}}(\mathbf{r}) = (\hbar k)^2e^{i\mathbf{k}\cdot\mathbf{r}}u_{\mathbf{k}}(\mathbf{r}) + e^{i\mathbf{k}\cdot\mathbf{r}}(2\hbar\mathbf{k}\cdot\mathbf{p})u_{\mathbf{k}}(\mathbf{r}) + e^{i\mathbf{k}\cdot\mathbf{r}}p^2u_{\mathbf{k}}(\mathbf{r}); \tag{56}$$

thus (55) may be written as

$$\left(\frac{1}{2m}(\mathbf{p} + \hbar\mathbf{k})^2 + U(\mathbf{r})\right)u_{\mathbf{k}}(\mathbf{r}) = \epsilon_{\mathbf{k}}u_{\mathbf{k}}(\mathbf{r}). \tag{57}$$

At $\mathbf{k} = 0$ we have $\psi_0 = u_0(\mathbf{r})$, where $u_0(\mathbf{r})$ has the periodicity of the lattice and near the ion cores will look somewhat like the wavefunction in the free atom.

It is usually much easier to find a good solution at $\mathbf{k} = 0$ than for a general $\mathbf{k}$. Consider the function

$$\psi = u_0(\mathbf{r})e^{i\mathbf{k}\cdot\mathbf{r}}. \tag{58}$$

This is of the Bloch form, but it is not an exact solution of (55) because we have suppressed the dependence of u on $\mathbf{k}$. But the function is likely to be a much better approximation than a plane wave to the correct wavefunction. The energy of the approximate solution depends on $\mathbf{k}$ as $(\hbar k)^2/2m$, exactly as for the plane wave, even though the modulation represented by $u_0(\mathbf{r})$ may be very strong. The energy follows from (57) on omitting the cross-product term in $\mathbf{p}\cdot\mathbf{k}$; then u_0 is a solution of the rest of (57) with energy $\epsilon_0 + (\hbar k)^2/2m$.

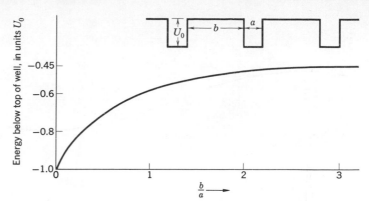

Figure 20 Ground state ($k = 0$) energy for an electron in a periodic square well potential of depth $|U_0| = 2\hbar^2/ma^2$. The energy is lowered as the wells come closer together. (Courtesy of C. Y. Fong.)

There is considerable interest in reliable calculations of $u_0(\mathbf{r})$, as this function often will give us a good picture of the distribution of charge within a unit cell. Wigner and Seitz developed a simple and fairly accurate method of calculating $u_0(\mathbf{r})$. Figure 19a shows the Wigner-Seitz wavefunction of lowest state in the conduction ($3s$) band of metallic sodium. The function is practically constant over 90 percent of the atomic volume. To the extent that the solutions for higher $\mathbf{k}$ may be approximated by $e^{i\mathbf{k}\cdot\mathbf{r}}u_0(\mathbf{r})$ as in (58), it will be true that the wavefunctions in the conduction band are similar to plane waves over most of the atomic volume, but may oscillate and increase markedly in the region of the ion core.

Lattice Effects on Cohesive Energy of Metals

In Chapter 8 we gave a primitive calculation of the binding energy of jellium, which is a uniform sea of electrons in which is imbedded the lattice of positive ion cores. We found in effect that the assembly was more tightly bound at a finite lattice constant than at an infinite lattice constant. Jellium is, however, less tightly bound than a free neutral hydrogen atom, so that it is unstable with respect to atomic hydrogen.[18] The minimum energy of the primitive model is found from Eq. (8.60) to be -0.37 rydberg, as compared with -1 rydberg (or -13.6 ev) for atomic hydrogen. To stabilize jellium we have to let the electron distribution pile up near the positive ions.

The stability of the alkali metals with respect to free atoms is due to the lowering of the energy of the Bloch state $\mathbf{k} = 0$ in the metal as compared with the ground electronic state in the free atom. This effect is illustrated by Fig. 20 for a linear periodic potential of attractive square wells. The ground state energy is much higher for isolated wells ($b/a \to \infty$) than for wells with close spacing. The decrease in the ground state energy for closely spaced wells in comparison with a single well is a consequence of the change in the boundary condition. For a single well we have the Schrödinger boundary condition that $\psi(x) \to 0$ as $x \to 0$; for the periodic array of wells the ground state is characterized by $d\psi/dx = 0$ at the midpoint of each potential barrier —this follows from the periodicity of ψ.

---

[18] And also with respect to molecular hydrogen.

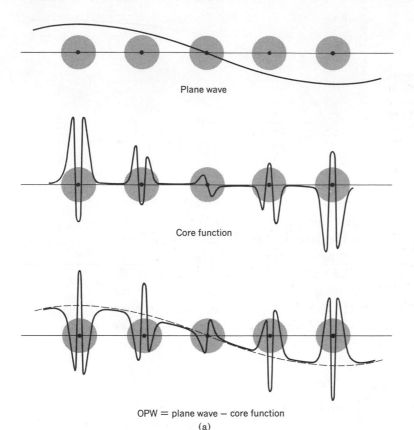

Plane wave

Core function

OPW = plane wave − core function

(a)

Figure 21a Construction of an orthogonalized plane wave, after Ziman.

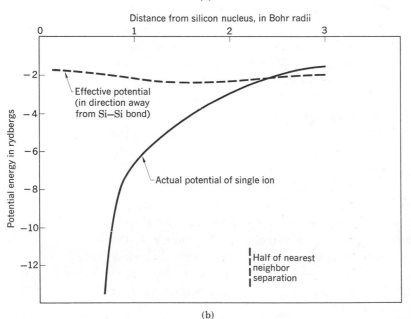

Distance from silicon nucleus, in Bohr radii

Effective potential (in direction away from Si–Si bond)

Actual potential of single ion

Half of nearest neighbor separation

Potential energy in rydbergs

(b)

Figure 21b The effective crystal potential which acts on an electron in the orthogonalized plane wave representation may be very much weaker than the actual crystal potential. The weak effective potential makes the energy band problem look much like a free electron problem. The curves are for silicon. (Courtesy of M. L. Cohen and T. K. Bergstresser.)

ORTHOGONALIZED PLANE WAVES

In (15) we expanded the Bloch function in plane waves:

$$\psi_k(r) = \sum_G C(k - G)e^{i(k-G)\cdot r}. \tag{59}$$

It takes very many plane waves in the summation to represent the rapid variation of the Bloch function near an ion core. It is possible to improve enormously the convergence of the procedure, in fact to reduce the expansion to a few terms, by working with a linear combination of a plane wave and an appropriate mixture of atomic wavefunctions from the occupied states of the ion cores, as in Fig. 21a. The new function is called an **orthogonalized plane wave** (OPW).

The admixture of core states provides the necessary structure, including nodes, in the wavefunction near each core. This theory[19] is given in QTS, Chap. 13. With the new OPW states it can be shown that the band energies may often be very close to the free electron energies, except for points in **k** space very near to a zone boundary. The explanation of this remarkable behavior is beyond the scope of this book. The essential result is that the effective potential which mixes two OPW's is very much less than the actual potential of the ion core which mixes two plane waves. Thus the model of nearly free electrons has the elements of the true problem. The actual and effective potentials for silicon are compared in Fig. 21b. The effective potentials for the OPW states are called **pseudopotentials.**

EXPERIMENTAL METHODS IN FERMI SURFACE STUDIES

A number of powerful experimental methods have been developed for studies of the Fermi surfaces of metals. These methods[20] include

a. Anomalous skin effect
b. Cyclotron resonance
c. Magnetoresistance
d. De Haas–van Alphen effect
e. Ultrasonic propagation in magnetic fields.

We shall discuss (b) and (d) for general Fermi surfaces. We have previously discussed (a) and (c), but only for free electrons.

---

[19] An application of the OPW method to the band structures of 14 semiconductor crystals is given by M. L. Cohen and T. K. Bergstresser, Phys. Rev. **141**, 789 (1966).

[20] Extensive discussions of the several methods are given by A. B. Pippard, *Dynamics of conductions electrons,* Gordon and Breach, 1965; and in W. A. Harrison and M. B. Webb (eds.), *The Fermi surface,* Wiley, 1960; and in *QTS.*

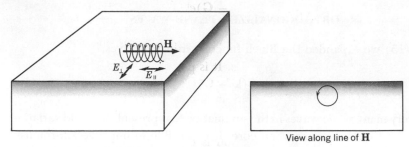

View along line of **H**

Figure 22 The Azbel-Kaner geometry is often employed for studies of cyclotron resonance in metals. The rf electric field **E** may be perpendicular or parallel to the static magnetic field **H**, but both **E** and **H** are parallel to the surface of the specimen. The penetration depth (skin depth) of the rf field is indicated by the shading. An electron orbit is shown. Near the top of each turn the electron enters the skin depth and experiences the rf electric field, gaining or losing energy from the field.

Cyclotron Resonance in Metals

The geometry employed in cyclotron resonance experiments in metals is sketched in Fig. 22. The radius of the orbit of an electron in a magnetic field of 10 kG is of the order of 10^{-3} cm, which is much larger than the skin depth at microwave frequencies in a pure metal at low temperatures. Electrons in orbits such as those drawn will see the rf electric field only for a small part of each cycle of their motion. Electrons can secure a net acceleration by the rf field if on successive cycles they arrive in the skin depth in the same phase of the rf field. The resonance condition is that the period T of the electron in its orbit should equal an integral number n of periods $2\pi/\omega$ of the rf field:

$$T = 2\pi n/\omega. \tag{60}$$

Now $T = 2\pi/\omega_c = 2\pi m_c^* c/eH$, where m_c^* denotes the effective mass for cyclotron resonance, so that the electrons will be in resonance at values of the magnetic field given by $2\pi m_c^* c/eH = 2\pi n/\omega$, or

$$H = \omega m_c^* c/en. \tag{61}$$

Many subharmonics ($n > 1$) have been observed, as in Fig. 23 for pure copper at helium temperatures. The results for copper support the model (Fig. 24) of the Fermi surface deduced by Pippard from work on the anomalous skin effect. The Fermi surface is distinctly nonspherical: necks make contact with the closest boundaries of the Brillouin zone.

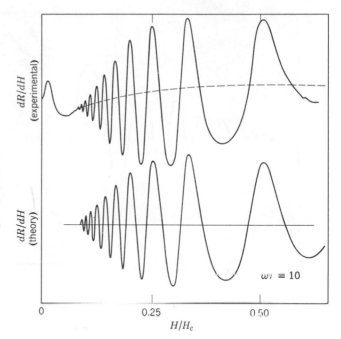

Figure 23 Cyclotron resonance in copper at 24 Gc/s. Comparison of calculations of the magnetic field dependence of the derivative of the surface resistivity with experimental results. Here H_c is the field (61) for $n = 1$. [After A. F. Kip, D. N. Langenberg, and T. W. Moore, Phys. Rev. **124**, 359 (1961).]

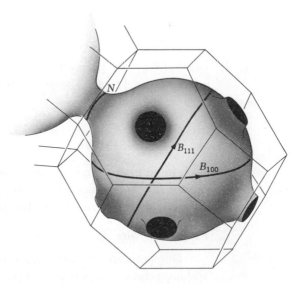

Figure 24 Fermi surface of copper, after Pippard. The Brillouin zone of the fcc structure is the truncated octahedron, as derived in Chapter 2. The Fermi surface makes contact with the boundary at the center of the hexagonal faces of the zone, in the [111] directions in **k** space. Two "belly" extremal orbits are shown, denoted by B, the extremal "neck" orbit is denoted by N.

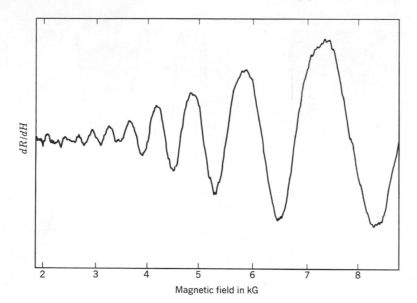

dR/dH

Magnetic field in kG

Figure 25 Experimental absorption derivative for cyclotron resonance in potassium at 68 Gc/s. The static magnetic field lies in a (110) plane; closely similar traces are obtained for all directions of **H** in this plane. [After C. C. Grimes and A. F. Kip, Phys. Rev. **132**, 1991 (1963).]

Resonance peaks for potassium are shown in Fig. 25: the measurements indicate that the Fermi surface is very nearly spherical, with an anisotropy of less than 1 percent. The measured effective mass is $m_c^* = (1.24 \pm 0.02)m$.

How is the period T related to the Fermi surface? From (41)

$$\frac{dk}{dt} = -\frac{eH}{\hbar^2 c} (\nabla \epsilon_{\mathbf{k}})_\perp, \tag{62}$$

where $(\nabla \epsilon_{\mathbf{k}})_\perp$ is proportional to the velocity component in real space in a plane normal to **H**. The period is found by integration of (62) around one cycle of the motion:

$$T = \oint dt = \frac{\hbar^2 c}{eH} \oint \frac{dk}{(\nabla \epsilon_{\mathbf{k}})_\perp}, \tag{63}$$

With some insight and ingenuity the essential features of the Fermi surface can usually be deduced from (63), given values of T measured for **H** in a variety of directions relative to the crystal axes.

Extremal Orbits

One point in the interpretation of cyclotron resonance in metals is subtle and important. For a spherical or ellipsoidal Fermi surface it can easily be shown that orbits on the Fermi surface in any plane normal to **H** have the identical period, independent of the value of k_H, the projection of **k** on the direction of **H**. But for a Fermi surface of general shape the sections at different values of k_H will have different periods. The power absorption will be the

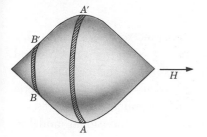

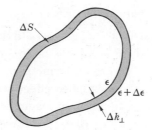

Figure 26   The orbits in the section AA' are extremal orbits: the cyclotron period is roughly constant over a reasonable section of the Fermi surface. Other orbits such as BB' vary in period over the section.

Figure 27   Orbits in **k** space at a constant value of k_H: one orbit is at energy ϵ, the other at energy $\epsilon + \Delta\epsilon$, where $\Delta\epsilon$ is constant. The spacing $\Delta k_\perp$ between the orbits may vary around an orbit. The shaded area between the orbits is ΔS.

sum of contributions from all sections or all orbits. But the *dominant response of the system comes from orbits whose periods are stationary with respect to small changes in k_H*. Such orbits are called **extremal orbits**. Thus in Fig. 26 the section AA' dominates the observed cyclotron period. The argument can be put in mathematical form, but we do not give the proof here. Essentially it is a question of phase cancellation: the contributions of different non-extremal orbits cancel, but near extrema the phase varies only slowly and there is a net signal from these orbits. Both theory and experiment agree that sharp resonances are obtained even from complicated Fermi surfaces because the experiments greatly accentuate the extremal orbits.

The expression (63) for the cyclotron period can be cast in a form which establishes the connection with the area S (in **k** space) of the Fermi surface section enclosed by the orbit. Let ΔS in Fig. 27 be the area between orbits having the same k_H but separated in energy by $\Delta\epsilon$. Because $(\nabla\epsilon_\mathbf{k})_\perp = (\Delta\epsilon)/(\Delta k)_\perp$, the integral in (63) may be writen as

$$\oint \frac{dk}{(\nabla\epsilon_\mathbf{k})_\perp} = \frac{1}{\Delta\epsilon}\oint (\Delta k)_\perp \, dk. \tag{64}$$

Now

$$\oint (\Delta k)_\perp \, dk = \Delta S \tag{65}$$

is the area between the two orbits, so that (63) may be written as

$$T = \frac{\hbar^2 c}{eH}\frac{\partial S}{\partial \epsilon} ; \qquad \omega_c = \frac{2\pi eH}{\hbar^2 c}\frac{\partial \epsilon}{\partial S} . \tag{66}$$

This expresses the cyclotron frequency in terms of the energy and the area of the orbit in **k** space in a section of Fermi surface normal to **H**. The orbits of extremal period which dominate the power absorption are also those whose area is extremal with respect to k_H.

De Haas–van Alphen Effect

In a strong[21] magnetic field the states of a free electron gas are not plane waves, and the energy is no longer given simply by $\epsilon_\mathbf{k} = \hbar^2 k^2/2m$. Several physical properties of the metal are changed remarkably by the magnetic field. The **de Haas–van Alphen effect** is concerned with oscillations in the magnetic moment as a function of magnetic field. The effect is much easier to discuss in two dimensions than in three dimensions; the two-dimensional model in most respects is not a bad approximation to reality because for real Fermi surfaces the extremal sections play the same dominant role as they played in cyclotron resonance. The de Haas–van Alphen effect arises from the periodic variation of the total electronic energy as a function of a static magnetic field. The energy variation is revealed experimentally as a periodic variation in the magnetic moment of the metal. We neglect the spin of the electron in the present discussion.

The energy levels of a free electron in two dimensions x, y in a magnetic field H normal to the xy plane are given by

$$\epsilon_l = \mu_B H(2l + 1), \tag{67}$$

where $\mu_B \equiv e\hbar/2mc$ and l is a quantum number which assumes integral values. This is the exact solution of a standard problem in elementary quantum mechanics. We do not give the derivation because when (67) is combined with the selection rule $\Delta l = \pm 1$ for transitions induced by a uniform electric field we have the standard result for the cyclotron resonance frequency

$$\hbar\omega_c = \epsilon_{l+1} - \epsilon_l = 2\mu_B H = e\hbar H/mc. \tag{68}$$

We now suppose that the energy of electrons on a general Fermi surface in two dimensions may be written as

$$\epsilon_l = (l + \tfrac{1}{2})\hbar\omega_c; \tag{69}$$

here ω_c is $2\pi/T$, with the period T given by (63) or (66). In the general case the phase factor in (69) need not be $\tfrac{1}{2}$, but we write it as $\tfrac{1}{2}$ to be concrete and to agree with (67) for free electrons.

If (68) is to agree with (66), we must have $\omega_c = eH/mc = (2\pi eH/\hbar^2 c)(\partial\epsilon/\partial S)$, or

$$S = \frac{2\pi eH}{\hbar c}(l + \tfrac{1}{2}) \tag{70}$$

for the area of the orbit in $\mathbf{k}$ space. Thus in a magnetic field the area of the orbit in $\mathbf{k}$ space is quantized! The flux quantum $\hbar c/e$ has the value 4.14×10^{-7} gauss/cm^2.

[21] By strong we mean fields such that an electron completes more than one cycle of a helical orbit before undergoing a collision, i.e., $\omega_c\tau \gg 1$, where ω_c is the cyclotron frequency. In practice we need low temperatures and pure specimens to satisfy this condition in the usual laboratory fields. The *dHvA* effect is not observable at room temperature.

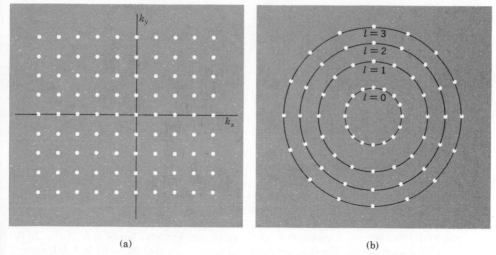

(a)   (b)

Figure 28   (a) Allowed electron states in two dimensions in absence of a magnetic field. (b) In a sufficiently strong magnetic field the points which represent the states of free electrons may be viewed as restricted to circles in the former $k_x k_y$ plane. The successive circles correspond to successive values of the quantum number l in the energy $(l + \frac{1}{2})\hbar\omega_c$. The area between successive circles is

$$\pi\,\Delta(k^2) = 2\pi k(\Delta k) = (2\pi m/\hbar^2)\,\Delta\epsilon = 2\pi m\omega_c/\hbar = 2\pi eH/\hbar c.$$

The angular position of the points has no significance. The number of states on a circle is constant and is equal to the area between successive circles times the number of states per unit area in (a), or $(2\pi eH/\hbar c)(L/2\pi)^2 = L^2 eH/2\pi\hbar c$, neglecting electron spin. By a sufficiently strong magnetic field we mean one such that an electron may complete at least several cycles of motion before colliding with a lattice imperfection, a phonon, or with the boundary of the specimen.

What happens in a magnetic field to the distribution of states in **k** space? The states are no longer described as in Fig. 28a by values of k_x and k_y, but instead are described by the quantum number l as in Fig. 28b. The number[22] of states of given l may be quite high, for every allowed state in (a) in the absence of the field has to be accommodated somewhere in (b) when the field is turned on. It is not hard to show[23] that for a square specimen of side L there are $(L/2\pi)^2(2\pi eH/\hbar c)$ states for each value of the quantum number l. This number of states is what we expect if each ring in Fig. 28b sweeps up the states in **k** space lying between it and an adjacent ring. We write for the degeneracy of a level l:

$$\boxed{\text{degeneracy} \equiv \xi H = (L/2\pi)^2(2\pi e/\hbar c)H,} \qquad (71)$$

where ξ is defined by this equation.

[22] This number is called the degeneracy. For $H = 0$, the density of states of a free electron gas in two dimensions is easily found by the arguments of Chap. 7 to be $\mathfrak{D}(\epsilon) = L^2 m/2\pi\hbar^2$, neglecting spin. The number of states in an energy range of extent $\hbar\omega_c$ is $\mathfrak{D}(\epsilon)\hbar\omega_c = L^2 eH/2\pi\hbar c$, in agreement with (71). Thus the application of a magnetic field collects the states of the continuum throughout an energy range $\hbar\omega_c$.

[23] *QTS*, Chap. 11.

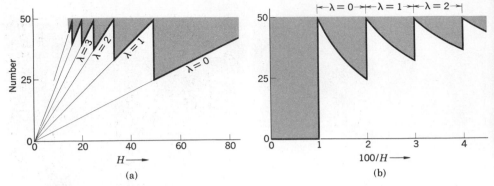

Figure 29 (a) The heavy line gives the number of particles in levels which are completely occupied in a magnetic field H, for a two-dimensional system with $N = 50$ and $\xi = 0.50$. The shaded area gives the number of particles in levels which are partially occupied. The value of λ denotes the quantum number of the highest level which is completely filled. Thus at $H = 40$ we have $\lambda = 1$: the levels $l = 0$ and $l = 1$ are filled and there are 10 particles in the level $l = 2$. At $H = 50$ the level $l = 2$ is empty. (b) The same points plotted against $1/H$; the periodicity in $1/H$ is evident.

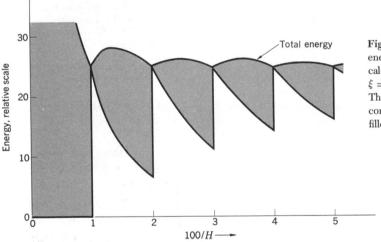

Figure 30 Plot of total energy versus $1/H$, calculated for $N = 50$, $\xi = 0.50$, and $\hbar\omega_c = H$. The shaded region is the contribution from partly filled levels.

Where does the Fermi level lie? For a system of N spinless electrons at absolute zero the energy levels are filled up to some quantum number λ, and states at the level $(\lambda + 1)$ will be partly filled to the extent needed to accommodate the electrons.[24] Because the degeneracy is proportional to H, the higher the field, the lower the value of λ. The distribution of electrons is shown in Fig. 29. As H is increased there occur certain values of H at which λ decreases abruptly by unity, as in Fig. 29. At these values of H no level is partly occupied, so that

$$\xi H_\lambda(\lambda + 1) = N, \tag{72}$$

---

[24] That is, λ is defined as the maximum value of l in (69) for which all states are filled with electrons.

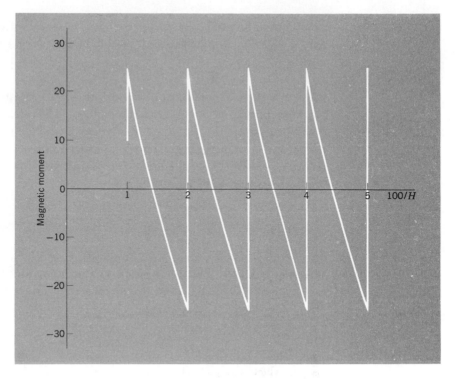

Figure 31 At absolute zero the magnetic moment is given by $-\partial E/\partial H$. The energy plotted in Fig. 30 leads to the magnetic moment shown here, which is an oscillatory function of $1/H$. The positive moments are paramagnetic (Chapter 14); the negative moments are diamagnetic. Effects of electron spin have not been included. In impure specimens or at finite temperatures the oscillations are reduced in amplitude or smudged out in part because the energy levels are no longer sharply defined.

This states that the degeneracy ξH_λ of a level times the number of filled levels $\lambda + 1$ is equal to the number of particles N. We rewrite (72) as

$$\frac{1}{H_\lambda} = \frac{\xi(\lambda + 1)}{N}. \tag{73}$$

It is now not surprising that certain properties of the system may be periodic in $1/H$, as in Fig. 29b, with the period ξ/N.

The energy of the electrons in *fully occupied* levels is

$$E_1 = \sum_{l=0}^{\lambda} (\xi H)(\hbar\omega_c)(l + \tfrac{1}{2}) = \tfrac{1}{2}(\xi H)(\hbar\omega_c)(\lambda + 1)^2 \tag{74}$$

where ξH is the number of electrons in each level, as in (71). The energy of the electrons in the *partly occupied* level $\lambda + 1$ is

$$E_2 = (\hbar\omega_c)(\lambda + \tfrac{3}{2})[N - (\xi H)(\lambda + 1)], \tag{75}$$

where $(\xi H)(\lambda + 1)$ is the number of electrons in the lower filled levels. The total energy of the system of N electrons is the sum of E_1 and E_2. The contributions to the energy are indicated in Fig. 30.

The magnetic moment μ of a system at absolute zero is given by $\mu = -\partial E/\partial H$. The moment for the system of Fig. 30 is an oscillatory function of $1/H$, as shown in Fig. 31. This oscillatory magnetic moment of the

Fermi gas at low temperatures is the de Haas–van Alphen effect. From (70) we see that the oscillations occur at equal intervals of $1/H$ such that

$$\Delta(1/H) = 2\pi e/\hbar cS, \tag{76}$$

where S is the extremal area of the Fermi surface normal to the direction of **H**. This period is identical with that of (73), for $\xi = L^2e/2\pi\hbar c$ and $N = (L/2\pi)^2S$.

From measurements of $\Delta(1/H)$ for different directions of **H** we can deduce the corresponding extremal areas S; thereby much can be inferred about the shape and size of the Fermi surface.[25]

EXAMPLE: *Fermi Surface of Gold.* In gold for quite a wide range of field directions Shoenberg finds the magnetic moment has a period of 2×10^{-9} gauss^{-1}. From (76) we see that this period corresponds to an extremal orbit of area

$$S = \frac{2\pi e/\hbar c}{\Delta(1/H)} \cong \frac{9.55 \times 10^7}{2 \times 10^{-9}} \cong 4.8 \times 10^{16} \text{ cm}^{-2}.$$

From Table 7.1 we have $k_F = 1.2 \times 10^8$ cm^{-1} for a free electron Fermi sphere for copper, which corresponds to an extremal area of 4.5×10^{16} cm^{-2}, in general agreement with the experimental value. The actual periods reported by Shoenberg are 2.05×10^{-9} gauss^{-1} for the orbit B_{111} of Fig. 32 and 1.95×10^{-9} gauss^{-1} for B_{100}. In the [111] direction in Au a large period of 6×10^{-8} gauss^{-1} is also found; the corresponding orbital area is 1.6×10^{15} cm^{-2}. This is the area of the "neck" orbit N of Fig. 24. Another extremal orbit, the "dog's bone," is shown in Fig. 32; its area in Au is about 0.4 of the belly area. Experimental results are shown in Figs. 33 and 34.

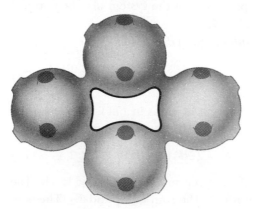

Figure 32 Dog's bone orbit of an electron on the Fermi surface of copper or gold in a magnetic field. The Fermi surface is also shown in Fig. 24.

---

[25] For references and a discussion of experimental methods, see D. Shoenberg, Proc. Phys. Soc. (London) **79**, 1–9 (1962).

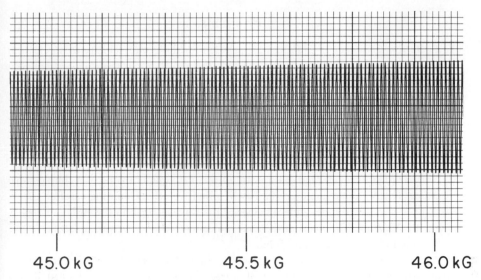

45.0 kG   45.5 kG   46.0 kG

Figure 33   De Haas-van Alphen effect in gold with **H** ∥ [110]. The oscillation is from the dog's bone orbit of Fig. 32. The signal is related to the second derivative of the magnetic moment with respect to field. The results were obtained by a field modulation technique in a high homogeneity superconducting solenoid at about 1.2°K. (Courtesy of I. M. Templeton.)

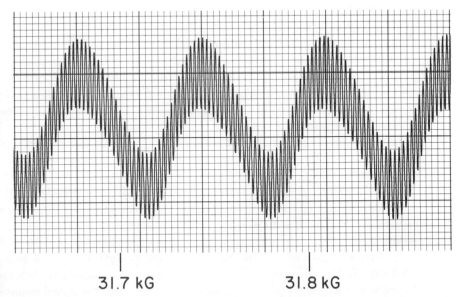

31.7 kG   31.8 kG

Figure 34   De Haas-van Alphen effect in gold with **H** ∥ [111], showing the belly (fine spacing) and neck (coarse spacing) oscillations. (Courtesy of I. M. Templeton.)

Problems

1. *Cyclotron frequency.* (a) Find an expression for the group velocity of an electron having energy $\epsilon_k = \hbar^2 k^2 / 2m^*$. (b) Show that $\omega_c = eH/m^*c$ is the angular frequency of the motion in a magnetic field H.

2. *Ellipsoidal energy surface.* Suppose that in an anisotropic crystal the electron energy is given by

$$\epsilon(\mathbf{k}) = \alpha_{xx}k_x^2 + \alpha_{yy}k_y^2 + \alpha_{zz}k_z^2.$$

Find the equations of motion which replace $\mathbf{F} = m\, d^2\mathbf{r}/dt^2$.

3. *Number of states.* (a) Derive the form of the first Brillouin zone of a simple cubic lattice. (b) A simple cubic crystal has N^3 primitive cells. Counting carefully, show that the number of independent values of the wavevector $\mathbf{k}$ in the Brillouin zone is exactly N^3. *Hint:* If p points of the zone are connected by a reciprocal lattice vector, they are to be counted as one point.

4. *Square lattice, free electron energies.* (a) Show for a simple square lattice (two dimensions) that the kinetic energy of a free electron at a corner of the first zone is higher than that of an electron at midpoint of a side face of the zone by a factor of 2. (b) What is the corresponding factor for a simple cubic lattice (three dimensions)? (c) What bearing might the result of (b) have on the conductivity of divalent metals?

5. *Brillouin zones of rectangular lattice.* Make a plot of the first two Brillouin zones of a primitive rectangular two-dimensional lattice with axes a, $b = 3a$.

6. *Brillouin zone, square lattice.* (a) Construct the fourth zone of the square lattice. (b) For the Fermi surface of Fig. 11, find in the reduced zone the form of that part of the Fermi surface which lies in the fourth zone.

7. *Cohesive energy for a square well potential.* (a) Find an expression for the binding energy of an electron in a single square well in one dimension of depth U_0 and width a. (This is the standard first problem in elementary quantum mechanics.) Assume that the solution is symmetric about the midpoint of the well. (b) Find a numerical result for the binding energy in terms of U_0 for the special case $|U_0| = 2\hbar^2/ma^2$ and compare with the appropriate limit of Fig. 20.

8. *Cyclotron resonance on spherical Fermi surface.* Show from (63) that the period of cyclotron resonance for a particle on a spherical Fermi surface is independent of the value of k_H, the projection of $\mathbf{k}$ on the direction of $\mathbf{H}$.

9. *De Haas–van Alphen period of potassium.* (a) Calculate the period $\Delta(1/H)$ expected for potassium on the free electron model. (b) What is the area in real space of the extremal orbit, for $H = 10$ kG?

10. *Properties of holes.* The energy near a valence band edge is given by $\epsilon_k = -1 \times 10^{-26} k^2$ ergs. An electron is removed from the state $\mathbf{k} = 1 \times 10^7\, \hat{\mathbf{k}}_x$ cm^{-1}. The band is otherwise full. (a) Give the sign and magnitude of the effective mass of the hole. (b) What is the direction and magnitude of the wavevector of the hole? (c) The crystal momentum of the hole? (d) The velocity of the hole? (e) The energy of the hole, referred to the valence band edge? (f) The electric current carried by the hole?

References

W. A. Harrison and M. B. Webb, ed., *The Fermi surface*, Wiley, 1960.

J. M. Ziman, *Principles of the theory of solids*, Cambridge University Press, 1964.

P. W. Anderson, *Concepts in solids*, Benjamin, 1963.

N. F. Mott and H. Jones, *Theory of the properties of metals and alloys*, Oxford, 1936. (Dover paperback reprint.)

R. Peierls, *Quantum theory of solids*, Oxford, 1955.

F. Seitz, *Modern theory of solids*, McGraw-Hill, 1940.

G. H. Wannier, *Elements of solid state theory*, Cambridge University Press, 1959.

A. H. Wilson, *Theory of metals*, 2nd ed., Cambridge University Press, 1953.

A. B. Pippard, *Dynamics of conduction electrons*, Gordon and Breach, 1965. (A geometrical discussion of Fermi surface phenomena.)

W. A. Harrison, *Pseudopotentials in the theory of metals*, Benjamin, 1966.

10

Semiconductor Crystals

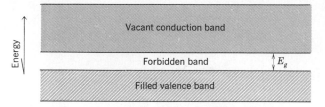

Figure 1 Band scheme for intrinsic conductivity in a semiconductor. At 0°K the conductivity is zero because all states in the valence band are filled and all states in the conduction band are vacant. As the temperature is increased, electrons are thermally excited from the valence band to the conduction band, where they become mobile.

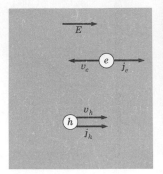

Figure 2 Motion of electrons and holes in electric field E. The directions of the carrier velocity and current are shown.

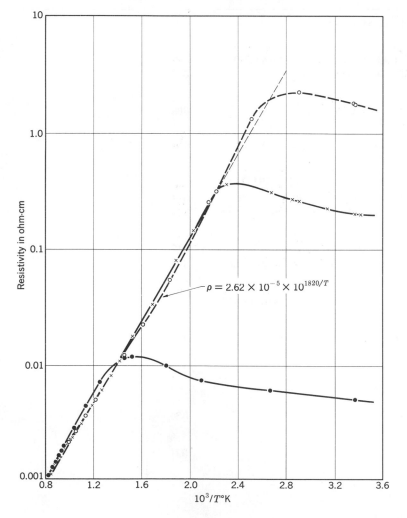

$$\rho = 2.62 \times 10^{-5} \times 10^{1820/T}$$

Figure 3 Log resistivity versus $1/T$ for three crystals of germanium with different concentrations of gallium as impurity. The impurity content affects the carrier concentration at low temperatures. The intrinsic region is at the left. In the intrinsic region the resistivity contains a factor exp $(E_g/2k_BT)$, where E_g is the energy gap. From these data $E_g = 0.72$ ev.

A semiconductor is an insulator in which in thermal equilibrium some charge carriers are mobile. At absolute zero a pure, perfect crystal of most semiconductors would be an insulator. The characteristic semiconducting properties are usually brought about by thermal agitation, impurities, lattice defects, or lack of stoichiometry (departure from nominal chemical composition). Semiconductors are understood in practice to be electronic conductors with values of the electrical resistivity at room temperature generally in the range $\sim 10^{-2}$ to $\sim 10^{9}$ ohm-cm, intermediate between good conductors ($\sim 10^{-6}$ ohm-cm) and insulators ($\sim 10^{14}$ to $\sim 10^{22}$ ohm-cm). The electrical resistivity of a semiconductor is usually strongly dependent on temperature. The devices based on the properties of semiconductors include transistors, rectifiers, modulators, detectors, thermistors, and photocells. We discuss in this chapter the central physical features of semiconductor crystals, particularly silicon and germanium; other important crystals include cuprous oxide (Cu_2O), selenium, PbTe, PbS, SiC, InSb, GaAs, and graphite.

INTRINSIC CONDUCTIVITY

Except at low temperatures a highly purified semiconductor exhibits intrinsic conductivity, as distinguished from the impurity conductivity of less pure specimens. We speak of the **intrinsic temperature range** as that in which the electrical properties of a semiconductor are not essentially modified by impurities in the crystal. The character of the electronic band scheme leading to intrinsic conductivity is indicated in Fig. 1. At absolute zero we postulate a vacant conduction band, separated by an energy gap E_g from a filled valence band. As the temperature is increased, electrons are thermally excited from the valence band to the conduction band. Both the electrons in the conduction band and the vacant states or holes left behind in the valence band will contribute to the electrical conductivity, as shown in Fig. 2. At temperatures below the intrinsic range the electrical properties are controlled by impurities, and here we speak of impurity conductivity or extrinsic conductivity. At sufficiently high temperatures, as in Fig. 3, the intrinsic conductivity is dominant, because there are more electrons in the valence band than there are electrons on the impurity atoms.

BAND GAP

The value of the intrinsic conductivity is controlled in large measure by the value of $E_g/k_B T$, the ratio of the band gap to the temperature. When this ratio is large, the concentration of intrinsic ionized carriers will be low. Values of the band gap of representative semiconductors are given in Table 1. These values usually are obtained in two ways, by optical absorption and by analysis of the dependence of conductivity on temperature.

Table 1   Values of the energy gap between the valence and conduction bands in semiconductors, at room temperature

Crystal	E_g, ev	Crystal	E_g, ev
Diamond	5.33	PbS	0.34–0.37
Si	1.14	PbSe	0.27
Ge	0.67	PbTe	0.30
InSb	0.23	CdS	2.42
InAs	0.33	CdSe	1.74
InP	1.25	CdTe	1.45
GaAs	1.4	ZnO	3.2
AlSb	1.6–1.7	ZnS	3.6
GaP	2.25	ZnSe	2.60
SiC	3	AgCl	3.2
Te	0.33	AgI	2.8
ZnSb	0.56	Cu_2O	2.1
GaSb	0.78	TiO_2	3

The threshold of continuous optical absorption at frequency ω_g determines the energy gap $E_g = \hbar\omega_g$ in Fig. 4a. Here a photon is absorbed by the crystal with the creation of an electron and a hole. This is the **direct process**. But if as in Fig. 4b the minimum energy gap involves electrons and holes separated by a substantial wavevector $\mathbf{k}_c$, a direct photon transition at the energy of the minimum gap cannot satisfy the requirement of conservation of wavevector: we cannot have $\mathbf{k}$ (photon) $= \mathbf{k}_c$ because photon wavevectors are negligible in magnitude at the energy range (~ 1 ev) of interest. If, however, a phonon

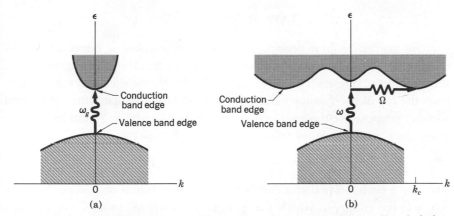

Figure 4 In (a) the lowest point of the conduction band occurs at the same value of **k** as the highest point of the valence band. A direct (vertical) optical transition is drawn with no significant change of **k**, because the absorbed photon has a very small wavevector. The threshold frequency ω_g for absorption by the direct transition determines the energy gap $E_g = \hbar\omega_g$. The indirect transition in (b) involves both a photon and a phonon because the band edges of the conduction and valence bands are widely separated in **k** space. The threshold energy for the indirect process in (b) is greater than the true band gap. The absorption threshold for the indirect transition between the band edges is at $\hbar\omega = E_g + \hbar\Omega$, where Ω is the frequency of an emitted *phonon* of wavevector $\mathbf{K} \cong -\mathbf{k}_c$. If a phonon is absorbed, the threshold energy is $\hbar\omega = E_g - \hbar\Omega$.

of wavevector **K** and frequency Ω is created in an **indirect process**,[1] then we can have

$$\mathbf{k}\,(\text{photon}) = \mathbf{k}_c + \mathbf{K} \cong 0; \qquad \hbar\omega = E_g + \hbar\Omega,$$

as required. The phonon energy $\hbar\Omega$ will generally be much less than E_g: in effect we use the phonon as an inexpensive source of crystal momentum, inexpensive because phonon energies are characteristically small ($\sim$0.01–0.03 ev) in comparison with the energy gap. If the temperature is sufficiently high that the necessary phonon is already available, it is possible to have also a process in which the phonon is absorbed.

The band gap may also be deduced from the temperature dependence of the conductivity or the carrier concentration in the intrinsic range. The carrier concentration may be obtained from the Hall effect (Chapter 8), sometimes supplemented by conductivity measurements.

---

[1] The band edges in Ge and in Si are connected as in Figs. 12 and 13 below by indirect transitions; the band edges in InSb, for example, are connected by a direct transition. See also the discussion of excitons in Chapter 17.

LAW OF MASS ACTION

We first calculate in terms of the chemical potential or Fermi level μ the number of electrons excited to the conduction band at temperature T. In semiconductor physics μ is called the **Fermi level**. We measure the energy ϵ from the top of the valence band, as in Fig. 5. At the temperatures of interest we may suppose for the conduction band that $\epsilon - \mu \gg k_B T$, and the Fermi-Dirac distribution function reduces to

$$f \cong e^{(\mu - \epsilon)\beta}, \qquad (\beta \equiv 1/k_B T). \tag{1}$$

This is the probability that a conduction electron state is occupied. We recall that μ is the energy at which $f = \frac{1}{2}$, but (1) is written in an approximation valid for $f \ll 1$. We suppose that in the conduction band

$$\epsilon_{\mathbf{k}} = E_g + \hbar^2 k^2 / 2m_e, \tag{2}$$

where m_e is the effective mass of an electron. Thus from (7.38) the number of states with energy between ϵ and $\epsilon + d\epsilon$ is

$$\mathcal{D}_e(\epsilon)\, d\epsilon = \frac{1}{2\pi^2} \left(\frac{2m_e}{\hbar^2} \right)^{3/2} (\epsilon - E_g)^{1/2}\, d\epsilon \tag{3}$$

per unit volume. Combining (1) and (3), we have for the number of electrons in the conduction band per unit volume

$$n = \int_{E_g}^{\infty} \mathcal{D}_e(\epsilon) f_e(\epsilon)\, d\epsilon = \frac{1}{2\pi^2} \left(\frac{2m_e}{\hbar^2} \right)^{3/2} e^{\mu\beta} \int_{E_g}^{\infty} (\epsilon - E_g)^{1/2} e^{-\epsilon\beta}\, d\epsilon, \tag{4}$$

which integrates to

$$n = 2(2\pi m_e k_B T/h^2)^{3/2} e^{(\mu - E_g)\beta}. \tag{5}$$

We have not solved the problem until μ is known. It is useful to calculate the equilibrium concentration of holes p. The distribution function f_h for holes is related to the electron distribution function f_e by $f_h = 1 - f_e$, because a hole is defined as the absence of an electron. We have

$$f_h = 1 - \frac{1}{e^{(\epsilon - \mu)\beta} + 1} = \frac{1}{e^{(\mu - \epsilon)\beta} + 1} \cong e^{(\epsilon - \mu)\beta}, \tag{6}$$

provided $(\mu - \epsilon) \gg k_B T$. If the holes near the top of the valence band behave as particles with effective mass m_h, the density of hole states is given by

$$\mathcal{D}_h(\epsilon)\, d\epsilon = \frac{1}{2\pi^2} \left(\frac{2m_h}{\hbar^2} \right)^{3/2} (-\epsilon)^{1/2}\, d\epsilon, \tag{7}$$

recalling that the energy is measured positive upwards from the top of the

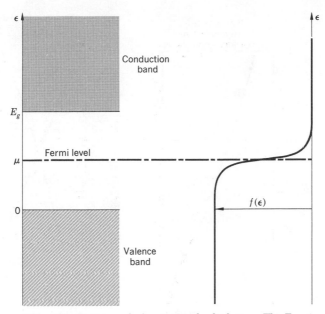

Figure 5   Energy scale for statistical calculations. The Fermi distribution function is shown on the same scale, for a temperature $k_B T \ll E_g$; the Fermi level μ is taken to lie in the band gap, as for an intrinsic semiconductor.

valence band. Proceeding as before, we find

$$p = \int_{-\infty}^{0} \mathfrak{D}_h(\epsilon) f_h(\epsilon) \, d\epsilon = 2(2\pi m_h k_B T / h^2)^{3/2} e^{-\mu\beta} \qquad (8)$$

for the concentration p of holes in the valence band.

On multiplying together the expressions for n and p we have the useful equilibrium relation:

$$\boxed{np = 4(2\pi k_B T / h^2)^3 (m_e m_h)^{3/2} e^{-E_g \beta}.} \qquad (9)$$

This result does not involve the Fermi level μ. It is an expression of the law of mass action.[1a] We have nowhere assumed in the derivation that the material is intrinsic: the result (9) holds in the presence of impurities as well. The only

[1a] A simple kinetic argument shows that the product np is constant at a given temperature. Suppose that the equilibrium population of electrons and holes is maintained by black-body photon radiation. The photons generate electron-hole pairs at a rate $A(T)$, while $B(T)np$ is the rate of the recombination reaction $e + h =$ photon. Then

$$dn/dt = A(T) - B(T)np = dp/dt.$$

In equilibrium $dn/dt = 0$; $dp/dt = 0$, whence $np = A(T)/B(T)$. Note that (9) does not involve the concentration of *atoms* in the crystal.

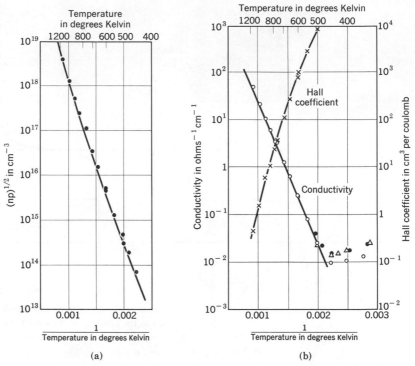

Figure 6 (a) Log of carrier concentration product $(np)^{1/2}$ in the intrinsic range of silicon as a function of reciprocal absolute temperature. The plotted points are derived from experiment. The solid curve is an empirical fit to the points below 700°K: $np = 1.5 \times 10^{33} \, T^3$ exp $(-1.21/k_B T)$, with the Boltzmann constant in ev/deg K. From this expression we find the energy gap $E_g(T = 0) = 1.21$ ev. (b) Conductivity and Hall coefficient in the intrinsic range of silicon. [After F. J. Morin and J. P. Maita, Phys. Rev. **96**, 28 (1954).]

assumption made in (9) is that the distance of the Fermi level from the edge of both bands should be large in comparison with $k_B T$. Experimental results[2] for silicon are shown in Fig. 6. At 300°K the value of np is 5.7×10^{26} cm^{-6} for Ge and 2.2×10^{20} cm^{-6} for Si.

We note from (9) that the product of the electron and hole concentrations is a constant independent of impurity concentration at a given temperature: introducing a small proportion of a suitable impurity to increase n, say, must decrease p, because the product must remain constant. This result is important in practice—we can reduce the total carrier concentration $n + p$, sometimes enormously, by the controlled introduction of suitable impurities. This reduction is called **compensation.**

---

[2] The coefficient of exp $(-E_g/k_B T)$ in Fig. 6 is considerably larger than the value calculated from (9). Note that if the gap depends on temperature as $E_g(T) = E_g(0)(1 - \alpha T)$, then a temperature-independent factor exp $(\alpha E_g/k_B)$ is introduced in front of exp $[-E_g(0)/k_B T]$.

INTRINSIC CARRIER CONCENTRATION

For an intrinsic semiconductor $n = p$: the thermal excitation of an electron from the valence band leaves behind a hole. Thus from (9) we have, letting the subscript i denote intrinsic,

$$n_i = p_i = 2(2\pi k_B T/h^2)^{3/2}(m_e m_h)^{3/4} e^{-E_g \beta/2}. \qquad (10)$$

The intrinsic carrier excitation depends exponentially on $E_g/2k_B T$, where E_g is the width of the forbidden gap. On setting (5) and (8) equal we have

$$e^{2\mu\beta} = (m_h/m_e)^{3/2} e^{E_g \beta} \qquad (11)$$

or

$$\mu = \tfrac{1}{2}E_g + \tfrac{3}{4}k_B T \log (m_h/m_e). \qquad (12)$$

If $m_h = m_e$, then $\mu = \tfrac{1}{2}E_g$ and the Fermi level is in the middle of the forbidden gap.

Mobility in the Intrinsic Region

The **mobility**[3] is defined as the magnitude of the drift velocity per unit electric field:

$$\mu = |v|/E.$$

The mobility is defined as positive for both electrons and holes, even though their drift velocities are opposite.

In an ideal intrinsic semiconductor the mobility is determined by lattice scattering; that is, by collisions between electrons and phonons. In actual intrinsic specimens there are always some impurity atoms that may dominate the scattering of electrons at low temperatures when phonons are not present, but at higher temperatures the lattice scattering is dominant.

The electrical conductivity in the presence of both electrons and holes is given by the sum of the separate contributions:

$$\sigma = (ne\mu_e + pe\mu_h), \qquad (13a)$$

where n and p are the concentrations of electrons and holes. On comparison with the expression (7.59) for the static conductivity we have

$$\mu_e = e\tau_e/m_e; \qquad \mu_h = e\tau_h/m_h. \qquad (13b)$$

The mobilities are likely to depend on temperature as a simple power law over an appropriate region. The temperature dependence of the conductivity in the intrinsic region will be dominated by the exponential dependence

---

[3] By writing μ_e or μ_h for the electron or hole mobility we can avoid any confusion between μ as the chemical potential and μ as the mobility.

Table 2 Carrier mobilities at room temperature
(Most of the values are probably representative of lattice scattering)

Crystal	Mobility, cm²/volt-sec		Crystal	Mobility, cm²/volt-sec	
	Electrons	Holes		Electrons	Holes
Diamond	1800	1200	GaSb	2500–4000	650
Si	1600	400	PbS	600	200
Ge	3800	1800	PbSe	900	700
InSb	77,000	1250	PbTe	17,000	–
InAs	23,000	~100	AgCl	50	–
InP	3400	650	KBr (100°K)	100	–

$\exp\left(-E_g/2k_BT\right)$ of the carrier concentration. This is the basis for the use of conductivity data in the determination of the energy gap.

Experimental values of the mobility[4] at room temperature are given in Table 2. By comparison, the mobility in metallic copper is 35 cm²/volt-sec at room temperature. In most substances quoted the values are probably representative of lattice scattering, i.e., scattering by phonons. There is a tendency for crystals with small energy gaps to have high values of the electron mobility. As discussed in Chapter 9, small gaps lead to small effective masses, which favor high mobilities.

The mobility in esu is expressed in cm²/statvolt-sec and is 300 times higher than the mobility expressed in cm²/volt-sec.

IMPURITY CONDUCTIVITY

Certain types of impurities and imperfections affect drastically the electrical properties of a semiconductor. The addition of boron to silicon in the proportion of 1 boron atom to 10^5 silicon atoms increases the conductivity of pure silicon by a factor of 10^3 at room temperature. In a compound semiconductor a stoichiometric deficiency of one constituent will act as an impurity; such semiconductors are known as **deficit semiconductors** (see Problem 6). The deliberate addition of impurities to a semiconductor is called **doping**.

We consider in particular the effect of impurities in silicon and ger-

[4] For electron mobilities in alkali halide crystals, see R. K. Ahrenkiel and F. C. Brown, Phys. Rev. **136**, A223 (1964).

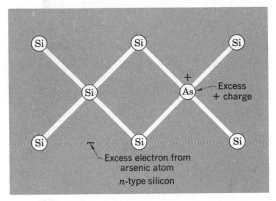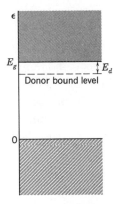

Figure 7 Charges associated with impurity atom in silicon: with arsenic impurity an electron is available for conduction; with boron impurity a positive hole is available. The arsenic atom is called a **donor** atom because when ionized it gives up an electron to the conduction band.

manium. These elements crystallize in the diamond structure, as shown in Fig. 1.29. Each atom forms four covalent bonds, one with each of its four nearest neighbors, corresponding to the chemical valence four. If an impurity atom of valence five, such as phosphorus, arsenic, or antimony, is substituted in the lattice in place of a normal atom, there will be one valence electron from the impurity atom left over after the four covalent bonds are established with the nearest neighbors, that is, after the impurity atom has been accommodated in the structure with as little disturbance as possible.

The situation shown in Fig. 7 is a structure with an excess positive charge from the impurity atom which has lost one electron, and there is also the excess electron. It is verified by lattice constant studies and by determining the density of carriers that the pentavalent impurities enter the lattice by substitution for normal atoms, rather than by going into interstitial positions. Impurity atoms which may be ionized to give up an electron are called **donors**. The crystal as a whole remains neutral.

The excess electron moves in the Coulomb potential $e/\epsilon r$ of the impurity ion, where ϵ in a covalent crystal is the static dielectric constant of the medium. The factor $1/\epsilon$ takes account of the reduction in the Coulomb force between charges caused by the electronic polarization of the medium. This treatment is valid for orbits large in comparison with the distance between atoms, and for slow motions of the electron such that the orbital frequency is low in comparison with the frequency ω_g corresponding to the energy gap. These conditions are satisfied quite well in Ge and Si by the extra electron of P, As, or Sb.

IMPURITY STATES

We now estimate the binding energy of the donor impurity. The Bohr theory of the hydrogen atom may readily be modified to take into account both the dielectric constant of the medium and the effective mass of an electron in the periodic potential of the crystal. We replace e^2 by e^2/ϵ and m by m^* in the standard result of the Bohr theory.

For an electron in atomic hydrogen in a state of principal quantum number n the energy is $-e^4m/2\hbar^2n^2$. On making the indicated replacements we have

$$E_n = -\frac{e^4m^*}{2\epsilon^2\hbar^2n^2} \tag{14}$$

in the semiconductor. The Bohr radius is $n^2\hbar^2/e^2m$ for the nth state of hydrogen; thus in the semiconductor

$$r_n = \frac{\epsilon n^2\hbar^2}{e^2m^*}. \tag{15}$$

The application to germanium and silicon is complicated by the anisotropic effective mass of the conduction electrons, as discussed in (28) and (29) below. But the dielectric constant is the most important correction to the energy: it enters the energy (14) as the square, whereas the effective mass enters only as the first power. We may obtain a general impression of the impurity levels by using an "average" value of $1/m^*$ to represent the anisotropic effective masses: we shall use $m^* \approx 0.1\ m$ for electrons in germanium and $m^* \approx 0.2\ m$ for electrons in silicon. The dielectric constant has the value 15.8 for germanium and 11.7 for silicon; these values apply with fair accuracy from low frequencies up to the frequencies corresponding to the energy gap, so that the values should be applicable to the present problem where the orbital frequency of motion of the electron about the donor atom is very much less than the frequency corresponding to the gap.

The ionization energy of the free hydrogen atom is 13.6 ev. For germanium the donor ionization energy E_d on our model is 0.006 ev, reduced with respect to hydrogen by the factor $m^*/m\epsilon^2 = 4 \times 10^{-4}$. The corresponding result for silicon is 0.02 ev. Calculations[5] using the correct anisotropic mass tensor predict 0.00905 ev for germanium and 0.0298 ev for silicon. Further corrections for silicon have been considered by Luttinger and Kohn. Observed values of donor ionization energies are given in Table 3. The values are obtained by thermal considerations to be described and also by direct optical absorption.

We note from (15) that the radius of the first Bohr orbit is increased by

[5] J. M. Luttinger and W. Kohn, Phys. Rev. **98**, 915 (1955); M. Lampert, Phys. Rev. **97**, 352 (1955); C. Kittel and A. H. Mitchell, Phys. Rev. **96**, 1488 (1954); see also QTS, Chap. 14.

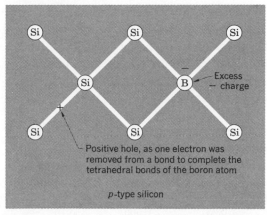
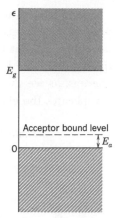

Figure 8 With boron impurity a positive hole is available for ionization and conduction. The boron atom is called an **acceptor** atom because when ionized it takes up an electron from the valence band. (The ionization of the hole associated with the acceptor corresponds to the addition of an electron to the acceptor, the hole moving to the former state of the valence electron.)

$\epsilon m/m^*$ over the value 0.53 Å for the free hydrogen atom. The corresponding radius is $(160)(0.53) \cong 80$ Å in germanium and $(60)(0.53) \cong 30$ Å in silicon.

Lithium acts as a donor in Ge and Si, although it enters the lattice interstitially between normal atom sites and not substitutionally. The $2s$ valence electron of Li is the donor electron.

Just as an electron may be bound to a pentavalent impurity, a hole may be bound to a trivalent impurity in germanium or silicon, as in Fig. 8. Typical trivalent impurities are B, Al, Ga, and In. Such impurities are called **acceptors,** because they can take up electrons from the valence band, leaving holes in the band. To ionize an acceptor, we must raise an electron in energy: we bring the electron to the acceptor, and take the hole into the valence band. The acceptor problem is similar in principle to that for electrons, although the initial strain of visualization on the reader is greater. On the usual energy band diagram an electron sinks when it loses energy, whereas a hole rises in losing energy.

Table 3 Donor ionization energies E_d
of pentavalent impurities in
germanium and silicon, in ev

	P	As	Sb
Si	0.045	0.049	0.039
Ge	0.0120	0.0127	0.0096

Experimental values of the ionization energies of acceptors in germanium and silicon are given in Table 4. It is seen that the ionization energies for acceptors are not unlike those for donors. The modified Bohr model applies qualitatively for holes just as for electrons, but in germanium and silicon there is, as we shall see, a degeneracy at the top of the valence band which complicates the effective mass problem.

Table 4   Acceptor ionization energies E_a of trivalent impurities in germanium and silicon, in ev

	B	Al	Ga	In
Si	0.045	0.057	0.065	0.16
Ge	0.0104	0.0102	0.0108	0.0112

A glance at Tables 3 and 4 shows that the donor and acceptor ionization energies may be comparable with $k_B T$ at room temperature (0.026 ev). We therefore expect the thermal ionization of donors and acceptors to be important in the electrical conductivity of germanium and silicon at room temperature. If donor atoms are present in considerably greater numbers than acceptors, the thermal ionization of donors will cause electrons to be freed in the conduction band. The conductivity of the specimen will be controlled by electrons (negative charges) and the material is said to be n type. If acceptors are dominant, holes will be freed in the valence band and the conductivity will be controlled by holes (positive charges): the material is p type. The sign of the Hall voltage (Chapter 8) is a rough test for n or p type.

We recall that the numbers of holes and electrons are equal in the absence of impurities: such material is described as intrinsic. The intrinsic electron concentration n_i at 300°K is 2.5×10^{13} cm^{-3} in germanium and 1.4×10^{10} cm^{-3} in silicon; the electrical resistivity of intrinsic material is 43 ohm-cm for germanium and 2.6×10^5 ohm-cm for silicon. The lowest impurity concentrations attained at present are of the order of 10^{12} impurity atoms per cm^3 so that we may obtain germanium intrinsic at room temperature, but not silicon. Impurities which do not ionize have no effect on the carrier concentration and may be present in higher proportions without being detected in electrical measurements.

THERMAL IONIZATION OF IMPURITIES

We now calculate the concentration n of conduction electrons from ionized donors at a temperature T. We assume that there are no acceptors. Further, we suppose there are sufficient donors ionized to suppress by (9) the concentration of holes to a value much below the intrinsic value (10). The suppression occurs because the product np is constant at a given temperature. If n is increased by adding donors, p must decrease. Let N_d, N_d^+, N_d^0 be the concentrations of donors, ionized donors, and neutral (un-ionized) donors respectively. The conduction electron concentration $n = N_d^+$, because each conduction electron results from the ionization of a donor atom, by virtue of the suppression of the intrinsic holes and electrons.

The Fermi distribution function gives us the fractional occupancy of any state. The donor level, referred to the top of the valence band as the zero of energy, is at $E_g - E_d$; thus

$$N_d^0 = N_d f(E_g - E_d - \mu) = \frac{N_d}{1 + \exp \beta(E_g - E_d - \mu)} \; ; \qquad (16)$$

$$N_d^+ = N_d - N_d^0 = \frac{N_d}{1 + \exp\left[-\beta(E_g - E_d - \mu)\right]} . \qquad (17)$$

But the conduction electron concentration n must satisfy (5); because $n - N_d^+$ we equate (5) and (17) to obtain

$$n = n_0 \exp \beta(\mu - E_g) = \frac{N_d}{1 + \exp \beta(\mu - E_g + E_d)}, \qquad (18)$$

where we have defined $n_0 \equiv 2(2\pi m_e k_B T/h^2)^{3/2}$.

We consider the low temperature limit $E_d/k_B T \gg 1$. Then (18) reduces to

$$\exp 2\beta(\mu - E_g) \cong (N_d/n_0) \exp(-\beta E_d); \qquad (19)$$

this determines the Fermi level. Thus (18) becomes

$$n \cong (n_0 N_d)^{1/2} \exp(-\tfrac{1}{2}\beta E_d). \qquad (20)$$

In this limit the electron concentration varies as the square root of the donor concentration. At low temperatures, however, there may be fewer conduction electrons than there are acceptor atoms present as an unavoidable impurity. A number of donor atoms are ionized in filling up the acceptors, and this process tends to pin down the Fermi level[6] at $E_g - E_d$, rather than as given by (19). Then n varies as $\exp(-E_d/k_B T)$ and not as $\exp(-E_d/2k_B T)$.

Identical results hold for acceptors, appropriate changes being made, under the assumption $N_d = 0$. If the donor and acceptor concentrations are comparable, then affairs are quite complicated, and one usually has to solve the equations by numerical methods.

---

[6] The steplike form of the Fermi function means that the Fermi level μ is likely to be close to a level which is neither nearly all ionized nor nearly all un-ionized.

Mobility in the Presence of Impurities

Scattering by phonons determines the mobility of carriers when relatively few impurity atoms are present, or at high temperatures. Scattering by impurity atoms may be important at higher impurity concentrations. The scattering will depend on whether the impurity is neutral or ionized. The neutral atom problem is equivalent to the scattering of an electron by a hydrogen atom. We note that the area of the first Bohr orbit is increased by $(\epsilon m/m^*)^2$. An exact solution for the neutral scattering cross-section is quite difficult in the energy range of interest in semiconductors. The scattering of carriers by ionized donors or acceptors has been treated by Conwell and Weisskopf, who utilized the Rutherford scattering formula. The effect of impurity scattering in reducing the mobility is shown in Fig. 9 for electrons in AgCl.

Analysis of Experimental Results

A good general picture of the physical behavior of a semiconductor can be obtained by measuring[7] the electrical conductivity and Hall coefficient as functions of temperature and impurity doping over wide ranges.

In a simple metal the Hall coefficient is given by

$$R_H = -\frac{1}{nec},\tag{21}$$

where n is the electron concentration. In semiconductors the connection between R_H and n may vary slightly from (21) according to the form of the dependence of the mean free path on velocity. Results on carrier concentration deduced from measurements of the Hall voltage versus temperature for a set of silicon crystals doped with arsenic donors are shown in Fig. 10a. Above room temperature the donors are essentially all ionized. Below $100°K$ the carrier concentration decreases as the donors become un-ionized. From the slope of the plot we estimate the ionization energy of the donors to be ~ 0.05 ev, using (20).

If the current carriers are predominantly of one type only, we may obtain the mobility μ simply from the product of the conductivity and the Hall coefficient

$$c|R_H|\sigma = c\left(\frac{1}{nec}\right)\left(\frac{ne^2\tau}{m^*}\right) = \frac{e\tau}{m^*} = \mu,\tag{22}$$

apart from factors of the order of unity. The product $c|R_H|\sigma$ is called the **Hall mobility.** The temperature dependence of the Hall mobility for the set of arsenic-doped silicon crystals is shown in Fig. 10b.

[7] For germanium see E. M. Conwell, Proc. I.R.E. **40**, 1327 (1952); P. P. Debye and E. M. Conwell, Phys. Rev. **93**, 693 (1954); for silicon see F. J. Morin and J. P. Maita, Phys. Rev. **96**, 28 (1954).

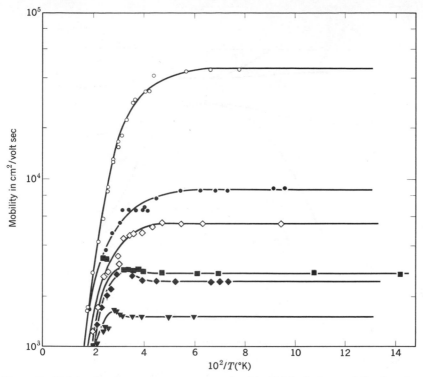

Figure 9 Mobility for electrons in various crystals of AgCl. The highest mobility found is 45000 cm²/volt-sec. The mobility at low temperatures is limited by crystal purity and at high temperatures by scattering by optical phonons. (After T. Masumi, R. K. Ahrenkiel, and F. C. Brown.)

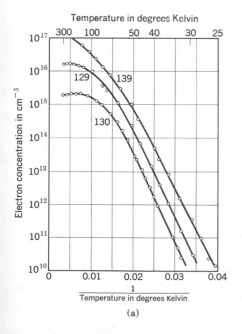

(a)

Figure 10 Silicon specimens containing arsenic. (a) Charge carrier concentration as a function of reciprocal absolute temperature; (b) Mobility as a function of temperature. (After Morin and Maita.)

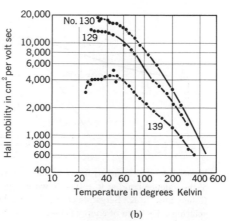

(b)

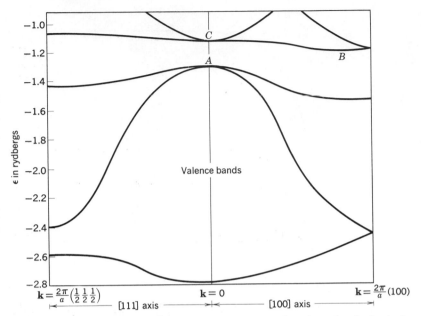

Figure 11 Calculated energy band structure of silicon. The valence band edge is at *A*; the conduction band edge is at *B*. Spin-orbit interaction has not been shown, it splits the valence band edge at *A* by 0.044 ev. The energy gap from *A* to *B* is 1.08 ev; the vertical gap *A* to *C* is 3.4 ev.

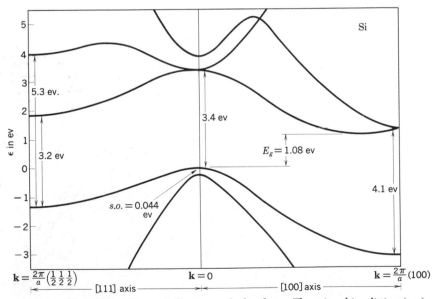

Figure 12 The band structure of silicon near the band gap. The spin-orbit splitting (s.o.) of the valence band at $k = 0$ is shown exaggerated. The band structure calculated by M. L. Cohen and T. K. Bergstresser has been adjusted slightly to fit the known experimental splittings. The zero of energy is taken at the top of the valence band.

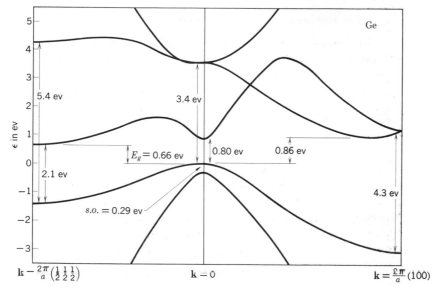

Figure 13 The band structure of germanium near the band gap. The spin-orbit splitting (s.o.) of the valence band at $k = 0$ is shown. The band structure calculated by M. L. Cohen and T. K. Bergstresser has been adjusted slightly to fit the known experimental splittings.

ENERGY BANDS IN Si AND Ge

The gross structure of the conduction and valence bands of silicon is shown in Fig. 11, based on a combination of theoretical and experimental results. Further details are given in Fig. 12 for Si and Fig. 13 for Ge.

The valence band edge in both crystals is at $k = 0$ and is derived from $p_{3/2}$ and $p_{1/2}$ states of the free atoms. The $p_{3/2}$ level is four-fold degenerate as in the atom; the four states correspond to m_J values $\pm\frac{3}{2}$ and $\pm\frac{1}{2}$. The $p_{1/2}$ level is doubly degenerate, with $m_J = \pm\frac{1}{2}$. The $p_{3/2}$ states are higher in energy than the $p_{1/2}$ states; the difference in energy is a measure of the spin-orbit interaction.

The conduction band edge is not at $k = 0$ in either Si or Ge. This is known from cyclotron resonance and from the existence of indirect optical absorption between the conduction and valence band edges (Fig. 4b).

Cyclotron Resonance in Semiconductors[8]

In a number of semiconductors it has been possible to determine by cyclotron resonance the form of the energy surfaces of the conduction and valence bands near the band edges;[9] that is, the energy $\epsilon(\mathbf{k})$ has been determined as a function of the wavevector $\mathbf{k}$. The determination of the energy surface is equivalent to a determination of the effective mass tensor, because

$$\left(\frac{1}{m^*}\right)_{ij} = \hbar^{-2}\frac{\partial^2\epsilon}{\partial k_i \partial k_j}. \tag{23}$$

Cyclotron resonance in a semiconductor is somewhat different than in a metal. If the carrier concentration is sufficiently low, the rf field will penetrate the entire specimen. The entire orbit of a carrier will therefore see a uniform rf field. The theory of the absorption under these conditions is given below. The current carriers are accelerated in spiral orbits about the axis of a static magnetic field H. The angular rotation frequency ω_c of the carriers is

$$\omega_c = eH/m^*c, \tag{24}$$

where m^* is the appropriate effective mass. Resonant absorption of energy from an rf electric field perpendicular to the static magnetic field (Fig. 14) occurs when the frequency of the rf field is equal to the cyclotron frequency. Holes and electrons will rotate in opposite senses in a magnetic field.

It is interesting to consider the order of magnitude of several physical quantities relevant to the experiment. We make the estimates using $m^*/m \cong 0.1$, which is not unrepresentative. For $f_c = 24{,}000$ Mcs, or $\omega_c = 1.5 \times 10^{11}$ sec^{-1}, we have $H \cong 860$ G at resonance. At $4°$K the mean velocity for a Maxwellian distribution is 4×10^6 cm/sec, and so the radius of the orbit is $r = v/\omega_c \cong 3 \times 10^{-5}$ cm. The line width is determined by the collision relaxation time τ, and it is necessary that $\omega_c\tau \geq 1$ in order to obtain a distinctive resonance. In other words, the mean free path must be long enough to permit the average carrier to get $1/2\pi$ of the way around a circle between successive collisions. For $\omega_c = 1.5 \times 10^{11}$ sec^{-1}, we require $\tau = 10^{-11}$ sec or longer. At room temperature the relaxation times of carriers in crystals are commonly in the range 10^{-13} to 10^{-15} sec. It is usually necessary to work with high-purity crystals in the liquid hydrogen or liquid helium range to obtain relaxation times long enough to permit the observation of cyclotron

---

[8] A useful bibliography is given in the article by B. Lax in *Semiconductors* (Italian Physical Society Course **22**), Academic Press, 1963.

[9] Recent advances in the analysis of ultraviolet reflectance measurements on semiconductors have led to the approximate determination of the overall shape of the energy surfaces; the experimental developments involve the modulation of the reflectance by electric fields and by elastic stress.

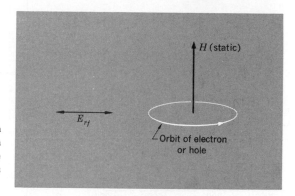

Figure 14 Arrangement of fields in a cyclotron resonance experiment in a semiconductor. The sense of the circulation is opposite for electrons and holes.

resonance in the microwave range. These requirements are relaxed significantly with the use of millimeter radiation because of the higher value of ω.

We give now a brief classical discussion of cyclotron resonance absorption[10] by a carrier of charge e and isotropic effective mass m^*, assuming an isotropic relaxation time τ independent of the velocity. The equation of motion for the drift velocity is

$$m^*\left(\frac{d\mathbf{v}}{dt} + \frac{1}{\tau}\mathbf{v}\right) = e\left(\mathbf{E} + \frac{\mathbf{v} \times \mathbf{H}}{c}\right). \tag{25}$$

We take H as the static field along the z axis and neglect the rf magnetic field. For plane-polarized radiation E_x we have

$$m^*\left(-i\omega + \frac{1}{\tau}\right)v_x = eE_x + \frac{e}{c}v_y H; \qquad m^*\left(-i\omega + \frac{1}{\tau}\right)v_y = -\frac{e}{c}v_x H. \tag{26}$$

We solve for v_x, finding the conductivity component

$$\sigma_{xx} = \frac{j_x}{E_x} = \frac{nev_x}{E_x} = \sigma_0\left[\frac{1 - i\omega\tau}{1 + (\omega_c{}^2 - \omega^2)\tau^2 - 2i\omega\tau}\right], \tag{27}$$

where $\sigma_0 = ne^2\tau/m^*$ is the static conductivity; n is the carrier concentration. This result exhibits the resonance at $\omega = \omega_c$. The tensor conductivity component $\sigma_{\mu\nu}$ is defined by $j_\mu = \sigma_{\mu\nu}E_\nu$, with the usual summation convention.

The neighborhood of the conduction band edge in both germanium and silicon consists of a set of spheroidal energy surfaces located in equivalent positions in $\mathbf{k}$ space, as illustrated below. We choose Cartesian coordinate axes with the z axis parallel to the figure axis of the spheroid, and we measure the wavevector components from the center of the spheroid. For points in $\mathbf{k}$ space

[10] References to early papers in the field are given by Dresselhaus, Kip, and Kittel, Phys. Rev. **98**, 368 (1955).

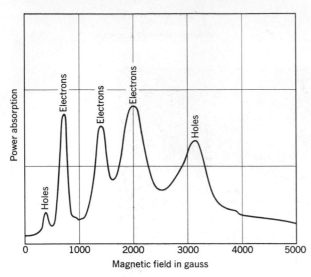

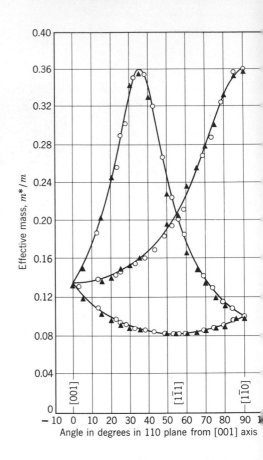

Figure 15 (*above*) Cyclotron resonance absorption in germanium near 24 Gcs and 4°K. The static magnetic field is in a (110) plane at 60° from a [100] axis. The holes and electrons were produced by photons from a light bulb.

Figure 16 (*right*) Effective cyclotron mass of electrons in germanium at 4°K for magnetic field directions in a (110) plane. (After Dresselhaus, Kip, and Kittel.)

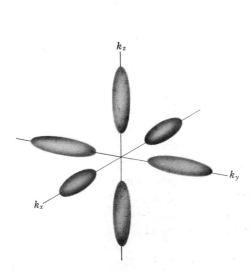

Figure 17 Constant energy ellipsoids for electrons in silicon, drawn for $m_l^*/m_t^* = 5$.

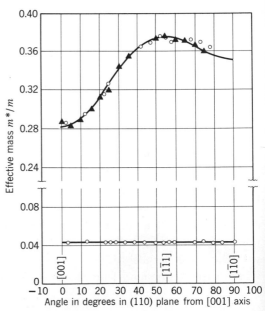

Figure 18 Effective cyclotron mass of holes in germanium at 4°K for magnetic field directions in a (110) plane.

sufficiently close to a band edge point, the energy is described by the equation

$$\epsilon(\mathbf{k}) = \hbar^2 \left(\frac{k_x{}^2 + k_y{}^2}{2m_t} + \frac{k_z{}^2}{2m_l} \right). \tag{28}$$

Here m_l is the mass parameter for the longitudinal axis of the spheroid, and m_t is the mass parameter for a transverse axis.

Shockley has given the solution of the cyclotron frequency problem for a general ellipsoidal energy surface. The effective mass determining the cyclotron frequency when the static magnetic field makes an angle θ with the longitudinal axis of the spheroidal energy surface (28) is

$$\left(\frac{1}{m^*} \right)^2 = \frac{\cos^2 \theta}{m_t{}^2} + \frac{\sin^2 \theta}{m_t m_l}. \tag{29}$$

A typical cyclotron resonance run in germanium is shown in Fig. 15. We see two hole masses and three electron masses; each electron mass originates from one or more spheroidal energy surfaces. For each mass the orientation of the spheroid with respect to the magnetic field is different. In Fig. 16 we give a plot of the experimental points obtained for electrons in germanium at 4°K as a function of the angle between the direction of the static magnetic field in a (110) plane and a [001] direction lying in the plane. The mass values derived from the theoretical fit to the experimental points[11] are $m_l = 1.59\, m$ and $m_t = 0.082\, m$. There is a set of crystallographically equivalent energy spheroids oriented along all $\langle 111 \rangle$ directions in the Brillouin zone. The center of each spheroid is known from other experiments to be at the edge of the zone.

In silicon the energy surfaces near the band edge of the conduction band are spheroids oriented along the equivalent $\langle 100 \rangle$ directions in the Brillouin zone, with mass parameters $m_l = 0.98\, m$ and $m_t = 0.19\, m$, as in Fig. 17.

The valence band edges in germanium and silicon are complicated. The holes observed in these crystals are characterized by two effective masses, and we speak of light and heavy holes. There is some anisotropy, easily apparent experimentally for the heavy hole (Fig. 18). The two hole masses arise from the two bands formed from the $p_{3/2}$ level of the atom. The energy surfaces are of the form

$$\epsilon(\mathbf{k}) = Ak^2 \pm [B^2 k^4 + C^2(k_x{}^2 k_y{}^2 + k_y{}^2 k_z{}^2 + k_z{}^2 k_x{}^2)]^{1/2}, \tag{30}$$

The choice of sign distinguishes the two masses. In units $\hbar^2/2m$,

$$\text{Si:} \quad A = -4.0; \quad |B| = 1.1; \quad |C| = 4.1$$

$$\text{Ge:} \quad A = -13.3; \quad |B| = 8.6; \quad |C| = 12.5$$

[11] B. W. Levinger and D. R. Frankel, J. Phys. Chem. Solids **20**, 281 (1961)

Roughly speaking, the holes in germanium have masses 0.04 m and 0.3 m; in silicon, 0.16 m and 0.5 m.

In InSb the conduction band edge is at $\mathbf{k} = 0$. The energy surface is spherical. The electron effective mass is isotropic and equal to 0.014 m. The low value of the effective mass is a consequence of the low value of the energy gap, which is only 0.23 ev.

CARRIER LIFETIME AND RECOMBINATION

It is possible in semiconductors to obtain departures from the thermal equilibrium concentrations of electrons and holes in several ways: by injecting carriers into the sample through a metal contact or by the creation of electron-hole pairs by light or by charged particle bombardment. Once disturbed, the system tends to return to equilibrium by recombination of the excess electrons and holes. The recombination rate can be observed by measuring the time variation of the conductance of the specimen after excitation or by detecting the drift in an electric field of excess carriers produced at one point and detected at another point.

In the simplest case excess electrons and holes are produced in equal numbers and they recombine both at the same rate. Letting

Δn = excess electron concentration above value at thermal equilibrium;

Δp = excess hole concentration above value at thermal equilibrium;

we have by assumption $\Delta n = \Delta p$. At small concentrations of excess carriers the decay is usually exponential and characterized by a constant lifetime τ.[12] We have then

$$\frac{dn}{dt} = -\frac{1}{\tau}\Delta n; \qquad \frac{dp}{dt} = -\frac{1}{\tau}\Delta p. \tag{31}$$

In practice it is often found that the decay of excess minority carrier concentration proceeds at different rates in n- and p-type material; thus we deal with a lifetime τ_n for excess electrons in p-type material and a lifetime τ_p for excess holes in n-type material.

The recombination mechanisms are still obscure, but direct radiative recombination of an electron and a hole with emission of a photon is infrequent in germanium and silicon. Shockley has calculated minority carrier lifetimes of the order of 1 sec for the radiative process in germanium at room tempera-

---

[12] It is standard practice to use the same symbol τ to denote both carrier relaxation time and carrier lifetime.

ture, whereas observed lifetimes are reported to be of the order of 0.01 sec in unusually pure germanium crystals. The emission of radiation accompanying minority carrier injection has been observed experimentally.

Recombination occurs both in the volume and on the surface of the crystal. The volume lifetime τ_v is particularly sensitive to small amounts of copper, iron, and nickel: a nickel contamination of 10^{12} atoms/cm^3 may shorten the lifetime observably. The volume lifetime is sensitive also to lattice imperfections. The lifetime for surface recombination τ_s is particularly sensitive to the condition of the surface. Because the carriers must diffuse to the surface before they can recombine there, the surface lifetime also depends on the dimensions of the specimen.

It is useful in connection with *p-n* junctions (see below) to find the average displacement distance of a carrier during its lifetime, considering only volume recombination. The hydrodynamic equation of continuity written for holes is

$$\frac{\partial p}{\partial t} + \text{div } p\mathbf{v}_p = \text{(generation minus recombination) rate per unit volume.} \quad (32)$$

Here $\mathbf{v}_p$ is the drift velocity of the holes. Now the diffusion equation is

$$p\mathbf{v}_p = -D_p \text{ grad } p; \quad (33)$$

this defines the **diffusivity** D_p. The diffusivity may be calculated from the mobility μ by the **Einstein relation**[13]

$$\mu k_B T = eD. \quad (34)$$

In germanium at room temperature

$$D_n = 93 \text{ cm}^2/\text{sec}; \quad D_p = 44 \text{ cm}^2/\text{sec}. \quad (35)$$

Let us consider the steady-state flow of holes from a region in which they are generated to a region where they recombine at the rate p/τ_p, according to (31). In the steady state $\partial p/\partial t = 0$. In the recombination region (32) and (33) reduce to

$$D_p \nabla^2 p - (p/\tau_p) = 0. \quad (36)$$

---

[13] This relation is easily proved. Suppose that the particles of charge e are in a constant electric field E. According to the Boltzmann distribution law the concentration of particles $n(x)$ at x is proportional to $\exp(-eEx/k_BT)$. The condition that in equilibrium no net current should flow is $\mu nE + D(dn/dx) = 0$, the definition of the diffusivity D being the net flux of particles per unit concentration gradient. From this equation we see that $n(x)$ is also proportional to $\exp(-\mu Ex/D)$; (34) follows on equating the exponents.

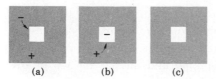

Figure 19 A recombination center captures alternately an electron and a hole and thus catalyzes their recombination, as shown successively in (a), (b), and (c).

For linear geometry we look for a solution of the form, for positive x,

$$p = p_0 e^{-x/L_p}. \tag{37}$$

We suppose that the holes are generated in the region of negative x and recombine in the region of positive x. Substituting (37) in (36) we find $L_p = (D_p \tau_p)^{1/2}$. The length L_p is known as the **diffusion length** for holes; it is a measure of the length a hole diffuses in a lifetime. For electrons $L_n = (D_n \tau_n)^{1/2}$ by a parallel argument. In germanium at room temperature a hole with a lifetime of 10^{-3} sec has a diffusion length of $L_p = (44 \times 10^{-3})^{1/2} \cong 0.2$ cm.

Shockley has suggested a mechanism whereby some imperfections may catalyze recombination. As indicated in Fig. 19, an electron and hole are initially free at stage (a); in (b) an electron is captured by the recombination center; a hole is attracted electrostatically by the captured electron, and in (c) the electron has dropped into the hole, leaving the recombination center ready to repeat the process with another electron and hole.

p-n JUNCTION RECTIFICATION

It is possible in a number of ways to produce a germanium or silicon crystal in which there are both p-type and n-type regions with a very thin internal boundary between them (Fig. 20). The interface between the different regions is called a p-n junction. A typical width is 10^{-4} cm. Such junctions have important electrical properties, including rectification and transistor action; the theory of the p-n junction is basic to a large amount of the development of transistor physics.

The thickness of the internal boundary between n- and p-type material is assumed here to be small in comparison with the diffusion length, the distance that a carrier diffuses in a lifetime. We saw above that the diffusion length L_p of holes in germanium at room temperature for a hole lifetime of 10^{-3} sec is 0.2 cm.

We give a qualitative description of the operation of a p-n junction as a rectifier. In equilibrium the conduction electrons contributed by the donors will be found chiefly in the n region where the electrons neutralize the space charge of the donor ions, whereas the holes contributed by the acceptor ions

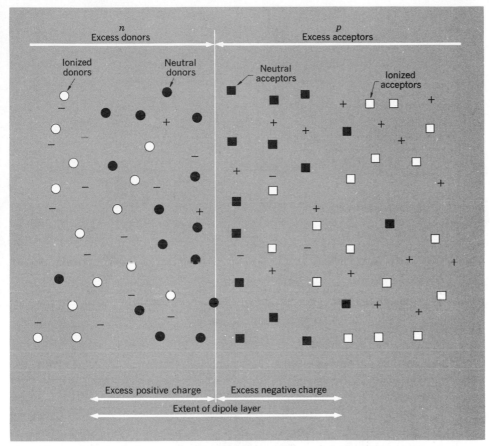

Figure 20   Structure of a *p-n* junction in thermal equilibrium. A hollow square represents an ionized acceptor and is charged negatively; a hollow circle represents an ionized donor and is charged positively. The ± signs represent mobile holes or conduction electrons.

will be found chiefly in the *p* region. Electrons and holes cannot remain separated in this way unless an electric field exists in the junction region, for without an electric field the electrons and holes would intermix by diffusion. If initially there is no electric field across the junction, holes will diffuse in one direction, leaving behind on one side of the junction negatively charged acceptor ions. Electrons will diffuse in the opposite direction, leaving behind positively charged donor ions. This initial diffusion of carriers will establish an electrostatic dipole layer at the junction. The dipole layer creates an electric field which opposes further diffusion across the junction.

   Even in thermal equilibrium there will be a small flow of electrons J_{nr} from the *n* region into the *p* region, the electrons ending their lives by recombination with holes. This flow will be balanced by the flow J_{ng} of electrons

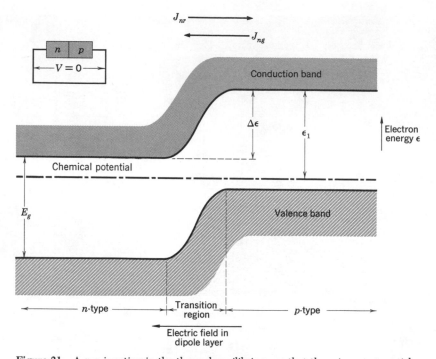

Figure 21 A p-n junction in the thermal equilibrium, so that there is no net particle flow through the circuit. By thermodynamics the chemical potential is everywhere constant in equilibrium. The position of the valence band edge relative to the Fermi level varies in the transition region of the junction. The band edge position is constant when well inside the n or p regions. It depends only on chemical composition and is independent of the rest of the circuit. We assume that the chemical composition changes abruptly at the center of the boundary. The transition region is distinguished by a gradual variation in the electron-hole concentrations. This variation produces an electrostatic dipole layer. The dipole layer produces a potential energy difference $\Delta\epsilon$ which prevents a net electron current and a net hole current from flowing across the boundary. The number of electrons in the conduction band is much greater on the n side than on the p side. The electron flux J_{nr} toward the right consists of those electrons which have enough energy to climb the potential energy barrier; these electrons then recombine with holes. The electron flux J_{ng} toward the left arises from those few electrons generated to maintain thermal equilibrium on the right; these can move downhill to the left. In equilibrium $J_{nr} + J_{ng} = 0$ at the boundary. The same argument applies to holes: $J_{pr} + J_{pg} = 0$.

which are generated thermally in the p region and which diffuse to the n region. Thermal equilibrium implies voltage $V = 0$. In this condition the recombination current of electrons must be equal but opposite to the thermal generation current of electrons; otherwise electrons would pile up on one side of the barrier. Thus

$$J_{nr}(0) + J_{ng}(0) = 0, \tag{38a}$$

as shown in Fig. 21.

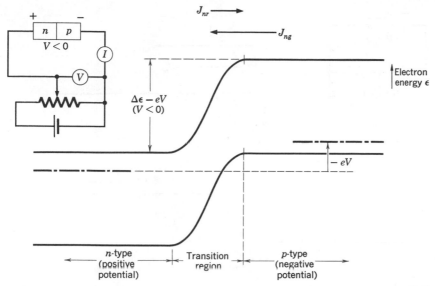

Figure 22   A *p-n* junction with *reverse* bias voltage $V < 0$. The net electron current is small and nearly independent of V. The hole current is also small and nearly independent of V.

We are now in a position to demonstrate the rectification action of a *p-n* junction. We assume that all or nearly all the applied voltage appears across the transition region. This is a reasonable assumption because the total carrier concentration $n + p$ is a minimum there, by the constancy of np shown in Eq. (9).

For reverse or back voltage bias (Fig. 22), negative voltage is applied to the *p* region and positive to the *n* region, so that the potential difference between the two regions is increased. Now practically no electrons can climb the potential energy hill from the low side of the barrier to the high side. The recombination current is reduced by the Boltzmann factor[14]:

$$J_{nr}(V\,back) = J_{nr}(0)\ \exp\,(-e|V|/k_BT). \tag{38b}$$

The generation flux of electrons is not particularly affected by the reverse or back bias voltage, because the generation electrons are flowing downhill anyway:

$$J_{ng}(V\,back) = J_{ng}(0). \tag{38c}$$

Thus for a back bias the generation current dominates the recombination current, but the generation current itself is always small in rectifiers at the temperatures of interest.

---

[14] The Boltzmann factor controls the number of electrons with enough energy to get over the barrier.

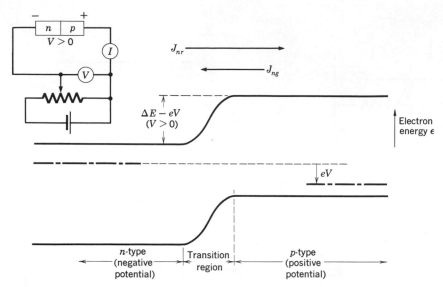

Figure 23 A *p-n* junction with *forward* bias voltage V > 0. The current is large and varies rapidly with V. Only the electron currents are shown, but the hole current is also large and sensitive to V.

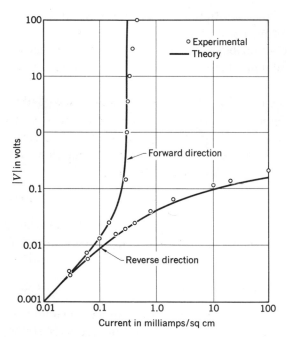

Figure 24 Rectification characteristic of a *p-n* junction in germanium, after Shockley.

When a **forward bias** voltage (Fig. 23) is applied, the recombination current increases by the Boltzmann factor because the potential energy barrier is lowered, enabling more electrons to flow from the n side to the p side:

$$J_{nr}(V \; forward) = J_{nr}(0) \exp \, (e|V|/k_B T). \tag{38d}$$

Again the generation current is unchanged:

$$J_{ng}(V \; forward) = J_{ng}(0). \tag{38e}$$

Positive eV is forward bias; negaitve eV is back or reverse bias.

The hole current flowing across the junction behaves similarly. The applied voltage which lowers the height of the barrier for electrons also lowers it for holes, so that large numbers of electrons flow from the n region to the p region under the same voltage conditions that produce large hole currents in the opposite direction.

The electrical currents due to holes and electrons add. The total electric current, including the effects of both holes and electrons, is given by

$$I = I_s(e^{eV/k_B T} - 1), \tag{40}$$

where I_s is the sum of the two generation currents. As shown in Fig. 24, this equation is well satisfied for p-n junctions in germanium.

POLARONS

An electron in a crystal lattice interacts via its electrical charge with the ions or atoms of the lattice and creates a local deformation of the lattice. The deformation tends to follow the electron as it moves through the lattice. The combination of the electron and its strain field is known as a **polaron**.[15] Perhaps the most important effect of the lattice deformation is the attendant increase in the effective mass of the electron: because the ion cores are set into motion when the electron moves, then the electron acts as if its mass were increased. We expect the effect to be large in ionic crystals because of the strong Coulomb interaction between charged ions and the electron. In covalent crystals the effect should be small because the crystals are composed of neutral atoms.

The strength of the electron-lattice interaction is measured by the dimensionless **coupling constant** α. The value of the coupling constant is given by

$$\frac{1}{2}\alpha = \frac{\text{deformation energy}}{\hbar \omega_L}, \tag{41}$$

---

[15] See *QTS*, Chap. 7; also C. G. Kuper and G. D. Whitfield, ed., *Polarons and excitons*, Plenum Press, New York, 1963, particularly the article "Experiments on the polaron" by F. C. Brown.

where ω_L is the longitudinal optical phonon frequency near zero wavevector. We view $\frac{1}{2}\alpha$ as "the number of phonons which surround a slow-moving electron in a crystal." Values of α deduced from diverse experiments and theory are given below, after F. C. Brown:

Crystal	KCl	AgCl	AgBr	ZnO	PbS	InSb	GaAs
α	5.6	1.9	1.6	0.85	0.16	0.014	0.06

Notice the high values in ionic crystals.

For $\alpha \ll 1$ the theory relates the effective mass of the polaron m_{pol}^* to the effective mass m^* of the electron in the undeformed lattice by the relation[16]

$$m_{pol}^* \cong m^*(1 + \tfrac{1}{6}\alpha). \tag{42}$$

Because α is always positive the polaron mass is always greater than the bare mass, as we expect from the inertia of the ions. For high α the mobility is low when the temperature is high enough to permit the excitation of optical phonons. Note the low electron mobility in AgCl and KBr, shown in Table 2.

Problems

1. **Impurity orbits.** Indium antimonide has $E_g = 0.23$ ev; dielectric constant $\epsilon = 17$; electron effective mass $m_e = 0.014\ m$. Calculate (a) the donor ionization energy; (b) the radius of the ground state orbit. (c) At what minimum donor concentration will appreciable overlap effects between the orbits of adjacent impurity atoms occur? This overlap tends to produce an impurity band—a band of energy levels which permit conductivity presumably by a hopping mechanism in which electrons move from one impurity site to a neighboring ionized impurity site.

2. **Ionization of donors.** In a particular semiconductor there are 10^{13} donors/cm^3 with an ionization energy E_d of 1×10^{-3} ev and an effective mass of $1 \times 10^{-2}\ m$. (a) What is the concentration of conduction electrons at 4°K? (b) What is the value of the Hall constant. *Note:* Assume no acceptor atoms are present.

3. **Hall effect with two carrier types.** Assuming concentrations n, p; relaxation times τ_e, τ_h; and masses m_e, m_h, show that the Hall constant is

$$R_H = \frac{1}{ec} \cdot \frac{p - nb^2}{(p + nb)^2},$$

where $b = \mu_e/\mu_h$ is the mobility ratio. In the derivation neglect terms of order H^2. *Hint:* In the presence of a longitudinal electric field, find the transverse electric field such that the transverse current vanishes.

[16] *QTS*, p. 141.

4. *Impurity conductivity.* A semiconductor with hole effective mass $m_h = m$ has 10^{18} acceptors per cubic centimeter. The energy level of these acceptors is 0.5 ev above the valence band of the crystal. If the mobility of holes in this band is 100 cm^2/volt-sec independent of temperature, calculate the conductivity of the material at room temperature (300°K).

5. *Impurity compensation.* (a) Explain the phenomenon of impurity compensation, which is the reduction of carrier concentration and conductivity in a semiconductor initially of one conductivity type (n or p) by the addition of impurities of the other type. (b) Does a nearly intrinsic resistivity prove the specimen is pure?

6. *Cuprous oxide.* Cu_2O is usually a p-type semiconductor in the impurity range. This circumstance is attributed to a deficiency of one of the components. (a) Which component must be missing in order to account for the conductivity type? (b) Cuprous oxide in thin sections is red by transmitted light. Why?

7. *Work function and charge layer.* The work function of two metals differs by 2 ev. If these metals are brought into contact, some electrons will flow from one into the other. The transferred electrons are localized near the surface of the metal. Assume that the electrons are displaced over a distance of 3×10^{-8} cm. How many electrons per square centimeter will be transferred?

8. *Mobility.* The mobility of electrons in a crystal is observed to be 5×10^4 cm^2/volt-sec or 15×10^6 cm^2/statvolt-sec. If the effective mass is the free electron mass, what is the relaxation time τ?

References[17]

R. L. Sproull, *Modern physics,* 2nd ed., Wiley, 1963. (Contains a good elementary discussion of semiconductor devices.)

R. A. Smith, *Semiconductors,* Cambridge University Press, 1959.

R. B. Adler, A. C. Smith, R. L. Longini, *Introduction to semiconductor physics,* Wiley, 1964.

R. A. Smith, ed., *Semiconductors* (Italian Physical Society Course **22**), Academic Press, 1963.

W. Shockley, *Electrons and holes in semiconductors,* Van Nostrand, 1950.

E. Spenke, *Electronic semiconductors,* McGraw-Hill, 1958.

A. F. Gibson, P. Aigrain, and R. E. Burgess, ed., *Progress in semiconductors,* Heywood, London; a continuing series of volumes starting in 1956.

J. L. Moll, *Physics of semiconductors,* McGraw-Hill, 1964. (For the physics of semiconductor devices.)

Selected constants related to semiconductors (Constantes sélectionées **12**), Pergamon, 1961.

L. B. Valdes, *Physical theory of transistors,* McGraw-Hill, 1961.

[17] For an excellent selective bibliography see P. Handler, "Resource letter Scr-1 on semiconductors," Am. J. Phys. **32**, 329 (1964).

11
Superconductivity

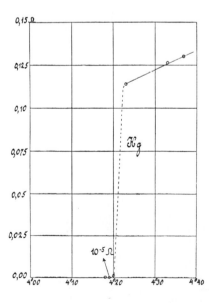

Figure 1 Resistance in ohms of a specimen of mercury versus absolute temperature. This plot by Kamerlingh Onnes marked the discovery of superconductivity.

The electrical resistivity of many metals and alloys drops suddenly to zero when the specimen is cooled to a sufficiently low temperature, often a temperature in the liquid helium range. This phenomenon was observed first by Kamerlingh Onnes[1] in Leiden in 1911, three years after he first liquified helium. His original measurements on mercury are shown in Fig. 1. Note the narrowness of the temperature interval in which the resistivity change occurs. We say that at a critical temperature T_c the specimen undergoes a phase transition from a state of normal electrical resistivity to a superconducting state.

EXPERIMENTAL SURVEY

In the superconducting state the dc electrical resistivity is exactly zero, or at least so close to zero that persistent electrical currents have been observed to flow without attenuation in superconducting rings for more than a year, until at last the experimentalist wearied of the experiment. The decay of supercurrents in a solenoid of $Nb_{0.75}\ Zr_{0.25}$ was studied by File and Mills[2] using precision nuclear magnetic resonance methods (Chapter 16) to measure the magnetic field associated with the supercurrent. They concluded that the decay time of the supercurrent is not less than 100,000 years. In some superconducting materials, particularly those used for superconducting magnets, finite decay times are observed because of an irreversible redistribution of magnetic flux in the material.

The magnetic properties exhibited by superconductors are as dramatic as their electrical properties. The magnetic properties cannot be accounted for by the assumption that the superconducting state is characterized properly by zero electrical resistivity. It is an experimental fact that a bulk superconductor in a weak magnetic field will act as a perfect diamagnet, with zero magnetic induction in the interior of a bulk superconductor. When a specimen is placed in a magnetic field and is then cooled through the transition temperature for superconductivity, the magnetic flux originally present is

[1] H. Kamerlingh Onnes, Akad. van Wetenschappen (Amsterdam) **14**, 113, 818 (1911): "The value of the mercury resistance used was 172.7 ohms in the liquid condition at 0°C; extrapolation from the melting point to 0°C by means of the temperature coefficient of solid mercury gives a resistance corresponding to this of 39.7 ohms in the solid state. At 4.3°K this had sunk to 0.084 ohms, that is, to 0.0021 times the resistance which the solid mercury would have at 0°C. At 3°K the resistance was found to have fallen below 3×10^{-6} ohms, that is to one ten-millionth of the value which it would have at 0°C. As the temperature sank further to 1.5°K this value remained the upper limit of the resistance." Historical references are given by C. J. Gorter, Rev. Mod. Phys. **36**, 1 (1964).

[2] J. File and R. G. Mills, Phys. Rev. Letters **10**, 93 (1963).

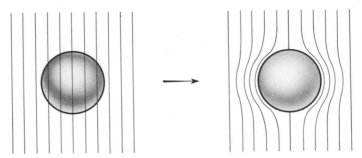

Figure 2 Meissner effect in a superconducting sphere cooled in a constant applied magnetic field; on passing below the transition temperature the lines of induction **B** are ejected from the sphere.

ejected from the specimen. This is called the **Meissner effect.** The sequence of events is shown in Fig. 2. The unique magnetic properties of superconductors are of central importance to the characterization of the superconducting state.

The superconducting state is known to be an ordered state of the conduction electrons of the metal. The order is in the formation of loosely associated pairs of electrons. The electrons are ordered at temperatures below the transition temperature, and they are disordered above the transition temperature. The nature and origin of the ordering was explained first in 1957 by Bardeen, Cooper, and Schrieffer.[3] In the present chapter we develop as far as we can in an elementary way the physics of the superconducting state. We shall also discuss the basic physics of the materials used for superconducting magnets, but not their technology.

Occurrence of Superconductivity

Superconductivity occurs[4] in many metallic elements of the periodic system and also in alloys, intermetallic compounds, and semiconductors.[5] The range of transition temperatures known at present extends from $18.05\,^{\circ}$K for the compound Nb_3Sn to $0.01\,^{\circ}$K for a semiconductor. In many metals superconductivity has not been found down to the lowest temperatures at which the metal was examined, usually well below $1\,^{\circ}$K. Thus Li, Na, and K have been investigated for superconductivity down to $0.08\,^{\circ}$K, $0.09\,^{\circ}$K, and $0.08\,^{\circ}$K,

[3] J. Bardeen, L. N. Cooper, and J. R. Schrieffer, Phys. Rev. **106**, 162 (1957); **108**, 1175 (1957).

[4] A review of data on the occurrence of superconductivity is given by B. T. Matthias, T. H. Geballe, and V. B. Compton, Rev. Mod. Phys. **35**, 1–22 (1963).

[5] Superconductivity in certain semiconductors was predicted theoretically by M. L. Cohen, Phys. Rev. **134**, 511 (1964); Rev. Mod. Phys. **36**, 240 (1964). For experiments on oxygen-deficient $SrTiO_3$, see J. F. Schooley et al., Phys. Rev. Letters **14**, 305 (1965); the lowest carrier concentration studied was 2×10^{18} cm^{-3}, and for this specimen $T_c \approx 0.01\,^{\circ}$K.

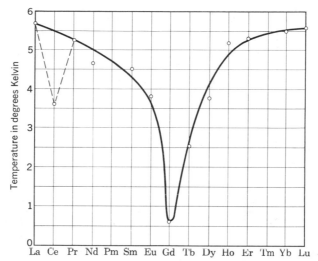

Figure 3 Superconducting transition temperatures of 1 at. percent solid solutions of rare earth elements in lanthanum, after Matthias, Suhl, and Corenzwit. Most of the rare earth elements in solid solution in lanthanum have electronic magnetic moments.

respectively, where they were still normal conductors. Similarly, Cu, Ag, and Au have been investigated down to 0.05°K, 0.35°K, and 0.05°K, where they were still normal conductors.

Will every metallic element become a superconductor at sufficiently low temperatures? We do not know. In experimental searches for superconductors with ultralow transition temperatures it is important to eliminate from the specimen even trace quantities of foreign paramagnetic elements, because these can lower the transition temperature severely. A few parts per million of Fe will destroy the superconductivity of Mo, which when pure has $T_c = 0.92°$K; and 1 at. percent of gadolinium lowers the transition temperature (Fig. 3) of lanthanum[6] from 5.6°K to 0.6°K. Nonmagnetic impurities have no very marked effect on the transition temperature, although they may affect the behavior of the superconductor in strong magnetic fields.

The elements known to be superconducting are displayed in Table 1, together with their transition temperatures. None of the monovalent metals are known to be superconductors; none of the ferromagnetic metals; and none of the rare earth elements except lanthanum (which has an entirely empty $4f$ electronic shell). The transition temperatures of a number of interesting superconducting compounds are listed in Table 2.

[6] H. Suhl and B. T. Matthias, Phys. Rev. Letters **2**, 5 (1959).

Table 1 Superconducting elements in the periodic system

Transition temperatures in °K for the common crystal forms of the elements, after Matthias, Geballe, and Compton. Columns not shown contain no known superconductors in the common crystal forms.

B												C
Al 1.18												**Si**
Sc	**Ti** 0.39	**V** 5.03	**Cr**	**Mn**	**Fe**	**Co**	**Ni**	**Cu**	**Zn** 0.85	**Ga** 1.09	**Ge**	
Y	**Zr** 0.55	**Nb** 9.1	**Mo** 0.92	**Tc** 11.2	**Ru** 0.49	**Rh**	**Pd**	**Ag**	**Cd** 0.52	**In** 3.41	**Sn** 3.72	
La(β) 6	**Hf** 0.16	**Ta** 4.48	**W** 0.01	**Re** 1.7	**Os** 0.66	**Ir** 0.14	**Pt**	**Au**	**Hg(α)** 4.15	**Tl** 2.37	**Pb** 7.19	
Ac												

	Ce	**Pr**	**Nd**
	Th 1.37	**Pa** 1.4	**U**

Table 2 Superconductivity of selected compounds

Compound	T_c, in °K	Compound	T_c, in °K
Nb_3Sn	18.05	V_3Ga	16.5
Nb_6Sn_5	2.07	V_3Si	17.1
Nb_3Al	17.5	UCo	1.70
Nb_3Au	11.5	Ti_2Co	3.44
NbN	16.0	La_3In	10.4
MoN	12.0	InSb°	1.9

° Metallic phase.

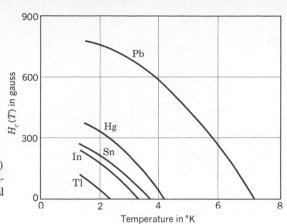

Figure 4 Threshold curves of the critical field $H_c(T)$ versus temperature for several superconductors. A specimen is superconducting below the curve and normal above the curve.

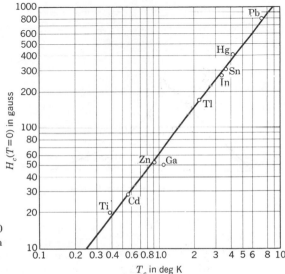

Figure 5 Log-log plot of critical field H_c at $T = 0$ versus transition temperature T_c for superconductors in bulk form.

Destruction of Superconductivity by Magnetic Fields

A sufficiently strong magnetic field will destroy superconductivity. The threshold or critical value of the magnetic field for the destruction of super-conductivity is denoted by $H_c(T)$ and is a function of the temperature. At the critical temperature the critical field is zero: $H_c(T_c) = 0$. The variation of the critical field with temperature for several superconducting elements is shown in Fig. 4. The threshold curves separate the superconducting state in the lower left of the figure from the normal state in the upper right. The de-pendence of $H_c(0)$ on T_c is shown in Fig. 5 for a number of superconductors.

Kamerlingh Onnes in 1913 found that the passage of an electric current down a superconducting wire destroyed superconductivity when a certain critical current was exceeded. Silsbee (1916) pointed out that the important factor in causing the transition back to the normal state was the magnetic field associated with the current, rather than the value of the current itself.

340

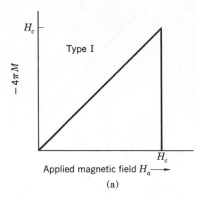

(a)

Figure 6a Magnetization versus applied magnetic field for a bulk superconductor exhibiting a complete Meissner effect (perfect diamagnetism). A superconductor with this behavior is called a type I superconductor. Above the critical field H_c the specimen is a normal conductor and the magnetization is too small to be seen on this scale. Note that *minus* $4\pi M$ is plotted on the vertical scale: the negative value of M corresponds to diamagnetism. In the notation of the text $4\pi M \equiv H_b$, where H_b is the magnetic field produced by the superconducting currents induced when an external field is applied.

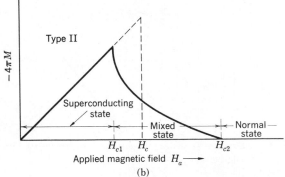

(b)

Figure 6b Superconducting magnetization curve of a type II superconductor. The flux starts to penetrate the specimen at a field H_{c1} which is lower than the thermodynamic critical field H_c. The specimen is in a **mixed state** between H_{c1} and H_{c2} and it has superconducting electrical properties up to H_{c2}. Above H_{c2} the specimen is a normal conductor in every respect, except for possible surface effects.

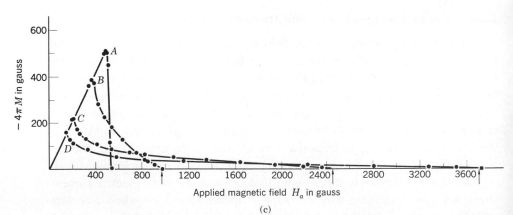

(c)

Figure 6c Superconducting magnetization curves of annealed polycrystalline lead and lead-indium alloys at 4.2°K. (A) lead; (B) lead–2.08 wt. percent indium; (C) lead–8.23 wt. percent indium; (D) lead–20.4 wt. percent indium. (After Livingston.)

Meissner Effect

Meissner and Ochsenfeld[7] found that if a superconductor is cooled in a magnetic field to below the transition temperature, then at the transition the lines of induction B are pushed out (Fig. 2). This phenomenon is called the Meissner effect. It shows that a bulk superconductor behaves in an applied external field H_a as if inside the specimen $B \equiv H_a + 4\pi M = 0$ or $\chi = -1/4\pi$; that is, a superconductor exhibits perfect diamagnetism.[8] This very important result cannot be derived merely from the characterization of a superconductor as a medium of zero resistivity. From Ohm's law $\mathbf{E} = \rho\mathbf{j}$ we see that if the resistivity ρ goes to zero while $\mathbf{j}$ is held finite, then $\mathbf{E}$ must be zero. By a Maxwell equation, $d\mathbf{B}/dt = -c$ curl $\mathbf{E}$, so that for zero resistivity

$$d\mathbf{B}/dt = 0. \tag{1}$$

This argument is not entirely transparent, but the result predicts that the flux through the metal cannot change on cooling through the transition. The Meissner effect contradicts this result and suggests that perfect diamagnetism is an essential property of the superconducting state.[9]

The magnetization curve expected for a superconductor under the conditions of the Meissner-Ochsenfeld experiment is sketched in Fig. 6a. This applies quantitatively to a specimen in the form of a long solid cylinder[10] placed in a longitudinal magnetic field. Pure specimens of many materials exhibit this behavior; they are called **type I superconductors**, or, formerly, soft superconductors. The values of H_c are always too low for type I superconductors to have any useful technical application in coils for superconducting magnets.

Other materials exhibit a magnetization curve of the form of Fig. 6b and are known as **type II superconductors**. They tend to be alloys (as in Fig. 6c) or transition metals with high values of the electrical resistivity in the normal state: that is, the electronic mean free path in the normal state is short. We shall see later why the mean free path is involved in the magnetization of superconductors. Type II superconductors have superconducting electrical properties up to a field denoted by H_{c2}, called the **upper critical field.** The value of

[7] W. Meissner and R. Ochsenfeld, Naturwiss. **21**, 787 (1933).

[8] Diamagnetism, the magnetization M, and the magnetic susceptibility $\chi = M/H$ are defined in Chapter 14. The magnitude of the diamagnetic susceptibility of bulk superconductors is very much larger than in typical diamagnetic substances.

[9] We expect another difference between a superconductor and a perfect conductor, defined as a conductor in which there is nothing to scatter the electrons. When the field penetration problem in a perfect conductor is solved in detail, it turns out that a perfect conductor when placed in a magnetic field cannot produce a permanent eddy current screen: the field will penetrate about 1 cm in an hour. See A. B. Pippard, *Dynamics of conduction electrons*, Gordon and Breach, 1965.

[10] In other geometries the field may not be homogeneous around the specimen and the field may penetrate below H_c; for a sphere the field penetrates at $\frac{2}{3}H_c$.

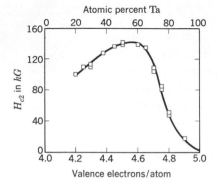

Figure 7 Applied magnetic field required for the destruction of superconductivity in Ti-Ta alloys, after Berlincourt and Hake. The measurements were made at 1.2°K and at a current density of 10 amps/cm².

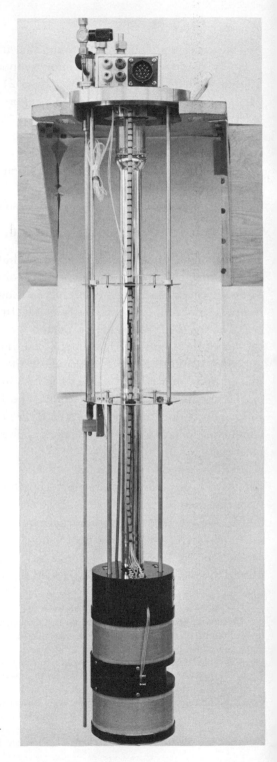

Figure 8 A superconducting magnet assembly for immersion in a liquid He cryostat. (Courtesy of Varian Associates.)

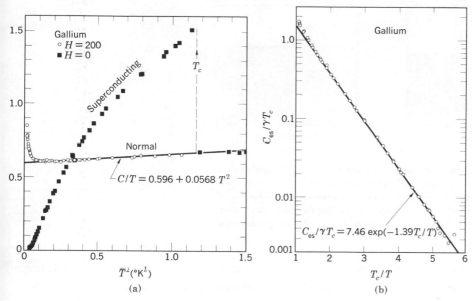

Figure 9 (a) The heat capacity of gallium in the normal and superconducting states. The normal state (which is restored by a 200 G field) has electronic, lattice, and (at low temperatures) nuclear quadrupole contributions. In (b) the electronic part C_{es} of the heat capacity in the superconducting state is plotted on a log scale versus T_c/T; the exponential dependence on $1/T$ is evident. Here $\gamma = 0.60$ mJ mole^{-1} deg^{-2}. [After N. E. Phillips, Phys. Rev. **134**, 385 (1964).]

H_{c2} may be 100 times or more higher than the value of the critical field H_c expected from other considerations, such as the thermodynamics (see below) of the transition in zero magnetic field. Fields H_{c2} of the order of 150 kG as in Fig. 7 have been observed.[11] Solenoids wound with wire of a hard super-conductor have produced field over 100 kG. A **hard superconductor** is a type II superconductor with a large amount of magnetic hysteresis induced by mechanical treatment.

Heat Capacity

In all superconductors the entropy decreases markedly on cooling below T_c in zero magnetic field. The decrease in entropy in cooling from the normal state to the superconducting state tells us that the superconducting state is more ordered than the normal state. The difference in entropy is of the order of $\sim 10^{-3} N k_B$ for N atoms. In an ordinary order-disorder or magnetic transition of the second order we expect (see Chapter 14) an entropy difference of the order of $k_B \log 2^N \approx N k_B$. The small entropy difference observed in the superconducting transition suggests that relatively few electrons are affected. The effect on the heat capacity is shown for gallium in Fig. 9: in

---

[11] For detailed data see T. G. Berlincourt and R. R. Hake, Phys. Rev. **131**, 140 (1963).

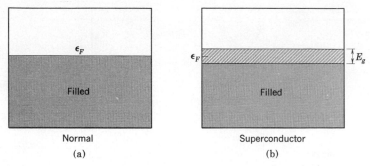

Figure 10 (a) Conduction band in the normal state; (b) energy gap at the Fermi level in the superconducting state. Electrons in excited states above the gap behave as normal electrons: in rf fields they cause resistance; at dc they are shorted out by the superconducting electrons. At absolute zero there are no electrons above the gap. The gap E_g is exaggerated in the figure: typically $E_g/\epsilon_F \sim 10^{-4}$.

(a) the normal and superconducting states are compared; in (b) it is seen the electronic contribution to the heat capacity in the superconducting state has an exponential form. This form is suggestive of excitation of electrons across an energy gap, as in Fig. 10. An energy gap is believed to be a characteristic (but not universal) feature of the superconducting state. It is accounted for by the Bardeen-Cooper-Schrieffer (BCS) theory of superconductivity discussed later in this chapter.

Table 3   Energy gaps in superconductors

Values of the gap $E_g(0) \equiv 2\Delta(0)$ at $T = 0$, as measured by tunneling experiments. (Selection of data assisted by M. Tinkham.)

Element	$2\Delta(0)$ in 10^{-3} ev	$2\Delta(0)/k_B T_c$	Ref
Hg	1.65 ± 0.04	4.6	a
Nb	3.05 ± 0.05	3.8	b
Ta	1.40 ± 0.05	3.6	b
Sn	1.15 ± 0.06	3.5	b
Al	0.34 ± 0.02	3.3	c
Pb°	2.67 ± 0.05	4.3	b
	2.90 ± 0.05	4.6	b
In	1.05 ± 0.03	3.6	d

°Two gaps were detected in Pb; in the other elements the gaps quoted are probably averages over the Fermi surface.

a. S. Bermon and D. M. Ginsberg, Phys. Rev. **135**, A306 (1964).

b. P. Townsend and J. Sutton, Phys. Rev. **128**, 591 (1962).

c. D. H. Douglass, Jr., and R. Meservey, Phys. Rev. **135**, A19 (1964).

d. I. Giaever and K. Megerle, Phys. Rev. **122**, 1101 (1961).

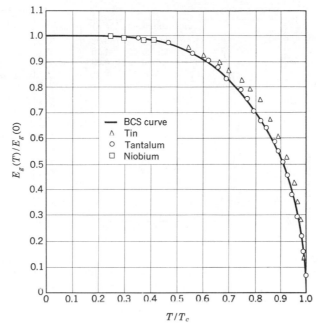

Figure 11 Reduced values of the observed energy gap $E_g(T)/E_g(0)$ as a function of the reduced temperature T/T_c, after Townsend and Sutton. The solid curve drawn is for the BCS theory.

Energy Gap

The energy gap in superconductors is of an entirely different nature than the energy gap in insulators.[12] But the argument of the exponential in the heat capacity is found[13] to be one-half of the gap. In Fig. 9b we see that the heat capacity of gallium varies as $e^{-\Delta/k_B T}$, with $\Delta \cong 1.4\ k_B T_c$. Thus the gap is $E_g \equiv 2\Delta = 2(1.4\ k_B T_c)$, or $E_g/k_B T_c = 2.8$. This value of the ratio $E_g/k_B T_c$ is representative. Values of the energy gaps[14] in several superconductors are given in Table 3; the values were obtained by the electron tunneling method to be described. The quantity Δ is often called the **energy gap parameter.**

The transition in zero magnetic field from the superconducting state to the normal state is observed to be a second-order phase transition (Chapter 13). In such a transition there is no latent heat, but there is a discontinuity in the heat capacity which is clearly evident in Fig. 9a. Further, the energy gap decreases continuously to zero as the temperature is increased to the transition temperature T_c, as shown in Fig. 11.

[12] In an insulator the gap is tied to the lattice; in a superconductor the gap is tied to the Fermi gas.

[13] From theory and from comparison with optical and other determinations of the gap.

[14] For a review, see D. H. Douglass, Jr., and L. M. Falicov, *Progress in low temperature physics* **4**, 97–193 (1964).

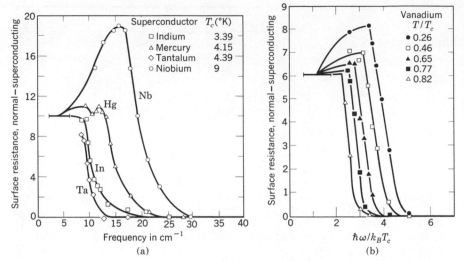

Figure 12 (a) Low temperature results on relative scale of (normal state surface resistance) minus (superconducting state surface resistance), as a function of frequency. The curves have been normalized so that the value at the lowest frequency is the same for each. (b) The same quantity for vanadium, as a function of temperature. (After Richards and Tinkham.)

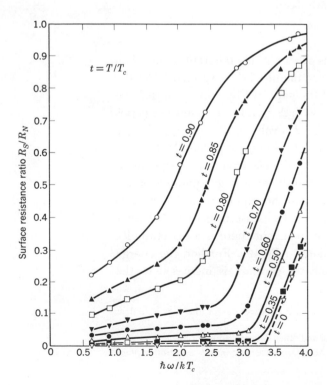

Figure 13 Isotherms of surface resistance ratio of aluminum versus photon frequency. (After Biondi and Garfunkel.)

Microwave and Infrared Properties

The existence of an energy gap in superconductors suggests that, as in semiconductors with a gap, photons of energy less than the gap energy can be transmitted through a superconducting metal. This has been established experimentally by Glover and Tinkham, and by several other workers.

For photon energies less than the energy gap, the resistivity of a superconductor vanishes at absolute zero. Experimental results in the far infrared[15] are shown in Fig. 12. Results in the microwave region[16] at different temperatures are shown in Fig. 13. It is seen that at $T \ll T_c$ the resistance in the superconducting state has a sharp threshold at the gap energy. Photons of lower energy see a resistanceless surface. Photons of higher energy see a resistance which approaches that of the normal state because such photons cause transitions to unoccupied "normal" energy levels above the gap. As the temperature is increased not only does the gap decrease in energy (as in Fig. 11) but the resistivity for photons below the gap no longer vanishes, except at zero frequency. At zero frequency the superconducting electrons short-circuit any normal electrons which have been thermally excited above the gap. Inertial effects present an exact short-circuit at $\omega > 0$.

Isotope Effect

It has been observed that the critical temperature of superconductors varies with isotopic mass. The first observations were made by Maxwell[17] and

Table 4   Isotope effect in superconductors

Experimental values of α in $M^\alpha T_c = $ constant, where M is the isotopic mass. (After a tabulation by J. W. Garland, Jr., Phys. Rev. Letters **11**, 114 (1963), with revisions suggested by Dr. V. Compton.)

Substance	α	Substance	α
Zn	0.45 ± 0.05	Ru	0.00 ± 0.05
Cd	0.51 ± 0.10	Os	0.15 ± 0.05
Sn	0.47 ± 0.02	Mo	0.33
Hg	0.50 ± 0.03	Nb_3Sn	0.08 ± 0.02
Pb	0.49 ± 0.02	Mo_3Ir	0.33 ± 0.03
Tl	0.61 ± 0.10	Zr	0.00 ± 0.05

[15] P. L. Richards and M. Tinkham, Phys. Rev. **119**, 575 (1960).

[16] M. A. Biondi and M. P. Garfunkel, Phys. Rev. Letters **2**, 143 (1959).

[17] E. Maxwell, Phys. Rev. **78**, 477 (1950).

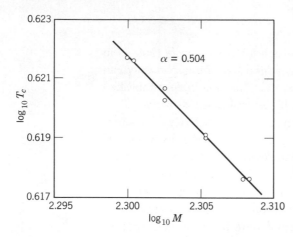

Figure 14 Log-log plot of transition temperature versus average mass number for separated isotopes of mercury. [After Reynolds, Serin, and Nesbitt, Phys. Rev. **84**, 691 (1951).]

by Reynolds and co-workers[18]. In mercury T_c varies from $4.185°$K to $4.146°$K as the average isotopic mass M varies from 199.5 to 203.4 atomic mass units.

The experimental results within each series of isotopes may be fitted by a relation of the form

$$M^\alpha T_c = \text{constant}, \tag{2}$$

as shown for mercury in Fig. 14. Observed values of α are given in Table 4.

It is often found that $\alpha \cong 0.5$. From Chapter 6 we know that the velocity of sound and the Debye temperature Θ are proportional to $M^{-1/2}$ so that $\alpha = 0.5$ means that $T_c/\Theta = \text{constant}$. From the constancy of T_c/Θ we learn that lattice vibrations and hence electron-lattice interactions have something to do with superconductivity![19]

THEORETICAL SURVEY

A theoretical understanding of the phenomena associated with superconductivity has been reached at several levels. Certain results follow directly from thermodynamics. Many important results can be described by phenomenological equations: the London equations and the Landau-Ginzburg equations. A successful quantum theory of superconductivity was given by Bardeen, Cooper, and Schrieffer, and in subsequent work the microscopic basis of their theory has been extended to give back the Landau-Ginzburg equations. Our survey will be somewhat sketchy because of the intrinsic advanced level of much of the theory.

---

[18] Reynolds, Serin, Wright, and Nesbitt, Phys. Rev. **78**, 487 (1950).

[19] The absence of an isotope effect in Ru and Os has been accounted for in terms of the band structure of these metals. J. W. Garland, Jr., Phys. Rev. Letters **11**, 114 (1963).

Thermodynamics of the Superconducting Transition

It was demonstrated experimentally by van Laer and Keesom[20] that the transition between the normal and superconducting states is thermodynamically reversible, just as the transition between liquid and vapor phases of a substance is reversible under conditions of slow evaporation. The Meissner effect also suggests that the transition is reversible. The superconducting currents do not die away with the production of Joule heat when superconductivity is destroyed by application of a magnetic field. If the transition is reversible, we may apply thermodynamics[21] to the transition. We thereby obtain an expression for the entropy difference between normal and superconducting states in terms of the critical field curve H_c versus T. We treat only a type I superconductor with a complete Meissner effect, so that $\mathbf{B} = 0$ inside the superconductor. We shall see that the critical field[22] H_c is a valuable measure of the energy difference between the superconducting and normal states at absolute zero.

We calculate the work done on a superconductor when a magnetic field is applied. The superconductor is in the form of a very long cylinder which is placed inside a solenoidal winding. Let H_a denote the magnetic field produced in the *empty* solenoid when a current i flows in the winding. The work done by the external power supply in building up the field H_a in the empty solenoid is

$$W \text{ (coil)} = \frac{1}{4\pi} \int H_a \, dH_a = \frac{1}{8\pi} H_a{}^2, \tag{3}$$

per unit volume of the solenoid. This is a standard result[23] of elementary electromagnetism. Work is done in building up the field because the changing flux through the coil induces a back emf. The integral $\int dt V i = \frac{1}{2} L i^2$ gives the work done, where L is the self-inductance of the coil. For an empty solenoid of cross-section area S, length l, and n turns, we have $H_a = (4\pi n/cl)i$ and $L = 4\pi n^2 S/c^2 l$, whence $W = H_a{}^2/8\pi$ per unit volume of the coil.

Now let the solenoid contain magnetic material which acquires a magnetization M when the current is turned on. The work done by the external power supply is

$$W \text{ (coil + matter)} = \frac{1}{4\pi} \int H_a \, dB = \frac{1}{8\pi} H_a{}^2 + \int H_a \, dM, \tag{4}$$

[20] P. H. van Laer and W. H. Keesom, Physica **5**, 993 (1938).

[21] C. Gorter and H. B. G. Casimir, Physica **1**, 306 (1934).

[22] The symbol H_c will always refer to a bulk specimen, never to a thin film. For type II superconductors H_c is understood to be the **thermodynamic critical field** which can be defined from (19) below.

[23] See C. Kittel, *Elementary statistical physics*, Wiley, 1958, pp. 77–85.

where $B = H_a + 4\pi M$. The term $\frac{1}{8\pi}H_a^2$ is common to (3) and (4), and we may call it the magnetic energy of the coil. The remaining term in (4) we associate with the work of magnetization, per unit volume:

$$W \text{ (matter)} = \int H_a \, dM; \qquad dW = H_a \, dM. \qquad (5)$$

In evaluating (5) we note that M is a function of the magnetizing field H_a.

The second law of thermodynamics is

$$dU = T \, dS + H_a \, dM, \qquad (6)$$

for a reversible process, using (5) for the external work done on the system. This may be compared with the form

$$dU = T \, dS - p \, dV \qquad (7)$$

for a gas. We see that H_a plays the role of p, and M plays the role of $-V$. (We could equally associate the minus sign with p instead of with V).

In discussions of thermodynamic equilibria at constant p and T it is useful to consider the thermodynamic potential

$$G(T, p) \equiv U - TS + pV, \qquad (8)$$

which is a minimum in equilibrium. For equilibrium at constant H_a and T we are guided by analogy to consider

$$G(T, H_a) \equiv U - TS - H_a M. \qquad (9)$$

On taking differentials we have

$$dG = dU - T \, dS - S \, dT - M \, dH_a - H_a \, dM. \qquad (10)$$

Using (6) this reduces to

$$dG = -S \, dT - M \, dH_a. \qquad (11)$$

For a process at constant temperature $dG = -M \, dH_a$.

Now suppose that the normal state of the metal is nonmagnetic, with zero magnetic susceptibility.[24] Then M is zero, and the thermodynamic potential G_N of a unit volume of the metal in the normal state N is not changed by the application of the external field:

$$G_N(T, H_a) = G_N(T, 0). \qquad (12)$$

---

[24] This is not always a good assumption because the Pauli spin susceptibility is believed in certain type II superconductors to limit the maximum field to which superconductivity persists, but it is a convenient assumption for an introductory discussion.

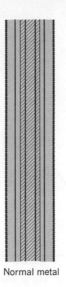
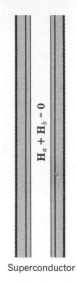

Figure 15 Static magnetic field inside an infinite solenoid when empty, when containing a normal metal, and when containing a superconductor. The magnetic field in the vacuum and in the normal metal is $\mathbf{H}_a$; it is also $\mathbf{H}_a$ in the region between the solenoid and the superconductor, but in the superconductor it is $\mathbf{H}_a + \mathbf{H}_b = 0$.

Vacuum   Normal metal   Superconductor

Consider the specimen[25] in the superconducting state S under the same conditions: A complete Meissner effect means that $B = 0$, or $M = -H_a/4\pi$, as in Fig. 15. At constant temperature

$$dG_S = -M\,dH_a = (H_a/4\pi)\,dH_a \qquad (13)$$

whence

$$G_S(T, H_a) = G_S(T, 0) + \frac{1}{8\pi}H_a{}^2. \qquad (14)$$

The thermodynamic potential of the superconductor is increased on placing it in a magnetic field.

The central result of the thermodynamic theory of equilibria[26] is that the thermodynamic potentials of two phases must be equal if the phases are to be in equilibrium at constant T and H_a. This follows from the minimal property of the total thermodynamic potential taken over the volume. For $V_S + V_N =$ constant the total potential $V_S G_S + V_N G_N$ is independent of V_S only if $G_S = G_N$. The critical field $H_c(T)$ is therefore characterized by the requirement that

$$G_N(T, H_c) = G_S(T, H_c). \qquad (15)$$

From (12) and (14) we have

---

25 Unless otherwise stated we shall always take the superconductor as a very long cylinder with H_a parallel to the axis of the cylinder.

26 A familiar application of the theory is the Clausius-Clapeyron equation for the equilibrium at constant pressure and temperature of a liquid with a gas.

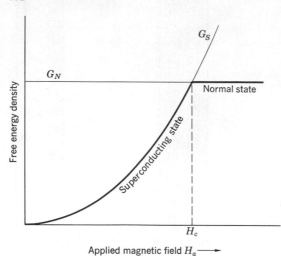

Free energy density

G_N

G_S

Normal state

Superconducting state

H_c

Applied magnetic field H_a ⟶

Figure 16   The thermodynamic potential density $G_N(H_a, T)$ of a nonmagnetic normal metal is approximately independent of the applied magnetic field intensity H_a. At the temperature for which this figure has been drawn the material is superconducting in zero magnetic field, so that $G_S(0, T)$ is lower than G_N. In the superconducting state in an applied magnetic field the Meissner effect increases G_S by $H_a^2/8\pi$, so that

$$G_S(H_a, T) = G_S(0, 0) + \frac{1}{8\pi} H_a^2.$$ For $H_a > H_c$ the thermodynamic potential density is lower in the normal state than in the superconducting state, so that now the normal state is stable.

$$G_N(T, 0) = G_S(T, 0) + \frac{1}{8\pi}H_c^2; \qquad G_N(T, 0) - G_S(T, 0) = \frac{1}{8\pi}H_c^2. \qquad (16)$$

When $H > H_c(T)$ we have $G_S > G_N$ and the normal state is stable (Fig. 16).

Equation (16) is an important result: $\frac{1}{8\pi}H_c^2$ is a direct experimental measure of the stabilization energy density of the superconductor. A typical value is 10^4 ergs/cm³, or 10^{-19} erg per conduction electron. The BCS theory shows how the stabilization is achieved.

The superconducting and normal states are in equilibrium along the critical field curve H_c vs. T, as in Fig. 4. It follows that $G_N(T, H_c) = G_S(T, H_c)$ along the critical field curve. Thus $dG_N = dG_S$ along the curve, so that

$$\left(\frac{\partial G_N}{\partial T}\right)_{H_c} dT + \left(\frac{\partial G_N}{\partial H_c}\right)_T dH_c = \left(\frac{\partial G_S}{\partial T}\right)_{H_c} dT + \left(\frac{\partial G_S}{\partial H_c}\right)_T dH_c. \qquad (17)$$

Using (11) we have

$$S = -(\partial G/\partial T)_{H_a}. \qquad (18)$$

From (12), (14), (17) it follows that the entropy S_N in the normal state is related to the entropy S_S in the superconducting state by

$$S_N = S_S - \frac{1}{8\pi}\frac{d}{dT}H_c^2, \qquad (19)$$

using the fact that G_N is independent of the magnetic field. The most useful form of this result is given in Problem 1. Because dH_c/dT is found to be always negative, as in Fig. 4, the entropy is always greater in the normal state than in the superconducting state. Entropy is a measure of order:

therefore the superconducting state is more ordered than the normal state. Because $dH_c{}^2/dT$ is observed to be nonzero (except at 0 and T_c where it is zero) there is a finite entropy change when the transition takes place in a magnetic field. A finite entropy change means that there is a latent heat.

London Equations

We have said that the Meissner effect implies a magnetic susceptibility $\chi = -1/4\pi$ in the superconducting state. This is a sweeping assumption which tends to cut off further discussion, and it does not account for observations on thin films. Can we avoid or restate the assumption and modify the electrodynamic equations in some other way to obtain the Meissner effect?

The assumption of zero resistivity leads to the acceleration equation[27]

$$m \, dv/dt = -e\mathbf{E}, \tag{20}$$

or, because $\mathbf{j} = -ne\mathbf{v}$,

$$\boxed{\frac{d\mathbf{j}}{dt} - \frac{ne^2}{m}\mathbf{E},} \tag{21}$$

with n the number of electrons per unit volume.

Taking the curl of both sides of (21), we have, with curl $\mathbf{E} = -\dot{\mathbf{H}}/c$,

$$\mathrm{curl}\,(\Lambda d\mathbf{j}/dt) = -\frac{1}{c}\dot{\mathbf{H}}, \tag{22}$$

where Λ denotes m/ne^2. We understand $\mathbf{H}$ to be the sum of the applied field $\mathbf{H}_a$ and the magnetic field $\mathbf{H}_b$ of the current $\mathbf{j}$. Because $4\pi\mathbf{j}/c = \mathrm{curl}\,\mathbf{H}$,

$$\mathrm{curl}\,\Lambda\,\frac{d\mathbf{j}}{dt} = \frac{c}{4\pi}\,\mathrm{curl\,curl}\,\Lambda\dot{\mathbf{H}} = -\frac{1}{c}\dot{\mathbf{H}}, \tag{23}$$

which reduces to

$$\frac{\Lambda c^2}{4\pi}\,\nabla^2\dot{\mathbf{H}} = \dot{\mathbf{H}}. \tag{24}$$

On integrating with respect to time we obtain

$$\frac{\Lambda c^2}{4\pi}\,\nabla^2(\mathbf{H} - \mathbf{H}_0) = \mathbf{H} - \mathbf{H}_0, \tag{25}$$

where $\mathbf{H}_0$ denotes the field at time $t = 0$.

---

[27] In a nonuniform electric field this expression and therefore the argument leading to (27) cannot be entirely correct because they neglect the mean free path of the electrons. The coherence length (see below) was introduced for this reason. We ran into a similar problem in the anomalous skin effect, Chapter 8.

Equation (25) is a direct consequence of the Maxwell equations and the acceleration equation. The result admits the particular solution $\mathbf{H} = \mathbf{H}_0$, where $\mathbf{H}_0$ is an arbitrary field existing at time $t = 0$; but the Meissner effect tells us that we cannot have frozen-in fields. We see therefore that (25) has more general solutions than nature allows in superconductors. In this discussion the currents are considered as the only internal source of magnetic field; no magnetization as such has been introduced.

F. and H. London[28] suggested that to eliminate $\mathbf{H}_0$ from (25) and to explain the Meissner effect we should postulate as a fundamental equation in a superconductor

$$c \operatorname{curl}(m\mathbf{j}/ne^2) = -\mathbf{H}. \tag{26}$$

We may introduce the vector potential $\mathbf{A}$ by the definition $\operatorname{curl} \mathbf{A} \equiv \mathbf{H}$; then (26) becomes, with $\mathbf{j}$ as the current density,

$$\boxed{\mathbf{j}(\mathbf{r}) = -\frac{ne^2}{mc}\mathbf{A}.} \tag{27}$$

This is called the **London equation.** It is a phenomenological empirical equation which replaces Ohm's law in superconductors. Sometimes (27) together with (21) are called the London equations. When applied to the superconducting electrons, they have considerable success in macroscopic descriptions of the electrodynamic behavior of type I superconductors. On taking the curl of both sides of the Maxwell equation $4\pi\mathbf{j}/c = \operatorname{curl}\mathbf{H}$ and using (26) we obtain

$$\frac{mc^2}{4\pi ne^2}\nabla^2\mathbf{H} = \mathbf{H}, \tag{28}$$

which should be contrasted with (25) obtained without using the London equation. Note that (28) does not admit a constant field as a solution.

London Penetration Depth

We look for a solution of (28) of the form

$$H = H_0 \exp(-x/\lambda_L), \tag{29}$$

---

[28] F. London and H. London, Proc. Roy. Soc. (London) A149, 72 (1935); Physica 2, 341 (1935). The London equation (27) is understood to be written in the London gauge in which div $\mathbf{A} = 0$, and $\mathbf{A}_n = 0$ on any external surface through which no external current is fed. Thus div $\mathbf{j} = 0$ and $\mathbf{j}_n = 0$.

[29] J. M. Lock, Proc. Roy. Soc. (London) A208, 391 (1951). The value of λ_L increases as $T \to T_c$, because the "concentration of superconducting electrons" decreases. That is, n in the definition of Λ in (22) might be interpreted as the concentration n_S of electrons in the superconducting state; however, n_S cannot really be defined without a theory of superconductivity.

where λ_L is a constant to be determined; it is a measure of the penetration depth of the field. Here x is the distance below the plane surface of a superconductor. On substitution of (29) in (28) we have

$$\lambda_L = (mc^2/4\pi ne^2)^{1/2}; \qquad \lambda_L^2 \nabla^2 \mathbf{H} = \mathbf{H}. \tag{30}$$

We may also write (30) as $\lambda_L = c/\omega_p$, with the definition (8.23) of the plasma frequency ω_p. At $0°$K the quantity n in (30) is the conduction electron concentration.

A typical experimental value[29] of λ_L in a metal at $0°$K is 500 Å, which is of the order of magnitude expected from (30) if n is the total concentration of conduction electrons. This quantity λ_L is known as the **London penetration depth**.

An applied magnetic field will penetrate a thin film fairly uniformly if the thickness is much less than λ_L. Thus H_b is $\ll H_a$ and there is no Meissner effect in a film of thickness $\ll \lambda_L$. In this situation there is little effect of H_a on the energy density (6) of the superconducting state. By reference to our thermodynamic argument it follows that the critical field H_c of thin films in parallel magnetic fields should be very high, as is in fact observed.

Coherence Length

The London penetration depth λ_L is a fundamental length characterizing a superconductor. There is another independent length of equal importance, the **coherence length** ξ. In a spatially varying magnetic field the energy gap parameter Δ can be a function of position, $\Delta(\mathbf{r})$. The coherence length is a measure of the distance within which the gap parameter cannot change drastically. The London equation (27) is a *local* equation because it relates the current density at a point $\mathbf{r}$ to the vector potential at the same point. But the coherence length ξ is a measure of nonlocal effects.

It is physically plausible that $\mathbf{j}(\mathbf{r})$ in (27) should not be able to follow very rapid spatial variations in $\mathbf{A}(\mathbf{r})$. We know that any spatial variation in the state of an electronic system requires extra energy.[30] It is reasonable to restrict the spatial variation in such a way that the extra energy is less than the energy gap, as this is a measure of the stabilization of the superconducting state. On the BCS theory[31] this restriction leads to the following relation

---

[30] A modulation of an eigenfunction increases the kinetic energy because the modulation will increase the integral of $(d\psi/dx)^2$.

[31] See QTS, pp. 173–174. This result emerges as an expression of the uncertainty principle $\Delta p \, \Delta x$ for superconducting electrons: the energy of a plane wave of wavevector $\mathbf{k}_F + \mathbf{q}$ is greater than that of a plane wave $\mathbf{k}_F$ by $\approx (\hbar^2/2m)(2k_F q)$, for $q \ll k_F$. Setting this equal to E_g we have an upper limit on q: $q \approx m/\hbar^2 k_F = 1/\hbar v_F$. The uncertainty principle becomes $(\hbar q)(\xi_0) \approx \hbar$, or $\xi_0 \approx \hbar v_F/E_g$.

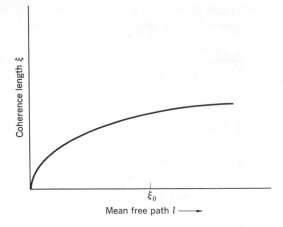

Figure 17 Schematic variation of superconducting coherence length ξ versus mean free path of conduction electrons in the normal state at low temperatures. The mean free path in an alloy series tends to vary inversely as the residual resistivity of the alloy in the normal state.

between the energy gap, the Fermi velocity, and the **intrinsic coherence length** ξ_0 of a pure superconductor:

$$\xi_0 = 2\hbar v_F/\pi E_g \sim 10^{-4} \text{ cm.} \tag{31}$$

In impure material and in alloys the coherence length[32] ξ is shorter than ξ_0 because of the effect of a short electron mean free path, as in (32b) below and in Fig. 17. We shall find that the type I or type II character of the superconductor is determined by the value of the coherence length.

The London equation (27) is modified by these considerations: $\mathbf{j}(\mathbf{r})$ now appears as a suitable weighted average of $\mathbf{A}(\mathbf{r}')$ over a finite region of extent $\approx \xi$ around the point $\mathbf{r}$ in a pure superconductor. We need not be concerned here with the exact form of the averaging function.

[32] The coherence length ξ first appeared in the solutions of a pair of phenomenological equations known as the Landau-Ginzburg equations. The Landau-Ginzburg equations follow from the BCS theory. These are a generalization of the London equations and were introduced to describe the structure of the transition layer between normal and superconducting phases in contact. In the transition layer the energy gap parameter Δ is a function of position. The intrinsic coherence length ξ_0 in (31) was introduced by Pippard to account for the results of experiments on the microwave properties of superconductors. Gorkov has determined the important connection between the actual coherence length ξ, the conduction electron mean free path l, and the intrinsic Pippard coherence length ξ_0 of a pure superconductor. In terms of the reduced temperature $t = T/T_c$ the results are, for t not too small:

Pure superconductor $\quad (l \gg \xi_0) \qquad \xi = 0.52\, \xi_0/(1 - t)^{1/2};$ (32a)

Impure superconductor $\quad (l \ll \xi_0) \qquad \xi = 0.60\, (l\xi_0)^{1/2}/(1 - t)^{1/2}.$ (32b)

Pippard has shown that in an impure superconductor the penetration depth λ is increased:

$$\lambda \cong \lambda_L(\xi_0/l)^{1/2}, \tag{32c}$$

with λ_L given by (30). The derivation of the set of results (32) is beyond the level of our text; see the book by de Gennes.

BCS Theory of Superconductivity

We have given above a simple unified discussion of the rich experimental and phenomenological knowledge of superconductors. There seems at present to be little need for fundamentally different theories of superconductivity for the different rows and columns of the periodic table, for pure metals and alloys, or for different crystal structures. These considerations affect the quantitative details of the superconducting properties, but apparently only within the framework of a general theory which we now discuss. The basis of a general quantum theory of superconductivity was laid by the classic 1957 papers of Bardeen, Cooper, and Schrieffer.[33]

The accomplishments of the BCS theory include:

1. An attractive interaction[34] between electrons can lead to a ground state of the entire electronic system which is separated from excited states by an energy gap. The critical field, the thermal properties,[35] and most of the electromagnetic properties are consequences of the energy gap. The mathematics which leads to the energy gap and to the special BCS ground state is discussed in Appendix E.

2. The electron-lattice-electron interaction is attractive and can overcome the Coulomb repulsion between electrons. The interaction leads to an energy gap of the observed magnitude. The indirect interaction proceeds roughly as follows: one electron interacts with the lattice and deforms it; a second electron sees the deformed lattice and adjusts itself to take advantage of the deformation to lower its energy. Thus in effect the second electron interacts with the first electron via the lattice deformation or phonon field. The Debye frequency of the phonon spectrum enters the theory of the interaction in a natural way and leads to the isotope effect, Eq. (2).

3. The London penetration depth and the Pippard coherence length emerge as natural consequences of the BCS ground state.[36] The London equation (27) is obtained for magnetic fields which vary slowly in space. This is very important because the London equation accounts for the central phenomenon in superconductivity, the Meissner effect.

4. The criterion for the occurrence of superconductivity and for the magnitude of the transition temperature in an element or alloy is found to involve the electron density of states $\mathfrak{D}(\epsilon_F)$ at the Fermi level and the electron-

---

[33] J. Bardeen, L. N. Cooper, and J. R. Schrieffer, Phys. Rev. **106**, 162 (1957); **108**, 1175 (1957).

[34] Strictly speaking, the net interaction does not have to be attractive, but it has to be less repulsive for the superconducting state than for the normal state.

[35] The observed ratios of $E_g(0)/k_B T_c$ listed in Table 3 are close to the prediction of the BCS theory. The character of the normal/superconductor phase transition is described correctly.

[36] For an elementary account, see Chapter 21 of Vol. 3 of R. P. Feynman, R. B. Leighton, and M. Sands, *Feynman lectures on physics*, Addison-Wesley, 1965.

lattice interaction U, which can be estimated from the electrical resistivity. For $U\mathfrak{D}(\epsilon_F) \ll 1$ the BCS theory predicts

$$T_c = 1.14\,\Theta\,\exp\,[-1/U\mathfrak{D}(\epsilon_F)],$$

where Θ is the Debye temperature. This relation assumes that U is an attractive interaction (positive as used here); otherwise the ground state is not superconducting. The result for T_c is satisfied at least qualitatively by the experimental data. There is an interesting apparent paradox: the higher the resistivity at room temperature,[37] the more likely it is that a metal will be a superconductor when cooled. This holds only if we compare metals with comparable densities of conduction electrons. Another simple conclusion is that elements with an even number of valence electrons per atom are less likely to be superconductors than elements with an odd number of valence electrons: this is just another way of saying as in Chapter 9 that an even number of valence electrons may favor filling a Brillouin zone, so that $\mathfrak{D}(\epsilon_F)$ will be small.

5. Several specialized effects have given impressive evidence for the BCS picture of the superconducting ground state. Of these we mention the quantization of magnetic flux through a superconducting ring: it is found that the flux is quantized and that effective unit of charge is $2e$ rather than e. The BCS ground state involves (Appendix E) pairs of one-electron states, and flux quantization[38] in terms of the pair charge $2e$ is a consequence of the BCS theory (QTS, Chap. 8).

BCS Ground State

We saw in Chapter 7 that the ground state of a Fermi gas of noninteracting electrons is just the filled Fermi sea (Fig. 18). This state, which we call the Fermi state, allows arbitrarily small excitations—we can form an excited state by taking an electron from the Fermi surface and raising it just above the Fermi surface. The BCS theory shows that with an appropriate attractive interaction between electrons the ground state is separated by a finite energy E_g from its lowest excited state.

The formation of the BCS ground state is indicated from one point of view in Fig. 19. The BCS state in (b) contains admixtures of one-electron states from above as well as below the Fermi energy ϵ_F. At first sight the BCS state appears to have a higher energy than the Fermi state. The comparison of (b) and (a) shows that the kinetic energy of the BCS state is higher than

---

[37] Because the resistivity at room temperature is a measure of the electron-phonon interaction. In the BCS relation quoted for T_c we should take $\mathfrak{D}(\epsilon_F)$ as the density of states of one spin.

[38] Early experiments on flux quantization are reported by H. S. Deaver and W. M. Fairbank, Phys. Rev. Letters **7**, 43 (1961); R. Doll and M. Näbauer, Phys, Rev. Letters **7**, 51 (1961). For a simple account of the theory, see QTS, pp. 175–177.

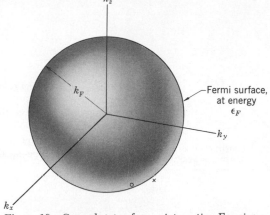

Figure 18   Ground state of a noninteracting Fermi gas; all one-particle states with $k \leq k_F$ are occupied; for $k > k_F$ all states are vacant. An excited state of arbitrarily low excitation energy can be formed by removing an electron from the point o just inside the Fermi surface and placing it at x just outside the Fermi surface.

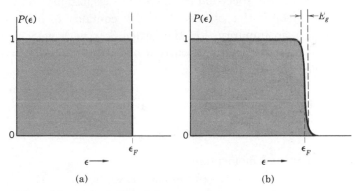

(a)   (b)

Figure 19   (a) Probability P that a one-electron state of energy ϵ is occupied in the ground state of the noninteracting Fermi gas; (b) the BCS ground state differs from the Fermi state in the distribution of probability over a region of width E_g at the Fermi surface.

that of the Fermi state. But the attractive potential energy of the BCS state, although not represented in the figure, acts to lower the total energy of the BCS state with respect to the Fermi state. One-particle states somewhat above the Fermi energy are brought into the BCS state because the value of the energy gap tends to be proportional to the number of states which participate in forming the BCS state. This point is explained in Appendix E.

If the BCS ground state of a many-electron system is described in terms of the occupancy of one-particle states, then those near ϵ_F are filled somewhat like a Fermi-Dirac distribution for some finite temperature. A further feature of the BCS state is that the one-particle states are occupied in pairs: if a state with wavevector $\mathbf{k}$ and spin up is occupied, then the state with wavevector $-\mathbf{k}$ and spin down is also occupied (see Appendix E). If $\mathbf{k}_1\uparrow$ is vacant, then $-\mathbf{k}_1\downarrow$ is also vacant.

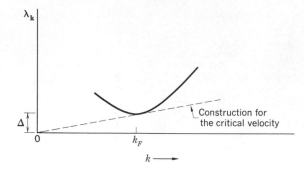

Figure 20 Spectrum of elementary excitations near the ground state of a superconductor. The vertical axis is the energy above the ground state of one member of a pair of two excited particles. The horizontal axis is the magnitude of the wavevector. The dashed line has a slope equal to $\hbar v_c$, where v_c is the critical velocity.

There are several arguments[38a] which can be given for the stability of persistent currents in a superconductor. The one easiest to grasp is due to Landau and concerns the spectrum of elementary excitations, shown in Fig. 20. Consider a crystal lattice of mass M which contains an imperfection, such as a phonon or an impurity. Let the lattice flow with velocity $\mathbf{v}$ relative to the electron gas (the persistent current has velocity $-\mathbf{v}$ relative to the lattice). The velocity $\mathbf{v}$ will decrease if the relative motion can generate excitations in the electron gas. In a collision event in which an excitation of energy $\lambda_\mathbf{k}$ and momentum $\hbar\mathbf{k}$ is created we must have

$$\tfrac{1}{2}Mv^2 = \tfrac{1}{2}Mv'^2 + \lambda_\mathbf{k}; \qquad M\mathbf{v} = M\mathbf{v}' + \hbar\mathbf{k},$$

from energy and momentum conservation.

If we combine these two equations we have

$$0 = \hbar\mathbf{k} \cdot \mathbf{v} + (\hbar^2 k^2 / 2M) + \lambda_\mathbf{k}.$$

For $M \to \infty$ we can neglect the term in $1/M$. The lowest value of v for which the equation $\lambda_\mathbf{k} = \hbar\mathbf{k} \cdot \mathbf{v}$ can be satisfied is

$$v_c = \min\,(\lambda_\mathbf{k}/\hbar k). \tag{33}$$

If there is an energy gap then $\lambda_\mathbf{k} > 0$, so that $v_c > 0$. Thus superconducting currents can flow with velocities less than v_c without risk of dissipation of energy by excitation of electrons from the superconducting state to the normal state. The values of the critical current density are quite high (Problem 4).

Essentially the same argument goes through for the excitation of a pair of electrons, one to energy $\lambda_\mathbf{k}$ and the other to $\lambda_{\mathbf{k}'}$.

[38a] An excellent discussion is given by V. F. Weisskopf, CERN report 62–30 (Oct. 1962).

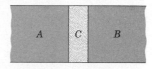

Figure 21   Two metals, *A* and *B*, separated by a thin layer of an insulator *C*.

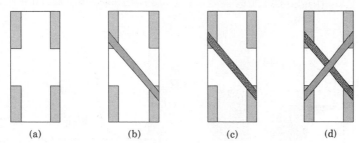

(a)   (b)   (c)   (d)

Figure 22   Preparation of an $Al/Al_2O_3/Sn$ sandwich. (a) Glass slide with indium contacts. (b) An aluminum strip 1 mm wide and 1000 to 3000 Å thick has been deposited across the contacts. (c) The aluminum strip has been oxidized. (d) A tin film has been deposited across the aluminum film, forming an $Al/Al_2O_3/Sn$ sandwich. The external leads are connected to the indium contacts; two contacts are used for the current measurement and two for the voltage measurement. The critical temperatures of Sn and Al are 3.7 and 1.2°K respectively; between these two temperatures the Sn strip is superconducting and the Al strip is normal. The Al_2O_3 layer is an insulator. (After Giaever and Megerle.)

Electron Tunneling

Consider two metals separated by an insulator, as in Fig. 21. The insulator normally acts as a barrier to the flow of conduction electrons from one metal to the other. If the barrier is sufficiently thin (less than 10 or 20 Å) there is a significant probability that an electron which impinges on the barrier will pass from one metal to the other: this is called **tunneling.** The concept that particles can tunnel through potential barriers is as old as quantum mechanics.[39] In many experiments the insulating layer is simply a thin oxide layer formed on one of two evaporated metal films, as in Fig. 22.

When both metals are normal conductors the current-voltage relation of the sandwich or tunneling junction is ohmic at low voltages, with the current directly proportional to the applied voltage (Fig. 23a). It is known from the theory[40] of tunneling that the current $I(NN)$ between two normal metals is

[39] See Born, pp. 208–210.
[40] See, for example, I. Giaever and K. Megerle, Phys. Rev. **122**, 1101 (1961); J. Bardeen, Phys. Rev. Letters **6**, 57 (1961).

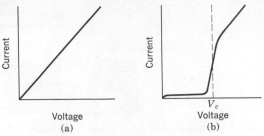

Figure 23 (a) Linear current-voltage relation for junction of normal metals separated by oxide layer; (b) current-voltage relation with one metal normal and the other metal superconducting.

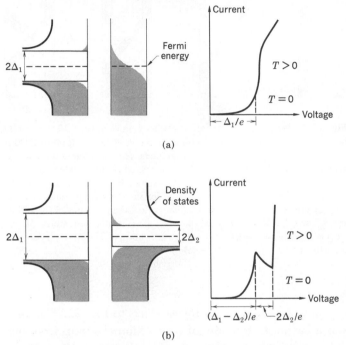

(a)

(b)

Figure 24 Energy diagram displaying the density of states and the current-voltage characteristics for a tunneling junction. The energy is plotted on the vertical scale and the density of states on the horizontal scale. (a) One metal in the normal state and one in the superconducting state. (b) Both metals in the superconducting state. In the drawings on the right the dashes indicate expected breaks at $T = 0$. (After Giaever and Megerle.)

proportional to the product of the density of electronic states of the conduction bands of the two metals A and B, evaluated at the Fermi surface:

$$I(NN) = C\mathcal{D}_A(\epsilon_F)\mathcal{D}_B(\epsilon_F)eV, \qquad (34)$$

where C is a constant; e is the elementary charge; V the applied voltage; and $\mathcal{D}_A$, $\mathcal{D}_B$ are the density of state functions for conduction electrons. Equation (34) is a plausible form: the density of states in the metal on one side of the junction determines the current density impinging on the junction and the density of states in the other metal determines the number of final states available for occupancy by an electron which has tunneled successfully. The $\mathcal{D}$'s are to be taken at the Fermi surface because only there are found filled and

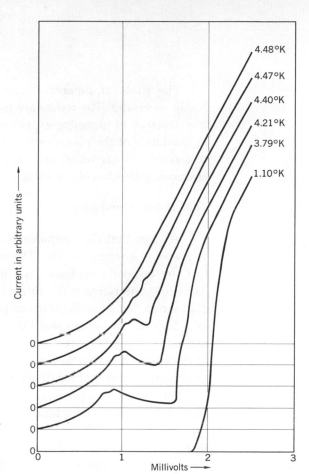

4.48°K
4.47°K
4.40°K
4.21°K
3.79°K
1.10°K

Current in arbitrary units ⟶

0
0
0
0
0
0

0   1   2   3

Millivolts ⟶

Figure 25   Current-voltage characteristics for a Ta/barrier/Pb sandwich as a function of temperature. (After Townsend and Sutton.)

empty states available at the same energy. The factor eV enters as the integral over energy of the difference $f(\epsilon) - f(\epsilon + eV)$ at the Fermi levels on opposite sides of the junction. The result (34) is for $T = 0°K$.

Giaever[41] discovered that if one of the metals becomes superconducting the current-voltage characteristic changes from a straight line of Fig. 23a to the curve shown in Fig. 23b. Figure 24a contrasts the electron density of states in the superconductor with that in the normal metal. In the superconductor there is an energy gap centered at the Fermi level. At absolute zero no current can flow until the applied voltage is $V = E_g/2e = \Delta/e$, which is one-half[42] the energy gap. At temperatures different from zero there is a small current flow even at low voltages, because of electrons in the superconductor which are thermally excited across the energy gap. Results for a Ta/barrier/Pb tunneling junction are shown in Fig. 25.

[41] I. Giaever, Phys. Rev. Letters **5**, 147, 464 (1960).

[42] The one-half enters because the full gap 2Δ corresponds to the break-up of a pair of electrons in the superconducting state, with the formation of two electrons in the normal state. The current starts when $2eV = 2\Delta$. Figure 24 is drawn in an unsophisticated representation; see Schrieffer, pp. 83–86.

The study of superconductors by single-electron tunneling has been highly successful. The results are in good agreement with the BCS theory. A fine structure in tunneling experiments[43] has been found which is attributed to the details of the phonon spectrum.[44] We do not have space to discuss the remarkable effects which arise in the tunneling of *pairs* of superconducting electrons, called Josephson tunneling.[45]

Type II Superconductors[46]

We saw that the thermodynamic potential of a bulk superconductor is increased in a magnetic field. The result (14) was derived on the assumption that the magnetic field does not penetrate significantly into the specimen. The field penetration is the subject of Problems 3 and 6. The integration of (30) shows that a parallel field can penetrate a very thin film nearly uniformly, as in Fig. 26a. It follows that $|M| \ll H_a$, and according to (11) the thermodynamic potential G of the superconducting film will increase relatively slowly as the external magnetic field is increased, causing a major increase in the field intensity required for the destruction of superconductivity.[47]

Persistence of superconductivity in films has been observed in magnetic fields 100 times or more higher than the critical field H_c defined for a bulk superconductor. If the field is not parallel to the plane of the film, the situation is complicated.[48] A thin film is not what is generally meant by a type II superconductor, but its behavior shows that superconductivity can exist in high magnetic fields, under suitable conditions.

The results for thin films suggest an important question: do there exist stable states of a homogeneous bulk superconductor in a magnetic field in which regions in the form of thin rods or plates are in the normal state, with each normal region surrounded by superconducting regions? In such a **mixed**

[43] I. Giaever, H. R. Hart, Jr., and K. Megerle, Phys. Rev. **126**, 941 (1962); J. M. Rowell, A. G. Chynoweth, and J. C. Phillips, Phys. Rev. Letters **9**, 59 (1962).

[44] J. M. Rowell, P. W. Anderson, and D. E. Thomas, Phys. Rev. Letters **10**, 334 (1963); J. R. Schrieffer, D. J. Scalapino, and J. W. Wilkins, Phys. Rev. Letters **10**, 336 (1963).

[45] B. D. Josephson, Physics Letters **1**, 251 (1962); P. W. Anderson and J. M. Rowell, Phys. Rev. Letters **10**, 230 (1963); R. C. Jaklevic, J. Lambe, A. H. Silver, and J. E. Mercereau, Phys. Rev. Letters **12**, 159 (1964).

[46] The theory of type II superconductors was developed by Ginzburg, Landau, Abrikosov, and Gorkov, whence the name GLAG theory. Later Kunzler and co-workers observed that Nb_3Sn wires can carry large supercurrents in fields approaching 100 kG. There is no difference in the mechanism of superconductivity in types I and II; the differences are in the sign of the interface energy between normal and superconducting regions. The surface energy is positive for type I and negative for type II. The consequences of the difference are spectacular with respect to critical fields, but of no importance for the transition temperature T_c.

[47] In a thin film in the superconducting state the magnitude of the apparent magnetic susceptibility may be much smaller than $1/4\pi$, but the film will have the usual energy gap and will be resistanceless.

[48] M. Tinkham, Phys. Rev. **129**, 2413 (1963).

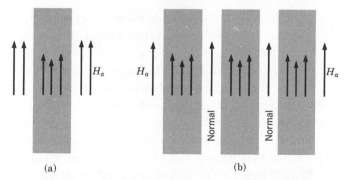

(a)   (b)

Figure 26 (a) Magnetic field penetration into a thin film of thickness, the London penetration depth λ_L. The arrows indicate the intensity of the magnetic field. (b) Magnetic field penetration in a homogeneous bulk structure in the mixed state, with alternate layers in normal and superconducting states. The superconducting layers are thin in comparison with λ_L. (The laminar structure is shown for convenience; the actual structure consists of rods of the normal state surrounded by the superconducting state.)

state the external magnetic field will penetrate the thin normal regions uniformly, and the field will also penetrate somewhat into the surrounding superconducting material, as in Fig. 26b. There is no chemical or crystallographic difference between the normal and superconducting regions in the mixed state; the mixed state will exist if its formation lowers the thermodynamic potential of the entire specimen in a magnetic field. A **type II superconductor** is characterized by a stable mixed state in a certain range of magnetic field strength. If the energy of the mixed state is lower, it is only because the penetration of the applied field into the superconducting material lowers the thermodynamic potential with respect to a pure superconducting state or pure normal state.

There is no difference in the mechanism of superconductivity in type I and type II superconductors. In both types the mechanism is the electron-phonon-electron interaction. Both types have similar thermal properties on going through the superconductor-normal transition in zero magnetic field. But the Meissner effect is entirely different in the two types (Fig. 6). A good type I superconductor excludes a magnetic field until superconductivity is destroyed suddenly and completely, at which point the field penetrates completely. A good type II superconductor excludes the field completely only for relatively weak fields, up to a field H_{c1}. Above H_{c1} the field is only partially excluded (Fig. 6c), but the specimen remains electrically superconducting. At a much higher field, sometimes 100 kG or more, the flux penetrates completely and all superconductivity vanishes; this field is called H_{c2}.

The essential difference between a type I and a type II superconductor is in the value of the mean free path of the conduction electrons in the normal state at low temperatures. If the coherence length ξ is longer than the penetration depth λ, then the superconductor will be type I. This is characteristic of most pure metals when superconductors. If the mean free path or the coherence length is much shorter than the penetration depth, then the superconductor will be type II. We can sometimes change a metal from type I to type II by a modest addition of an alloying element. Thus (Fig. 6c) the addition of 2 wt. percent of indium to lead changes lead from type I to type II, although the transition temperature is scarcely changed at all by this amount of alloying. Neither would we expect the energy gap to be changed, nor the discontinuity in heat capacity at the transition temperature. Nothing very fundamental has been done to the intrinsic electronic structure or superconducting nature of lead by this amount of alloying, but the behavior in a magnetic field has changed drastically.

The question of the stability of the mixed state involves two contributions to the energy. The normal regions have an energy density higher by $(H_c{}^2 - H_a{}^2)/8\pi$ than for a superconductor in the field H_a. The radius of a normal rod[49] will be no smaller than the coherence length ξ, because it is costly in energy to go from S to N to S in a shorter distance. Thus the energy per unit length of a rod-shaped normal region is, referred to S,

$$g_N \cong \frac{1}{8\pi}(H_c{}^2 - H_a{}^2) \cdot \pi\xi^2, \tag{35}$$

where H_c is the thermodynamic critical field.[50]

The second contribution to the energy comes from the penetration of the applied field H_a into the superconductor. The field in the normal rod is of the order[51] of H_a and will penetrate into the superconductor for a distance of the order of λ, as in Fig. 27. There is an area $\approx \pi(\lambda^2 - \xi^2)$ in the superconductor in which $|M| \ll H_a$. Per unit length of rod the energy of the superconductor is thereby lowered by

$$g_S \cong -\frac{1}{8\pi}H_a{}^2\pi(\lambda^2 - \xi^2), \tag{36}$$

referred to a bulk superconductor without the rod, but in the field H_a.

---

[49] We phrase the discussion in terms of rods because rods give a lower energy than plates. For brevity we often say energy density for thermodynamic potential density.

[50] The **thermodynamic critical field** H_c of a type II superconductor is defined so that $H_c{}^2/8\pi$ equals the difference of thermodynamic potential density between the normal and superconducting states in zero magnetic field. The difference may be determined by calorimetric measurements.

[51] This can be demonstrated for $H_a = H_{c1}$.

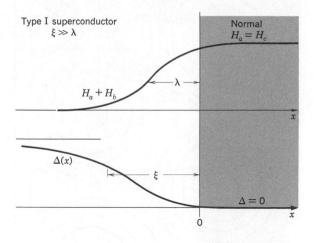

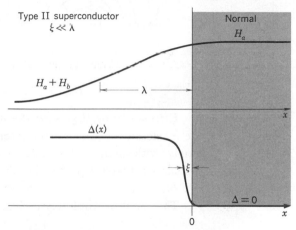

Figure 27 Variation of the magnetic field and energy gap parameter $\Delta(x)$ at the interface of superconducting and normal regions, for type I and type II superconductors.

In a type I superconductor $\xi > \lambda$ and g_S is positive; in a type II superconductor $\xi < \lambda$ and g_S is negative.

Estimation of H_{c1}. The thermodynamic potential of the mixed state with a single rod is

$$g_M = g_N + g_S = \tfrac{1}{8}(\xi^2 H_c{}^2 - \lambda^2 H_a{}^2), \qquad (37)$$

per unit length. The formation of a rod becomes favorable when g_M is negative, for the zero of energy of (37) is referred to the superconductor in the field H_a. The threshold value of H_a marks the initiation of the mixed state and is denoted by H_{c1}:

$$H_{c1} = (\xi/\lambda)H_c. \qquad (38)$$

We see that $H_{c1} < H_c$ as in Fig. 6b, provided that the assumption $\xi < \lambda$ for a type II superconductor is satisfied.

Figure 28 Contour diagram of the local spatial variation of the superconducting energy gap in a type II superconductor just below the upper critical field H_{c2}, after W. H. Kleiner, L. M. Roth, and S. H. Autler, Phys. Rev. **133**, A1226 (1964). At the center of each fluxoid the energy gap goes to zero. A triangular lattice of this nature has been found experimentally by neutron diffraction at Saclay.

Abrikosov[52] has carried out more carefully the calculation of H_{c1}: he finds

$$H_{c1} = H_c(\xi/\lambda)\,[\log(\lambda/\xi) - 0.27].\qquad(39)$$

Estimation of H_{c2}. Near the upper critical field the rods or fluxoids are packed closely together and the external field infiltrates the specimen almost uniformly, with small ripples on the scale of the fluxoid lattice. The lattice has triangular symmetry,[53] as in Fig. 28. The structure of a fluxoid is indicated in Fig. 29.

The result of Abrikosov is that

$$H_{c2} = \sqrt{2}(\lambda/\xi)H_c,\qquad(40)$$

so that H_{c2} may be $\gg H_c$ if $\lambda \gg \xi$. Using (32) we may rewrite (40) as

$$H_{c2} \approx (\lambda_L/l)H_c\qquad(41)$$

in the limit of a dirty superconductor ($l \ll \xi_0$). The shorter the mean free path l, the higher will be H_{c2}. This agrees qualitatively with Fig. 6c.

It is difficult to obtain the Abrikosov result (40) without detailed calculation. The same result, however, applies to thin films in a perpendicular magnetic field; here a simple derivation has been given by Tinkham.[54]

To summarize this chapter, the BCS theory is believed to give a satisfactory general account, in broad outline, of the central phenomena observed in superconductors.

[52] A. A. Abrikosov, Soviet Phys.–JETP **5**, 1174 (1957); his original prediction of type II superconductors was made long before there was a quantum theory of superconductivity.

[53] This has been observed at Saclay by neutron diffraction (D. Cribier et al.).

[54] M. Tinkham, Phys. Rev. **129**, 2413 (1963).

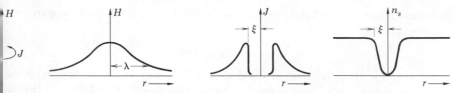

Figure 29 Structure of fluxoid in the mixed state is supported by a circulating supercurrent. The core of the flux line of size $\approx\xi$ is in the normal state, and contains most of the flux, but the field extends into the superconducting region over a distance $\approx\lambda$. The current density is J; the density of superconducting electrons is n_S. Each flux line contains one flux quantum $hc/2e = 2 \times 10^{-7}$ gauss-cm². (After Y. B. Kim, Physics Today, September 1964, pp. 21–30.)

Problems

1. **Discontinuity in heat capacity.** Show from (19) that at T_c the discontinuity in heat capacity per unit volume is given by

$$C_S - C_N = \frac{T_c}{4\pi}\left(\frac{dH_c}{dT}\right)^2.$$

This has been verified experimentally. In a type II superconductor this relation can be used to determine H_c. *Hint:* Note that $H_c = 0$ at T_c.

2. **Thermodynamics of the transition.** Often the observed threshold field curve of H_c versus T is represented fairly well by the parabola $H_c(T) = H_0[1 - (T/T_c)^2]$, where H_0 is the value of the critical field at absolute zero. (a) Show that this relation leads to

$$C_N - C_S = \frac{H_0^2}{2\pi T_c}\left[\frac{T}{T_c} - 3\left(\frac{T}{T_c}\right)^3\right]$$

for the heat capacity differences per unit volume between the normal state N and the superconducting state S. (b) It is known experimentally that the heat capacity C_S of a metal in the superconducting state does not contain a term linear in T, so that the linear term in the equation above is to be identified with the electronic contribution γT to the heat capacity of the metal in the normal state, as in (7.49). Compare for Al and Cd the experimental values of γ and of $H_0^2/2\pi T_c^2$, using Table 7.2 and 11.1, with $H_0 = 99$ G for Al and 30 G for Cd.

3. **Magnetic field penetration in a plate.** The London equation may be written as $\lambda_L^2\nabla^2 H = H$, where λ_L is the London penetration depth as defined by (30). (a) Show that $H(x)$ inside a superconducting plate of thickness δ is given by

$$H(x) = H_a\frac{\cosh(x/\lambda_L)}{\cosh(\delta/2\lambda_L)},$$

where H_a is the field outside the plate; here $x = 0$ is at the center of the plate. We assume that H_a is parallel to the surface of the plate. (b) The effective magnetization $M(x)$ in the plate is defined by $H(x) = H_a + 4\pi M(x)$. Show that

$$4\pi M(x) = -H_a(1/8\lambda_L^2)(\delta^2 - 4x^2),$$

for $\delta \ll \lambda_L$.

4. **Critical velocity.** (a) Find the critical velocity v_c of Eq. (33) if the elementary excitation spectrum is given by

$$\lambda_k = [\Delta^2 + \epsilon_k^2]^{1/2},$$

for $\Delta = 1 \times 10^{-16}$ erg and m equal to the free electron mass. Here ϵ_k is the free electron energy referred to the Fermi level. Take $k_F = 0.66 \times 10^8$ cm^{-1}. (b) Estimate the critical current density, using the value of v_c found in part (a) and with $n = 1 \times 10^{22}$ electrons per cm^3. Express the result in amperes per cm^2.

5. **Superconductor parameters.** Consider a metal with a conduction electron concentration $n = 1 \times 10^{23}$ electrons per cm^3; Debye temperature $\Theta = 300\,°$K; and superconducting transition temperature $0.3\,°$K. (a) Find for a free electron model the density of states $\mathfrak{D}(\epsilon_F)$ at the Fermi level. (b) From the BCS relation given in the text, find the electron-electron interaction U in the specimen. (c) The BCS theory predicts $E_g \cong 3.5k_B T_c$ for the energy gap and $\frac{1}{2}\mathfrak{D}(\epsilon_F)\,\Delta^2$ for the stabilization energy density $G_N(0, 0) - G_S(0, 0)$ of the superconducting state, with $E_g = 2\Delta$. Find the value of the critical field H_c at $T = 0\,°$K. (d) Find the intrinsic coherence length ξ_0. *Note:* In BCS relations as usually stated in the literature, $\mathfrak{D}(\epsilon_F)$ is the density of one electron states for *one* spin direction.

6. **Critical field of thin films.** (a) Using the result of Problem 3b, show that the thermodynamic potential density within a superconducting film of thickness δ in an external magnetic field H_a is given by, for $\delta \ll \lambda_L$,

$$G_S(x, H_a, T) = G_S(0, T) + \frac{1}{64\pi\lambda_L^2}(\delta^2 - 4x^2)H_a^2.$$

(b) Show that the magnetic contribution to G_S when averaged over the thickness of the film is

$$\frac{1}{96\pi} H_a^2 \left(\frac{\delta}{\lambda_L}\right)^2.$$

(c) Show that the critical field of the thin film is proportional to $(\lambda_L/\delta)H_c$, where H_c is the bulk critical field. (We consider only the magnetic contribution to G_S, and we neglect possible coherence effects on λ_L.)

References

E. A. Lynton, *Superconductivity*, Wiley, 1962. (An excellent short introduction.)

M. Tinkham, "Superconductivity," in De Witt et al., ed., *Low temperature physics*, Gordon and Breach, 1962.

Superconductivity conference, Rev. Mod. Phys. **36**, 1–331 (1964).

J. R. Schrieffer *Theory of superconductivity*, Benjamin, 1964.

F. London, *Superfluids*, Vol. I., Wiley, 1950.

G. Rickayzen, *Theory of superconductivity*, Interscience, 1965.

D. Shoenberg, *Superconductivity*, Cambridge University Press, 1960, 2nd ed.

B. W. Roberts, "Superconducting materials," *Progress in cryogenics* **4**, 161 (1964). (Tables of properties.)

TYPE II SUPERCONDUCTIVITY

P. G. de Gennes, *Superconductivity of metals and alloys*, Benjamin, 1966.

B. B. Goodman, Rev. Mod. Phys. **36**, 12–19 (1964).

T. G. Berlincourt, Rev. Mod. Phys. **36**, 19–26 (1964).

DEVICES

V. L. Newhouse, *Applied superconductivity*, Wiley, 1964.

12

Dielectric Properties

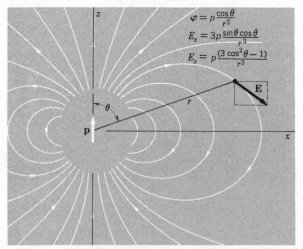

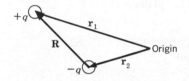

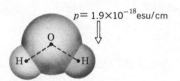

Figure 1 The dipole moment of the pair of charges $\pm q$ is $\mathbf{p} = q\mathbf{r}_1 - q\mathbf{r}_2 = q\mathbf{R}$ and is directed from the negative charge toward the positive charge.

Figure 2 The permanent dipole moment of a molecule of water has the magnitude 1.9×10^{-18} esu/cm and is directed from O^{--} ion toward the midpoint of the line connecting the H^+ ions.

Figure 3 Electrostatic potential and field components at position r, θ for a dipole $\mathbf{p}$ directed along the z axis. For $\theta = 0$, we have $E_x = E_y = 0$ and $E_z = 2p/r^3$; for $\theta = \pi/2$ we have $E_x = E_y = 0$ and $E_z = -p/r^3$. (After E. M. Purcell.)

We discuss first the relationship between the external applied electric field and the local electric field which acts on an atom. The interaction of the local field with the atom determines the polarization, yet the local field is itself a function of the polarization. We then discuss the electric polarization of atoms, molecules, and crystals, in static fields and at high frequencies. The Lyddane-Sachs-Teller relation used in Chapter 5 is derived in detail.

Polarization

The **polarization** $\mathbf{P}$ is defined[1] as the *dipole moment per unit volume*. The total dipole moment is defined (Fig. 1) as

$$\mathbf{p} = \Sigma q_n \mathbf{r}_n, \tag{1}$$

where $\mathbf{r}_n$ is the position vector of the charge q_n. The value of the sum will be independent of the origin chosen for the position vectors, provided that the system is neutral. The dipole moment of a water molecule is shown in Fig. 2.

The electric field at a point $\mathbf{r}$ from a point dipole of moment $\mathbf{p}$ is given by a standard result of elementary electrostatics:

$$\mathbf{E}(\mathbf{r}) = \frac{3(\mathbf{p} \cdot \mathbf{r})\mathbf{r} - r^2 \mathbf{p}}{r^5}. \tag{2}$$

The lines of force for a dipole pointing along the z axis are shown in Fig. 3.

LOCAL ELECTRIC FIELD AT AN ATOM

The calculation of the local field at an atom or ion as affected by the polarization of the specimen as a whole is a problem of central importance in dielectric and magnetic theory. Consider first a solid dielectric with a cubic crystal structure: we suppose that the specimen is in the form of an ellipsoid with one of the axes parallel to the applied electric field (Fig. 4). It is known[2] that the polarization is uniform for a homogeneous ellipsoid in a uniform external field.

---

[1] By far the clearest elementary exposition of electric fields in polarized dielectrics is given by E. M. Purcell, *Electricity and magnetism*, Vol. II of the Berkeley Physics Course, McGraw-Hill, 1965, Chap. 9. Our treatment below is unnecessarily complicated if one needs only the local field (9) at atom sites which have cubic symmetry, because if the specimen is spherical the symmetry argument following (7) gives $E_{\text{loc}} = E_0$ in (3). On going from a sphere to a long rod (or to a capacitor) we increase the local field by $4\pi P/3$, the negative of the depolarization field E_1 of the sphere, and thus we obtain the result (9). For atoms in surroundings of low symmetry, as in many ferroelectrics, it is advantageous to make the detailed decomposition implied by (3).

[2] This is demonstrated in the classical texts on electricity, such as Maxwell, Jeans, and Abragam and Becker, Vol. I.

The electric field at any atom is called the **local field** E_{loc}. It is an idealized field measured under certain conditions: (a) in the absence of the atom; (b) by an infinitesimal test charge; (c) in surroundings undistorted by the test charge and by the imagined removal of the atom; and (d) at the center of the atom, with no allowance for the spatial extent of the atom. In spite of these important idealizations there is an operational value in speaking of E_{loc}. It is important to realize that E_{loc} is *not* the same as the macroscopic electric field E of Maxwell's equation, for E is defined as the space-average electric field over the volume of a unit cell of the crystal.

The local field is the sum of the electric field E_0 from external sources and the field of the dipoles within the specimen. It is traditional and convenient to decompose the dipole field into several parts in order that part of the summation over dipoles may be replaced by integration. We write

$$E_{loc} = E_0 + E_1 + E_2 + E_3. \tag{3}$$

Here

E_0 = external electric field, from external charges;

E_1 = depolarization field, from polarization charges on the outer surface of the specimen;

E_2 = Lorentz cavity field: field from polarization charges on inside of a spherical cavity cut (as a mathematical fiction) out of the specimen with the reference atom as center;

E_3 = field of atoms inside cavity.

E = macroscopic average field over the volume of the specimen; this is the electric field of Maxwell's equations and is equal to $E_0 + E_1$.

The result $E = E_0 + E_1$ can be seen by considering a long thin specimen in an applied field E_0 parallel to the long axis. For this geometry the field component parallel to the axis but just outside the specimen must be E_0, because the effect of the ends of the specimen can be made vanishingly small. But this means that $E_1 = 0$ for this shape. Now the average field component parallel to the axis but over any path just inside the specimen must also be E_0, because the integral of the electric field around a closed path is zero in a static problem. For a specimen with a depolarization field, the average field in the interior becomes $E_0 + E_1$.

The contribution $E_1 + E_2 + E_3$ to the local field is the total field at one atom caused by the dipole moments of all the other atoms in the specimen:

$$E_1 + E_2 + E_3 = \sum_i \frac{3(p_i \cdot r_i)r_i - r_i^2 p_i}{r_i^5}, \tag{4}$$

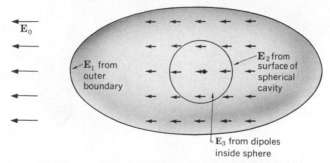

Figure 4   The internal electric field on an atom in a crystal is the sum of the external applied field E_0 and of the field due to the other atoms in the crystal. The standard method of summing the dipole fields of the other atoms is first to sum individually over a moderate number of neighboring atoms inside an imaginary sphere concentric with the reference atom: this defines the field E_3, which vanishes at a reference site with cubic symmetry. The atoms outside the sphere can be treated as a uniformly polarized dielectric. Their contribution to the field at the reference point is $E_1 + E_2$, where E_1 is the depolarization field associated with the other boundary and E_2 is the field associated with the surface of the spherical cavity.

where p_i is the dipole moment of atom i. If we are far enough away from the individual dipoles of a uniformly polarized specimen, we may, according to an elementary transformation occurring in electrostatics, calculate the field of the specimen as equal to the field of a surface charge distribution of density P_n on the surfaces of the specimen. Here P_n is the normal component of the polarization P at the surfaces. The reason for creating the cavity is that we may treat the field E_3 of the dipoles within the cavity by evaluating the sum (4) over the dipoles within the cavity, while the dipoles in the rest of the specimen are treated by means of integrals over the equivalent surface charges which simulate a uniform macroscopic polarization. One integral is taken over the outer surface of the specimen, and it gives E_1; the other integral is taken over the surface of the spherical cavity, and it gives E_2. The field E_1 is seen from Fig. 5 to be opposite in direction to the polarization; it is called the **depolarization field**.

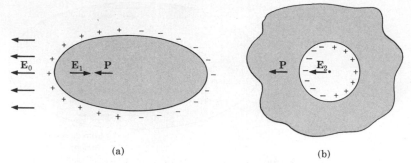

(a)   (b)

Figure 5 Effective surface charges. (a) The depolarization field E_1 is opposite to P; (b) the Lorentz field E_2 is parallel to P.

Depolarization Field, E_1

The calculation of the depolarization field is a well-known problem in classical electricity, and we summarize the results here. Specimens of homogeneous composition will be uniformly polarized when placed in a uniform external field if the external form of the specimen is a general ellipsoid or a limiting case of a general ellipsoid. If the ellipsoid is oriented with a principal axis parallel to the applied field, the polarization and the depolarization field will be parallel to the applied field. In this configuration E_1 is related to the polarization P by

$$E_1 = -NP, \quad \text{and} \quad E = E_0 + E_1 = E_0 - NP. \tag{5}$$

The constant N is known as the **depolarization factor.** Its value depends on the axial ratios of the ellipsoid. Values of N are plotted in Fig. 6 for ellipsoids of revolution, and additional cases have been calculated by Osborn[3] and by Stoner. In the several limiting cases N has the following values:

Shape	Axis	N
Sphere	any	$4\pi/3$
Thin slab	normal	4π
Thin slab	in plane	0
Long circular cylinder	longitudinal	0
Long circular cylinder	transverse	2π

The depolarization factor has a rigorous meaning only for homogeneous general ellipsoids in uniform applied fields. An important property is that $N_a + N_b + N_c = 4\pi$, where N_a, N_b, N_c are the depolarization factors along the three principal axes of a general ellipsoid.

[3] J. A. Osborn, Phys. Rev. **67**, 351 (1945); E. C. Stoner, Phil. Mag. **36**, 803 (1945).

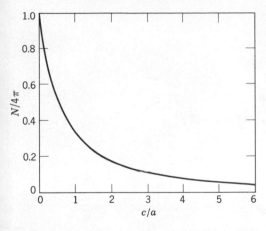

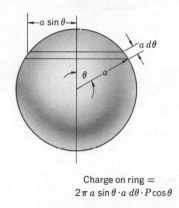

Charge on ring $=$
$2\pi a \sin\theta \cdot a\, d\theta \cdot P\cos\theta$

Figure 6 Depolarization factor N parallel to the figure axis of ellipsoids of revolution, as a function of the axial ratio c/a.

Figure 7 Calculation of the field in a spherical cavity in a uniformly polarized medium.

Lorentz Field, E_2

The field $\mathbf{E}_2$ due to the polarization charges on the surface of the fictitious cavity was calculated first by Lorentz. If θ is the polar angle (Fig. 7) referred to the polarization direction as axis, the surface charge density on the surface of the cavity is $-P\cos\theta$. The electric field at the center of the spherical cavity of radius a is

$$\mathbf{E}_2 = \int_0^\pi (a^{-2})\,(2\pi a \sin\theta)\,(a\,d\theta)\,(\mathbf{P}\cos\theta)\,(\cos\theta) = 4\pi\mathbf{P}/3. \qquad (6)$$

Field of Dipoles Inside Cavity, E_3

The field $\mathbf{E}_3$ due to the dipoles within the cavity is the only term which depends on the crystal structure. We shall first consider a reference site with cubic surroundings; here we can show that $\mathbf{E}_3 = 0$ if all the atoms may be replaced by point dipoles *parallel* to each other. The axis of the dipoles is taken as the z axis; at the reference point the field caused by the other dipoles p_i is

$$E_3^z = \sum_i \frac{3p_i z_i^2 - p_i r_i^2}{r_i^5}. \qquad (7)$$

By the symmetry of the lattice and the cavity

$$\Sigma\,(z_i^2/r_i^5) = \Sigma\,(y_i^2/r_i^5) = \Sigma\,(x_i^2/r_i^5),$$

so that $\Sigma\,(r_i^2/r_i^5) = 3\,\Sigma\,(z_i^2/r_i^5)$, whence $\mathbf{E}_3 = 0$. This result applies only at points such that the surroundings have cubic or spherical symmetry. Values of $\mathbf{E}_3$ for tetragonal and simple hexagonal lattices have been given by Mueller.[4]

[4] H. Mueller, Phys. Rev. **47**, 947 (1935); **50**, 547 (1936); see also L. W. McKeehan Phys. Rev. **43**, 1022, 1025 (1933).

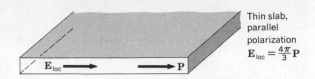

Thin slab, parallel polarization
$$\mathbf{E}_{loc} = \tfrac{4\pi}{3}\mathbf{P}$$

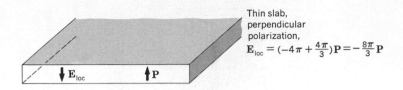

Thin slab, perpendicular polarization,
$$\mathbf{E}_{loc} = (-4\pi + \tfrac{4\pi}{3})\mathbf{P} = -\tfrac{8\pi}{3}\mathbf{P}$$

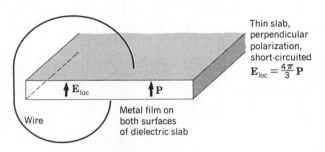

Thin slab, perpendicular polarization, short-circuited
$$\mathbf{E}_{loc} = \tfrac{4\pi}{3}\mathbf{P}$$

Wire   Metal film on both surfaces of dielectric slab

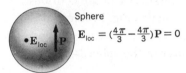

Sphere
$$\mathbf{E}_{loc} = (\tfrac{4\pi}{3} - \tfrac{4\pi}{3})\mathbf{P} = 0$$

Figure 8

(a) Local electric fields due to polarization alone, as seen at atom sites with cubic local surroundings, for four important geometries.

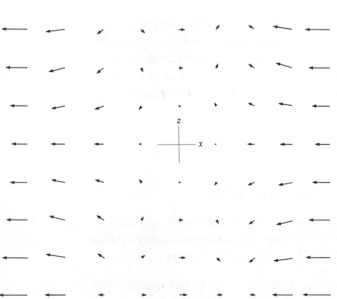

(b) Electric fields at points within a square in the [020] plane of a sc crystal. The origin is at the center of a cell. The lattice carries dipoles uniformly polarized in the $+x$ direction. The crystal is in the form of sphere. The tails of the $\mathbf{E}$ field vectors are situated at the points for which the fields were calculated. The field at the center is zero. (Courtesy of C. Y. Fong.)

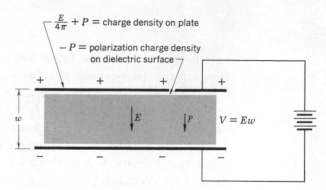

Figure 9 The voltage V across the capacitor plates is E times the separation w, if we neglect the air gaps between the plates and the dielectric. The macroscopic E is the average over the volume of the microscopic electric field.

Local fields for several geometries are shown in Fig. 8a. The variation of the local or microscopic field over a plane in a simple cubic lattice is shown in Fig. 8b.

Field in Dielectric Between Capacitor Plates

The macroscopic electric field intensity $\mathbf{E}$ of Maxwell's equations is defined as the spatial average of the electric field in the material, averaged over a volume at least as large as a unit cell. The displacement $\mathbf{D}$ is defined as

$$\mathbf{D} \equiv \mathbf{E} + 4\pi\mathbf{P}. \tag{8a}$$

Measurements of the polarization $\mathbf{P}$ or of the dielectric constant $\epsilon = D/E$ are usually made by measuring the capacitance $C = Q/V$ of a capacitor filled with the dielectric (Fig. 9). In the absence of the dielectric we suppose that the field between the plates of the capacitor is E', so that the surface charge density on each plate is $\pm E'/4\pi$. When the dielectric is inserted, polarization surface charge densities $\pm P$ are induced on the surface of the dielectric, and these charges are neutralized by a flow of charge around the circuit to the capacitor plates. The space-average field E inside the dielectric is the sum of a field $E_1 = -4\pi P$ from the polarization charges on the dielectric and $E_0 = E' + 4\pi P$ from the original and the neutralization charges on the plates. Thus for the capacitor arrangement the space-average field in the dielectric is

$$E = E_0 + E_1 = E' + 4\pi P - 4\pi P = E', \tag{8b}$$

and

$$E_{\text{loc}} = E_0 + E_1 + E_2 + E_3 = (E + 4\pi P) + (-4\pi P) + (4\pi P/3) + (0)$$

at atom sites for which $E_3 = 0$.

Thus for a cubic site

$$\boxed{E_{\text{loc}} = E + \frac{4\pi}{3}P,} \tag{9}$$

where the coefficient of P is known as the Lorentz local field factor. If the site has a lower symmetry, the factor will not be given by $4\pi/3$ (see footnote 4). Here E is the space-average field inside the dielectric.

The relation (9) is the **Lorentz relation**: the field acting at the center of an atom is E plus a contribution $4\pi P/3$ from the field produced by the polarization of the other atoms in the specimen, where the value of the macroscopic average field E is the same as the field existing between the capacitor planes before the dielectric was inserted. Evidence for the approximate validity of (9) in ionic crystals is given by Tessman, Kahn, and Shockley.[5]

DIELECTRIC CONSTANT AND POLARIZABILITY

The **dielectric constant** ϵ of an isotropic or cubic medium is defined as

$$\epsilon = D/E = 1 + 4\pi(P/E) = 1 + 4\pi\chi, \tag{10}$$

where $\chi = P/E$ is the **electric susceptibility** and E is the macroscopic average field. The **polarizability** α of an atom is defined as

$$\alpha = p/E_{\mathrm{loc}}, \tag{11}$$

where p is the dipole moment of the atom and E_{loc} is the local electric field at the atom. Notice that α is defined as an atomic or ionic property, whereas χ and ϵ will depend also on the manner in which the atoms are assembled in the crystal, because E is not in general equal to E_{loc}. For an anisotropic molecule the polarizability is a tensor, with components $\alpha_{\mu\nu}$ defined by $p_\mu = \alpha_{\mu\nu}E_\nu$, where ν is summed over x, y, z.

The polarization is the dipole moment per unit volume:

$$P = \sum_i N_i\alpha_i E_{\mathrm{loc}}(i), \tag{12}$$

where N_i is the number per unit volume of atoms of polarizability α_i, and $E_{\mathrm{loc}}(i)$ is the local field at atoms of type i.

If the local field is connected with the applied field by the Lorentz relation (9), we have

$$\frac{P}{E} = \frac{\sum N_i\alpha_i}{1 - \dfrac{4\pi}{3}\sum N_i\alpha_i} = \frac{\epsilon - 1}{4\pi}, \tag{13}$$

which may be solved for $\sum N_i\alpha_i$ to give

$$\frac{\epsilon - 1}{\epsilon + 2} = \frac{4\pi}{3}\sum N_i\alpha_i. \tag{14}$$

This is the **Clausius-Mossotti relation**.

[5] J. Tessman, A. Kahn, and W. Shockley, Phys. Rev. **92**, 890 (1953).

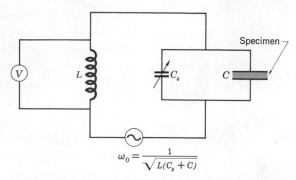

$$\omega_0 = \frac{1}{\sqrt{L(C_s + C)}}$$

Figure 10 Schematic diagram of apparatus for the measurement of dielectric constants.

Measurement of Dielectric Constant

The usual methods of measuring the dielectric constant are based on a comparison of the capacity C'' of a capacitor filled with the substance and the capacity C' of the empty capacitor. The ratio $C''/C' = \epsilon$, the dielectric constant. The determination of the value of the capacitance may in principle be accomplished by an LC resonant circuit as shown in Fig. 10, where C_s is a calibrated variable capacitor and C is the capacitor in which the specimen may be placed. By varying the calibrated capacitor so as to keep the resonance frequency $\omega_0 = [L(C_s + C)]^{-1/2}$ constant when C is inserted and then filled, we may determine C' and C'', and thus ϵ.

Descriptions of the actual circuits employed are abundant in the literature. At microwave frequencies the technique of measurement is altered somewhat, and here one often measures essentially the wavelength λ of the microwave radiation in the specimen, obtaining the dielectric constant from the relation λ (vacuum)$/\lambda$ (specimen) $= (\epsilon\mu)^{1/2}$, where μ is the permeability.

384

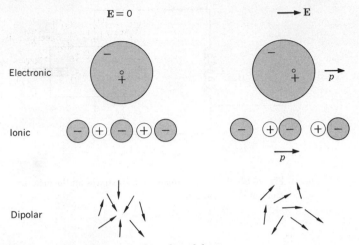

E = 0   ⟶ E

Electronic

Ionic

Dipolar

Figure 11   Contributions to the polarizability.

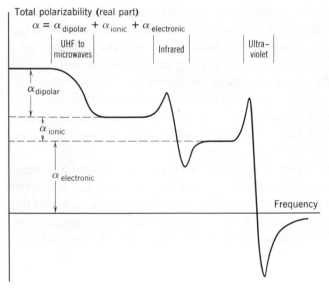

Total polarizability (real part)

$$\alpha = \alpha_{dipolar} + \alpha_{ionic} + \alpha_{electronic}$$

UHF to microwaves

Infrared

Ultra-violet

$\alpha_{dipolar}$

α_{ionic}

$\alpha_{electronic}$

Frequency

Figure 12   Frequency dependence of the several contributions to the polarizability (schematic).

Electronic Polarizability

The total polarizability α may usually be separated into three parts:[6] electronic, ionic, and orientational (dipolar), as in Fig. 11. The electronic contribution arises from the displacement of electrons in an atom relative to

[6] In heterogeneous materials there is usually also an *interfacial polarization* arising from the accumulation of charge at structural interfaces. This is of little fundamental interest, but it is of considerable practical interest because commercial insulating materials are usually heterogeneous.

the nucleus, that is, from the deformation of the electron shell about a nucleus. The ionic contribution comes from the displacement and deformation of a charged ion with respect to other ions. The orientational or dipolar polarizability arises when the substance is built up of molecules possessing a permanent electric dipole moment which may be more or less free to change orientation in an applied electric field. One way to separate experimentally the different contributions is indicated in Fig. 12. The ionic and the dipolar contributions are seldom both large in the same substance; in ordinary ionic crystals there is no dipolar contribution.

In the optical frequency range the dielectric constant arises almost entirely from the electronic polarizability. The dipolar and ionic contributions are small at high frequencies because of the inertia of the molecules and ions. In the optical range (14) reduces to

$$\frac{n^2 - 1}{n^2 + 2} = \frac{4\pi}{3} \Sigma N_i \alpha_i \text{ (electronic)};\tag{15}$$

here we have used the relation $n^2 = \epsilon$, where n is the refractive index. By applying this relation to large numbers of crystals we may determine empirical values of the electronic polarizabilities which are reasonably consistent with the observed values of the refractive index. Values obtained in this way are given in Table 1. The scheme is not entirely self-consistent, as the electronic polarizability of an ion may depend slightly on the environment in which it is placed. Notice that the negative ions have high values of α.

Table 1   Electronic polarizabilities of ions in 10^{-24} cm^3

Values from L. Pauling, Proc. Roy. Soc. (London) **A114**, 181 (1927) and from Tessman, Kahn, and Shockley, Phys. Rev. **92**, 890 (1953). The TKS polarizabilities are for the D lines of sodium.

			He	Li$^+$	Be^{2+}	B^{3+}	C^{4+}
Pauling			0.201	0.029	0.008	0.003	0.0013
TKS				0.03			
	O^{2-}	F$^-$	Ne	Na$^+$	Mg^{2+}	Al^{3+}	Si^{4+}
Pauling	3.88	1.04	0.390	0.179	0.094	0.052	0.0165
TKS	(2.4)	0.652		0.14			
	S^{2-}	Cl$^-$	Ar	K$^+$	Ca^{2+}	Sc^{3+}	Ti^{4+}
Pauling	10.2	3.66	1.62	0.83	0.47	0.286	0.185
TKS	(5.5)	2.97		1.33	1.1		(0.19)
	Se^{2-}	Br$^-$	Kr	Rb$^+$	Sr^{2+}	Y^{3+}	Zr^{4+}
Pauling	10.5	4.77	2.46	1.40	0.86	0.55	0.37
TKS	(7.)	4.17		1.98	1.6		
	Te^{2-}	I$^-$	Xe	Cs$^+$	Ba^{2+}	La^{3+}	Ce^{4+}
Pauling	14.0	7.10	3.99	2.42	1.55	1.04	0.73
TKS	(9.)	6.44		3.34	2.5		

Classical Theory of Electronic Polarizability. An electron bound harmonically to an atom will show resonance absorption at a frequency $\omega_0 = (\beta/m)^{1/2}$, where β is the force constant. The displacement x of the electron occasioned by the application of a field E_{loc} is given by

$$eE_{loc} = \beta x = m\omega_0^2 x, \tag{16}$$

so that the static electronic polarizability is

$$\alpha \text{ (electronic)} = \frac{p}{E_{loc}} = \frac{ex}{E_{loc}} = \frac{e^2}{m\omega_0^2}. \tag{17}$$

The electronic polarizability will depend on frequency, and it is shown in the following example that for frequency ω

$$\alpha \text{ (electronic)} = \frac{e^2/m}{\omega_0^2 - \omega^2}, \tag{18}$$

but in the visible region the frequency dependence (dispersion) is not usually very important in most dielectric materials.

EXAMPLE: *Frequency dependence.* Find the frequency dependence of the electronic polarizability of an electron having the resonance frequency ω_0, treating the system as a simple harmonic oscillator.

The equation of motion in the local electric field $E_{loc} \sin \omega t$ is

$$m\, d^2x/dt^2 + m\omega_0^2 x = eE_{loc} \sin \omega t, \tag{19}$$

so that, for $x = x_0 \sin \omega t$,

$$m(-\omega^2 + \omega_0^2)x_0 = eE_{loc}.$$

The dipole moment has the amplitude

$$p_0 = ex_0 = \frac{e^2 E_{loc}}{m(\omega_0^2 - \omega^2)}, \tag{20}$$

from which (18) follows.

In quantum theory the expression corresponding to (18) is

$$\alpha \text{ (electronic)} = \frac{e^2}{m} \sum_j \frac{f_{ij}}{\omega_{ij}^2 - \omega^2}, \tag{21}$$

where f_{ij} is the **oscillator strength** of the electric dipole transition between the atomic states i and j. The oscillator strength is defined in Appendix B. Equation (21) is written for atoms and should be modified slightly for solids.

Ionic Polarizability

The difference $\Delta\epsilon$ between the static and optical dielectric constants is a measure of the contribution of the ionic polarizability; in sodium chloride $\Delta\epsilon = 5.9 - 2.25 = 3.7$. The ionic polarization arises from the relative displacement of ions of opposite sign when an electric field is applied. The total relative displacement $\mathbf{u}$ of the positive and negative ion lattices is given by setting $\omega = 0$ in Eq. (5.42). Then

$$u = \xi - \eta = \frac{qE_{loc}}{\omega_T^2}\left(\frac{1}{M_1} + \frac{1}{M_2}\right), \qquad (22)$$

where E_{loc} is the electric field at the ions; ω_T is the transverse optical phonon frequency; q is the charge on an ion. The dipole moment per molecule is $p = qu = q(\xi - \eta)$, so that the ionic polarization is

$$\mathbf{P}_{ion} = Nq\mathbf{u}, \qquad (23)$$

where N is the number of molecules per unit volume.

Orientational Polarizability

The polarizability arising from the orientation in an applied electric field of molecules possessing a permanent electric dipole moment[7] is usually discussed with reference to gases and liquids. It is occasionally of importance in solids (see Problem 14.7). By assuming that molecules have permanent dipole moments Debye explained the high dielectric constant of water, alcohol, and similar liquids, and the temperature dependence of their dielectric constants.

The static dielectric constant of water is 81 at room temperature, but the dielectric constant at optical frequencies is only 1.77. The difference is caused chiefly by the orientational polarization which is effective at low frequencies, but is damped out for frequencies above 10^{10} cps. The characteristic temperature dependence of the orientational polarizability of polar molecules is shown in Fig. 13; CH_3Cl has a permanent electric dipole moment; CH_4 and CCl_4 do not.

The orienting tendency of the electric field on a permanent dipole is opposed by thermal agitation. We consider the effect of the thermal motion on molecules which are free to rotate. The potential energy U of a molecule of permanent moment $\mathbf{p}$ in a field $\mathbf{E}$ is

$$U = -\mathbf{p}\cdot\mathbf{E} = -pE\cos\theta, \qquad (24)$$

where θ is the angle between the moment and the field direction. The

---

[7] A molecule with a permanent electric dipole moment is called a **polar molecule**.

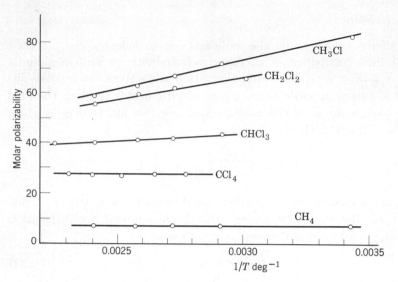

Figure 13 Plot of $[(\epsilon - 1)/(\epsilon + 1)]$ times the molar volume, which is known as the molar polarizability, for polar and nonpolar substituted methane compounds in gaseous form. [After R. Sanger, Physik Z. **27**, 556 (1926).]

polarization is

$$P = Np \langle \cos \theta \rangle, \tag{25}$$

where N is the number of molecules per unit volume and $\langle \cos \theta \rangle$ is the average over a distribution in thermal equilibrium.

According to the Boltzmann distribution law the relative probability of finding a molecule in an element of solid angle $d\Omega$ is proportional to $\exp(-U/k_BT)$, and

$$\langle \cos \theta \rangle = \frac{\int e^{-\beta U} \cos \theta \, d\Omega}{\int e^{-\beta U} \, d\Omega}, \tag{26}$$

where $\beta \equiv 1/k_BT$. The integration is to be carried out over all solid angles, so that

$$\langle \cos \theta \rangle = \frac{\int_0^\pi 2\pi \sin \theta \cos \theta \, e^{\beta pE \cos \theta} \, d\theta}{\int_0^\pi 2\pi \sin \theta \, e^{\beta pE \cos \theta} \, d\theta}. \tag{27}$$

We let $s \equiv \cos \theta$ and $x \equiv pE/k_BT$, so that

$$\langle \cos \theta \rangle = \int_{-1}^1 e^{sx}s \, ds \bigg/ \int_{-1}^1 e^{sx} \, ds = \frac{d}{dx} \log \int_{-1}^1 e^{sx} \, ds$$

$$= \frac{d}{dx} \log (e^x - e^{-x}) - \frac{d}{dx} \log x = \text{ctnh } x - \frac{1}{x} \equiv L(x). \tag{28}$$

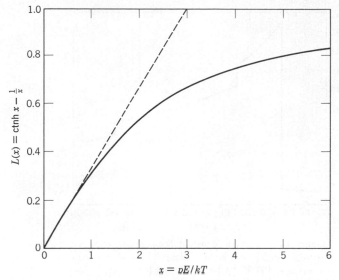

Figure 14   Plot of Langevin function $L(x)$ versus $x = pE/k_BT$. The initial slope is shown by the dashed line. The polarization is 80 percent of saturation when $pE/k_BT = 5$.

This defines the **Langevin function** $L(x)$. The function[8] is plotted in Fig. 14, where the saturation property for $pE \gg k_BT$ is clearly seen.

The most important situation experimentally is when $pE \ll k_BT$. Dipole moments are of the order of 10^{-18} esu, so that for $E = 3000$ v/cm $= 10$ statv/cm we have $pE \approx 10^{-17}$ erg. At room temperature $k_BT \approx 4 \times 10^{-14}$ erg, so that $x \equiv pE/k_BT \approx 1/4000$. In the limit of $x \ll 1$, we have

$$\mathrm{ctnh}\, x = \frac{1}{x} + \frac{x}{3} - \frac{x^3}{45} + \cdots; \qquad L(x) \cong x/3 = pE/3k_BT, \qquad (29)$$

and so the polarization is

$$P = Np \langle \cos \theta \rangle = Np^2E/3k_BT. \qquad (30)$$

The orientational polarizability per molecule is

$$\alpha\,(\text{dipolar}) = p^2/3k_BT. \qquad (31)$$

At room temperature this is of the order of $(10^{-18})^2/10^{-13} \approx 10^{-23}$ cm^3, of the same order of magnitude as the electronic polarizability. The total polarizability may then be written, if α_0 denotes the sum of the electronic and ionic contributions,

$$\alpha = \alpha_0 + p^2/3k_BT. \qquad (32)$$

---

[8] The Langevin function is tabulated in Jahnke-Emde-Lösch, *Tables of higher functions*, McGraw-Hill, 6th ed., 1960, table 51.

390

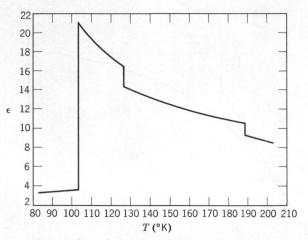

Figure 15 Dielectric constant temperature curve of hydrogen sulfide at 5 kc/sec. The solid-liquid transition occurs near 190°K. [After Smyth and Hitchcock, J. Am. Chem. Soc. **56**, 1084 (1934).]

This is the **Langevin-Debye equation.** It has been of great importance to chemists in interpreting molecular structures.

The dipole moment p is determined in practice by plotting either α or $(\epsilon - 1)/(\epsilon + 2)$ from (14) as a function of $1/T$ as in Fig. 13; the slope is simply related to p. In this way one obtains, for example, the following dipole moments: p (HCl) $= 1.03 \times 10^{-18}$ esu; p (HBr) $= 0.79 \times 10^{-18}$ esu; p (HI) $= 0.38 \times 10^{-18}$ esu; p (H_2O) $= 1.87 \times 10^{-18}$ esu. The moments are often expressed in **Debye units** equal to 10^{-18} esu, which is of the order of the electronic charge times an interatomic distance.

Dipole Orientation in Solids

The ability of a molecule to reorient in a solid depends very much on its shape and on the strength of its interactions with the environment. The nearer to sphericity and the lower the dipole moment, the more easily and faster the molecule will reorient in a changing electric field. Solid methane (CH_4), a symmetrical nonpolar molecule, rotates fairly freely in the solid state;[9] the molecules in solid hydrogen also rotate quite freely. Less symmetrical molecules such as HCl and H_2O have several stable orientations and change direction relatively slowly from one stable orientation to another. The average time between changes is called the **relaxation time.**

The dielectric constant of solid H_2S as a function of temperature is shown in Fig. 15. Notice the sharp increase in the dielectric constant as the tempera-

[9] For an account of the nuclear resonance experiments from which supporting evidence is derived, see N. L. Alpert, Phys. Rev. **75**, 398 (1949).

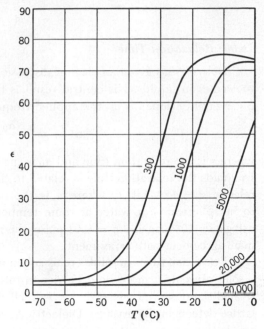

Figure 16 Variation of the dielectric constant of ice with temperature and frequency. [After Smyth and Hitchcock, J. Am. Chem. Soc. **54**, 4631 (1932).]

ture is lowered; the sudden drop below 105°K is thought to mark the transition to an ordered state in which the directions of the H_2S molecules form a regular array. The variation of the dielectric constant above the transition temperature is suggestive of free rotation, but a similar variation with temperature arises when there are only a discrete number of allowed orientations for each dipole, so that the variation is not evidence of free rotation.

DIELECTRIC RELAXATION AND LOSS

In solids and liquids composed of polar molecules the principal part of the difference between the low frequency dielectric constant and the optical frequency dielectric constant (the square of the optical refractive index) measures the orientational contribution to the dielectric constant. We have introduced the relaxation time as the time interval characterizing the restoration of a disturbed system to its equilibrium configuration; the **relaxation frequency** is the reciprocal of the relaxation time. When the frequency of an applied field is higher than the relaxation frequency, the system will not follow or respond to the field. The orientation relaxation frequencies vary over a wide range and may be strongly dependent on the temperature. In water at room temperature, relaxation occurs at about 3×10^{10} cps. In ice at $-20°C$ the relaxation frequency is of the order of 1 kc, as we see from Fig. 16.

Debye Relaxation Time

Debye[10] has given an elegant discussion of dielectric relaxation of polar molecules in liquids. His central result is that the orientational part of the polarizability depends on the applied frequency ω as, for $E \propto \exp(-i\omega t)$,

$$\alpha(\omega) = \frac{\alpha_0}{1 - i\omega\tau}, \tag{33}$$

where τ is the relaxation time and α_0 is the static orientational polarizability. In liquids the relaxation time is related to the viscosity η by the approximate relation $\tau = 4\pi\eta a^3/k_B T$, where a is the radius of the molecule, supposed to be spherical. For water at room temperature we obtain $\tau \approx 10^{-11}$ sec, using $a \approx 10^{-8}$ cm and $\eta = 0.01$ poise; this relaxation frequency is in approximate agreement with experiment.

Relaxation times in solids are usually much longer than in liquids, because a solid presents a more rigid barrier to internal motion. Breckenridge[11] has related the observed dielectric losses in alkali halide crystals to the motion of lattice defects in the crystals. Dielectric losses due to electrons hopping from one lattice site to another in transition metal oxides are discussed by S. van Houten and A. J. Bosman, Proc. 1963 Buhl Int. Conf. Transition Metal Compounds, pp. 123–136.

Shepherd and Feher[12] have reported that OH^- ions substituted for Cl^- ions in a KCl crystal have a relaxation time less than 10^{-10} sec near $1°K$. The OH^- ion has six equally likely orientations in the solid, with the dipole moment along the direction of each cube edge.

Complex Dielectric Constant

In the presence of relaxation effects the dielectric constant may conveniently be written as complex. For a polarizability $\alpha(\omega) = \alpha_0/(1 - i\omega\tau)$ as in (33) the dielectric constant is, using (12) and taking the local field as equal to the applied field,

$$\epsilon = \epsilon' + i\epsilon'' = 1 + \frac{4\pi\alpha_0 N}{1 - i\omega\tau} = 1 + \frac{4\pi\alpha_0 N}{1 + \omega^2\tau^2} + i\frac{4\pi\alpha_0\omega\tau N}{1 + \omega^2\tau^2}, \tag{34}$$

as plotted in Fig. 17. Notice that the decrease of the real part of ϵ occurs near the peak of the imaginary part; this is an example of the general result that if $\epsilon'(\omega)$ changes with frequency then $\epsilon''(\omega)$ also changes[13] with frequency.

[10] P. Debye, *Polar molecules*, Chemical Catalog Co., New York, 1929, Chap. V. For a discussion of the transition from resonance to relaxation-type behavior, see J. H. Van Vleck and V. F. Weisskopf, Revs. Modern Phys. **17**, 227 (1945).

[11] R. G. Breckenridge, in *Imperfections in nearly perfect crystals*, eds., Shockley, Hollomon, Maurer, and Seitz, Wiley, 1952; J. Volger, *Prog. semiconductors* **4**, 207 (1959).

[12] I. Shepherd and G. Feher, Phys. Rev. Let. **15**, 194 (1965).

[13] The connection between $\epsilon'(\omega)$ and $\epsilon''(\omega)$ is known as the Kramers-Kronig relation; see, for example, C. Kittel, *Elementary statistical physics*, Wiley, 1958, pp. 206–210.

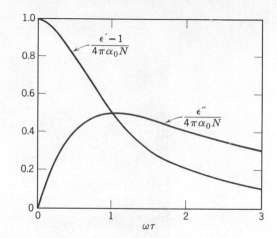

Figure 17 Frequency dependence of real and imaginary parts of the dielectric constant $\epsilon = \epsilon' + i\epsilon''$, for a relaxation mechanism.

LYDDANE-SACHS-TELLER RELATION

The LST relation[14] was given in (5.49), but without a full derivation. From the Clausius-Mossotti relation (14) we have

$$\epsilon = \frac{1 + 2\beta}{1 - \beta}, \qquad \beta \equiv \frac{4\pi}{3} \Sigma N_j \alpha_j. \tag{35}$$

In a diatomic ionic crystal the electronic contribution to the polarizability is $N(\alpha_+ + \alpha_-)$, where N is the number of molecules per unit volume. We define $\beta_{el} \equiv (4\pi/3)N(\alpha_+ + \alpha_-)$.

The static ionic displacement is determined by a force constant C defined by

$$C\mathbf{u} = q\mathbf{E}_{loc}, \tag{36}$$

where q is the charge on a negative ion and $\mathbf{u}$ is the displacement between positive and negative ion lattices. The ionic polarization is $\mathbf{P}_{ion} = Nq\mathbf{u} = (Nq^2/C)\mathbf{E}_{loc}$. The static ionic polarizability is $\alpha_{ion} = q^2/C$, and we define $\beta_{ion} \equiv (4\pi/3)Nq^2/C$.

The static dielectric constant is

$$\epsilon(0) = \frac{1 + 2(\beta_{el} + \beta_{ion})}{1 - (\beta_{el} + \beta_{ion})}, \tag{37}$$

from (35) written in terms of the β's.

The high frequency dielectric constant involves only the electronic polarizability, because the inertia of the ions eliminates the ionic contribution. We use $\epsilon(\infty)$ to denote the dielectric constant at a frequency at which the electronic polarizability is effective, but not the ionic polarizability. Note then that $\epsilon(\infty)$ does not mean the dielectric constant at infinite frequency. From

[14] For the generalization of the LST relation to noncubic structures or to crystals with more than two atoms per primitive cell, see W. Cochran, Z. Krist. **112**, 465 (1959); also A. S. Barker, Jr., Phys. Rev. **136**, A1290 (1964).

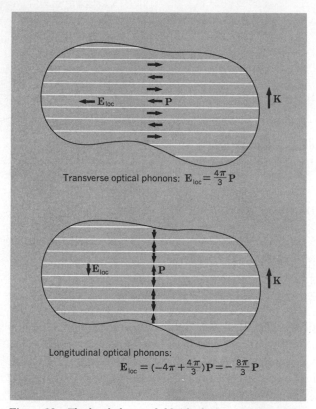

Transverse optical phonons: $E_{loc} = \frac{4\pi}{3} P$

Longitudinal optical phonons:
$$E_{loc} = (-4\pi + \frac{4\pi}{3})P = -\frac{8\pi}{3} P$$

Figure 18 The local electric field (the long range part of the interaction) tends to assist the lattice distortion associated with a transverse optical phonon (a), but tends to resist the deformation for a longitudinal optical phonon (b). Thus $\omega_L > \omega_T$. The values of the local fields shown are for ions in cubic surroundings. The rulings indicate the lines (or planes) of nodes. It is supposed that the wavevectors are nearly zero, but still large enough that there are many wavelengths within the specimen.

(37) with β_{ion} omitted we have

$$\epsilon(\infty) = \frac{1 + 2\beta_{el}}{1 - \beta_{el}}. \tag{38}$$

The frequency ω_T of transverse optical phonons in the limit of long wavelengths is determined by the equation of motion

$$\mu \frac{d^2u}{dt^2} + Cu = qE_{loc} = q \cdot \frac{4\pi}{3} P, \tag{39}$$

where μ is the reduced mass of a molecule. All vector components are parallel to the plane of the wavefronts. In the absence of an applied electric field, the local field is $4\pi P/3$, as in Fig. 18a. Thus

$$P = P_{el} + P_{ion} = N(\alpha_+ + \alpha_-)(4\pi P/3) + Nqu = \beta_{el}P + Nqu, \quad (40)$$

so that (39) yields

$$\mu\omega_T^2 = C\left(1 - \frac{\beta_{ion}}{1 - \beta_{el}}\right). \quad (41)$$

The frequency ω_L of longitudinal optical phonons is determined by (39), with the addition of the depolarization field $-4\pi P$, as in Fig. 18b. The local field for longitudinal phonons is $\mathbf{F}_{loc} = \mathbf{E}_0 - 4\pi\mathbf{P} + \dfrac{4\pi}{3}\mathbf{P}$. In the absence of an applied field $E_0 = 0$, and in place of (40) we have

$$P = N(\alpha_+ - \alpha_-)(-8\pi P/3) + Nqu = -2\beta_{el}P + Nqu, \quad (42)$$

where now all components are normal to the wavefronts. The equation of motion for longitudinal optical phonons is

$$\mu\frac{d^2u}{dt^2} + Cu = q\left(-\frac{8\pi}{3}P\right) = -\frac{8\pi}{3}\frac{Nq^2u}{1 + 2\beta_{el}}, \quad (43)$$

using (42). We have

$$\mu\omega_L^2 = C\left(1 + \frac{2\beta_{ion}}{1 + 2\beta_{el}}\right). \quad (44)$$

From (41) and (44) we have

$$\frac{\omega_T^2}{\omega_L^2} = \frac{1 - (\beta_{el} + \beta_{ion})}{1 + 2(\beta_{el} + \beta_{ion})} \cdot \frac{1 + 2\beta_{el}}{1 - \beta_{el}}. \quad (45)$$

From (37) and (38) we have

$$\frac{\epsilon(\infty)}{\epsilon(0)} = \frac{1 - (\beta_{el} + \beta_{ion})}{1 + 2(\beta_{el} + \beta_{ion})} \cdot \frac{1 + 2\beta_{el}}{1 - \beta_{el}}. \quad (46)$$

On comparing (45) and (46) we have the Lyddane-Sachs-Teller relation

$$\boxed{\frac{\omega_T^2}{\omega_L^2} = \frac{\epsilon(\infty)}{\epsilon(0)}.} \quad (53)$$

This has implications for ferroelectricity, for it predicts that $\epsilon(0) \to \infty$ as $\omega_T \to 0$.

We compare values of ω_L/ω_T obtained by inelastic neutron scattering[15] with experimental values of $[\epsilon(0)/\epsilon(\infty)]^{1/2}$:

	NaI	KBr	GaAs
ω_L/ω_T	1.44 ± 0.05	1.39 ± 0.02	1.07 ± 0.02
$[\epsilon(0)/\epsilon(\infty)]^{1/2}$	1.45 ± 0.03	1.38 ± 0.03	1.08

The agreement is excellent.

[15] A. D. B. Woods et al., Phys. Rev. **131**, 1025 (1963); J. L. T. Waugh and G. Dolling, Phys. Rev. **132**, 2410 (1963).

Problems

1. *Polarizability of atomic hydrogen.* Consider a semiclassical model of the ground state of the hydrogen atom in an electric field normal to the plane of the orbit Fig. (19), and show that for this model $\alpha = a_H^3$, where a_H is the radius of the unperturbed orbit. *Note:* If the applied field is in the x direction, then the x component of the field of the nucleus at the displaced position of the electron orbit must be equal to the applied field. The correct quantum-mechanical result is larger than this by the factor $\frac{9}{2}$.

2. *Field of cubical cavity.* In the local field problem the cavity need not be chosen as spherical, but may be a cube (Fig. 20) with a face normal to the polarization. In this case the polarization charge density on the upper and lower faces of the cube is uniform and equal to $\mp P$, whereas the other faces do not carry any charge. Show that at the center of this cavity $E_2 = 4\pi P/3$, just as for the spherical cavity.

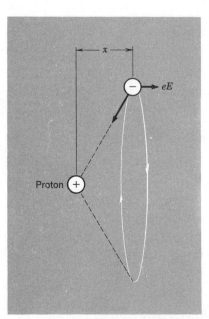

Figure 19 An electron in a circular orbit of radius a_H is displaced a distance x on application of an electric field E in the $-x$ direction. The force on the electron due to the nucleus is e^2/a_H^2.

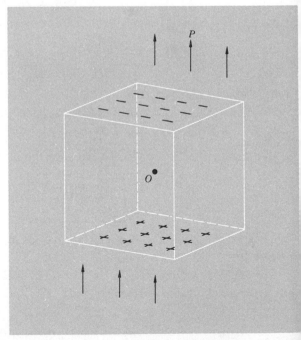

Figure 20 The field is $-4\pi P/3$ at the center O of a cubical cavity bearing charges of uniform surface density $\pm P$ on the upper and lower faces. Solve this problem by finding the vertical component of the field due to a rectangular strip of width dx and integrating over one face.

3. *Polarizability of conducting sphere.* Show that the polarizability of a conducting metallic sphere of radius a is $\alpha = a^3$. This result is most easily obtained by noting that $E = 0$ inside the sphere and then using the depolarization factor $4\pi/3$ for a sphere (Fig. 21). The result gives values of α of the order of magnitude of the observed polarizabilities of atoms. A lattice of N conducting spheres per unit volume has dielectric constant $\epsilon = 1 + 4\pi Na^3$, for $Na^3 \ll 1$.

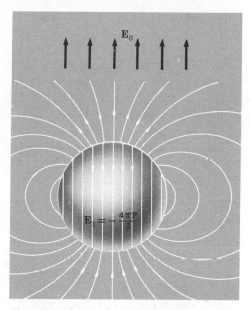

Figure 21   The total field inside a conducting sphere is zero. If a field E_0 is applied externally, then the field E_1 due to surface charges on the sphere must just cancel E_0, so that $E_0 + E_1 = 0$ within the sphere. But E_1 can be simulated by the depolarization field $-4\pi P/3$ of a uniformly polarized sphere of polarization P. Relate P to E_0 and calculate the dipole moment p of the sphere.

4. *Effect of air gap.* Discuss the effect of an air gap (Fig. 22) between condenser plates and dielectric on the measurement of high dielectric constants. What is the highest apparent dielectric constant possible if the air gap thickness is 10^{-3} of the total thickness?

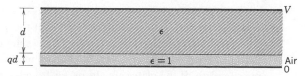

Figure 22   An air gap of thickness qd is in series in a capacitor with a dielectric slab of thickness d.

5. *Interfacial polarization.* Show that a parallel-plate capacitor made up of two parallel layers of material—one layer with dielectric constant ϵ, zero conductivity, and thickness d, and the other layer with $\epsilon = 0$ for convenience, finite conductivity σ, and thickness qd—behaves as if the space between the condenser plates were filled with a homogeneous dielectric with dielectric constant

$$\epsilon_{\text{eff}} = \frac{\epsilon(1 + q)}{1 - (i\epsilon\omega q/4\pi\sigma)},$$

where ω is the angular frequency [K. W. Wagner, Arch. Elektrotech. **2**, 371 (1941)]. Values of ϵ_{eff} as high as 10^4 or 10^5 caused largely by the Maxwell-Wagner mechanism, are sometimes found, but the high values are always accompanied by large losses. An analysis of the dielectric properties of a nickel zinc ferrite is given by C. G. Koops, Phys. Rev. **83**, 121 (1951).

6. *Refractive indexes.* Estimate using Table 1 the refractive index of solid xenon.

7. *Dielectric constant of damped oscillator.* Suppose that a damped oscillator of mass m and charge q has the equation of motion

$$m\left(\frac{d^2x}{dt^2} + \frac{1}{\tau}\frac{dx}{dt} + \omega_0^2 x\right) = qE_0 e^{-i\omega t},$$

where ω_0 is the resonant frequency and τ, the relaxation frequency, represents the damping effects. (a) Neglecting interactions among the oscillators, show that the contribution of the N such oscillators per unit volume to the dielectric constant is

$$\epsilon = 1 + \frac{4\pi Nq^2/m}{\omega_0^2 - \omega^2 - i\omega/\tau}.$$

(b) Assuming $\omega\tau \gg 1$, sketch roughly the dependence of ϵ' and ϵ'' on ω/ω_0, where ϵ' is the real part and ϵ'' is the imaginary part of ϵ.

8. *Dielectric constant of PbTe, using LST relation.* Experiments by R. S. Allgaier and W. W. Scanlon, Phys. Rev. **111**, 1029 (1958), on the mobility at low temperatures of electrons in the semiconductor lead telluride suggest that the static dielectric constant may be very large. The electrical conductivity interferes with low frequency measurements of the dielectric constant. It is found by neutron diffraction [W. Cochran, Phys. Letters **13**, 193 (1964)] that the low wavevector limit of the frequencies of the longitudinal and transverse optical phonons are $\nu_L = 3.2 \times 10^{12}$ cps and $\nu_T = 1.0 \times 10^{12}$ cps. With $\epsilon(\infty) = 28$, use the Lyddane-Sachs-Teller relation to show that $\epsilon(0) \approx 300$.

9. *Polarization of sphere.* A sphere of dielectric constant ϵ is placed in a uniform external electric field E_0. (a) What is the volume average electric field E in the sphere? (b) Show that the polarization in the sphere is $P = \chi E_0/[1 + (4\pi\chi/3)]$, where $\chi = (\epsilon - 1)/4\pi$. *Hint:* You do not need to calculate E_{loc} in this problem; in fact it is confusing to do so, because ϵ and χ are defined so that $P = \chi E$. Should you wish to know E_{loc} for this problem, utilize Eq. (9) if the site is cubic. Note further that we want E_0 to be unchanged by insertion of the sphere. We can produce a fixed E_0 by placing positive charges on one thin plate of an insulator and negative charges on an opposite plate. If the plates are always far from the sphere, the field of the plates will remain unchanged when the sphere is inserted between them.

References

H. Fröhlich, *Theory of dielectrics: dielectric constant and dielectric loss*, Oxford, 1949.

C. P. Smyth, *Dielectric behavior and structure*, McGraw-Hill, 1955.

J. H. Van Vleck, *Theory of electric and magnetic susceptibilities*, Oxford, 1932.

A. R. von Hippel, *Dielectrics and waves*, Wiley, 1954.

A. R. von Hippel, ed., *Dielectric materials and applications*, Wiley, 1954.

W. F. Brown, Jr., "Dielectrics," *Encyclo. of physics* **17**, 1–263 (1956).

13

Ferroelectric Crystals

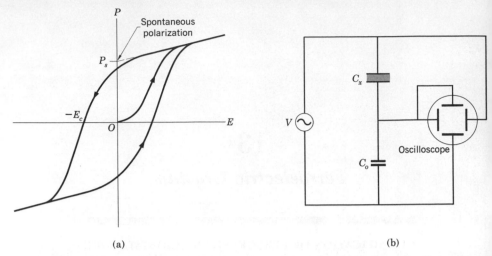

(a) (b)

Figure 1 (a) Ferroelectric hysteresis loop; the coercive force is E_c. (b) Circuit for display of loop. The voltage across the ferroelectric crystal C_x is applied to the horizontal plates of the oscilloscope. The linear capacitor C_0 is in series with C_x. The voltage across C_0 is proportional to the polarization of C_x and is applied to the vertical plates. [After C. B. Sawyer and C. H. Tower, Phys. Rev. **35**, 269 (1930).]

Table 1 Ferroelectric crystal data°

		T_c, °K	P_s(esu), at $T°$K	
Rochelle salt group	NaK$(C_4H_4O_6) \cdot 4H_2O$	297 (upper) 255 (lower)	800	[278°K]
	NaK$(C_4H_2D_2O_6) \cdot 4D_2O$	308 (upper) 251 (lower)	1100	[279]
	LiNH$_4(C_4H_4O_6) \cdot H_2O$	106	660	[95]
KDP group	KH$_2$PO$_4$	123	16,000	[96]
	KD$_2$PO$_4$	213	27,000	–
	RbH$_2$PO$_4$	147	16,800	[90]
	RbH$_2$AsO$_4$	111	–	–
	KH$_2$AsO$_4$	96	15,000	[80]
	KD$_2$AsO$_4$	162	–	–
	CsH$_2$AsO$_4$	143	–	–
	CsD$_2$AsO$_4$	212	–	–
Perovskites	BaTiO$_3$	393	78,000	[296]
	SrTiO$_3$†	32	(9000)	[4]
	WO$_3$	223	–	–
	KNbO$_3$	712	90,000	[523]
	PbTiO$_3$	763	>150,000	[300]
Ilmenite (approx.)	LiTaO$_3$	–	70,000	[720]
TGS group	Tri-glycine sulfate	322	8400	[293]
	Tri-glycine selenate	295	9600	[273]

°A table of 76 ferroelectric crystals (excluding solid solutions) known up to 1960 is given in App. A of F. Jona and G. Shirane, *Ferroelectric crystals*, Pergamon, 1962. This reference is an excellent source of data on the crystal structure of ferroelectrics. For further data, see E. Nakumura, T. Mitsui, and J. Furuichi, J. Phys. Soc. Japan **18**, 1477 (1963).

†It is not at all certain that SrTiO$_3$ has a ferroelectric phase; it may be paraelectric down to at least 1°K. Possibly a ferroelectric phase can be induced by an electric field at low temperatures.

A ferroelectric crystal exhibits an electric dipole moment even in the absence of an external electric field. In the **ferroelectric state** the center of positive charge of the crystal does not coincide with the center of negative charge.

A typical plot of polarization versus electric field[1] for the ferroelectric state is shown in Fig. 1. The loop is called a **hysteresis loop;** it is a sign of a ferroelectric state. A crystal in a normal dielectric state usually does not show perceptible hysteresis when the electric field is increased and reversed slowly.

Ferroelectricity usually disappears above a certain temperature called the **transition temperature;** above the transition the crystal is said to be in a **paraelectric** state. The term paraelectric suggests an analogy with paramagnetism (Chapter 14) and implies a rapid decrease in the dielectric constant as the temperature increases.

CLASSIFICATION OF FERROELECTRIC CRYSTALS

We list in Table 1 some of the crystals commonly considered to be ferroelectric, along with the transition temperature or Curie point T_c at which the crystal changes from the low temperature polarized state to the high temperature unpolarized state. Thermal motion tends to destroy the ferroelectric order. Rochelle salt has both an upper and a lower Curie point, between which the crystal is ferroelectric. Ferroelectric crystals are known which have no Curie point because they melt before leaving the ferroelectric phase. The table also includes values of the spontaneous polarization P_s. We note that $P(esu)$ is obtained by multiplying $P(\mu coul/cm^2)$ by 3×10^3 and by multiplying the MKS value $P(coul/m^2)$ by 3×10^5.

The crystals in the table may be classified into several groups. First there is Rochelle salt[2] and related isomorphous salts. Rochelle salt is a complicated crystal, and little progress has been made toward understanding its behavior

---

[1] In some crystals the ferroelectric dipole moment may not be changed by an electric field of the maximum intensity which it is possible to apply without causing electrical breakdown of the crystal. In these crystals we are often able to observe a change in the spontaneous moment when they are heated: changing the temperature changes the value of the dipole moment. Such crystals are called **pyroelectric,** whereas crystals such that the direction of the spontaneous moment can be altered by an electric field are called ferroelectric.

[2] Discovered by J. Valasek, Phys. Rev. **17,** 475 (1921); for summary of properties see H. Mueller, Ann. N.Y. Acad. Sci. **40,** 321 (1940); the isomorphous Ta-Na and Rb-Na salts are also ferroelectric.

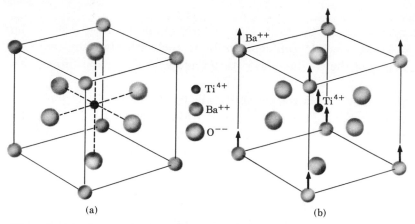

Figure 2 (a) The perovskite crystal structure of barium titanate. The prototype crystal is calcium titanate (perovskite). The structure is cubic, with Ba^{2+} ions at the cube corners, O^{2-} ions at the face centers, and a Ti^{4+} ion at the body center. (b) Below the Curie temperature the structure is slightly deformed, with Ba^{++} and Ti^{4+} ions displaced relative to the O^{--} ions, thereby developing a dipole moment. It is possible that the upper and lower oxygen ions move downward slightly.

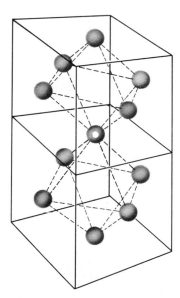

Figure 3 Two cubic cells of barium titanate, with only O^{--} ions shown. These ions form interconnected octahedra with Ti^{4+} ions at the centers. The local symmetry about each oxygen ion is not cubic: thus the O^{--}, Ti^{4+} or Ba^{++} ions are not cubic with respect to the ion marked with a white spot.

on a microscopic basis, although Mueller[3] and others have formulated a phenomenological theory which correlates a number of experimental facts.

The second group of ferroelectric crystals consists of crystals with hydrogen bonds in which the motion of the protons is related to the ferroelectric properties; the group comprises potassium dihydrogen phosphate[4] (KH_2PO_4) and the isomorphous salts. The behavior of crystals in which the hydrogen has been replaced by deuterium is interesting:

	KH_2PO_4	KD_2PO_4	KH_2AsO_4	KD_2AsO_4
Curie temperature	123°K	213°K	96°K	162°K
Saturation polarization	16,000 esu	27,000 esu		

The substitution of deuterons for protons nearly doubles both T_c and P_s, although the fractional change in the molecular weight of the compound is less than 2 percent. This extraordinarily large isotope shift is believed to be a quantum effect[5] involving the mass-dependence of the de Broglie wavelength, which is $\lambda = h/(2ME)^{1/2}$ for a particle of energy E.

Neutron diffraction data[6] show that above the Curie temperature the proton distribution along the hydrogen bond is symmetrically elongated, whereas below the Curie temperature the distribution is more concentrated and asymmetric with respect to neighboring ions.

The third group of ferroelectrics consists of ionic crystals with crystal structures closely related to the perovskite and ilmenite structures. The perovskite structure is the simplest crystal structure (Figs. 2 and 3) to exhibit ferroelectricity. We shall devote ourselves primarily to crystals which have the perovskite structure.

[3] H. Mueller, Phys. Rev. **57**, 829 (1940); **58**, 565 (1940).

[4] G. Busch and P. Scherrer, Naturwiss. **23**, 737 (1935).

[5] J. Pirenne, Physica **15**, 1019 (1949). A theory of the transition is given by J. C. Slater, J. Chem. Phys. **9**, 16 (1941); see also T. Nagamiya, Prog. Theor. Phys. **7**, 275 (1952); H. B. Silsbee, E. A. Uehling, and V. H. Schmidt, Phys. Rev. **133**, A165 (1964).

[6] B. C. Frazer and R. Pepinsky, Acta Cryst. **6**, 273 (1953); R. S. Pease and G. E. Bacon, Proc. Roy. Soc. (London) **A220**, 397 (1953); **A236**, 359 (1955).

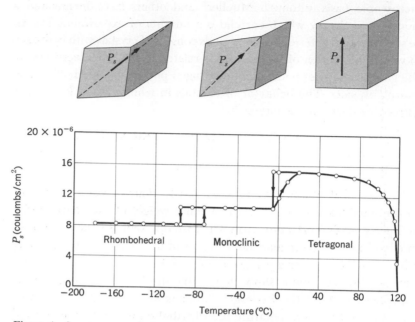

Figure 4 Spontaneous polarization projected on cube edge of barium titanate as a function of temperature. The discontinuities near $0°C$ and $-80°C$ are caused by small changes in the crystal structure. The direction of spontaneous polarization is parallel to a cube edge above $0°C$, becomes parallel to a face diagonal below $0°C$ and parallel to a body diagonal below $-80°C$. [After W. J. Merz, Phys. Rev. **76**, 1221 (1949).]

Ferroelectricity in Ionic Crystals

Consider first the order of magnitude of the ferroelectric effects in barium titanate: The observed saturation polarization P_s at room temperature (Fig. 4) is 8×10^4 esu. The volume of a unit cell is $(4 \times 10^{-8})^3 = 64 \times 10^{-24}$ cm^3, so that the dipole moment of a unit cell is

$$p \cong (8 \times 10^4)(64 \times 10^{-24}) \cong 5 \times 10^{-18} \text{ esu.} \tag{1}$$

If in the ideal perovskite structure the positive ions (Ba^{++} and Ti^{4+}) were moved[7] by $\delta = 0.1$ Å with respect to the negative O^{--} ions, the dipole moment of a unit cell would be $6e\delta = 6 \times (4.8 \times 10^{-10}) \times 10^{-9} \cong 3 \times 10^{-18}$ esu.

---

[7] The actual shifts are not accurately known. G. Shirane, H. Danner, and R. Pepinsky [Phys. Rev. **105**, 856 (1957)] report the following displacements in the tetragonal phase referred to the central four O^{--} ions: $\delta(\text{Ba}) = 0.09$ Å; $\delta(\text{Ti}) = 0.15$ Å; $\delta(\text{O}_I) = -0.03$ Å.

THE POLARIZATION CATASTROPHE

Two related viewpoints contribute to an understanding of the occurrence of ferroelectricity. We may speak in terms of a polarization catastrophe in which for some critical condition the polarization becomes very large; or we may speak in terms of a transverse optical phonon of very low frequency.[8] The two viewpoints are related by the Lyddane-Sachs-Teller relation derived in Chapter 12.

In a polarization catastrophe the local electric field caused by the polarization increases faster than the elastic restoring force on an ion in the crystal, thereby leading to an asymmetrical shift in ionic positions. The shift is ultimately limited to a finite displacement by higher order restoring forces. The occurrence of ferroelectricity in an appreciable number of crystals with the perovskite structure suggests that this structure is favorably disposed to a polarizability catastrophe. Calculations of local fields by Slater[9] and others have made clear the physical reason for the favored position of the perovskite structure.

We give first the simple form of the catastrophe theory, supposing that the Lorentz local field factors as defined following (12.9) are all equal to $4\pi/3$. The theory as given now assumes implicitly that the transition is a second-order transition,[10] but we shall see that the physical ideas can be carried over in part to a first-order transition.

We may rewrite (12.14) for the dielectric constant in the form

$$\epsilon = \frac{1 + \dfrac{8\pi}{3} \Sigma \, N_i \alpha_i}{1 - \dfrac{4\pi}{3} \Sigma \, N_i \alpha_i}, \tag{2}$$

where α_i is the electronic plus ionic polarizability of an ion of type i and N_i is the number of ions i per unit volume. The numerical factors multiplying $\Sigma \, N_i \alpha_i$ are the consequence of the Lorentz local field $E + (4\pi/3)P$.

The dielectric constant becomes infinite, corresponding to a finite

[8] P. W. Anderson, Moscow dielectric conference, 1960; W. Cochran, Adv. in Physics **9**, 387 (1960); V. L. Ginzburg, Sov. Physics (Solid State) **2**, 1824 (1960).

[9] J. C. Slater, Phys. Rev. **78**, 748 (1950). We note that the O^{--} ions in the perovskite structure do not have cubic surroundings. The local field factors at these ions turn out to be large.

[10] In a second-order transition there is no latent heat; the order parameter (in this instance, the polarization) is not discontinuous at the transition temperature. In a first-order transition there is a latent heat; the order parameter changes discontinuously at the transition temperature.

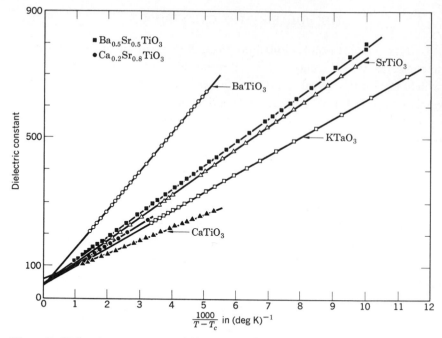

Figure 5 Dielectric constant versus $1/(T - T_c)$ in the paraelectric state $(T > T_c)$ of perovskites, after G. Rupprecht and R. O. Bell, Phys. Rev. **135**, A748 (1964). A plot versus $1/(T - T_0)$ would also be of interest.

polarization for zero applied field, when

$$\Sigma \, N_i \alpha_i = 3/4\pi. \tag{3}$$

This is the condition for a polarization catastrophe.

The value of ϵ in (2) is sensitive to small departures of $\Sigma \, N_i \alpha_i$ from the critical value $3/4\pi$. If we write

$$(4\pi/3) \, \Sigma \, N_i \alpha_i = 1 - 3s, \tag{4}$$

where $s \ll 1$, we have for the dielectric constant in (2)

$$\epsilon \cong 1/s. \tag{5}$$

Let us suppose that near the critical temperature the value of s in (4) varies with temperature in a linear fashion:[11]

$$s \cong (T - T_c)/\xi \tag{6}$$

[11] This might come about in part from the normal thermal expansion of the lattice. Our assumption (6) is not as arbitrary as it may look at first.

where ξ is a constant, then above the transition temperature we have a law for the dielectric constant of the form

$$\epsilon \cong \frac{\xi}{T - T_c}.$$
(7)

This is close to the form of the observed temperature variation in the paraelectric state, as shown in Fig. 5.

Nature of the Phase Transition[12]

We can obtain a consistent thermodynamic theory of the behavior of a ferroelectric crystal by considering the form of the expansion of the energy as a function of the polarization P. We assume that the free energy density F in one dimension may be expanded formally as

$$F(P, T) = g_0 + \tfrac{1}{2}g_2 P^2 + \tfrac{1}{4}g_4 P^4 + \tfrac{1}{6}g_6 P^6 + \cdots,$$
(8)

where the coefficients g_n may depend on the temperature. This series expresses the dependence of the free energy on the quadratic and higher powers of the polarization. The series will not contain terms in odd powers of P if the unpolarized crystal has a center of inversion symmetry. For convenience we take g_0 as zero. From Problem 4 we have $(\partial F/\partial P)_T = E$, the electric field intensity.

To obtain a ferroelectric state we must suppose that g_2 passes through zero at some temperature T_0:

$$g_2 = \gamma(T - T_0),$$
(9)

where γ is taken as a positive constant and T_0 may be equal to or lower than the transition temperature. A small positive value of g_2 means that the lattice is "soft" and is close to instability. The variation of g_2 with temperature can be accounted for by anharmonic interactions of thermal vibrations in the lattice.

---

[12] An example of a first-order phase transition is given by the liquid-vapor transition at constant pressure (the boiling of water). A ferroelectric with a first-order phase transition between the ferroelectric and the paraelectric state is distinguished by a discontinuous change (as in Fig. 8a) of the saturation polarization at the transition temperature. An example of a second-order phase transition is given by the transition between the ferromagnetic and paramagnetic states (Chapter 15). A good discussion of second-order phase transitions is given in Chap. 18 of J. C. Slater, *Introduction to Chemical physics*, McGraw-Hill, 1939; and in Chap. 14 of L. Landau and E. Lifshitz, *Statistical physics*, Pergamon, 1958. It is not clear that a power series expansion such as (8) can always be made. For example, the transition in KH_2PO_4 appears to have a logarithmic singularity in the heat capacity at the transition. Such a singularity is not classifiable as either first- or second-order.

Second-order Transition

If g_4 is positive, nothing new is added by the term in g_6, which may then be neglected. Because $(\partial F/\partial P)_T = E$ as shown in Problem 4, the polarization for zero applied electric field is given by

$$\frac{\partial F}{\partial P} = 0 = \gamma(T - T_0)P_s + g_4 P_s^3, \tag{10}$$

so that either $P_s = 0$ or

$$P_s^2 = (\gamma/g_4)(T_0 - T). \tag{11}$$

For $T \geqq T_0$ the only real root of (10) is at $P_s = 0$, because γ and g_4 are positive. Thus T_0 is the Curie temperature.

For $T < T_0$ the minimum free energy is at

$$|P_s| = (\gamma/g_4)^{1/2}(T_0 - T)^{1/2}, \tag{12}$$

as plotted in Fig. 6a. The phase transition is a second-order phase transition because the polarization (12) goes continuously to zero at the transition temperature. Plots of the free energy versus P^2 are given in Fig. 6b for three representative temperatures. The transition in rubidium bisulfate[13] is an example of an apparent second-order transition.

[13] R. Pepinsky and K. Vedam, Phys. Rev. **117**, 1502 (1960).

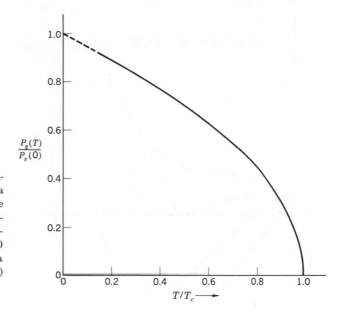

Figure 6a Spontaneous polarization versus temperature, for a second-order phase transition. (The curve is not realistic at low temperatures: the third law of thermodynamics requires that $dP_s/dT \to 0$ as $T \to 0$. Thus Eq. (9) cannot be a valid assumption near $T = 0$.)

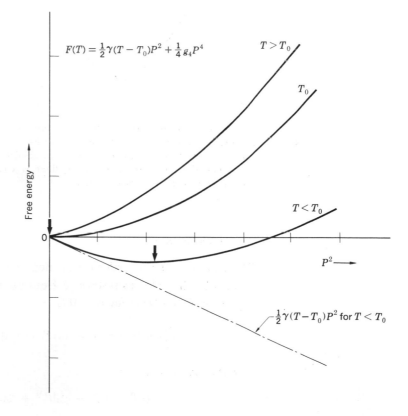

Figure 6b Free energy versus (polarization)^2 at representative temperatures. As the temperature drops below T_0 the equilibrium polarization gradually increases, as defined by the position of the minimum of the free energy. The arrows mark the minima.

$$F(T) = \tfrac{1}{2}\gamma(T - T_0)P^2 + \tfrac{1}{4}g_4 P^4$$

$T > T_0$

T_0

$T < T_0$

$-\tfrac{1}{2}\gamma(T - T_0)P^2$ for $T < T_0$

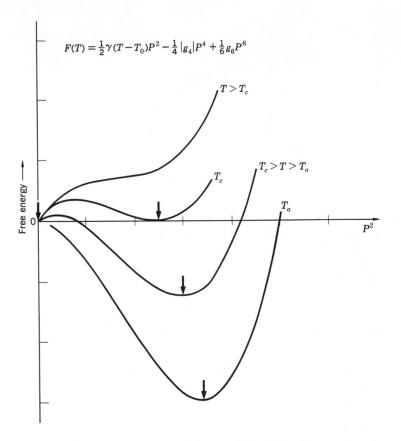

Figure 7 Free energy versus (polarization)^2 in a first-order transition, at representative temperatures. At T_c the free energy has equal minima at $P = 0$ and at a finite P as shown. For T below T_c the absolute minimum is at larger values of P; as T passes through T_c there is a discontinuous change in the position of the absolute minimum.

First-order Transition

The transition is first-order if g_4 is negative. We must now retain g_6 and take it positive in order to restrain F from going to minus infinity (Fig. 7). The equilibrium condition for $E = 0$ is

$$\frac{\partial F}{\partial P} = 0 = \gamma(T - T_0)P_s - |g_4|P_s^3 + g_6 P_s^5, \tag{13}$$

so that either $P_s = 0$ or

$$\gamma(T - T_0) - |g_4|P_s^2 + g_6 P_s^4 = 0. \tag{14}$$

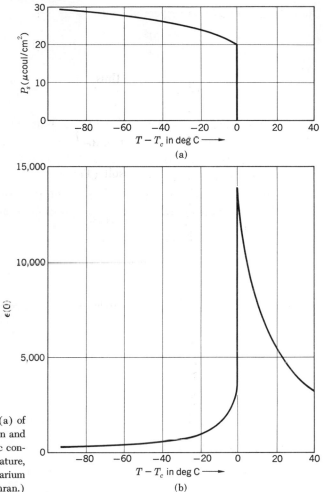

Figure 8 Calculated values (a) of the spontaneous polarization and (b) of the static dielectric constant as a function of temperature, with parameters as for barium titanate. (After W. Cochran.)

At the transition temperature T_c the free energies of the paraelectric and ferroelectric phases will be equal. That is, the value of F for $P_s = 0$ will be equal to the value of F at the minimum given by (14). In Fig. 8 we show the characteristic variation with temperature of P_s for a first-order phase transition; contrast this with the variation shown in Fig. 6a for a second-order phase transition. The transition in $BaTiO_3$ is first order.

The dielectric constant is calculated from $(\partial F/\partial P)_T = E$, with

$$F(P, T) = \tfrac{1}{2}\gamma(T - T_0)P^2 + \tfrac{1}{4}g_4 P^4 + \tfrac{1}{6}g_6 P^6. \qquad (15)$$

In equilibrium at temperatures over the Curie temperature the terms in P^4

and P^6 may usually be neglected; thus

$$\frac{\partial F}{\partial P} = E = \gamma(T - T_0)P, \tag{16}$$

or

$$\epsilon(T > T_c) = 1 + 4\pi\frac{P}{E} = 1 + \frac{4\pi/\gamma}{T - T_0}. \tag{17}$$

This has the form of (7). The result (17) applies whether the transition is of the first or second order, but if second order we have $T_0 = T_c$; if first order, then $T_0 < T_c$. We recall that T_0 is defined by (9), while T_c is the temperature at which the transition actually occurs.

If we write the temperature-dependent part of (17) as $C/(T - T_0)$, then selected experimental data may be represented as in Table 2.

Table 2   Ferroelectric constants

Crystal	C, in 10^4 °K	T_c, in °K	T_0, in °K
$BaTiO_3$	17	381	370
$KNbO_3$	27	683	623
$PbTiO_3$	11	763	693
KH_2PO_4	0.3	123	123

LOW FREQUENCY OPTICAL PHONONS

The Lyddane-Sachs-Teller relation (Chapter 12) says that

$$\omega_L^2/\omega_T^2 = \epsilon(0)/\epsilon(\infty). \tag{18}$$

Here ω_T is the frequency of a transverse optical phonon near zero wavevector. Note that $\epsilon(0) \to \infty$ as $\omega_T \to 0$. The range of values of $\epsilon(\infty)$ observed for crystals is not very wide. Thus whenever the intrinsic static dielectric constant $\epsilon(0)$ is observed to have very high values, such as 100 to 10,000 or above, we expect that ω_T will have very low values. It has been reported[14] that $BaTiO_3$ at 24°C has a low frequency optical mode centered at 12 cm^{-1}: this is a very low frequency for an optical mode.

In 12.41 we found that the transverse optical phonon frequency in a cubic diatomic crystal is given by

$$\mu\omega_T^2 = C - \frac{\frac{4}{3}\pi N q^2}{1 - \frac{4}{3}\pi N \alpha}, \tag{19}$$

where μ is the reduced mass of a molecule, C is the interlattice force constant

---

[14] J. M. Ballantyne, Phys. Rev. **136**, A429 (1964).

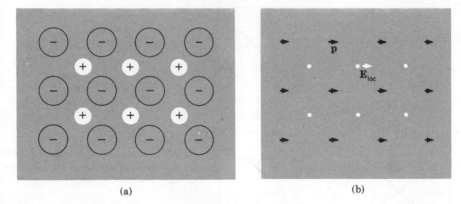

(a)   (b)

Figure 9 In an optical phonon mode of zero wavevector the negative ion lattice is displaced as a whole with respect to the positive ion lattice, as in (a). As seen by a positive ion, the long-range electrostatic effects of the displacement of the negative ion lattice can be simulated by the lattice of dipoles shown in (b). The dipoles are directed opposite to the negative ion displacement. The local field of these dipoles is $\frac{4\pi}{3} \, P$ at a positive ion site, for the geometry of a *transverse* optical phonon. Thus the local field tends to increase the amplitude of the deformation.

apart from effects of the local electric field, N is the number of molecules per unit volume, and $\alpha = \alpha_+ + \alpha_-$ is the sum of the electronic polarizabilities of a positive and a negative ion. The second term on the right-hand side is caused by the local electric field[15] created by the polarization of the lattice during the passage of a transverse optical phonon (Fig. 9). The local electric field provides feedback; it tends to increase the amplitude of the deformation and to lower the frequency.

The short-range force constant C may have a conventional value even if ω_T has an abnormally low value. To obtain $\omega_T = 0$ we see from (19) that we must have

$$C = \frac{\frac{4}{3}\pi N q^2}{1 - \frac{4}{3}\pi N \alpha}. \tag{20}$$

This relation expresses the cancellation of the short-range interaction by the long-range Coulomb interaction. Here α refers to the electronic polarizability. If ω_T is zero, the crystal is unstable, for there is no effective restoring force.

If the transition to a ferroelectric state is first order, we do not find $\omega_T = 0$ or $\epsilon(0) = \infty$ at the transition. The result (17), for example, tells us only that $\epsilon(0)$ extrapolates to a singularity at a temperature T_0. In the usual first-order transition the transition occurs at a temperature T_c which is higher than T_0. In a first-order transition ω_T never becomes zero and $\epsilon(0)$ never becomes infinite.

[15] For a detailed treatment of a simple line of ions, see B. D. Silverman, Phys. Rev. **125**, 1921 (1962).

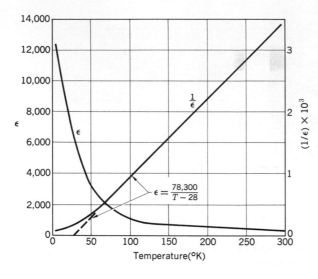

Figure 10 Dielectric constant of a SrTiO₃ crystal versus temperature, after T. Mitsui and W. B. Westphal, Phys. Rev. **124**, 1354 (1961).

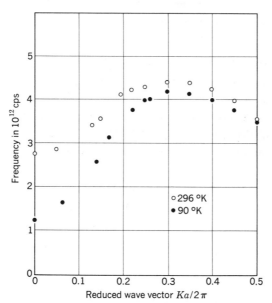

Figure 11 The dispersion curve of the lowest frequency transverse optic branch in strontium titanate along [100] at 90°K and 296°K, after R. A. Cowley, Phys. Rev. Letters **9**, 159 (1962).

Experiments with Strontium Titanate

The association of a high dielectric constant with a low frequency optical mode is supported very well by experiments on strontium titanate, SrTiO₃. The dielectric constant (Fig. 10) takes on very large values near 30°K and below.[16] Neutron diffraction experiments (Fig. 11) show a large decrease in the frequency of the lowest optical phonon between room temperature and

---

[16] At present definite proof of the state of the crystal below 30°K is lacking.

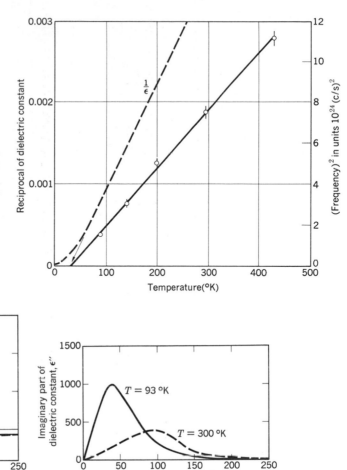

Figure 12 Plot of the square of the frequency of the $K = 0$ transverse optic mode against temperature, for $SrTiO_3$, as observed in neutron diffraction experiments by Cowley. The solid line gives a Curie temperature of $32 \pm 5°K$. The broken line represents the reciprocal of the dielectric constant from the measurements of Mitsui and Westphal.

Figure 13 (a) Real and (b) imaginary parts of the dielectric constant of $SrTiO_3$ as a function of frequency at $93°K$ and $300°K$, after A. S. Barker, Jr., and M. Tinkham, Phys. Rev. **125**, 1527 (1962).

$90°K$.[17] The extrapolation in Fig. 12 of the phonon frequency goes through zero near $32°K$, in approximate agreement with the extrapolation of the reciprocal of the dielectric constant. According to the theory, if the reciprocal of the static dielectric constant has a temperature dependence $1/\epsilon(0) \propto (T - T_0)$ over some region of temperature, then the square of the optical mode frequency will have a similar temperature dependence: $\omega_T{}^2 \propto (T - T_0)$, if ω_L is independent of temperature. The result for $\omega_T{}^2$ is very well confirmed by Fig. 12. The neutron measurements are supported by the far infrared optical measurements shown in Fig. 13.

[17] For a discussion of the lattice dynamics of $SrTiO_3$ see R. A. Cowley, Phys. Rev. **134**, A981 (1964). It is possible to obtain large changes in the frequency of the lowest transverse optical phonon by only slight changes in the parameters which describe the interatomic forces.

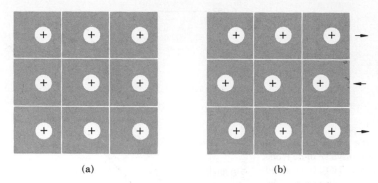

Figure 14 Comparison of (a) ferroelectric and (b) antiferroelectric deformations. Only the displacement of positive ions is shown.

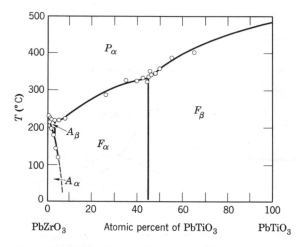

Figure 15 Phase diagram of $PbZrO_3$–$PbTiO_3$ system; A, F, P denote antiferroelectric, ferroelectric, and paraelectric, respectively. [After F. Sawaguchi. J. Phys. Soc. Japan **8**, 615 (1953).]

Antiferroelectricity

A ferroelectric type of displacement is not the only type of instability which may develop in a dielectric crystal. In the perovskite structure other deformations occur. These deformations, even if they do not give a spontaneous polarization, may be accompanied by changes in the dielectric constant. One class of deformation is called **antiferroelectric**[18] and has neighboring lines of ions displaced in opposite senses, as in Fig. 14.

The perovskite structure appears to be susceptible to many types of deformation, often with little difference in energy between them. The phase diagrams of mixed perovskite systems, such as the $PbZrO_3$–$PbTiO_3$ system in Fig. 15, show transitions between para-, ferro-, and antiferroelectric states.

Ordered antiferroelectric arrangements of permanent electric dipole moments occur at low temperatures in ammonium salts and in hydrogen halides. Several other crystals believed to have a nonpolar (or nearly so) ordered state are listed in Table 3.

Table 3   Antiferroelectric crystals
(From a compilation by Walter J. Merz)

Crystal	Transition temperature to antiferroelectric state, in °K.
WO_3	1010
$NaNbO_3$	793, 911
$PbZrO_3$	506
$PbHfO_3$	488
$NH_4H_2PO_4$	148
$ND_4D_2PO_4$	242
$NH_4H_2AsO_4$	216
$ND_4D_2AsO_4$	304
$(NH_4)_2H_3IO_6$	254

[18] C. Kittel, Phys. Rev. **82**, 729 (1951); M. H. Cohen, Phys. Rev. **84**, 369 (1951).

Piezoelectricity

All crystals in a ferroelectric state are also piezoelectric: a stress Z applied to the crystal will change the electric polarization (Fig. 16). Similarly, an electric field E applied to the crystal will cause the crystal to become strained. In schematic one-dimensional notation, the piezoelectric equations are

$$P = Zd + E\chi; \qquad e = Zs + Ed, \tag{21}$$

where P is the polarization, Z the stress, d the **piezoelectric strain constant,** E the electric field, χ the dielectric susceptibility, e the elastic strain, and s the elastic compliance constant.

These relations exhibit the development of polarization by an applied stress and the development of elastic strain by an applied electric field. The first aspect is exploited in strain gauges and in the detection of ultrasonic waves; the second aspect is exploited in ultrasonic generators.

A crystal may be piezoelectric without being ferroelectric: a schematic example of such a structure is given[19] in Fig. 17. Quartz is piezoelectric, but is not ferroelectric; barium titanate is both. For order of magnitude, in quartz $d \approx 10^{-7}$ cm/statvolt and in barium titanate $d \approx 10^{-5}$ cm/statvolt.

The general definition of the piezoelectric strain constants is

$$d_{ik} = (\partial e_k/\partial E_i)_Z, \tag{22}$$

where $i \equiv x, y, z$ and $k \equiv xx, yy, zz, yz, zx, xy$. To convert to cm/statvolt from values of d_{ik} given in meters/volt, multiply by 3×10^4.

For a detailed account of piezoelectricity, see the book by Nye cited at the end of Chapter 4 and also the book by Mason.

[19] See also Chap. 11 of A. Holden and P. Singer, *Crystal and crystal growing,* Doubleday Anchor, 1960.

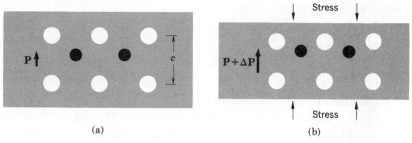

(a)   (b)

Figure 16 (a) Unstressed ferroelectric crystal and (b) stressed ferroelectric crystal. The stress changes the polarization by **ΔP**, the induced piezoelectric polarization.

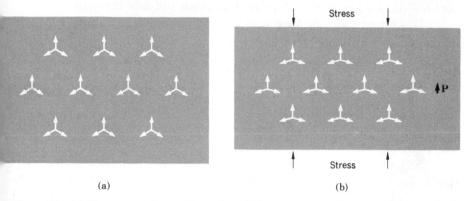

(a)   (b)

Figure 17 (a) The unstressed crystal has a three-fold symmetry axis. The arrows represent dipole moments; each set of three arrows represents a planar group of ions denoted by $A_3^+B^{---}$, with a B^{---} ion at each vertex. The sum of the three dipole moments at each vertex is zero. (b) The crystal when stressed develops a polarization in the direction indicated. The sum of the dipole moments about each vertex is no longer zero.

Ferroelectric Domains

Consider a ferroelectric crystal (such as barium titanate in the tetragonal phase) in which the spontaneous polarization may be either up or down the c axis of the crystal. A ferroelectric crystal generally consists of regions called **domains** within each of which the polarization is in the same direction, but in adjacent domains the polarization is in different directions. In our example in Fig. 18 the polarization is in opposite directions. The net polarization of the crystal will depend on the difference in the volumes of the upward- and downward-directed domains. The crystal as a whole will appear to be unpolarized, as measured by the charge on electrodes covering the ends, when the volumes of domains in opposite senses are equal. The total dipole moment of the crystal may be changed by the movement of the walls (boundaries) between domains or by the creation (nucleation) of new domains.

We exhibit in Fig. 19 a series of photomicrographs of a single crystal of barium titanate in an electric field normal to the plane of the photographs and parallel to the tetragonal axis. The closed curves are boundaries between domains polarized into and out of the plane of the photographs. The domain boundaries move sidewise and change size and shape when the intensity of the electric field is altered. In $BaTiO_3$ the domain widths are characteristically 10^{-4} to 10^{-2} cm; the thickness of the boundary between domains may be only one lattice constant.

The motion of domain walls in ferroelectrics is not simple: it is known[20] that in an electric field a 180° wall[21] in $BaTiO_3$ does not move as a whole perpendicular to itself, but the wall motion appears to result from the repeated nucleation by thermal fluctuations of steps along the parent wall. The nucleation rate[22] is the controlling factor in the propagation of the wall. This is rather unlike the usual situation with ferromagnetic domains (Chapter 15).

[20] W. J. Merz, Phys. Rev. **95**, 690 (1954); R. Landauer, J. Appl. Phys. **28**, 227 (1957); R. C. Miller and A. Savage, Phys. Rev. **115**, 1176 (1959).

[21] A "180° wall" is the boundary between regions having opposite polarization directions.

[22] R. C. Miller and G. Weinreich, Phys. Rev. **117**, 1460 (1960).

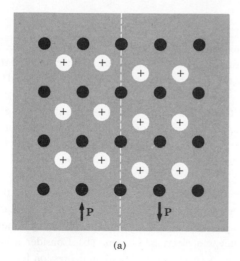 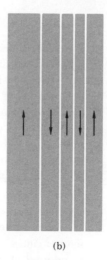

(a)   (b)

Figure 18 (a) Schematic drawing of atomic displacements on either side of a boundary between domains polarized in opposite directions in a ferroelectric crystal; (b) view of a domain structure, showing 180° boundaries between domains polarized in opposite directions.

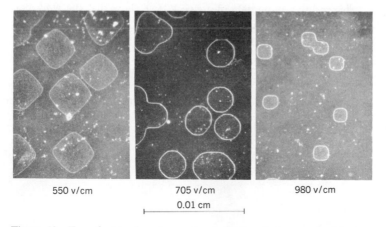

550 v/cm   705 v/cm   980 v/cm

|———————— 0.01 cm ————————|

Figure 19 Ferroelectric domains on the face of a single crystal of barium titanate. The face is normal to the tetragonal or *c* axis. The net polarization of the crystal as judged by domain volumes is increased markedly as the electric field intensity parallel to the axis is increased from 550 volts/cm to 980 volts/cm. The domain boundaries are made visible by etching the crystal in a weak acid solution. (Courtesy of R. C. Miller.)

Problems

1. **Ferroelectric criterion for neutral atoms.** Consider a system of two neutral atoms separated by a fixed distance a, each atom having a polarizability α. Find the relation between a and α for such a system to be ferroelectric. *Hint:* The dipolar field is strongest along the axis of the dipole.

2. **Saturation polarization at Curie point.** In a first-order transition the equilibrium condition (14) with T set equal to T_c gives one equation for polarization $P_s(T_c)$. A further condition at the Curie point is that $F(P_s, T_c) = F(0, T_c)$. (a) Combining these two conditions, show that $P_s^2(T_c) = 3|g_4|/4g_6$. (b) Using this result, show that $T_c = T_0 + (3g_4^2)/(16\gamma g_6)$.

3. **Piezoelectricity.** (a) Consider a flat plate of a piezoelectric crystal with the plane of the plate normal to the direction of E and Z considered in (21). Find expressions for the effective elastic compliance constants when the surfaces of the plate are short-circuited and when they are electrically open. (b) Consider a longitudinal sound wave of strain $e(x, t) = A \cos(kx - \omega t)$. Find an expression for the polarization $P(x, t)$. Using the Maxwell equation div $(\mathbf{E} + 4\pi\mathbf{P}) = 0$, find $E(x, t)$. This electric field is important in determining the interaction of electrons with elastic waves in piezoelectric semiconductors.

°4. **Thermodynamics of polarization.** A parallel-plate capacitor of capacitance C is charged to a potential difference V. (a) Show that the work done by an external power supply in charging the capacitor is $\frac{1}{2}CV^2$. (b) If the capacitor is empty, show that the work done is

$$W \text{ (vacuum)} = \frac{1}{8\pi}E^2$$

per unit volume. *Hint:* For an empty capacitor, the capacitance is given by $C = A/4\pi s$, where A is the area and s the separation of the plates. The charge Q on a plate is $Q = CV$. (c) If a dielectric is introduced, show using the discussion of Eq. (12.8) that

$$W \text{ (vacuum + matter)} = \frac{1}{4\pi}\int E \, dD = \frac{1}{8\pi}E^2 + \int E \, dP,$$

where $D = E + 4\pi P$. We call $\frac{1}{8\pi}E^2$ the electric energy of the vacuum, and we associate the left-hand term with the work of polarization, per unit volume:

$$W \text{ (matter)} = \int E \, dP,$$

which may be compared with Eq. (11.5) for the work of magnetization. The second law of thermodynamics becomes $dU = T \, dS + E \, dP$. (d) Show that the free energy density $F(P, T) = U - TS$ is a minimum in equilibrium at constant T and P, by virtue of the relation $\delta(\text{heat}) \leq T \, \delta S$, where the inequality applies in an irreversible process. Here $E = 0$. (e) Show that $(\partial F/\partial P)_T = E$, as used in Eq. (16).

References

A. F. Devonshire, "Theory of ferroelectrics," Advances in Physics **3**, 85–130 (1954).

W. P. Mason, *Piezoelectric crystals*, Van Nostrand, 1950.

F. Jona and G. Shirane, *Ferroelectric crystals*, Pergamon, 1962.

W. Cochran, "Crystal stability and the theory of ferroelectricity," Advances in Physics **9**, 387 (1960); **10**, 401–420 (1961).

W. Känzig, "Ferroelectrics and antiferroelectrics," *Solid state physics* **4**, 1–197 (1957).

P. W. Forsbergh, "Piezoelectricity, electrostriction, and ferroelectricity," *Encyclo. of physics* **17**, 264–392 (1956).

M. Tinkham, "Spectroscopy of solids in the far-infrared," Science **145**, 240 (1964).

14

Diamagnetism and Paramagnetism

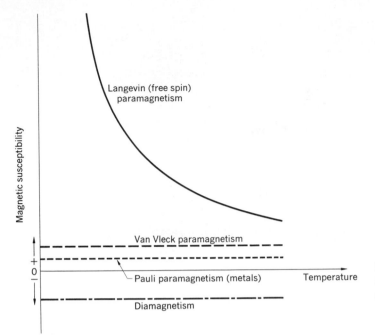

Figure 1   Characteristic magnetic susceptibilities of diamagnetic and paramagnetic substances.

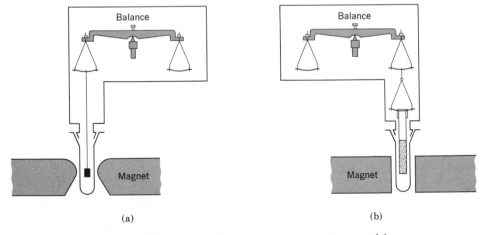

Figure 2   (a) Faraday and (b) Gouy methods for measuring magnetic susceptibility. The magnet pole pieces in the Faraday method are designed to produce high values of $H \, dH/dx$ constant over a small volume. Values of 10 $(\text{kG})^2/\text{cm}$ are found in good commercial equipment, so that the force on 1 cm^3 of a specimen having $\chi \sim 10^{-6}$ is 10 dynes. In the Gouy method a high value of H is desired.

This is the first of three chapters on magnetism. Chapter 15 treats ferromagnetism and antiferromagnetism, and Chapter 16 treats magnetic resonance.

The **magnetization M** is defined as the magnetic moment per unit volume. The magnetic susceptibility per unit volume is defined as

$$\chi = M/H; \tag{1}$$

here H is the macroscopic magnetic field intensity.[1] In Gaussian units χ is dimensionless. Quite frequently a susceptibility is defined referred to unit mass or to a mole of the substance. The molar susceptibility is written as χ_M; the magnetic moment per gram is sometimes written as σ.

Substances with a negative magnetic susceptibility are called **diamagnetic.** Substances with a positive susceptibility are called **paramagnetic,** as in Fig. 1. Ordered arrays of magnetic moments are discussed in Chapter 15; the arrays may be ferromagnetic, ferrimagnetic, antiferromagnetic, helical, or more complex in form. Nuclear magnetic moments give rise to **nuclear paramagnetism.** Magnetic moments of nuclei are of the order of 10^{-3} times smaller than the magnetic moment of the electron.

Measurement of Susceptibility

The magnetic contribution to the energy density of a magnetized specimen is $\frac{1}{2}\chi H^2$, provided χ is independent of H. The force on a unit volume is the gradient of the energy density. The x component of the force on a small specimen of volume V is

$$F_x = \frac{1}{2}\chi V \frac{d}{dx} H^2 = \chi V \mathbf{H} \cdot (d\mathbf{H}/dx), \tag{2}$$

provided the field $\mathbf{H}$ and the derivative $d\mathbf{H}/dx$ do not vary appreciably over the volume (this is why the specimen must be small). Equation (2) is the basis of the Faraday method (Fig. 2a) which is used with small samples and a sensitive microbalance. The sensitivity of the Faraday method is high: a susceptibility change of 10^{-10} may be measured.

In the Gouy method (Fig. 2b) a long cylindrical sample is suspended halfway into a strong field H: one end of the sample is in the maximum field and the other end is in a region where the field is negligible. The total force

[1] We could well write B in place of H for the magnetic field intensity in the absence of the specimen, but our usage of H is established in the literature of magnetism. We shall express both B and H in gauss (G) or kilogauss (kG). The matter of names and symbols in magnetism is treated definitively in Chap. 10 of E. M. Purcell, *Electricity and magnetism*, Berkeley physics course, Vol. 2, McGraw-Hill, 1965.

under these conditions on a specimen of cross-sectional area A is

$$F_x = \frac{1}{2}\chi A \int dx \frac{d}{dx} H^2 = \frac{1}{2}\chi A H^2. \tag{3}$$

LANGEVIN DIAMAGNETISM EQUATION

Diamagnetism is associated with the tendency of electrical charges partially to shield the interior of a body from an applied magnetic field. In electromagnetism we are familiar with Lenz's law, which states that when the flux through an electrical circuit is changed, an induced current is set up in such a direction as to oppose the flux change. In a resistanceless circuit, in a superconductor, or in an electron orbit within an atom, the induced current persists as long as the field is present. The magnetic field produced by the induced current is opposite to the applied field, and the magnetic moment associated with the current is a diamagnetic moment.

The usual treatment of the diamagnetism of atoms and ions employs the Larmor theorem,[2] which states that in a magnetic field the motion of the electrons around a central nucleus is, to the first order in H, the same as a possible motion in the absence of H except for the superposition of a precession of angular frequency

$$\omega = eH/2mc. \tag{4}$$

If the field is applied slowly, the motion in the rotating reference system will be the same as the original motion in the rest system before the application of the field. If the average electron current around the nucleus was zero initially, then the application of the magnetic field will cause a finite average current around the nucleus. The current thus established is equivalent to a magnetic moment. The direction of the moment is opposite to the direction of the applied field.

The Larmor precession of the electron distribution is equivalent to an electric current

$$I = -(Ze)(eH/2mc)/2\pi c, \tag{5}$$

in electromagnetic units. The magnetic moment μ of a current loop is given by the product of the current (in emu) times the area of the loop. The area of a loop of radius ρ is $\pi\rho^2$. We have

$$\mu = -(Ze^2H/4mc^2)\langle\rho^2\rangle, \tag{6}$$

for Z electrons; here $\langle\rho^2\rangle = \langle x^2\rangle + \langle y^2\rangle$ is the average of the square of the perpendicular distance of the electron from the field axis.

The mean square distance of the electrons from the nucleus is $\langle r^2\rangle = \langle x^2\rangle + \langle y^2\rangle + \langle z^2\rangle$. For a distribution of charge which is spherically sym-

[2] H. Goldstein, *Classical mechanics*, Addison-Wesley, 1953, pp. 176–178.

metrical $\langle x^2 \rangle = \langle y^2 \rangle = \langle z^2 \rangle$, so that

$$\langle r^2 \rangle = \tfrac{3}{2}\langle \rho^2 \rangle. \tag{7}$$

From (6) and (7) the diamagnetic susceptibility per unit volume is, if N is the number of atoms per unit volume,

$$\boxed{\chi = N\mu/H = -\frac{Ze^2N}{6mc^2}\langle r^2 \rangle.} \tag{8}$$

This is the classical Langevin result. A quantum-theoretical derivation is given in Appendix F.

The problem of calculating the diamagnetic susceptibility of an isolated atom is reduced to the calculation of $\langle r^2 \rangle$ for the electron distribution within the atom. The distribution can be calculated by quantum mechanics. Experimental values for neutral atoms are most easily obtained for the inert gases. Typical experimental values of the molar susceptibilities are the following:

	He	Ne	Ar	Kr	Xe
χ_M in 10^{-6} cm^3/mole:	-1.9	-7.2	-19.4	-28.0	-43.0

In dielectric solids the diamagnetic contribution of the ion cores is described roughly by the Langevin result. The contribution of conduction electrons is more complicated, as is evident from the de Haas–van Alphen effect discussed in Chapter 9.

Diamagnetism of Molecules

The derivation of the Larmor equation assumes implicitly that the field direction is an axis of symmetry of the system. In most molecular systems this condition is not satisfied, and the general theory of Van Vleck (Appendix G) must be applied. For a polyatomic molecule with spin quantum number zero we have, according to (G.7), the total molar susceptibility

$$\chi_M = -\frac{N_0 e^2}{6mc^2}\sum\langle r^2 \rangle + 2N_0 \sum_s \frac{|\langle s|\mu_z|0\rangle|^2}{E_s - E_0}, \tag{9}$$

where N_0 is the Avogadro number, $\langle s|\mu_z|0\rangle$ is the matrix element of the z component of the orbital magnetic moment connecting the ground state 0 with the excited state s, and $E_s - E_0$ is the energy separation of the two states. The material is diamagnetic or paramagnetic according to whether the first or second term of (9) is greater. The second term is known as **Van Vleck paramagnetism.**

For the normal state of the H_2 molecule Van Vleck and Frank[3] calculate

$$\chi_M = -4.71 \times 10^{-6} + 0.51 \times 10^{-6} = -4.20 \times 10^{-6},$$

cm^3/mole. The experimental values are between -3.9 and -4.0×10^{-6}.

[3] J. H. Van Vleck and A. Frank, Proc. Natl. Acad. Sci. U.S. **15**, 539 (1929).

PARAMAGNETISM

Electronic paramagnetism (positive contribution to χ) is found in:

a. Atoms, molecules, and lattice defects possessing an odd number of electrons, as here the total spin of the system cannot be zero. Examples: free sodium atoms; gaseous nitric oxide (NO); organic free radicals such as triphenylmethyl, $C(C_6H_5)_3$; F centers in alkali halides.

b. Free atoms and ions with a partly filled inner shell: transition elements; ions isoelectronic with transition elements; rare earth and actinide elements. Examples: Mn^{2+}, Gd^{3+}, U^{4+}. Paramagnetism is exhibited by many of these ions when incorporated into solids, but not invariably.

c. A few compounds with an even number of electrons, including molecular oxygen and organic biradicals.

d. Metals.

We shall consider classes (b) and (d).

LANGEVIN PARAMAGNETISM EQUATION AND THE CURIE LAW

We treat a medium containing N atoms per unit volume, each bearing a magnetic moment μ. Magnetization results from the orientation of the magnetic moments in an applied magnetic field; thermal disorder resists the tendency of the field to orient the moments. The energy of interaction with an applied magnetic field $\mathbf{H}$ is

$$U = -\boldsymbol{\mu} \cdot \mathbf{H}. \tag{10}$$

The magnetization in thermal equilibrium is calculated by following exactly the steps (12.25) to (12.28) in the derivation of the Debye orientational polarizability, with μ written for $\mathbf{p}$ and $\mathbf{H}$ for $\mathbf{E}$. The magnetization is then given by the Langevin equation

$$M = N\mu L(x), \tag{11}$$

where $x \equiv \mu H / k_B T$, and the Langevin function $L(x)$ is

$$L(x) \equiv \operatorname{ctnh} x - \frac{1}{x}. \tag{12}$$

For $x \ll 1$, we have $L(x) \cong x/3$ from (12.29), so that the magnetization is

$$M \cong N\mu^2 H / 3k_B T. \tag{13}$$

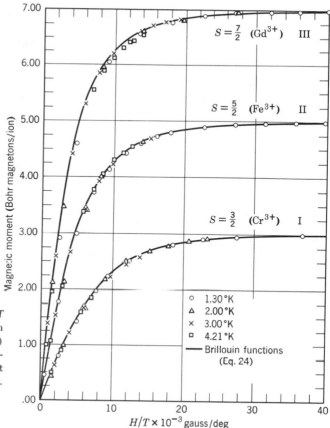

Figure 3 Plot of magnetic moment versus H/T for spherical samples of (I) potassium chromium alum, (II) ferric ammonium alum, and (III) gadolinium sulfate octahydrate. Over 99.5% magnetic saturation is achieved at $1.3\,°K$ and about 50,000 gauss. [After W. E. Henry, Phys. Rev. **88**, 559 (1952).]

For an electron $\mu \approx 10^{-20}$ erg/gauss. At room temperature in a field of 10^4 gauss we have $\mu H/k_B T \approx 2 \times 10^{-3}$, so that under these conditions we may safely approximate the Langevin function by $\mu H/3k_B T$. At low temperatures saturation effects have been observed, as shown in Fig. 3.

The magnetic susceptibility in the limit $\mu H/k_B T \ll 1$ is

$$\chi = \frac{M}{H} = \frac{N\mu^2}{3k_B T} = \frac{C}{T}, \tag{14}$$

where the **Curie constant** $C \equiv N\mu^2/3k_B$. The result (14) is known as the **Curie law**.

QUANTUM THEORY OF PARAMAGNETISM

The magnetic moment of an atom or ion in free space is given by

$$\mu = \gamma \hbar \mathbf{J} = -g\mu_B \mathbf{J}, \tag{15}$$

where the total angular momentum $\hbar \mathbf{J}$ is the sum of the orbital $\hbar \mathbf{L}$ and spin $\hbar \mathbf{S}$ angular momenta. The constant γ is the ratio of the magnetic moment to the angular momentum; γ is called the **magnetomechanical ratio** or **gyromagnetic ratio.**

For electronic systems a quantity g is defined as in (15) by

$$g\mu_B \equiv -\gamma \hbar. \tag{15a}$$

The quantity g is called the **g factor** or the **spectroscopic splitting factor.** It represents the ratio of the number of Bohr magnetons to the units of $\hbar$ of angular momentum. For an electron spin $g = 2.0023$, usually taken as 2.00. For a free atom with an orbital angular momentum the g factor is given by the Landé equation[4]

$$g = 1 + \frac{J(J+1) + S(S+1) - L(L+1)}{2J(J+1)}. \tag{16}$$

The **Bohr magneton** μ_B is defined as $e\hbar/2mc$ and has the value 0.927×10^{-20} erg/gauss.

The energy levels of the system in a magnetic field are

$$E = m_J g \mu_B H, \tag{17}$$

where m_J is the azimuthal quantum number and has the values $J, J-1, \cdots,$ $-J$. For a single spin with no orbital moment we have $m_J = \pm\frac{1}{2}$ and $g = 2$, whence

$$E = \pm\mu_B H. \tag{18}$$

This splitting is shown in Fig. 4a.

If a system has only two levels the equilibrium populations are, with $\beta \equiv 1/k_B T$,

$$\frac{N_1}{N} = \frac{\exp(\beta\mu H)}{\exp(\beta\mu H) + \exp(-\beta\mu H)};$$

$$\frac{N_2}{N} = \frac{\exp(-\beta\mu H)}{\exp(\beta\mu H) + \exp(-\beta\mu H)}; \tag{19}$$

---

[4] For a derivation see Born, pp. 164 and 370.

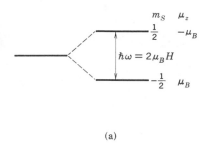

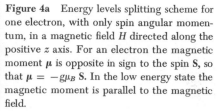

(a)

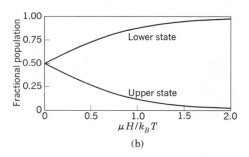

(b)

Figure 4a Energy levels splitting scheme for one electron, with only spin angular momentum, in a magnetic field H directed along the positive z axis. For an electron the magnetic moment μ is opposite in sign to the spin S, so that $\mu = -g\mu_B S$. In the low energy state the magnetic moment is parallel to the magnetic field.

Figure 4b Fractional populations of a two-level spin system in thermal equilibrium at temperature T in a magnetic field H. The magnetic moment is proportional to the difference between the two curves.

here N_1, N_2 are the populations of the lower and upper levels, and $N = N_1 + N_2$ is the total number of atoms. The fractional populations are plotted in Fig. 4b.

The projection of the magnetic moment of the upper state along the field direction is $-\mu$ and of the lower state is μ. The resultant magnetization for N atoms per unit volume is

$$M = (N_1 - N_2)\mu = N\mu \cdot \frac{e^x - e^{-x}}{e^x + e^{-x}} = N\mu \tanh x, \qquad (20)$$

where $x \equiv \mu H/k_B T$. Note that the function L in (11) and $\tanh$ in (20) are different because of the difference between continuous orientation and quantized orientation. The low field expansions of the functions are also different.

For $x \ll 1$, $\tanh x \cong x$, and we have

$$M \cong N\mu(\mu H/k_B T). \qquad (21)$$

The susceptibility in this limit is also of the Curie form:

$$\chi = N\mu^2/k_B T. \qquad (22)$$

Results for a copper salt are shown in Fig. 5.

In a magnetic field an atom with angular momentum quantum number J has $2J + 1$ equally spaced energy levels. The magnetization is given by

$$M = NgJ\mu_B B_J(x), \qquad (x \equiv gJ\mu_B H/k_B T) \qquad (23)$$

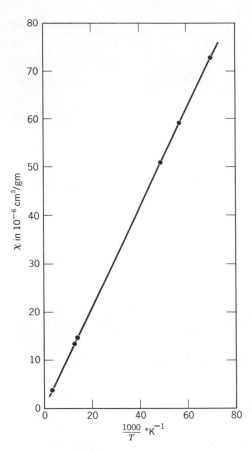

Figure 5 Plot of susceptibility per gm versus reciprocal temperature for powdered $CuSO_4 \cdot K_2SO_4 \cdot 6H_2O$, showing the Curie law temperature dependence. [After J. C. Hupse, Physica **9**, 633 (1942).]

where the **Brillouin function** B_J is defined by

$$B_J(x) = \frac{2J + 1}{2J} \operatorname{ctnh} \left(\frac{(2J + 1)x}{2J} \right) - \frac{1}{2J} \operatorname{ctnh} \left(\frac{x}{2J} \right). \tag{24}$$

Equation (20) is a special case of (23) for $J = \frac{1}{2}$. For $x \ll 1$, we have

$$\operatorname{ctnh} x = \frac{1}{x} + \frac{x}{3} - \frac{x^3}{45} + \cdots,$$

whence the susceptibility M/H is given from (23) and (24) by

$$\chi \cong NJ(J + 1)g^2\mu_B{}^2/3k_BT = Np^2\mu_B{}^2/3k_BT = C/T. \tag{25}$$

Here p is the **effective number of Bohr magnetons**, defined as

$$p \equiv g[J(J + 1)]^{1/2}. \tag{26}$$

Rare Earth Ions

The preceding discussion applies to atoms which have a $(2J + 1)$-fold degenerate ground state, the degeneracy being lifted by a magnetic field. The influence of all higher energy states of the system is neglected. These assumptions appear to be satisfied by a number of rare-earth ions, Table 1. The calculated magneton numbers are obtained with g values from the Landé formula (16) and the ground state level assignment predicted by the Hund theory of spectral terms (discussed in books on atomic spectroscopy). The **Hund rules** tell us that for electrons from the same shell the ground state has the maximum multiplicity $2S + 1$ allowed by the Pauli principle and the maximum L consistent with this multiplicity; furthermore, the J value is equal to $|L - S|$ when the shell is less than half full and $L + S$ when the shell is more than half full.

Consider several examples of the Hund rules: The ion Ce^{3+} has a single f electron; an f electron has $l = 3$ and $s = \frac{1}{2}$. Because the f shell is less than half full, the J value by the preceding rule is $|L - S| = L - \frac{1}{2} = \frac{5}{2}$. The ion Pr^{3+} has two f electrons: one of the rules tells us that the spins add to give $S = 1$. Both f electrons cannot have $m_l = 3$ without violating the Pauli exclusion principle, so that the maximum L consistent with the Pauli principle is not 6, but 5. The J value is $|L - S| = 5 - 1 = 4$.

The discrepancy between the experimental magneton numbers and those

Table 1   **Effective magneton numbers p for trivalent lanthanide group ions**
(Near room temperature)

Ion	Configuration	Basic level	p (calc) $=$ $g[J(J + 1)]^{1/2}$	p (exp), approximate
Ce^{3+}	$4f^1 5s^2 p^6$	$^2F_{5/2}$	2.54	2.4
Pr^{3+}	$4f^2 5s^2 p^6$	$^3H_4$	3.58	3.5
Nd^{3+}	$4f^3 5s^2 p^6$	$^4I_{9/2}$	3.62	3.5
Pm^{3+}	$4f^4 5s^2 p^6$	$^5I_4$	2.68	–
Sm^{3+}	$4f^5 5s^2 p^6$	$^6H_{5/2}$	0.84	1.5
Eu^{3+}	$4f^6 5s^2 p^6$	$^7F_0$	0	3.4
Gd^{3+}	$4f^7 5s^2 p^6$	$^8S_{7/2}$	7.94	8.0
Tb^{3+}	$4f^8 5s^2 p^6$	$^7F_6$	9.72	9.5
Dy^{3+}	$4f^9 5s^2 p^6$	$^6H_{15/2}$	10.63	10.6
Ho^{3+}	$4f^{10} 5s^2 p^6$	$^5I_8$	10.60	10.4
Er^{3+}	$4f^{11} 5s^2 p^6$	$^4I_{15/2}$	9.59	9.5
Tm^{3+}	$4f^{12} 5s^2 p^6$	$^3H_6$	7.57	7.3
Yb^{3+}	$4f^{13} 5s^2 p^6$	$^2F_{7/2}$	4.54	4.5

calculated on these assumptions is quite marked for Eu^{3+} and Sm^{3+} ions. For these ions it is necessary to consider the influence of the higher states of the $L - S$ multiplet,[5] as the intervals between successive states of the multiplet are not large compared to k_BT at room temperature.

The full theoretical expression for the susceptibility if higher states are considered may be quite complicated. In Appendix G we consider two limiting cases, when the level splitting is $\ll k_BT$ or $\gg k_BT$. Levels $\gg k_BT$ above the ground state may contribute a Van Vleck term (9) to the susceptibility, independent of temperature over the appropriate range.

Iron Group Ions

Table 2 shows that the experimental magneton numbers for salts of the iron transition group of the periodic table are in poor agreement with (26). The values often agree quite well with magneton numbers $p = 2[S(S + 1)]^{1/2}$ calculated as if the orbital moment were not there at all. One expresses this situation by saying that the orbital moments are "quenched."

Table 2   Effective magneton numbers for iron group ions

Ion	Config-uration	Basic level	$p\,(calc) = g[J(J + 1)]^{1/2}$	$p\,(calc) = 2[S(S + 1)]^{1/2}$	$p\,(exp)$°
Ti^{3+}, V^{4+}	$3d^1$	$^2D_{3/2}$	1.55	1.73	1.8
V^{3+}	$3d^2$	$^3F_2$	1.63	2.83	2.8
Cr^{3+}, V^{2+}	$3d^3$	$^4F_{3/2}$	0.77	3.87	3.8
Mn^{3+}, Cr^{2+}	$3d^4$	$^5D_0$	0	4.90	4.9
Fe^{3+}, Mn^{2+}	$3d^5$	$^6S_{5/2}$	5.92	5.92	5.9
Fe^{2+}	$3d^6$	$^5D_4$	6.70	4.90	5.4
Co^{2+}	$3d^7$	$^4F_{9/2}$	6.63	3.87	4.8
Ni^{2+}	$3d^8$	$^3F_4$	5.59	2.83	3.2
Cu^{2+}	$3d^9$	$^2D_{5/2}$	3.55	1.73	1.9

°Representative values.

Crystal Field Splitting

The basic reason for the difference in behavior of the rare earth and the iron group salts is that the $4f$ shell responsible for paramagnetism in the rare earth ions lies deep inside the ions, inside the $5s$ and $5p$ shells, whereas in the iron group ions the $3d$ shell responsible for paramagnetism is the outermost shell. The $3d$ shell experiences the intense local electric field produced by

[5] A multiplet is the set of levels of different J values arising out of a given L and S. The levels of a multiplet are split by the spin-orbit interaction.

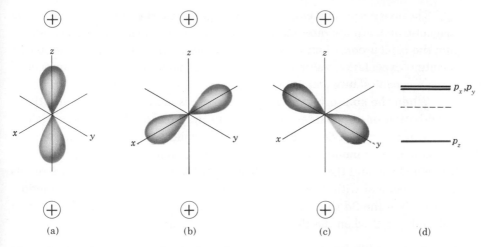

(a)   (b)   (c)   (d)

Figure 6 Consider an atom with orbital angular momentum $L = 1$ placed in the uniaxial crystal-line electric field of the two positive ions along the x axis. In the free atom the states $m_L = \pm 1, 0$ have identical energies—they are degenerate. In the crystal the atom has a lower energy when the electron cloud is close to positive ions as in (a) than when it is oriented midway between them, as in (b) and (c). The wavefunctions which give rise to these charge densities are of the form $zf(r)$, $xf(r)$ and $yf(r)$ and are called the p_z, p_x, and p_y orbitals, respectively. In an axially symmetric field as shown the p_x and p_y orbitals are degenerate. The energy levels referred to the free atom (dotted line) are shown in (d). If the electric field does not have axial symmetry, all three states will have different energies.

neighboring ions. This inhomogeneous electric field is called the **crystal field.** The interaction of the paramagnetic ions with the crystal field has two major effects: the coupling of **L** and **S** vectors is largely broken up, so that the states are no longer specified by their J values; further, the $2L + 1$ sublevels belonging to a given L which are degenerate in the free ion may now be split up by the crystal field, as in Fig. 6. This splitting diminishes the contribution of the orbital motion to the magnetic moment.

Quenching of the Orbital Angular Momentum

In an electric field directed toward a fixed nucleus, the plane of a classical orbit is fixed in space, so that all the orbital angular momentum components L_x, L_y, L_z are constant. In quantum theory one angular momentum component, usually taken as L_z, and the square of the total orbital angular momentum L^2 are constant in a central field. In a noncentral field the plane of the orbit will move about; the angular momentum components are no longer constant and may average to zero. In a crystal, as shown in detail in Appendix H, L_z will no longer be a constant of the motion, although to a good approximation L^2 may continue to be constant. When L_z averages to zero the orbital angular momentum is said to be **quenched.**

The magnetic moment of a state is given by the average value of the magnetic moment operator $\mu_B(\mathbf{L} + 2\mathbf{S})$. In a magnetic field along the z direction the orbital contribution to the magnetic moment is proportional to the quantum expectation value of L_z; the orbital magnetic moment is quenched if the mechanical moment L_z is quenched.

When the spin-orbit interaction energy is introduced as an additional perturbation on the system, the spin may drag some orbital moment along with it. If the sign of the interaction favors parallel orientation of the spin and orbital magnetic moments, the total magnetic moment will be larger than for the spin alone, and the g value will be larger than 2. The experimental results are in agreement with the known variation of sign of the spin-orbit interaction: $g > 2$ when the $3d$ shell is more than half full, $g = 2$ when the shell is half full, and $g < 2$ when the shell is less than half full.

Nuclear Paramagnetism

Magnetic moments of nuclei are smaller than the magnetic moment of the electron by a factor $\sim m/M_p \sim 10^{-3}$, where M_p is the proton mass. According to (14) the susceptibility of a nuclear paramagnetic system for the same number of particles will be smaller by a factor $\sim 10^{-6}$ than that of an electronic paramagnetic system. The susceptibility of solid hydrogen, which is diamagnetic with respect to electrons but paramagnetic with respect to protons, was measured at very low temperatures by Lasarew and Schubnikow.[6] Nuclear magnetism is discussed in Chapter 16.

COOLING BY ADIABATIC DEMAGNETIZATION OF A PARAMAGNETIC SALT

The universal method at present for attaining temperatures below $0.3\,^\circ$K is that of adiabatic demagnetization.[7] By its use temperatures of $10^{-3}\,^\circ$K and lower have been reached. The method rests on the fact that at a fixed temperature the entropy of a system of magnetic moments is lowered by the application of a magnetic field. (The entropy is a measure of the disorder of a system: the greater the disorder, the higher is the entropy.) In the magnetic field the moments will be partly lined up (partly ordered), so that the entropy is lowered by the field. The entropy is also lowered if the temperature is lowered, as more of the moments line up.

If the magnetic field can be removed without changing the entropy of

---

[6] B. Lasarew and L. Schubnikow, Physik. Z. Sowjetunion **11**, 445 (1937); see also D. F. Evans, Phil. Mag. **1**, 370 (1956).

[7] The method was suggested independently by P. Debye, Ann. Physik **81**, 1154 (1926); and W. F. Giauque, J. Am. Chem. Soc. **49**, 1864 (1927). To obtain temperatures from $4\,^\circ$K to $1\,^\circ$K one pumps on liquid helium; from $1\,^\circ$K to $0.3\,^\circ$K one pumps on liquid He^3.

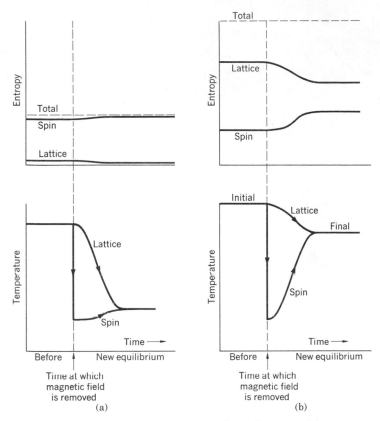

Figure 7 During adiabatic demagnetization the total entropy of the specimen is constant, but situation (a) is favorable for cooling, whereas (b) is not. In (a) the initial entropy of the lattice is small in comparison with the entropy of the spin system, whereas in (b) the initial lattice entropy is large, so that the low spin temperature reached just after the magnetic field is switched off is chiefly wasted in a slight cooling off of the lattice.

the spin system, the order of the spin system will correspond to a lower temperature than the same degree of order in the presence of the field. When the specimen is demagnetized adiabatically, entropy can flow into the spin system only from the system of lattice vibrations, as in Fig. 7. At the temperatures of interest the entropy of the lattice vibrations is usually negligible; thus the entropy of the spin system will be essentially constant during adiabatic demagnetization of the specimen.

We first find an expression for the spin entropy of a system of N ions each of spin S at a temperature sufficiently high so that the spin system is entirely disordered. That is, T is supposed to be much higher than some temperature Δ which characterizes the energy of the interactions ($E_{int} \equiv k_B \Delta$) tending to

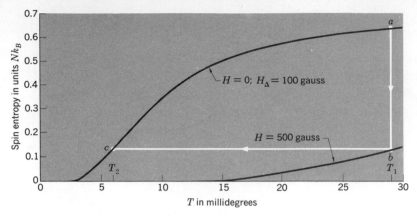

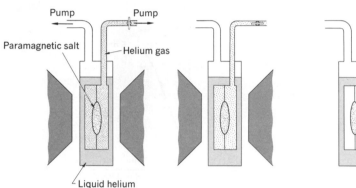

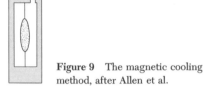

Figure 8 Entropy for a spin ½ system as a function of temperature, assuming an internal random magnetic field H_Δ of 100 gauss. The specimen is magnetized isothermally along ab, and is then insulated thermally. The external magnetic field is turned off along bc. In order to keep the figure on a reasonable scale the initial temperature T_1 is lower than would be used in practice, as is also the external magnetic field.

Figure 9 The magnetic cooling method, after Allen et al.

orient the spins preferentially. Some of these interactions are discussed in Chapter 16. The Boltzmann definition of the entropy σ of a distribution of objects is

$$\sigma = k_B \log W, \tag{27}$$

where W is the number of independent arrangements of the objects. At a temperature so high that all of the $2S + 1$ states of each ion are nearly equally populated, the number of arrangements is the number of ways of arranging N spins in $2S + 1$ states. Thus

$$W = (2S + 1)^N, \tag{28}$$

whence the spin entropy[8] is

$$\sigma_S = k_B \log (2S + 1)^N = Nk_B \log (2S + 1). \tag{29}$$

It is this spin entropy which is reduced by a magnetic field. The field separates the $2S + 1$ states in energy, and the lower levels gain in population.

The steps carried out in the cooling process are shown in Figs. 8 and 9. The field is applied at temperature T_1 with the specimen in good thermal contact with the surroundings, giving the isothermal path ab. The specimen

---

[8] Here σ_S denotes the entropy of the spin system.

442

is then insulated ($\Delta\sigma = 0$) and the field removed; the specimen follows the constant entropy path bc, ending up at temperature T_2. The thermal contact at T_1 is provided by helium gas, and the thermal contact is broken by removing the gas with a pump.

EXAMPLE. Consider a unit volume of a crystal containing N unpaired electrons of spin $\frac{1}{2}$ and magnetic moment μ. Let the heat capacity of the lattice be $C_{\text{lat}} = 3AT^3$, where A is a constant. The lattice entropy is

$$\sigma_{\text{lat}} = \int_o^T (C_{\text{lat}}/T)\, dT = AT^3. \tag{30}$$

The entropy of the spin system in a magnetic field H is found readily. The partition function per spin is

$$Z = e^{-\beta\delta} + e^{\beta\delta} \equiv 2 \cosh \beta\delta, \tag{31}$$

where $\beta \equiv 1/k_B T$ and $\delta \equiv \mu H$. The free energy of N spins of $S = \frac{1}{2}$ is

$$F_S = -Nk_B T \log Z = -Nk_B T \log (2 \cosh \beta\delta), \tag{32}$$

and the spin entropy σ_S is

$$\sigma_S = -(\partial F_S/\partial T)_H = Nk_B[\log (2 \cosh \beta\delta) - \beta\delta \tanh \beta\delta]. \tag{33}$$

This is plotted in Fig. 10 as a function of $\mu H/k_B T$.

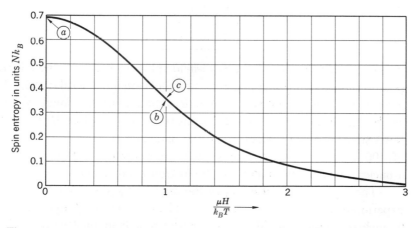

Figure 10   Entropy of a spin ½ system as a function of $\mu H/k_B T$. In a realistic experiment the specimen is initially at $1°$K and the internal random magnetic field H_Δ is of the order of 100 gauss. Then $\mu_B H_\Delta/k_B T_1 \approx 10^{-18}/10^{-16} \approx 10^{-2}$, and the specimen is at the point a in the figure. If we magnetize the specimen isothermally in a 10,000 gauss field, then $\mu_B H/k_B T_1 \approx 1$ and the specimen is brought to point b. (The total lattice entropy is assumed to be much smaller than the amount by which the entropy of the spin system has been lowered.) If now we remove the external magnetic field the entropy is constant, so that $\mu_B H_\Delta/k_B T$ must be ≈ 1, or $T_2 \approx 0.01°$K at point c.

The constant A in the expression (30) for the lattice entropy may be of the order of $10^{-6} N_a k_B$ for a representative solid, as we see from Chapter 6. Here N_a is the number of atoms, which may be 10 to 100 times larger than the number of spins in the paramagnet, according to the chemical composition and dilution. When we compare σ_{lat} at $1°K$ with σ_S, we see that at and below this temperature the lattice entropy is negligible in comparison with the spin entropy. This is usually the situation in practice, provided the initial temperature is not too high. If initially the lattice entropy is higher than the spin entropy, the cooling effect following demagnetization will be negligible.

In Fig. 10, $T_1 = 1°K$ and $H = 10$ kG; the specimen will be cooled to $0.01°K$. The ultimate temperature reached by adiabatic demagnetization is limited by the intrinsic or **zero-field splitting** of the spin energy levels—the splitting which occurs in the absence of external magnetic fields. The zero-field splitting may be caused by electrostatic interaction with the other ions in the crystal, by the interaction of the magnetic moments with each other, or by interactions of nuclear moments. In Fig. 10 the zero-field splitting of the spin levels is equivalent to an internal magnetic field H_Δ of 100 gauss. The zero-field splitting makes the entropy at a and at c in Fig. 8 less than for a smaller zero-field splitting; thus the final temperature is not as low as for a smaller splitting.

Nuclear Demagnetization

The result of the preceding discussion of cooling by adiabatic demagnetization of a paramagnetic salt is that T_2, the final temperature reached, is given as in Fig. 10 by $H/T_1 = H_\Delta/T_2$, or

$$\boxed{T_2 = T_1(H_\Delta/H),} \qquad (34)$$

where H_Δ corresponds to the zero-field splitting and T_1 is the starting temperature. Because nuclear magnetic moments are much weaker than electronic magnetic moments, nuclear magnetic interactions are much weaker than similar electronic interactions. If in this relation we replace H_Δ by a value 100 times smaller than is usual for a dilute paramagnetic salt (say 1 gauss instead of 100 gauss), we expect to reach a temperature 100 times lower with a nuclear paramagnet than with an electron paramagnet.

The initial temperature T_1 of the nuclear stage in a nuclear spin-cooling experiment must be lower than in an electron spin-cooling experiment. For a nuclear moment of 10^{-23} erg/gauss in a field of 10 kG at $T_1 = 1°K$ we have $\mu H/k_B T_1 \approx 10^{-3}$; with this low value the entropy (Fig. 10) in the magnetized state is imperceptibly less than in the unmagnetized state at the same temperature.

We do not want to use up the decrease in spin entropy to cool the lattice. We therefore want a larger entropy change on magnetization and a

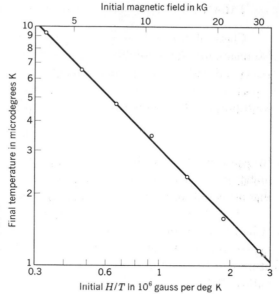

Figure 11 Nuclear demagnetizations of copper nuclei in the metal, starting from 0.012°K and various fields. [After M. V. Hobden and N. Kurti, Phil. Mag. 4, 1092 (1959).]

lower lattice heat capacity.[9] We can obtain these by starting at a higher field and lower temperature: if we start at $H = 50$ kC and $T_1 = 0.01°$K, the picture is more favorable. Now $\mu H/k_B T_1 \approx 0.5$, and the entropy decrease on magnetization is over 10 percent of the maximum spin entropy. This is sufficient to overwhelm the lattice and to allow us to use (34), from which we estimate a final temperature $T_2 \approx 10^{-7}°$K.

The first[10] nuclear cooling experiment was carried out on Cu nuclei in the metal, starting from a first stage at about 0.02°K as attained by electronic cooling. Results of Hobden and Kurti are shown in Fig. 11. The lowest temperature reached was $1.2 \times 10^{-6}°$K. The results fit a line of the form of (34): $T_2 = T_1(3.1/H)$ with H in gauss, so that $H_\Delta = 3.1$ gauss. The motivation for using nuclei in a metal rather than in an insulator is that conduction electrons help ensure rapid thermal contact of lattice and nuclei at the temperature of the first stage. The value of H_Δ in this experiment is the effective magnetic interaction field of the magnetic moments of the Cu nuclei: $\mu(\text{Cu}^{63}) = 2.22$ nuclear magnetons; $\mu(\text{Cu}^{65}) = 2.38$ nuclear magnetons.

---

[9] If the nuclei are in a metal, we must also be concerned with the heat capacity of the conduction electrons.

[10] N. Kurti, F. N. H. Robinson, F. E. Simon, and D. A. Spohr, Nature **178**, 450 (1956); R. E. Walstedt, E. L. Hahn, C. Froidevaux, and E. Geissler, Proc. Roy. Soc. (London) **A284**, 499 (1965); for reviews see N. Kurti, Cryogenics **1**, 2 (1960); Adv. in Cryogenic Engineering **8**, 1 (1963).

PARAMAGNETIC SUSCEPTIBILITY OF CONDUCTION ELECTRONS

Classical free electron theory gives an unsatisfactory account of the paramagnetic susceptibility of the conduction electrons. An electron has associated with it a magnetic moment of one Bohr magneton, μ_B. One might expect that the conduction electrons would make a Curie-type paramagnetic contribution (22) to the susceptibility of the metal:

$$\chi = N\mu_B{}^2/k_BT. \tag{35}$$

Instead it is observed that the susceptibility of most normal nonferromagnetic metals is *independent of temperature;* the magnitude is perhaps only 0.01 of that expected from (35) at room temperature.

Pauli[11] showed that the application of the Fermi-Dirac distribution (Chapter 7) would correct the theory as required. We first give a qualitative explanation of the situation. The result (21) tells us that the probability an atom will be lined up parallel to the field H exceeds the probability of the antiparallel orientation by roughly $\mu H/k_BT$. For N atoms, this gives a net magnetic moment $\sim N\mu^2 H/k_BT$, the standard result. Most conduction electrons in a metal, however, have zero probability of turning over when a field is applied, because the states with parallel spin are already occupied. Only the electrons within a range of the order of k_BT of the top of the Fermi distribution have a chance to turn over in the field; thus only the fraction T/T_F of the total number of electrons contribute to the susceptibility. Hence

$$\chi \approx (N\mu^2/k_BT)(T/T_F) = N\mu^2/k_BT_F,$$

which is independent of temperature and of the observed order of magnitude.

We now calculate the expression for the paramagnetic susceptibility of a free electron gas at $T \ll T_F$. We follow the method of calculation suggested by Fig. 12. The concentration of electrons with magnetic moments parallel to the magnetic field is

$$N_+ = \frac{1}{2} \int_{-\mu H}^{\epsilon_F} d\epsilon\, f(\epsilon)\, \mathfrak{D}(\epsilon + \mu H) \cong \frac{1}{2} \int_0^{\epsilon_F} d\epsilon\, f(\epsilon)\, \mathfrak{D}(\epsilon) + \frac{1}{2}\mu H\, \mathfrak{D}(\epsilon_F), \tag{36}$$

where $f(\epsilon)$ is the Fermi-Dirac distribution function and $\frac{1}{2}\mathfrak{D}(\epsilon + \mu H)$ is the density of states of one spin orientation, with allowance for the downward shift of energy by $-\mu H$. The approximation is written for $k_BT \ll \epsilon_F$. The

[11] W. Pauli, Z. Physik **41**, 81 (1927).

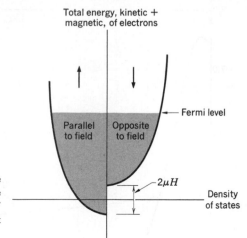

Total energy, kinetic +
magnetic, of electrons

Fermi level

Parallel to field | Opposite to field

$2\mu H$

Density of states

Figure 12 Pauli paramagnetism at $0°$K; the levels in the shaded regions are occupied. The numbers of electrons in the "up" and "down" band will adjust to make the energies equal at the Fermi level.

concentration of electrons with magnetic moments antiparallel to H is

$$N_- = \frac{1}{2} \int_{\mu H}^{\cdot \epsilon_F} d\epsilon \, f(\epsilon) \, \mathfrak{D}(\epsilon - \mu H) = \frac{1}{2} \int_0^{\epsilon_F} d\epsilon \, f(\epsilon) \, \mathfrak{D}(\epsilon) - \frac{1}{2} \mu H \, \mathfrak{D}(\epsilon_F).$$

$$(37)$$

The magnetization is given by

$$M = \mu(N_+ - N_-), \qquad (38)$$

so that, with (7.47) for $\mathfrak{D}(\epsilon_F)$,

$$M \simeq \mu^2 \, \mathfrak{D}(\epsilon_F) H; \qquad \chi = \mu^2 \, \mathfrak{D}(\epsilon_F) = 3N\mu^2/2k_B T_F. \qquad (39)$$

This result gives the **Pauli spin susceptibility** of the conduction electrons.

In deriving the paramagnetic susceptibility we have supposed that the spatial motion of the electrons is not affected by the magnetic field. We saw in Chapter 8 and 9 that the wavefunctions are modified by the magnetic field; Landau[12] has shown that for free electrons this causes a diamagnetic moment equal to $-\frac{1}{3}$ of the paramagnetic moment. Thus the total susceptibility χ_{tot} of a free electron gas is

$$\chi_{tot} = N\mu_B^2/k_B T_F. \qquad (40)$$

Before comparing (40) with the observed susceptibility we must take account of the diamagnetism of the ionic cores, of band effects, and of electron-electron

[12] L. Landau, Z. Physik **64**, 629 (1930).

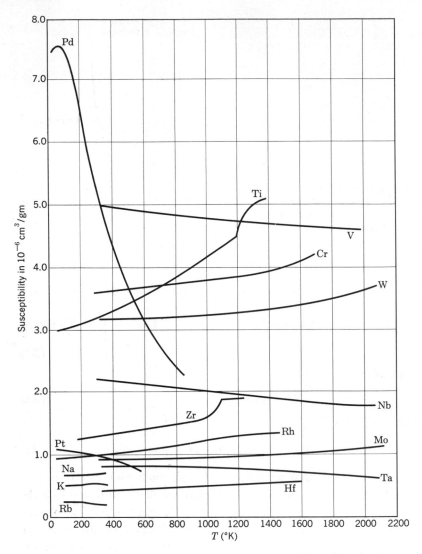

Figure 13 Temperature dependence of the magnetic susceptibility of metals. (Courtesy of C. J. Kriessman.)

interactions. Detailed calculations and comparison with experiment for the alkali metals are reported by Silverstein.[13]

The magnetic susceptibility is considerably higher for most transition metals (with unfilled inner electron shells) than for the alkali metals (Fig. 13). The high values suggest that the density of electron states in (39) is unusually high for transition metals in agreement with the electronic heat capacity. We saw in Chapter 9 how this arises on band theory.

Problems

1. *Diamagnetic susceptibility of atomic hydrogen.* The wavefunction of the hydrogen atom in its ground state (1s) is

$$\psi = (\pi a_0^3)^{-1/2} e^{-r/a_0},$$

where $a_0 = \hbar^2/me^2 = 0.529 \times 10^{-8}$ cm. The charge density is $\rho(x, y, z) = -e|\psi|^2$, according to the statistical interpretation of the wave function. Show that for this state $\langle r^2 \rangle = 3a_0^2$, and calculate the molar diamagnetic susceptibility of atomic hydrogen (-2.36×10^{-6} cm³/mole).

2. *Langevin paramagnetism.* Show that on the Langevin theory the first two terms in a series expansion of the differential susceptibility are

$$\chi = dM/dH = (N\mu^2/3k_BT)[1 - \tfrac{1}{5}(\mu H/k_BT)^2 + \cdots].$$

3. *Hund rules.* Apply the Hund rules to find the ground state (the basic level in the notation of Table 1) of (a) Eu^{++}, in the configuration $4f^7\, 5s^2p^6$; (b) Yb^{3+}; (c) Tb^{3+}. The results for (b) and (c) are in Table 1, but you should give the separate steps in applying the rules.

4. *Triplet excited states.* Some organic molecules have a triplet ($S = 1$) excited state at an energy $k_B\Delta$ above a singlet ($S = 0$) ground state. (a) Find an expression for the magnetic moment $\langle \mu \rangle$ in a field H. (b) Show that the susceptibility for $T \gg \Delta$ is approximately independent of Δ.

[13] S. D. Silverstein, Phys. Rev. **130**, 1703 (1963).

5. *Heat capacity from internal degrees of freedom.* (a) Consider a two-level system with an energy splitting $k_B\Delta$ between upper and lower states; the splitting may arise from a magnetic field or in other ways. Show that the heat capacity per system is

$$C = \left(\frac{\partial E}{\partial T}\right)_\Delta = k_B \frac{(\Delta/T)^2 \, e^{\Delta/T}}{(1 + e^{\Delta/T})^2}.$$

The function is plotted in Fig. 14. Peaks of this type in the heat capacity are often known as Schottky anomalies. The maximum heat capacity is quite high, but for $T \ll \Delta$ and for $T \gg \Delta$ the heat capacity is low. (b) Show that for $T \gg \Delta$ we

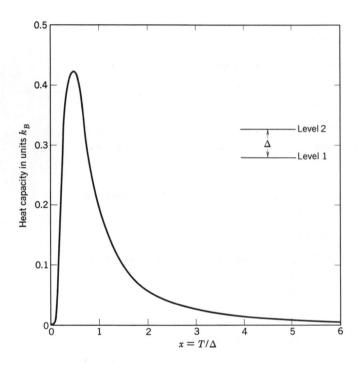

Figure 14 Heat capacity of a two-level system as a function of T/Δ, where Δ is the level splitting.

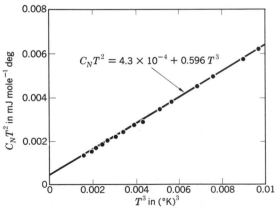

Figure 15 The normal-state heat capacity of gallium at $T < 0.21°$K. The nuclear quadrupole ($C \propto T^{-2}$) and conduction electron ($C \propto T$) contributions dominate the heat capacity at very low temperatures. [After N. E. Phillips, Phys. Rev. **134**, 385 (1964).]

have $C \cong k_B(\Delta/2T)^2 + \cdots$. The hyperfine interaction between nuclear and electronic magnetic moments in paramagnetic salts (and in systems having electron spin order) causes splittings with $\Delta \simeq 0.001$ to $0.1°$K. These splittings are often detected experimentally by the presence of a term in $1/T^2$ in the heat capacity in the region $T \gg \Delta$. Nuclear electric quadrupole interactions (see Chapter 16) with crystal fields also cause splittings, as in Fig. 15.

6. *Spin entropy and lattice entropy.* Making *rough* calculations, compare the entropy (for $H = 0$) at $2°$K of 1 cm³ of the salt iron ammonium alum, $FeNH_4(SO_4)_2 \cdot 12H_2O$, with that of 1 cm³ of sodium at the same temperature. (The result shows that one may use the salt to cool other substances). At $2°$K, $T/\Delta > 10$ for iron ammonium alum, where $k_B\Delta$ is the zero field splitting. Neglect nuclear spin effects.

7. *Paraelectric cooling.* It is known that OH^- ions substitute for Cl^- ions in KCl crystals. Suppose that the electric dipole moment of the OH^- ion may be oriented freely. The electric dipole moment is $\sim 4 \times 10^{-18}$ esu. (a) What is the overall splitting in ergs for $E = 60$ kv/cm parallel to [100]? (b) For what temperature is k_BT equal to this overall splitting? *Note:* Paraelectric cooling was first observed for this system by W. Känzig, H. R. Hart, Jr., and S. Roberts, Phys. Rev. Letters **13**, 543 (1904). I. Sheperd and G. Feher, Phys. Rev. Letters **13**, 194 (1965) cooled a crystal with 2.9×10^{18} OH^- ions/cm³ from $1.27°$K to about $0.4°$K by adiabatic depolarization with an initial electric field of 75 kv/cm.

References

L. F. Bates, *Modern magnetism*, Cambridge University Press, 4th ed., 1961.

P. W. Selwood, *Magnetochemistry*, Interscience, 2nd ed., 1956.

J. H. Van Vleck, *The theory of electric and magnetic susceptibilities*, Oxford, 1932.

ADIABATIC DEMAGNETIZATION

H. B. G. Casimir, *Magnetism and very low temperatures*, Cambridge University Press, 1940.

C. G. B. Garrett, *Magnetic cooling*, Harvard, 1954.

N. Kurti, Nuovo Cimento (Supplemento) **6**, 1101–1139 (1957).

D. de Klerk, "Adiabatic demagnetization," *Encyclo. of physics* **15**, 38–209 (1956). This reference contains detailed entropy data for many paramagnetic salts.

W. A. Little, "Magnetic cooling," *Prog. in cryogenics* **4**, 101 (1964).

15

Ferromagnetism
and
Antiferromagnetism

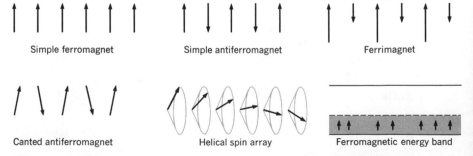

Figure 1 Possible ordered arrangements of electron spins. Note that the particular helix shown has a magnetic moment along the axis.

FERROMAGNETIC ORDER

A ferromagnet has a spontaneous magnetic moment—a magnetic moment even in zero applied magnetic field. A spontaneous moment suggests that electron spins and magnetic moments are arranged in a regular manner. The order need not be simple: all of the spin arrangements sketched in Fig. 1 except the simple antiferromagnet (and except the helix if the spin directions lie in a plane) have a spontaneous magnetic moment, usually called the saturation moment.

Curie Point and the Exchange Integral

Consider a paramagnet with a concentration of N ions of spin S. Given an internal interaction tending to line up the magnetic moments parallel to each other, we shall have a ferromagnet. Let us postulate such an interaction and call it the exchange field or molecular field.[1] The orienting effect of the exchange field is opposed by thermal agitation, and at elevated temperatures the spin order is destroyed.

We treat the exchange field as equivalent to a magnetic field $\mathbf{H}_E$. The magnitude of the exchange field may be as high as 10^7 gauss. We assume further that $\mathbf{H}_E$ is proportional to the magnetization $\mathbf{M}$. The magnetization $\mathbf{M}(\mathbf{H}, T)$ is defined as the magnetic moment per unit volume; unless otherwise specified it is understood to be the value in thermal equilibrium in the field $\mathbf{H}$ at the temperature T. If domains (regions magnetized in different directions) are present, the magnetization refers to the value within a domain. Thus we assume

$$\mathbf{H}_E = \lambda \mathbf{M}, \tag{1}$$

where λ is a constant, independent of temperature. According to (1) each spin sees the average magnetization of all the other spins. Actually, it may see only near neighbors, but our oversimplification of the situation is good for a first look at the problem.

The **Curie temperature** T_c is the temperature above which the spontaneous magnetization vanishes; it separates the disordered paramagnetic phase at $T > T_c$ from the ordered ferromagnetic phase at $T < T_c$. We can find T_c in terms of λ. Consider the paramagnetic phase: an applied field H will cause a finite magnetization and this in turn will cause a finite exchange field H_E. If χ is the susceptibility,

$$M = \chi(H + H_E). \tag{2}$$

---

[1] Also called the Weiss field, after Pierre Weiss who was the first to imagine such a field.

We saw in Chapter 14 that we can write the magnetization as a constant χ times a field only if the fractional alignment is small: this is where the assumption enters that the specimen is in the paramagnetic phase. The susceptibility χ is given by the Curie law $\chi = C/T$, where C is the Curie constant. Using (1) and (2), $MT = C(H + \lambda M)$ and

$$\chi = M/H = C/(T - C\lambda). \tag{3}$$

The susceptibility has a singularity at $T = C\lambda$. At this temperature (and below) there exists a spontaneous magnetization, for if χ is infinite we can have a finite M for zero H. From (3) we have the **Curie-Weiss law**

$$\chi = \frac{C}{T - T_c}; \qquad T_c = C\lambda. \tag{4}$$

This expression describes fairly well the observed susceptibility variation in the paramagnetic region above the Curie point. Detailed calculations[2] predict $\chi \propto (T - T_c)^{-4/3}$ for $T_c < T \lesssim 1.5T_c$; experiments also favor the exponent $-\frac{4}{3}$ at temperatures close to T_c. Results for nickel are shown in Fig. 2. From (4) and the definition (14.25) of the Curie constant C we may determine the value of the molecular field constant λ:

$$\lambda = T_c/C = 3k_B T_c/Ng^2 S(S + 1)\mu_B^2. \tag{5}$$

For iron $T_c \approx 1000°\text{K}$, $g \approx 2$, and[3] $S \approx 1$; from (5) we have $\lambda \approx 5000$. With $M_s \approx 1700$ we have $H_E \approx \lambda M \approx (5000)(1700) \approx 10^7$ G. The exchange field in iron is very much stronger than the real magnetic field due to the other magnetic ions in the crystal: a magnetic ion produces a field $\approx \mu_B/a^3$ or about 10^3 G at a neighboring lattice point.

The exchange field gives an approximate representation of the quantum-mechanical exchange interaction. On certain assumptions it can be shown[4] that the energy of interaction of atoms i, j bearing spins $\mathbf{S}_i$, $\mathbf{S}_j$ contains a term

$$U = -2J\mathbf{S}_i \cdot \mathbf{S}_j, \tag{6}$$

where J is the exchange integral and is related to the overlap of the charge distributions of the atoms i, j. Equation (6) is called the **Heisenberg model.**

[2] Experimentally the susceptibility for $T \gg T_c$ is given quite accurately by $C/(T - \theta)$, where θ is appreciably greater than the actual transition temperature T_c. See the review by C. Domb in *Magnetism*, Vol. 2A, G. T. Rado and H. Suhl, eds., Academic Press, 1965. For experimental references see R. W. Kedzie and D. H. Lyons, Phys. Rev. Letters **15**, 632 (1965).

[3] We assume $S = 1$ for iron; Table 1 shows that the moment per atom in the metal is close to $2\mu_B$.

[4] See most texts on quantum theory; also J. H. Van Vleck, Revs. Modern Phys. **17**, 27 (1945). We do not have space to give a useful discussion of exchange interactions in crystals. The origin of exchange in insulators is reviewed by P. W. Anderson in Rado and Suhl, Vol. I, 25 (1963); in metals by C. Herring in Vol. IV, to appear.

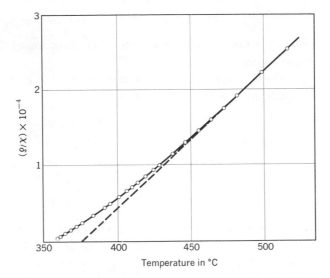

Figure 2 Reciprocal of the susceptibility per gram of nickel in the neighborhood of the Curie temperature ($358°C$). The density is ρ. The dashed line is a linear extrapolation from high temperatures. After P. Weiss and R. Forrer. An analysis of the curve near T_c has been given by J. S. Kouvel and M. E. Fisher, Phys. Rev. **136**, A1626 (1964).

The exchange energy has no classical analog, but the energy is of electrostatic origin. It expresses the difference in Coulomb interaction energy of the systems when the electron spins are parallel or antiparallel, as in Fig. 3.13. Because of the Pauli exclusion principle we cannot change the relative direction of two spins without changing[5] the spatial distribution of charge. The resulting changes in the Coulomb energy of the system may be written in the form[6] (6), as if there were a direct coupling between the directions of the spins S_i, S_j.

We establish an approximate connection between the exchange integral J in (6) and the exchange constant λ in (1). We suppose that the atom under consideration has z nearest neighbors, each connected with the central atom by the interaction J. For more distant neighbors we take J as zero. The energy required to reverse the spin under consideration in the presence of all other spins may be written, neglecting components of S perpendicular to the average magnetization, as

[5] If two spins are parallel, the spatial part of the wavefunction must be antisymmetric under the exchange of the two electrons. If the spins are antiparallel, the spatial part of the wavefunction is symmetric.

[6] Equation (6) is an equation in the spin operators S_i, S_j; for many purposes in ferromagnetism it is a good approximation to treat the spins as classical angular momentum vectors.

$$U = 4Jz\overline{S}^2 = 2\mu H_E = 2\mu(\lambda M_s) = 2\mu(\lambda\mu/\Omega) \tag{7}$$

where $\overline{S}$ is the average value of S in the direction of the magnetization and Ω is the volume per atom.

The average magnetic moment of a spin is $\mu = g\overline{S}\mu_B$, and the saturation magnetization is $M_s = \mu/\Omega$. Thus from (7)

$$\lambda = 2Jz\Omega/g^2\mu_B{}^2, \tag{8}$$

where z is the number of nearest neighbors.

Using (5) and $\Omega = 1/N$, we have the molecular field theory result:

$$J = \frac{3k_B T_c}{2zS(S + 1)}. \tag{9}$$

Better approximations to the quantum-statistical problem give somewhat different results for $zJ/k_B T_c$. For the *sc*, *bcc*, and *fcc* structures with $S = \frac{1}{2}$, Rushbrooke and Wood[7] give $k_B T_c/zJ = 0.28; 0.325;$ and 0.346, respectively, as compared with 0.500 from (9) for all three structures. If iron is represented by the Heisenberg model (6) with $S = 1$, then the observed Curie temperature corresponds to $J = 1.19 \times 10^{-2}$ ev.

Temperature Dependence of the Saturation Magnetization

We can also use the molecular field approximation below the Curie temperature to find the magnetization as a function of temperature. We proceed as before, but instead of the Curie law we use the complete Brillouin expression (14.23) for the magnetization. For spin $\frac{1}{2}$ this is[8] $M = N\mu \tanh (\mu H/k_B T)$, according to (14.20). If we omit the applied magnetic field and replace H by the molecular field $H_E = \lambda M$, then

$$M = N\mu \tanh (\mu\lambda M/k_B T). \tag{10}$$

We shall see that solutions of this equation with nonzero M exist in the temperature range between 0 and T_c.

To solve (10) we write it in parametric form as

$$M = N\mu \tanh \xi; \qquad \mu\lambda M/k_B T = \xi, \tag{11}$$

and plot M versus ξ for both equations. The intercept of the two curves gives the value of M at the temperature of interest, as in Fig. 3. As $M \to 0$, we have $M \to N\mu(\mu\lambda M/k_B T_c)$, or $T_c = \lambda(N\mu^2/k_B)$, in agreement with (5) for $S = \frac{1}{2}$.

The curves of M versus T obtained in this way reproduce roughly the features of the experimental results, as shown in Fig. 4 for nickel. As T

---

[7] G. S. Rushbrooke and P. J. Wood, Molecular Physics **1**, 257 (1958).

[8] We often write M_s for the spontaneous or saturation magnetization, but where no ambiguity is possible we shall use M. Compare Fig. 37.

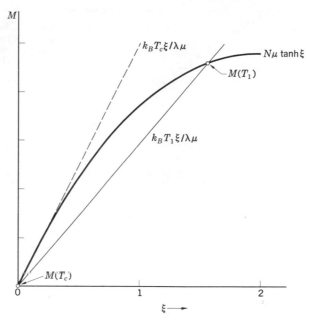

Figure 3 Solution of the equations (11) for the spontaneous magnetization. For $T_1 < T_c$ the intercept of the two curves gives $M(T_1)$. The slope of the straight line $M = k_B T \xi / \lambda \mu$ increases as T increases; for $T > T_c$ the intercept is at $M = 0$. The value of T_c determined in this way is consistent with Eq. (4). As $T \rightarrow 0$ the intercept moves up to $M(0) = N\mu$, so that all magnetic moments are lined up at absolute zero.

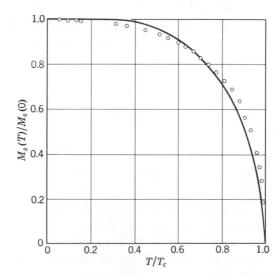

Figure 4 Saturation magnetization of nickel as a function of temperature, together with the theoretical curve for $S = \frac{1}{2}$ on the molecular field theory. Experimental values by P. Weiss and R. Forrer, Ann. phys. **5**, 153 (1926).

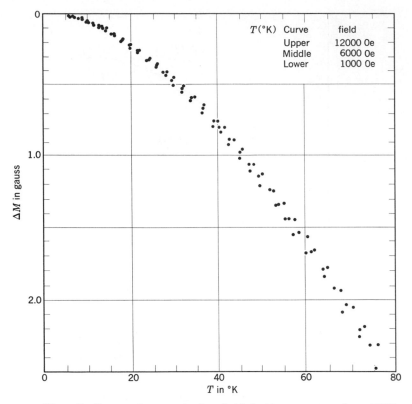

Figure 5 Decrease in magnetization of nickel with temperature above 4.2°K, after Argyle, Charap, and Pugh. In the plot $\Delta M \equiv 0$ at 4.2°K.

increases the magnetization decreases smoothly to zero at $T = T_c$. This behavior (or the absence of a latent heat of transition) classifies the usual ferromagnetic/paramagnetic transition as second-order (see Chapter 13).

The molecular field theory does not give a good description of the variation of M at low temperatures. For $T \ll T_c$ the argument of tanh in (11) is large, and

$$\tanh \xi \cong 1 - 2e^{-2\xi} \dots \tag{12}$$

To lowest order the deviation $\Delta M \equiv M(0) - M(T)$ is

$$\Delta M \cong 2N\mu \exp(-2\lambda N\mu^2/k_B T). \tag{13}$$

The argument of the exponential is equal to $-2T_c/T$, from (5) with $g = 2$ and $S = \frac{1}{2}$. For $T = 0.1T_c$ we have $\Delta M/N\mu \cong 2 \exp(-20) \cong 4 \times 10^{-9}$.

The experimental results show a much more rapid dependence of ΔM on temperature at low temperatures than predicted by (13). At $T = 0.1T_c$ we have $\Delta M/M \cong 2 \times 10^{-3}$ from the data of Fig. 5. The leading term in ΔM is observed from experiment to have the form

$$\Delta M/M(0) = C_{3/2}T^{3/2}, \tag{14}$$

where[9] the constant $C_{3/2}$ has the experimental value $(7.5 \pm 0.2) \times 10^{-6}$ $deg^{-3/2}$ for Ni and $(3.4 \pm 0.2) \times 10^{-6}$ $deg^{-3/2}$ for Fe. The result (14) finds a natural explanation in terms of spin wave theory, as discussed below.

Saturation Magnetization at Absolute Zero

Table 1 gives representative values of the saturation magnetization M_s, the effective magneton number n_B, and the ferromagnetic Curie temperature.

Table 1   Number n_B of Bohr magnetons per magnetic atom, and data on saturation magnetization and Curie points

(Data selected with the assistance of R. M. Bozorth. General references: A.I.P. Handbook, 1963, Sec. 5g; Landolt-Bornstein **2**, pt. 9, 6th ed., 1962)

Substance	Saturation magnetization M_s, in gauss		$n_B(0°K)$, per formula unit	Ferromagnetic Curie temperature, in °K
	Room temperature	0°K		
Fe	1707	1740	2.22	1043
Co	1400	1446	1.72	1400
Ni	485	510	0.606	631
Gd	–	2010	7.10	292
Dy	–	2920	10.0	85
Cu_2MnAl	500	(550)	(4.0)	710
MnAs	670	870	3.4	318
MnBi	620	680	3.52	630
Mn_4N	183	–	1.0	743
MnSb	710	–	3.5	587
MnB	152	163	1.92	578
CrTe	247	–	2.5	339
$CrBr_3$	–	–	–	37
CrO_2	515	–	2.03	392
$MnOFe_2O_3$	410	–	5.0	573
$FeOFe_2O_3$	480	–	4.1	858
$CoOFe_2O_3$	400	–	3.7	793
$NiOFe_2O_3$	270	–	2.4	858
$CuOFe_2O_3$	135	–	1.3	728
$MgOFe_2O_3$	110	–	1.1	713
UH_3	–	230	0.90	180
EuO	–	1920	6.8	69
$GdMn_2$	–	215	2.8	303
$Gd_3Fe_5O_{12}$	0	605	16.0	564
$Y_3Fe_5O_{12}$ (YIG)	130	200	5.0	560

[9] B. E. Argyle, S. Charap, and E. W. Pugh, Phys. Rev. **132**, 2051 (1963).

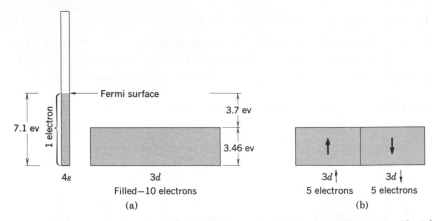

Figure 6a   Schematic relationship of 4s and 3d bands in metallic copper. The 3d band holds ten electrons per atom and is filled in copper. The 4s band can hold two electrons per atom; it is shown half-filled, as copper has one valence electron outside the filled 3d shell. The energies shown are from calculations by Howarth; it is coincidental that the bottoms of both bands fall nearly at the same energy.

Figure 6b   The filled 3d band of copper shown as two separate sub-bands of opposite electron spin orientation, each band holding five electrons. With both sub-bands filled as shown, the net spin (and hence the net magnetization) of the d band is zero.

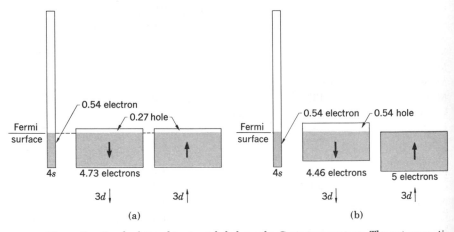

Figure 7a   Band relationships in nickel above the Curie temperature. The net magnetic moment is zero, as there are equal numbers of holes in both 3d↓ and 3d↑ bands.

Figure 7b   Schematic relationship of bands in nickel at absolute zero. The energies of the 3d↑ and 3d↓ sub-bands are separated by an exchange interaction. The 3d↑ band is filled; the 3d↓ band contains 4.46 electrons and 0.54 hole. The 4s band is usually thought to contain approximately equal numbers of electrons in both spin directions, and so we have not troubled to divide it into sub-bands. The net magnetic moment of 0.54 μ_B per atom arises from the excess population of the 3d↑ band over the 3d↓ band. It is often convenient to speak of the magnetization as arising from the 0.54 hole in the 3d↓ band.

The effective magneton number of a ferromagnet is defined by $M_s(0) = n_B N \mu_B$, where N is the number of formula units of the element or compound per unit volume. Do not confuse n_B with the paramagnetic effective magneton number p defined by (14.26).

Observed values of n_B are often nonintegral. There are many possible causes. One is the spin-orbit interaction which adds or subtracts some orbital magnetic moment. Another cause in ferromagnetic metals is the conduction electron magnetization induced locally about a paramagnetic ion core. A third cause is suggested by the drawing in Fig. 1 of the spin arrangement in a ferrimagnet: if there is one atom of spin projection $-S$ for every two atoms $+S$, the average spin is $\frac{1}{3}S$.

A band model[10] may be applicable to the explanation of $n_B = 0.60$ for nickel, for example. The approach is indicated in Figs. 6 and 7. The relationship of $4s$ and $3d$ bands is shown in Fig. 6 for copper, which is not ferromagnetic. If we remove one electron from copper, we obtain nickel which has the possibility of a vacant state in the $3d$ band. In the band structure of nickel shown in Fig. 7a for $T > T_c$ we have taken $2 \times 0.27 = 0.54$ of an electron away from the $3d$ band and 0.46 away from the $4s$ band, as compared with copper. The band structure of nickel at absolute zero is shown in Fig. 7b. Nickel is ferromagnetic and at absolute zero $n_B = 0.60$ Bohr magnetons per atom. After allowance[11] for the magnetic moment contribution of orbital electronic motion, nickel has an excess of 0.54 electron per atom having spin preferentially oriented in one direction.

Are there in fact any simple ferromagnetic insulators, with all ionic spins parallel in the ground state? The few simple ferromagnets known at present include[12] $CrBr_3$, EuO, and EuS.

---

[10] E. C. Stoner, Repts. Prog. Phys. **11**, 43 (1948); Proc. Roy. Soc. (London) **A165**, 372 (1938); C. Herring and C. Kittel, Phys. Rev. **81**, 869 (1951); E. C. Mattis, *Theory of magnetism*, Harper and Row, 1965, Chap. 7; C. Herring in Rado and Suhl, Vol. IV (to appear).

[11] P. Argyres and C. Kittel, Acta Met. **1**, 241 (1953). The number of effective ferromagnetic electrons n_e is just n_B corrected for the orbital contribution. We have $n_e = 2n_B/g$, where g is the spectroscopic splitting factor defined in Chapters 14 and 16. In metallic Ni, $g = 2.20$.

[12] A review of the properties of ferromagnetic europium compounds is given by T. R. McGuire and M. W. Shafer, J. Appl. Phys. **35**, 984 (1964); numerous references to work on $CrBr_3$ are given by H. L. Davis and A. Narath, Phys. Rev. **134**, A433 (1964).

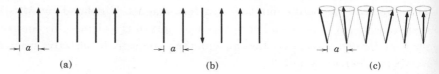

(a) (b) (c)

Figure 8 (a) Classical picture of the ground state of a simple ferromagnet; all spins are parallel. (b) A possible excitation; one spin is reversed. (c) The low-lying elementary excitations are spin waves. The ends of the spin vectors precess on the surfaces of cones, with successive spins advanced in phase by a constant angle.

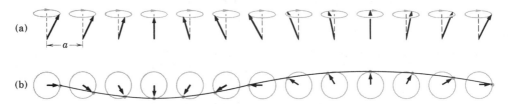

(a)

(b)

Figure 9 A spin wave on a line of spins. (a) The spins viewed in perspective. (b) Spins viewed from above, showing one wavelength. The wave is drawn through the ends of the spin vectors.

Spin Waves

The ground state of a simple ferromagnet has all spins parallel, as in Fig. 8a. Consider N spins each of $S = \frac{1}{2}$ on a line or a ring, with nearest neighbor spins coupled by the Heisenberg interaction (6):

$$U = -2J \sum_{p=1}^{n} \mathbf{S}_p \cdot \mathbf{S}_{p+1}; \tag{15}$$

here J is the exchange integral and $\hbar\mathbf{S}_p$ is the angular momentum of the spin at site p. If we treat the spins $\mathbf{S}_p$ as classical vectors, then in the ground state $\mathbf{S}_p \cdot \mathbf{S}_{p+1} = S^2$ and the exchange energy of the system is $U_0 = -2NJS^2$. What is the energy of the first excited state? Consider an excited state with one particular spin reversed, as in Fig. 8b. We see from (15) that this increases the energy by $8JS^2$, so that $U_1 = U_0 + 8JS^2$.

We can form an excitation of much lower energy if we let all the spins share the reversal, as in Fig. 8c. The elementary excitations of a spin system have a wavelike form and are called **spin waves** or, when quantized, **magnons**. These are analogous to lattice vibrations or phonons.

We now give a classical derivation of the magnon dispersion relation for the problem described by the interaction (15), which we rewrite as[13]

$$U = -\frac{1}{2} \sum_p \boldsymbol{\mu}_p \cdot \mathbf{H}_p; \tag{16}$$

---

[13] A factor $\frac{1}{2}$ appears to avoid double-counting; otherwise each moment would be counted once as a source of the field and once as a moment in the field.

as in (14.15) the magnetic moment at site p is given by $\mu_p \equiv -g\mu_B S_p$, and the effective magnetic field acting on this moment is

$$\mathbf{H}_p \equiv (-2J/g\mu_B)(\mathbf{S}_{p-1} + \mathbf{S}_{p+1}), \tag{17}$$

by comparison of (16) with (15).

From elementary mechanics the rate of change of the angular momentum $\hbar\mathbf{S}_p$ is equal to the torque $\mu_p \times \mathbf{H}_p$ which acts on the spin:

$$\hbar\frac{d\mathbf{S}_p}{dt} = \mu_p \times \mathbf{H}_p, \tag{18}$$

or

$$\frac{d\mathbf{S}_p}{dt} = (-g\mu_B/\hbar)\mathbf{S}_p \times \mathbf{H}_p = (2J/\hbar)(\mathbf{S}_p \times \mathbf{S}_{p-1} + \mathbf{S}_p \times \mathbf{S}_{p+1}). \tag{19}$$

In Cartesian components

$$dS_p{}^x/dt = (2J/\hbar)[S_p{}^y(S_{p-1}^z + S_{p+1}^z) - S_p{}^z(S_{p-1}^y + S_{p+1}^y)], \tag{20}$$

and similarly for $dS_p{}^y/dt$ and $dS_p{}^z/dt$. These equations involve products of spin components and are nonlinear.

If the amplitude of the excitation is small (if $S_p{}^x$, $S_p{}^y \ll S$), we may obtain an approximate set of linear equations by taking all $S_p{}^z = S$, and by neglecting terms in the product of S^x and S^y which appear in the equation for dS^z/dt. The linearized equations are

$$dS_p{}^x/dt = (2JS/\hbar)(2S_p{}^y - S_{p-1}^y - S_{p+1}^y); \tag{21a}$$

$$dS_p{}^y/dt = -(2JS/\hbar)(2S_p{}^x - S_{p-1}^x - S_{p+1}^x); \tag{21b}$$

$$dS_p{}^z/dt = 0. \tag{21c}$$

By analogy with the phonon problems in Chapter 5 we look for traveling wave solutions of (21) of the form

$$S_p{}^x = ue^{i(pka-\omega t)}; \qquad S_p{}^y = ve^{i(pka-\omega t)}, \tag{22}$$

where u, v are constants, p is an integer, and a is the lattice constant. On substitution into (21ab) we have

$$-i\omega u = (2JS/\hbar)(2 - e^{-ika} - e^{ika})v = (4JS/\hbar)(1 - \cos ka)v; \tag{23a}$$

$$-i\omega v = -(2JS/\hbar)(2 - e^{-ika} - e^{ika})u = -(4JS/\hbar)(1 - \cos ka)u. \tag{23b}$$

These equations have a solution for u and v if the determinant of the coefficients is equal to zero:

$$\begin{vmatrix} i\omega & (4JS/\hbar)(1 - \cos ka) \\ -(4JS/\hbar)(1 - \cos ka) & i\omega \end{vmatrix} = 0, \tag{24}$$

whence

$$\hbar\omega = 4JS(1 - \cos ka). \tag{25}$$

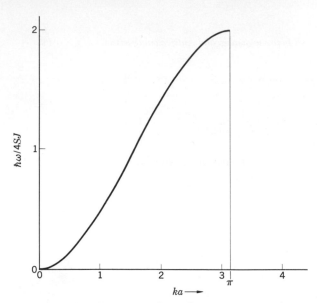

Figure 10 Dispersion relation for spin waves in a ferromagnet in one dimension with nearest-neighbor interactions.

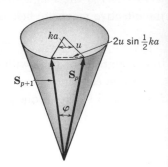

Figure 11 Construction relating the angle φ between two successive spin vectors to the spin wave amplitude u and the phase angle ka. The length of the dashed line is $2u \sin \frac{1}{2}ka$; if the length of a spin is S, then

$$S \sin \tfrac{1}{2}\varphi = u \sin \tfrac{1}{2}ka.$$

This result is plotted in Fig. 10. With this solution we find from (23) that $v = -iu$, corresponding to circular precession[14] of each spin about the z axis.

Equation (25) is the dispersion relation $\omega(k)$ for spin waves in one dimension with nearest-neighbor interactions.[15] At long wavelengths $ka \ll 1$, so that $(1 - \cos ka) \cong \frac{1}{2}(ka)^2$. In this limit (25) becomes

$$\hbar\omega \cong (2JSa^2)k^2. \tag{26}$$

Notice that the frequency is proportional to k^2, whereas the frequency of a phonon in the same limit is proportional to k.

The dispersion relation for a ferromagnetic cubic lattice (*sc*, *bcc*, or *fcc*) with nearest-neighbor interactions may be shown to be (see Problem 1)

$$\hbar\omega = 2JS[z - \sum_{\delta} \cos(\mathbf{k} \cdot \boldsymbol{\delta})], \tag{27}$$

where the summation is over the z vectors denoted by $\boldsymbol{\delta}$ which join the central atom to its nearest neighbors.

The leading terms in the expansion of (27) for $ka \ll 1$ is

$$\hbar\omega = (2JSa^2)k^2 \tag{28}$$

for all three cubic lattices, where a is the lattice constant.[16]

---

[14] We see this on taking real parts of (22), with v set equal to $-iu$. Then

$$S_p{}^x = u \cos(pka - \omega t); \quad S_p{}^y = u \sin(pka - \omega t).$$

[15] Precisely the same result is obtained from the quantum-mechanical solution; see *QTS*, Chap. 4.

[16] The coefficient of k^2 in (28) often may be determined accurately by spin wave resonance in thin films; see, for example, R. Weber and P. E. Tannenwald, Phys. Rev. **140**, A498 (1965). The principle of the method is treated by C. Kittel, Phys. Rev. **110**, 1295 (1958).

Quantization of Spin Waves

The values of the total spin quantum number of a system of N spins S are NS, $NS - 1$, $NS - 2, \ldots$, according to the quantum mechanics of angular momenta. In the ferromagnetic ground state the total spin quantum number has the value NS: all spins are parallel in the ground state. The excitation of a spin wave lowers the total spin because the spins are no longer parallel. We look for the relation between the amplitude of the spin wave and the reduction in the z component of the total spin quantum number.

Consider the spin wave (22) with $v = -iu$, as we found earlier:

$$S_p{}^x = ue^{i(pka-\omega t)}; \qquad S_p{}^y = -iue^{i(pka-\omega t)}. \qquad (29)$$

The spin component perpendicular to the z direction is u, independent of the site position p and of the time. The z component of a spin is

$$S_z = (S^2 - u^2)^{1/2} \cong S - u^2/2S, \qquad (30)$$

for small amplitudes $u/S \ll 1$. Quantum theory allows only integral values for $S - S_z$.

If N is the total number of spins and $NS - n_k$ is the total spin quantum number when a spin wave k is excited, then by (30)

$$n_k \cong Nu_k{}^2/2S, \qquad (31)$$

where n_k is an integer. Equation (31) is the semiclassical quantization condition on u_k. We call $n_\mathbf{k}$ the number of **magnons** of wavevector $\mathbf{k}$ which are excited. Each magnon lowers the z component of the total spin by one. Quantum theory allows only integral values for $S - S_z$.

Does the energy $\epsilon_\mathbf{k}$ satisfy the same quantum condition

$$\epsilon_\mathbf{k} = n_\mathbf{k}\hbar\omega_\mathbf{k}, \qquad (32)$$

as for photons and phonons? The exchange energy (15) depends on the cosine of the angle between the spins at sites p and $p + 1$. The *phase difference* at the same time t between successive spins is ka radians, according to (29). The tips of the two spin vectors in Fig. 11 are separated by a distance $2u \sin \frac{1}{2}ka$, so that the angle φ between the spin vectors is given by

$$\sin \tfrac{1}{2}\varphi = (u/S) \sin \tfrac{1}{2}ka. \qquad (33)$$

For $u/S \ll 1$ the cosine of φ is

$$\cos \varphi = 1 - 2(u/S)^2 \sin^2 \tfrac{1}{2}ka. \qquad (34)$$

Thus the energy (15) is

$$U \cong -2JNS^2 + 4Ju^2 \sin^2 \tfrac{1}{2}ka = -2JNS^2 + 2JNu^2(1 - \cos ka). \quad (35)$$

The excitation energy of a spin wave of amplitude $u_\mathbf{k}$ and wavevector k is $\epsilon_\mathbf{k} = 2JNu_k{}^2(1 - \cos ka)$. With the quantization condition (31) we have

$$\epsilon_\mathbf{k} = 4JS(1 - \cos ka)n_\mathbf{k} = n_\mathbf{k}\hbar\omega_\mathbf{k}, \qquad (36)$$

where $\hbar\omega_k$ is given by (25). Equation (36) is of the form (32).

Thermal Excitation of Magnons

In thermal equilibrium the average value of $n_{\mathbf{k}}$ is given by the Bose distribution:[17]

$$\langle n_{\mathbf{k}} \rangle = \frac{1}{\exp(\beta\hbar\omega_{\mathbf{k}}) - 1}, \tag{37}$$

where $\beta = 1/k_BT$. The total number of magnons excited at a temperature T is

$$\sum_{\mathbf{k}} n_{\mathbf{k}} = \int d\omega\, \mathfrak{D}(\omega)\langle n(\omega)\rangle, \tag{38}$$

where $\mathfrak{D}(\omega)$ is the number of magnon states $\mathbf{k}$ per unit frequency range, as in Chapter 6 for phonons. The integral is to be taken over the allowed range of $\mathbf{k}$, which is the first Brillouin zone. At sufficiently low temperatures we may carry the integral between 0 and ∞ because $\langle n(\omega)\rangle \to 0$ exponentially as $\omega \to \infty$.

Magnons have only a single polarization for each value of $\mathbf{k}$. In three dimensions the number of states of wavevector less than k is $(1/2\pi)^3(4\pi k^3/3)$ per unit volume, whence the number of magnons $\mathfrak{D}(\omega)d\omega$ with frequency in $d\omega$ at ω is $(1/2\pi)^3(4\pi k^2)(dk/d\omega)\ d\omega$. In the approximation (28)

$$d\omega/dk = 4JSa^2k/\hbar = 2(2JSa^2/\hbar)^{1/2}\omega^{1/2}.$$

Thus the density of states for magnons is

$$\mathfrak{D}(\omega) = \frac{1}{4\pi^2} \cdot \left(\frac{\hbar}{2JSa^2}\right)^{3/2} \omega^{1/2}. \tag{39}$$

Using (39), we evaluate (38):

$$\sum_{\mathbf{k}} n_{\mathbf{k}} = \frac{1}{4\pi^2}\left(\frac{\hbar}{2JSa^2}\right)^{3/2}\int_0^\infty d\omega\, \frac{\omega^{1/2}}{e^{\beta\hbar\omega} - 1} = \frac{1}{4\pi^2}\left(\frac{k_BT}{2JSa^2}\right)^{3/2}\int_0^\infty dx\, \frac{x^{1/2}}{e^x - 1}. \tag{40}$$

The definite integral is found in tables and has the value $(0.0587)(4\pi^2)$.

The number N of atoms per unit volume is Q/a^3, where $Q = 1, 2, 4$ for sc, bcc, fcc lattices respectively. Now $(\Sigma n_{\mathbf{k}})/NS$ is equal to the fractional change of magnetization $\Delta M/M(0)$, so that

$$\boxed{\frac{\Delta M}{M(0)} = \frac{0.0587}{SQ} \cdot \left(\frac{k_BT}{2JS}\right)^{3/2}.} \tag{41}$$

---

[17] The argument is exactly as for phonons or photons. The Bose distribution follows whenever all excited states of a harmonic oscillator may be populated without restriction.

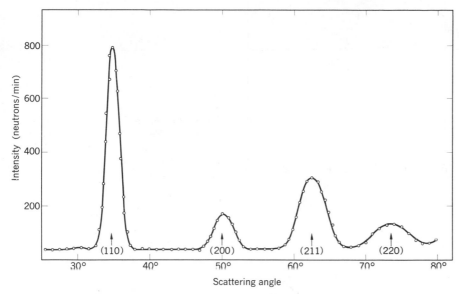

Figure 12   Neutron diffraction pattern for iron. The observed reflections satisfy the index rule for a body-centered cubic structure: the sum of the reflection indices is an even integer. [After C. G. Shull, E. O. Wollan, and W. C. Koehler, Phys. Rev. **84**, 912 (1951).]

This result[18] due to Felix Bloch[19] is known as the **Bloch $T^{3/2}$ law**; it has the form (14) found experimentally.

Neutron Scattering: Elastic and Inelastic

In Chapter 5 we discussed the determination of phonon spectra by inelastic x-ray or neutron scattering. An x-ray photon sees the spatial distribution of electronic charge, whether or not the charge density is magnetized or unmagnetized. But a neutron sees two aspects of a crystal: the distribution of nuclei and the distribution of electronic magnetization. The neutron diffraction pattern for iron is shown in Fig. 12.

The magnetic moment of the neutron interacts with the magnetic moment of the electron. The cross-section for the neutron-electron interaction is of the same order of magnitude as for the neutron-nuclear interaction. Diffraction of neutrons by a magnetic crystal allows the determination of the distribution, direction, and order of the magnetic moments. Further, a neutron can be inelastically scattered by the magnetic structure, with the creation or

---

[18] The result (41) is the correct leading term on the Heisenberg model. To go further we need to use the full dispersion relation; to carry out the integration over the first Brillouin zone; to take account of magnon-magnon interactions; and to take account of external magnetic fields, anisotropy fields, and dipolar interactions among the spins. An elementary method for taking account of magnon-magnon interactions, as far as possible at present, is given by M. Bloch, Phys. Rev. Letters **9**, 286 (1962); J. Appl. Phys. **34**, 1151 (1963).

[19] F. Bloch, Z. Physik **61**, 206 (1931).

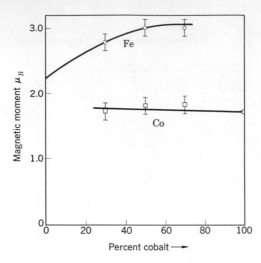

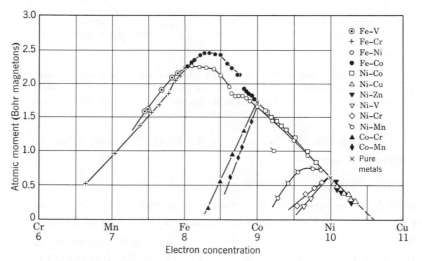

Figure 13   Moments attributable to 3*d* electrons in Fe-Co alloys as a function of composition, after M. F. Collins and J. B. Forsyth, Phil. Mag. **8**, 401 (1963).

Figure 14   Average atomic moments of binary alloys of the elements in the iron group, after Bozorth.

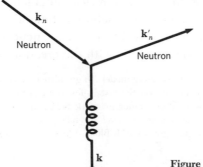

Figure 15   Scattering of a neutron with creation of a magnon.

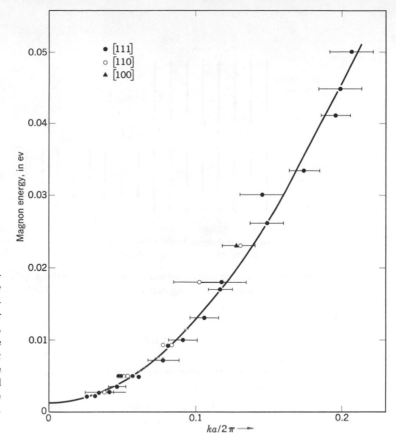

Figure 16 Magnon spectrum of a fcc cobalt alloy (92 Co 8 Fe) at room temperature, after R. N. Sinclair and B. N. Brockhouse, Phys. Rev. **120**, 1638 (1960). The solid line is the best-fit theoretical curve. The results shown do not extend very far out into the Brillouin zone.

annihilation of a magnon; such events make possible the experimental determination of magnon spectra.

The magnetic moments associated with particular components of alloys may be investigated by neutron diffraction. Results for the Fe-Co binary alloy system (which is ferromagnetic) are shown in Fig. 13. Notice that the magnetic moment on the cobalt atom does not appear to be affected by alloying, but that on the iron atom increases to about $3\mu_B$ as the cobalt concentration increases. (The neutron results relate essentially to the difference of the Fe and Co moments; the sum of the moments is taken from magnetization data, as in Fig. 14.)

In an inelastic scattering event a neutron may create or destroy a magnon (Fig. 15). If the incident neutron has wavevector $\mathbf{k}_n$ and is scattered to $\mathbf{k}'_n$ with the creation of a magnon of wavevector $\mathbf{k}$, then by conservation of crystal momentum

$$\mathbf{k}_n = \mathbf{k}'_n + \mathbf{k} + \mathbf{G},\tag{42}$$

where $\mathbf{G}$ is a reciprocal lattice vector. By conservation of energy

$$\frac{\hbar^2 k_n{}^2}{2M_n} = \frac{\hbar^2 k'_n{}^2}{2M_n} + \hbar\omega_{\mathbf{k}},\tag{43}$$

where $\hbar\omega_{\mathbf{k}}$ is the energy of the magnon created in the process. The observed magnon spectrum for a cobalt-rich alloy is shown in Fig. 16.

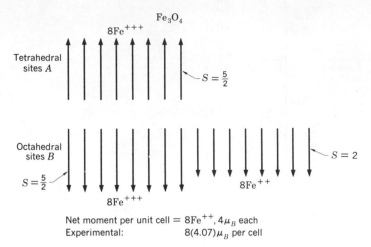

Net moment per unit cell $= 8Fe^{++}, 4\mu_B$ each
Experimental: $8(4.07)\mu_B$ per cell

Figure 17 Schematic spin arrangements in magnetite, $FeO \cdot Fe_2O_3$, showing that the moments of the Fe^{3+} ions cancel out, leaving only the moments of the Fe^{++} ions. The types of interstices are defined in Fig. 19.

FERRIMAGNETIC ORDER

In many ferromagnetic crystals the saturation magnetization at $T = 0°K$ does not correspond to parallel alignment of the magnetic moments of the constituent paramagnetic ions, even in crystals for which there is strong evidence that the individual paramagnetic ions have their normal magnetic moments. The most familiar example is magnetite, Fe_3O_4 or $FeO \cdot Fe_2O_3$. From Table 14.2 we see that ferric (Fe^{+++}) ions are in a state with spin $S = \frac{5}{2}$ and zero orbital moment. Thus each ion should contribute $5\mu_B$ to the saturation moment. The ferrous (Fe^{++}) ions have a spin of 2 and should contribute $4\mu_B$, apart from any residual orbital moment contribution. Thus the effective number of Bohr magnetons per Fe_3O_4 formula unit should be about $2 \times 5 + 4 = 14$ if all spins were parallel. The observed value (Table 1) is 4.1. The discrepancy[20] is accounted for if the moments of the Fe^{+++} ions are antiparallel to each other: then the observed moment arises only from the Fe^{++} ion, as in Fig. 17. The neutron diffraction results in Fig. 18 agree with this model.

A systematic discussion of the consequences of this type of spin order was given by L. Néel with reference to an important class of magnetic oxides known as ferrites.[21] The term **ferrimagnetic** was coined originally to describe the ferrite-type ferromagnetic spin order such as Fig. 17, and by extension the term covers almost any compound in which some ions have a moment antiparallel to other ions. Many ferrimagnets are poor conductors of electricity, a quality which is exploited in device applications.

[20] L. Néel, Ann. phys. **3**, 137 (1948).

[21] The usual chemical formula of a **ferrite** is $MO \cdot Fe_2O_3$, where M is a divalent cation, often Zn, Cd, Fe, Ni, Cu, Co, or Mg.

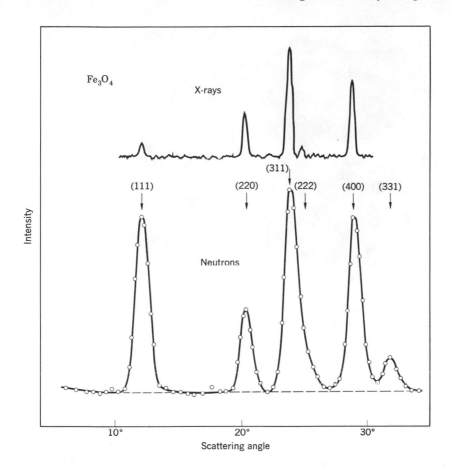

Figure 18   X-ray and neutron diffraction patterns for magnetite at room temperature. A pronounced magnetic scattering contribution is found in the neutron pattern:
note the strength of the (111) neutron line. The relative intensities of the neutron
diffraction lines are sensitive to the order of the Fe^{++} and Fe^{3+} electronic magnetic
moments. The intensities calculated for the Néel ferrimagnetic structure agree well
with the observed intensities:

Reflection:	(111)	(220)	(311) + (222)	(400)	(331)
Calculated intensity	934	343	1060	765	110
Observed intensity	860	360	1070	780	135

(After Shull, Wollan, and Koehler.)

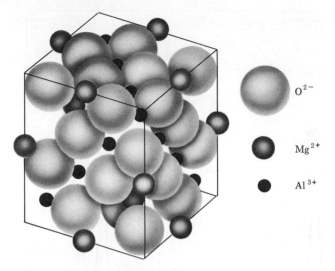

Figure 19 Crystal structure of the mineral spinel $MgAl_2O_4$; the Mg^{++} ions occupy tetrahedral sites, each surrounded by four oxygen ions; the Al^{3+} occupy octahedral sites, each surrounded by six oxygen ions. This is a **normal spinel** arrangement: the divalent metal ions occupy the tetrahedral sites. In the **inverse spinel** arrangement the tetrahedral sites are occupied by trivalent metal ions, while the octahedral sites are occupied half by divalent and half by trivalent metal ions.

The cubic ferrites have the **spinel** crystal structure shown in Fig. 19. There are eight occupied tetrahedral (or A) sites and sixteen occupied octahedral (or B) sites in a unit cube. The lattice constant is about 8 Å. A remarkable feature of the spinels is that all exchange interactions (AA, AB, and BB) are believed to favor *antiparallel* alignment of the spins connected by the interaction. But the AB interaction is the strongest, so that the A spins are parallel to each other and the B spins are parallel to each other, just in order that the A spins may be antiparallel to the B spins.

The assumption that all exchange integrals J_{AA}, J_{AB}, and J_{BB} are negative[22] can account (as we show below) for spin structure of Fe_3O_4 in Fig. 17; it also explains why zinc ferrite, $ZnO \cdot Fe_2O_3$, has zero saturation magnetization: it is an antiferromagnet (Fig. 20). The theory explains in a natural way the saturation magnetization curves shown in Fig. 21. The moments for zero zinc content agree quite well with the idea that the Fe^{3+} ions do not contribute, and the trend of the moments toward zero for $ZnO \cdot Fe_2O_3$ is also plausible. In the intermediate region the zinc ions cause an unbalance in the system, increasing the total moment. The situation is discussed by Went and Gorter.

We now prove that three antiferromagnetic interactions can result in

---

[22] If J in (6) is positive, we say that the exchange integral is ferromagnetic; if J is negative, the exchange integral is antiferromagnetic.

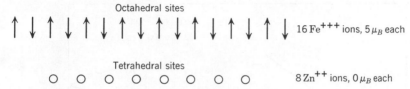

Octahedral sites

16 Fe^{+++} ions, 5 μ_B each

Tetrahedral sites

8 Zn^{++} ions, 0 μ_B each

Figure 20   Explanation of zero saturation magnetization in zinc ferrite; the zinc ions occupy the tetrahedral sites of Fig. 19. The antiferromagnetic interaction of the ferric ions on the octahedral sites controls the magnetic structure.

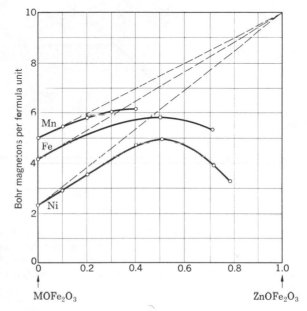

Figure 21   Saturation magnetization of mixed Mn-Zn, Fe-Zn, and Ni-Zn ferrites as a function of the zinc content, after J. J. Went and E. W. Gorter, Philips Tech. Rev. **13**, 181 (1952). At the left we have MnO · Fe$_2$O$_3$; FeO · Fe$_2$O$_3$ and NiO · Fe$_2$O$_3$; at the right we have ZnO · Fe$_2$O$_3$.

ferrimagnetism. The molecular fields acting on the A and B spin lattices may be written

$$\mathbf{H}_A = -\lambda\mathbf{M}_A - \mu\mathbf{M}_B; \qquad \mathbf{H}_B = -\mu\mathbf{M}_A - \nu\mathbf{M}_B; \qquad (44)$$

taking λ, μ, ν to be positive. The minus sign then corresponds to an antiparallel interaction. The interaction energy is

$$U = -\tfrac{1}{2}(\mathbf{H}_A \cdot \mathbf{M}_A + \mathbf{H}_B \cdot \mathbf{M}_B) = \tfrac{1}{2}\lambda M_A{}^2 + \mu\mathbf{M}_A \cdot \mathbf{M}_B + \tfrac{1}{2}\nu M_B{}^2; \quad (45)$$

this is lower when $\mathbf{M}_A$ is antiparallel to $\mathbf{M}_B$ than when $\mathbf{M}_A$ is parallel to $\mathbf{M}_B$. The energy when antiparallel should be compared with zero, because a possible solution is $M_A = M_B = 0$. Thus when

$$\mu M_A M_B > \tfrac{1}{2}(\lambda M_A{}^2 + \nu M_B{}^2), \qquad (46)$$

the ground state will have M_A directed oppositely to M_B. Under certain conditions there may be spin arrays of still lower energy.

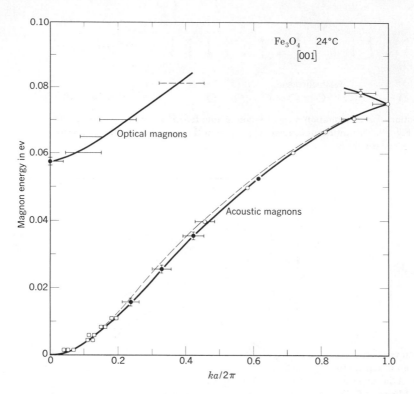

Figure 22 Experimental dispersion curve for magnons in Fe_3O_4 at room temperature. The dashed curve gives the results before correction for resolution. The results indicate a value $J_{AB} = 2.3 \times 10^{-3}$ ev, and a much smaller value of J_{BB}; the results are not sensitive to J_{AA}. (After B. N. Brockhouse and H. Watanabe.)

The magnon spectrum[23] of Fe_3O_4 has acoustic and optical branches. There are six magnetic atoms in the primitive unit cell, so that there should be six branches, one acoustic and five optical, to the magnon spectrum. The experiments in Fig. 22 show the acoustic and one of the optical branches. The spectrum agrees with the ferrimagnetic model of Fig. 17, with the dominant interaction the antiparallel interaction between the spins on the A and B sites.

[23] H. Kaplan, Phys. Rev. **86**, 121 (1952); J. S. Kouvel, Harvard University thesis, 1955; T. A. Kaplan, Phys. Rev. **109**, 782 (1958).

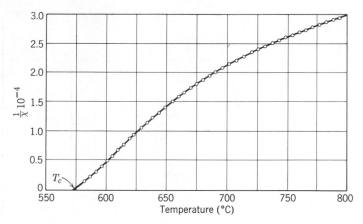

Figure 23 Reciprocal susceptibility of magnetite, $FeO \cdot Fe_2O_3$, above the Curie temperature.

Curie Temperature and Susceptibility of Ferrimagnets

We define separate Curie constants C_A and C_B for the A and B sites.[24] Let all interactions be zero except for an antiparallel interaction between the A and B sites: $\mathbf{H}_A = -\mu\mathbf{M}_B$; $\mathbf{H}_B = -\mu\mathbf{M}_A$. In analogy to the argument of (1) to (4) we have

$$M_A T = C_A(H - \mu M_B); \qquad M_B T = C_B(H - \mu M_A). \tag{47}$$

These equations have a nonzero solution for M_A and M_B in zero applied field H if

$$\begin{vmatrix} T & \mu C_A \\ \mu C_B & T \end{vmatrix} = 0, \tag{48}$$

so that the ferrimagnetic Curie temperature is given by $T_c = \mu(C_A C_B)^{1/2}$.

We solve (47) for M_A and M_B to obtain the susceptibility at $T > T_c$:

$$\chi = \frac{M_A + M_B}{H} = \frac{(C_A + C_B)T - 2\mu C_A C_B}{T^2 - T_c^2}, \tag{49}$$

a result more complicated than (4). Experimental values for Fe_3O_4 are plotted in Fig. 23. The curvature of the plot of $1/\chi$ versus T is a characteristic feature of a ferrimagnet. In (51) below we consider the case $C_A = C_B$.

---

[24] We need separate C's for the two lattices because the numbers and types of paramagnetic ions will usually be different on the two lattices. The values of C_A, C_B will be given by (14.25).

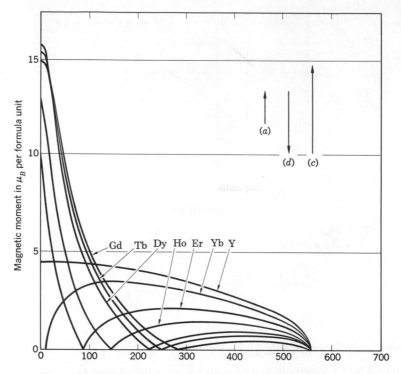

Figure 24 Experimental values of the saturation magnetization versus temperature of various iron garnets, after R. Pauthenet. The formula unit is $M_3Fe_5O_{12}$, where M is a trivalent metal ion. The temperature at which the magnetization crosses zero is called the compensation temperature; here the magnetization of the M sublattice is equal and opposite to the net magnetization of the ferric ion sublattices. Per formula unit there are 3 Fe^{3+} ions on tetrahedral sides d; 2 Fe^{3+} ions on octahedral sites a; and 3 M^{3+} ions on sites denoted by c. The ferric ions contribute $(3 - 2)5\mu_B = 5\mu_B$ per formula unit. The ferric ion coupling is strong and determines the Curie temperature. If the M^{3+} ions are rare earth ions they are magnetized opposite to the resultant of the Fe^{3+} ions. The M^{3+} contribution drops rapidly with increasing temperature because the M-Fe coupling is weak.

Iron Garnets. The iron garnets are cubic ferrimagnetic insulators with the general formula $M_3Fe_5O_{12}$, where M is a trivalent metal ion and the Fe is the trivalent ferric ion ($S = \frac{5}{2}$, $L = 0$). An example is yttrium iron garnet $Y_3Fe_5O_{12}$, known as YIG. Here Y^{+++} is diamagnetic.

The net magnetization of YIG is due to the resultant of two oppositely magnetized lattices of Fe^{+++} ions. At absolute zero each ferric ion contributes $\pm5\mu_B$ to the magnetization, but in each formula unit the three Fe^{+++} ions on sites denoted as d sites are magnetized in one sense and the two Fe^{+++} ions

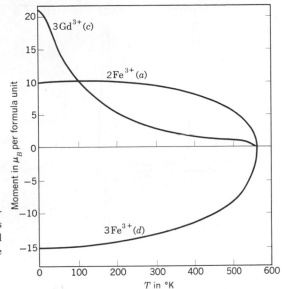

Figure 25 Magnetization of the sublattices in gadolinium iron garnet, as calculated by R. Pauthenet. The total moment is zero near 280°K; the Curie temperature is near 560°K.

on a sites are magnetized in the opposite sense, giving a resultant of $5\mu_B$ per formula unit. The molecular field[25] at an a site due to the ions on the d sites is $\mathbf{H}_a = -(1.5 \times 10^4)\mathbf{M}_d$. The observed Curie temperature 559°K of YIG is due to the $a-d$ interaction.

The only magnetic ions in YIG are the ferric ions. Because these are in an $L=0$ state with a spherical charge distribution their interaction with lattice deformations and phonons is weak. As a result YIG is characterized by very narrow linewidths in ferromagnetic resonance experiments (Chapter 16).

In the rare-earth iron garnets[26] the ions M^{+++} are paramagnetic trivalent rare-earth ions. Magnetization curves are given in Fig. 24. The rare-earth ions occupy sites labeled c; the magnetization M_c of the ions on the c lattice is opposite to the net magnetization of the ferric ions on the $a+d$ sites. At low temperatures (Fig. 25) the combined moments of the three rare-earth ions in a formula unit may dominate the net moment of the Fe^{+++} ions, but because of the weak c-a and c-d coupling the rare-earth lattice loses its magnetization rapidly with increasing temperature. The total moment can pass through zero and then increase again as the Fe^{+++} moment starts to be dominant. In GdIG the molecular field at a c site can be represented by $\mathbf{H}_c \cong -(2 \times 10^3)(\mathbf{M}_a + \mathbf{M}_d)$, much weaker than the field at an a site as given for YIG in the preceding paragraph.

[25] R. Pauthenet, *Ann. phys.* **3**, 424 (1958); see also E. E. Anderson, *Phys. Rev.* **134**, A1581 (1964).

[26] A review of their properties is given by L. Néel, R. Pauthenet, and B. Dreyfus, *Prog. in low temperature physics* **4**, 344–383 (1964).

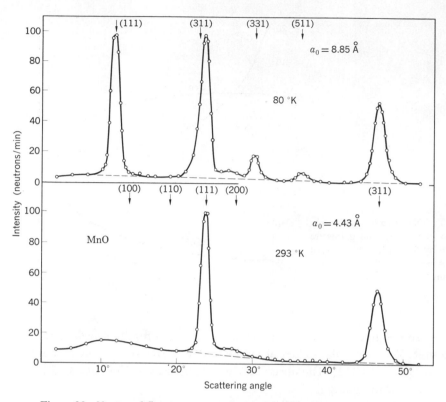

Figure 26 Neutron diffraction patterns for MnO below and above the spin-ordering temperature of 120°K, after C. G. Shull, W. A. Strauser, and E. O. Wollan, Phys. Rev. **83**, 333 (1951). The reflection indices are based on an 8.85 Å cell at 80°K and on a 4.43 Å cell at 293°K. At the higher temperature the Mn^{++} ions are still magnetic, but they are no longer ordered.

ANTIFERROMAGNETIC ORDER[27]

A classical example of magnetic structure determination by neutrons is shown in Fig. 26 for MnO, which has the NaCl structure. At 80°K there are extra neutron reflections not present at 293°K. The reflections at 80°K may be classified in terms of a cubic unit cell of lattice constant 8.85 Å. At 293°K the reflections correspond to an *fcc* unit cell of lattice constant 4.43 Å. But the lattice constant determined by x-ray reflection is 4.43 Å at *both* temperatures, 80°K and 293°K. We conclude that the chemical unit cell has the 4.43 Å lattice parameter, but that at 80°K the electronic magnetic moments

---

[27] Data on antiferromagnetic structures studied by neutron diffraction are given in Table 5g-22 of the *A.I.P. handbook*, McGraw-Hill, 1963, 2nd ed.

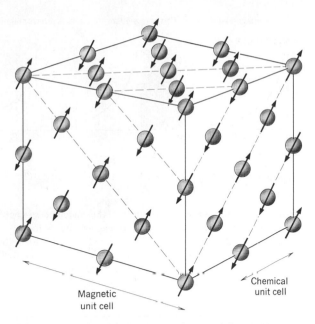

Figure 27   Ordered arrangement of spins of the Mn^{++} ions in manganese oxide, MnO, as determined by neutron diffraction. The O^{--} ions are not shown.

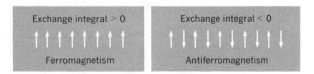

Figure 28   Spin ordering in ferromagnets $(J > 0)$ and antiferromagnets $(J < 0)$.

of the Mn^{++} ions[28] are ordered in some nonferromagnetic arrangement. If the ordering were ferromagnetic, the chemical and magnetic cells would give the same reflections. The spin arrangement shown in Fig. 27 is consistent with the neutron diffraction results and with magnetic measurements. The spins in a single [111] plane are parallel, but adjacent [111] planes are antiparallel. Thus MnO is an antiferromagnet, as in Fig. 28.

In an **antiferromagnet** the spins are ordered in an antiparallel arrangement with zero net moment at temperatures below the ordering or **Néel**

---

[28] Mn^{++} has a magnetic moment of $5\mu_B$.

482

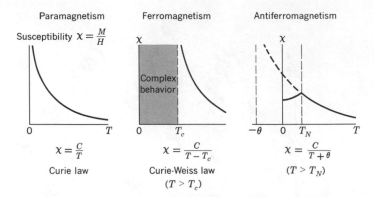

Figure 29 Temperature dependence of the magnetic susceptibility in paramagnets, ferromagnets, and antiferromagnets. Below the Néel temperature of an antiferromagnet the spins have antiparallel orientations; the susceptibility attains its maximum value at T_N where there is a well-defined kink in the curve of χ versus T. The transition is also marked by peaks in the heat capacity and the thermal expansion coefficient.

temperature. The susceptibility of an antiferromagnet is not infinite at $T = T_N$, but has a weak cusp, as in Figs. 29 and 30.

An antiferromagnet is a special case of a ferrimagnet for which both sublattices A and B have equal saturation magnetizations. Thus $C_A = C_B$ in (47), and the Néel temperature is given by

$$T_N = \mu C, \tag{50}$$

where C refers to a single sublattice. The susceptibility in the paramagnetic region $T > T_N$ is obtained from (49):

$$\chi = \frac{2CT - 2\mu C^2}{T^2 - (\mu C)^2} = \frac{2C}{T + \mu C} = \frac{2C}{T + T_N}. \tag{51}$$

The experimental results at $T > T_N$ are of the form

$$\chi = \frac{2C}{T + \theta}. \tag{52}$$

Experimental values of θ/T_N listed in Table 2 often differ substantially from the value unity expected from (51). Values of θ/T_N of the observed magnitude may be obtained when next-nearest-neighbor interactions[29] are provided for, and when general sublattice arrangements[30] are considered. It is shown in Problem 3 that if a molecular field constant $-\epsilon$ is introduced to describe interactions within a sublattice, then $\theta/T_N = (\mu + \epsilon)/(\mu - \epsilon)$.

[29] L. Néel, Ann. phys, 3, 137 (1948).
[30] P. W. Anderson, Phys. Rev. 79, 350, 705 (1950); J. M. Luttinger, Phys. Rev. 81, 1015 (1951).

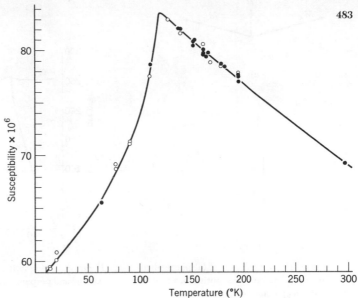

Figure 30 Magnetic susceptibility of MnO, after Bizette, Squire, and Tsai.

Table 2   Summary of antiferromagnetic data

The Néel temperatures T_N often vary considerably between samples, and in some cases there is large thermal hysteresis. For a bibliography relating to experimental data on antiferromagnetic substances, see T. Nagamiya, K. Yosida, and R. Kubo, Advances in Physics **4**, 1–112 (1955); and the A.I.P. Handbook. The value of θ is obtained by fitting an expression of the form $\chi = C/(T + \theta)$ to the susceptibility above the actual transition temperature T_N.

Substance	Paramagnetic ion lattice	Transition temperature, T_N in °K	Curie-Weiss θ in °K	$\dfrac{\theta}{T_N}$	$\dfrac{\chi(0)}{\chi(T_N)}$
MnO	fcc	116	610	5.3	$\frac{2}{3}$
MnS	fcc	160	528	3.3	0.82
MnTe	hex. layer	307	690	2.25	
MnF$_2$	bc tetr	67	82	1.24	0.76
FeF$_2$	bc tetr	79	117	1.48	0.72
FeCl$_2$	hex. layer	24	48	2.0	<0.2
FeO	fcc	198	570	2.9	0.8
CoCl$_2$	hex. layer	25	38.1	1.53	
CoO	fcc	291	330	1.14	
NiCl$_2$	hex. layer	50	68.2	1.37	
NiO	fcc	525	~2000	~4	
α-Mn	complex	~100			
Cr	bcc	308			
CrSb	hex. layer	723	550	0.76	~$\frac{1}{4}$
Cr$_2$O$_3$	complex	307	485	1.58	
FeCO$_3$	complex	35	14	0.4	~$\frac{1}{4}$

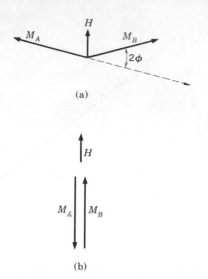

(a)

(b)

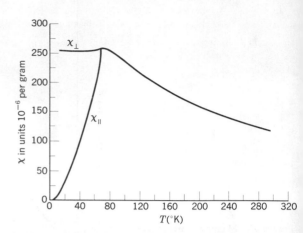

Figure 31 Calculation of (a) perpendicular and (b) parallel susceptibilities at 0°K, in the molecular field approximation.

Figure 32 Magnetic susceptibility of manganese fluoride, MnF$_2$, parallel and perpendicular to the tetragonal axis. (After S. Foner.)

Susceptibility below the Néel Temperature

There are two situations: with the applied magnetic field perpendicular to the axis of the spins; and with the field parallel to the axis of the spins. At the Néel temperature the susceptibility is nearly independent of the direction of the field relative to the spin axis.

For $\mathbf{H} \perp \mathbf{M}_A$, $\mathbf{M}_B$ we can calculate the susceptibility by elementary considerations. The energy density in the presence of the field is, with $M = |M_A| = |M_B|$,

$$U = \mu \mathbf{M}_A \cdot \mathbf{M}_B - \mathbf{H} \cdot (\mathbf{M}_A + \mathbf{M}_B) \cong -\mu M^2 [1 - \tfrac{1}{2}(2\varphi)^2] - 2HM\varphi, \quad (53a)$$

where 2φ is the angle the spins make with each other (Fig. 31a). The energy is a minimum when

$$dU/d\varphi = 0 = 4\mu M^2 \varphi - 2HM; \qquad \varphi = H/2\mu M, \qquad (53b)$$

so that
$$\chi_\perp = 2M\varphi/H = 1/\mu. \qquad (53c)$$

In the parallel orientation (Fig. 31b) the magnetic energy is not changed if the spin systems A and B make equal angles with the field. Thus the susceptibility at $T = 0°K$ is zero:

$$\chi_\parallel(0) = 0. \qquad (54)$$

The parallel susceptibility increases smoothly with temperature up to T_N. Measurements on MnF$_2$ are shown in Fig. 32. In very strong fields the spin

484

systems will flop from the parallel orientation to the perpendicular orientation, because the energy is lower here.

Antiferromagnetic Magnons

We obtain simply an expression for the dispersion relation of magnons in a one-dimensional antiferromagnet by making the appropriate substitutions in the treatment of the ferromagnetic line. Let spins with even indices $2p$ compose sublattice A, that with spins up ($S_z = S$); and let spins with odd indices $2p + 1$ compose sublattice B, that with spins down ($S_z = -S$). We consider only nearest-neighbor interactions, with J negative. Then (21ab) written for A becomes, with a careful look at (20),

$$dS_{2p}^x/dt = (2JS/\hbar)(-2S_{2p}^y - S_{2p-1}^y - S_{2p+1}^y); \tag{55a}$$

$$dS_{2p}^y/dt = -(2JS/\hbar)(-2S_{2p}^x - S_{2p-1}^x - S_{2p+1}^x). \tag{55b}$$

The corresponding equations for a spin on B are

$$dS_{2p+1}^x/dt = (2JS/\hbar)(2S_{2p+1}^y + S_{2p}^y + S_{2p+2}^y); \tag{56a}$$

$$dS_{2p+1}^y/dt = -(2JS/\hbar)(2S_{2p+1}^x + S_{2p}^x + S_{2p+2}^x). \tag{56b}$$

We form $S^+ = S_x + iS_y$; then

$$dS_{2p}^+/dt = (2iJS/\hbar)(2S_{2p}^+ + S_{2p-1}^+ + S_{2p+1}^+); \tag{57}$$

$$dS_{2p+1}^+/dt = -(2iJS/\hbar)(2S_{2p+1}^+ + S_{2p}^+ + S_{2p+2}^+). \tag{58}$$

We look for solutions of the form

$$S_{2p}^+ = ue^{i[2pka-\omega t]}; \qquad S_{2p+1}^+ = ve^{i[(2p+1)ka-\omega t]}, \tag{59}$$

so that (57) and (58) become, with $\omega_{ex} \equiv -2JS/\hbar = 2|J|S/\hbar$,

$$\omega u = \omega_{ex}(2u + ve^{-ika} + ve^{ika}); \tag{60a}$$

$$-\omega v = \omega_{ex}(2v + ue^{-ika} + ue^{ika}). \tag{60b}$$

Equations (60ab) have a solution if

$$\begin{vmatrix} \omega_{ex} - \omega & \omega_{ex}\cos ka \\ \omega_{ex}\cos ka & \omega_{ex} + \omega \end{vmatrix} = 0. \tag{61}$$

Thus
$$\omega^2 = \omega_{ex}^2(1 - \cos^2 ka); \qquad \omega = \omega_{ex}|\sin ka|. \tag{62}$$

The dispersion relation (62) for magnons in an antiferromagnet is quite different from (25) for magnons in a ferromagnet. For $ka \ll 1$ we see that (62) is linear[31] in k:

$$\omega \cong \omega_{ex}|ka|. \tag{63}$$

---

[31] A physical discussion of the difference between the dispersion relations for ferromagnetic and antiferromagnetic magnons is given by F. Keffer, H. Kaplan, and Y. Yafet, Am. J. Phys. **21**, 250 (1953).

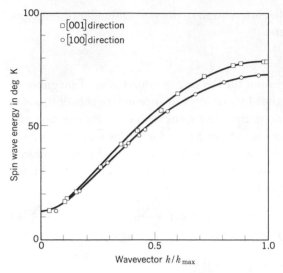

Figure 33 Antiferromagnetic magnons in tetragonal MnF_2 at $4.2\,°K$ observed by neutron inelastic scattering. [After A. Okazaki, K. C. Turberfield, and R. W. H. Stevenson, Phys. Letters **8**, 9 (1964).]

The magnon spectrum of MnF_2 is shown in Fig. 33, as determined by inelastic neutron scattering experiments. The observed magnon frequency does not approach zero as $k \to 0$, because of an interaction known as the anisotropy field which has been omitted from our discussion. The frequency at $k = 0$ is discussed in Chapter 16. Well-resolved magnons were observed in these experiments at specimen temperatures up to 0.93 of the Néel temperature. Thus even at high temperatures the magnon approximation is useful. Further details concerning antiferromagnetic magnons are given in *QTS*, Chap. 4.

Helical Order[32]

Helical or screwlike arrangements of spins have been observed; the idea was originated by Yoshimori to explain the magnetic properties of MnO_2. We show with a simple classical model that a helical arrangement can minimize the energy, given suitable interactions.

Consider as in Fig. 34 a line of identical spins normal to the line and coupled by the exchange energy

[32] A. Yoshimori, J. Phys. Soc. Japan **14**, 807 (1959); J. Villain, J. Phys. Chem. Solids **23**, 287 (1962). A review of the theory of general spin configurations is given by E. F. Bertaut in Rado and Suhl, Vol. III.

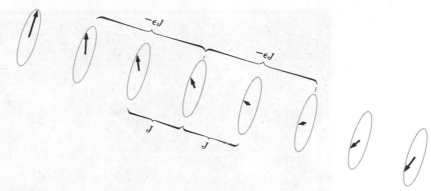

Figure 34 A helical array of spins. Nearest-neighbor atoms are coupled by the ferromagnetic exchange J; next-nearest-neighbor atoms are coupled by the antiferromagnetic exchange $-\epsilon J$, where ϵ is a positive constant.

$$U = -2J\left(\sum_p \mathbf{S}_p \cdot \mathbf{S}_{p+1} - \epsilon \sum_p \mathbf{S}_p \cdot \mathbf{S}_{p+2}\right), \qquad (64)$$

where J and ϵ are positive. This couples nearest neighbors ferromagnetically and next-nearest neighbors antiferromagnetically. Suppose that adjacent spins make an angle θ with each other; then (64) becomes

$$U = -2JNS^2(\cos\theta - \epsilon\cos 2\theta), \qquad (65)$$

for N spins S. This is an extremum when

$$\partial U/\partial\theta = -2JNS^2(-\sin\theta + 2\epsilon\sin 2\theta) = 0, \qquad (66)$$

or

$$\epsilon = \frac{\sin\theta}{2\sin 2\theta} = \frac{1}{4\cos\theta}; \qquad \theta = \cos^{-1}\left(\frac{1}{4\epsilon}\right). \qquad (67)$$

The maximum value of the cosine is one, so that the helical arrangement is possible[33] only if $\epsilon > \frac{1}{4}$. If $\epsilon < \frac{1}{4}$ the solution gives the simple ferromagnet, $\theta = 0$. The repeat distance of the spin arrangement is $2\pi/\theta$ lattice constants and need not be an integer.

Several of the rare-earth metals, notably Tb, Dy, and Ho, have helical magnetic structures. The structures are discussed by Yosida,[34] Elliott, and Rocher.

---

[33] It is easily shown that the extremum (66) is a minimum.

[34] K. Yosida, *Prog. low temperature physics* 4, 265 (1964); R. J. Elliott in Rado and Suhl, Vol. IIA, 385 (1965); Y. Rocher, Adv. in Physics 11, 232 (1962).

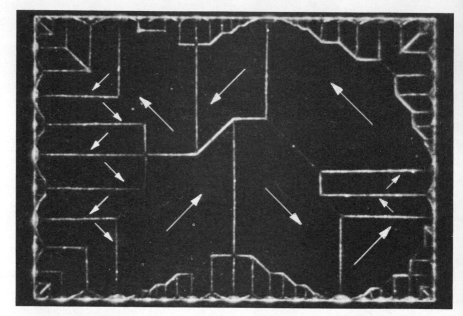

Figure 35 Ferromagnetic domain pattern on the surface of a single crystal platelet of nickel. The domain boundaries are made visible by the Bitter technique. The direction of magnetization within a domain is determined by observing growth or contraction of the domain in an applied magnetic field, as in Fig. 36a. (Courtesy of R. W. De Blois.)

FERROMAGNETIC DOMAINS

At temperatures well below the Curie point the electronic magnetic moments of a ferromagnet are essentially all lined up when regarded on a microscopic scale. Yet, looking at a specimen as a whole, the magnetic moment may be very much less than the saturation moment, and the application of an external magnetic field may be required to saturate the specimen. The behavior observed in single crystals is similar to that in polycrystalline specimens.

Weiss explained this behavior by assuming that actual specimens are composed of a number of small regions called domains, within each of which the local magnetization is saturated. The directions of magnetization of different domains, however, need not necessarily be parallel. An arrangement of domains with approximately zero resultant magnetic moment is shown in Fig. 35.

The increase in the magnetic moment of the specimen under the action

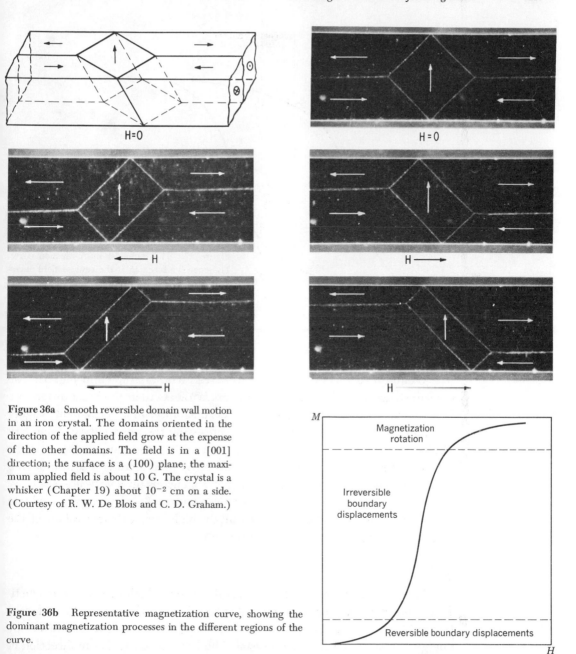

Figure 36a Smooth reversible domain wall motion in an iron crystal. The domains oriented in the direction of the applied field grow at the expense of the other domains. The field is in a [001] direction; the surface is a (100) plane; the maximum applied field is about 10 G. The crystal is a whisker (Chapter 19) about 10^{-2} cm on a side. (Courtesy of R. W. De Blois and C. D. Graham.)

Figure 36b Representative magnetization curve, showing the dominant magnetization processes in the different regions of the curve.

of an applied magnetic field takes place by two independent processes: (1) in weak applied fields the volume of domains (Fig. 36) which are favorably oriented with respect to the field increases at the expense of unfavorably oriented domains; (2) in strong applied fields the magnetization rotates toward the direction of the field.

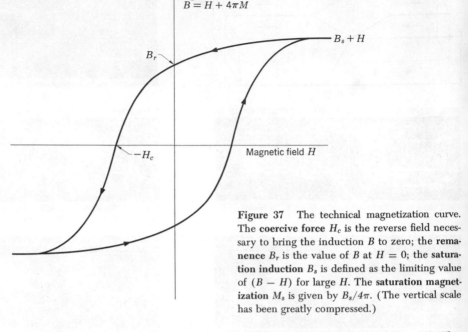

Figure 37 The technical magnetization curve. The **coercive force** H_c is the reverse field necessary to bring the induction B to zero; the **remanence** B_r is the value of B at $H = 0$; the **saturation induction** B_s is defined as the limiting value of $(B - H)$ for large H. The **saturation magnetization** M_s is given by $B_s/4\pi$. (The vertical scale has been greatly compressed.)

Technical terms defined by the hysteresis loop are shown in Fig. 37. The domain structure of ferromagnetic materials affects their practical properties. In a transformer core we want a high permeability; in a permanent magnet we want a high coercive force.[35] By suppressing the possibility of boundary displacement we may achieve a high coercivity; the suppression may be accomplished by using very fine particles or by precipitating a second metallurgical phase so that the specimen is heterogeneous on a very fine scale. By making the material pure, homogeneous, and well oriented we facilitate boundary displacement and thereby attain high permeability; values of the permeability up to 3.8×10^6 have been reported.

Anisotropy Energy

There is an energy in a ferromagnetic crystal which directs the magnetization along certain definite crystallographic axes called directions of easy magnetization. This energy is called the **magnetocrystalline** or **anisotropy energy.** Cobalt is a hexagonal crystal. The hexagonal axis is the direction of easy magnetization at room temperature, as shown in Fig. 38.

One origin of the anisotropy energy[36] is illustrated by Fig. 39. The

---

[35] The **coercive force** is defined as the reverse field needed to reduce the induction B or the magnetization M to zero, starting in a saturated condition. Usually the definition is understood to refer to B, except in theoretical work. When referred to M, one writes $_IH_c$ or $_MH_c$.

[36] The theory of anisotropy is reviewed by J. Kanamori in Rado and Suhl, Vol. I, 127 (1963).

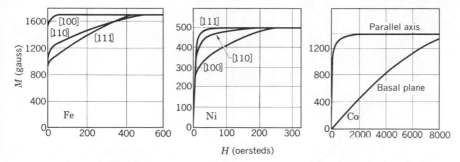

Figure 38 Magnetization curves for single crystals of iron, nickel, and cobalt. From the curves for iron we see that the [100] directions are easy directions of magnetization and the [111] directions are hard directions. (After Honda and Kaya.)

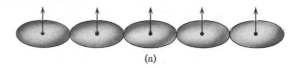

(a)

Figure 39 Asymmetry of the overlap of electron distributions on neighboring ions is one mechanism of magnetocrystalline anisotropy. Because of spin-orbit interaction the charge distribution is not spherical. The asymmetry is tied to the direction of magnetization by the spin-orbit coupling; changing the spin direction changes the overlap energy.

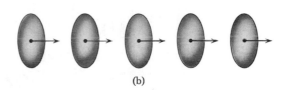

(b)

magnetization of the crystal "sees" the crystal lattice through orbital overlap of the electrons: the spin interacts with the orbital motion by means of the spin-orbit coupling, and the orbital motion in turn interacts with the crystal structure by means of the electrostatic fields and overlapping wavefunctions associated with neighboring atoms in the lattice.

In cobalt the anisotropy energy density is given by

$$U_K = K_1' \sin^2 \theta + K_2' \sin^4 \theta, \tag{68}$$

where θ is the angle the magnetization makes with the hexagonal axis. At room temperature $K_1' = 4.1 \times 10^6$ ergs/cm^3; $K_2' = 1.0 \times 10^6$ ergs/cm^3.

Iron is a cubic crystal, and the cube edges are the directions of easy magnetization. To represent the anisotropy energy of iron magnetized in an arbitrary direction with direction cosines α_1, α_2, α_3 referred to the cube edges, we are guided by cubic symmetry. The expression for the anisotropy energy must be an even power[37] of each α_i, and it must be invariant under interchanges of the α_i among themselves. The lowest order combination

---

[37] Because opposite ends of a crystal axis are equivalent magnetically.

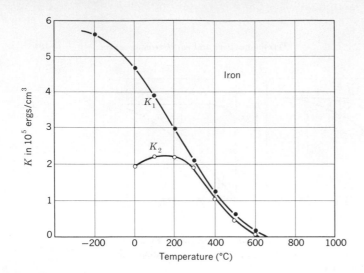

Figure 40 Temperature dependence of anisotropy constants of iron.

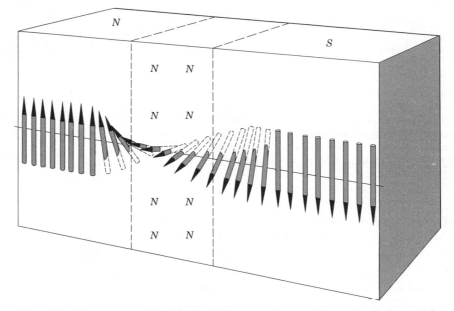

Figure 41 The structure of the Bloch wall separating domains. In iron the thickness of the transition region is about 300 lattice constants.

satisfying the symmetry requirements is $\alpha_1{}^2 + \alpha_2{}^2 + \alpha_3{}^2$, but this is identically equal to unity and does not describe anisotropy effects. The next combination is of the fourth degree: $\alpha_1{}^2\alpha_2{}^2 + \alpha_1{}^2\alpha_3{}^2 + \alpha_3{}^2\alpha_2{}^2$, and then of the sixth degree: $\alpha_1{}^2\alpha_2{}^2\alpha_3{}^2$. Thus

$$U_K = K_1(\alpha_1{}^2\alpha_2{}^2 + \alpha_2{}^2\alpha_3{}^2 + \alpha_3{}^2\alpha_1{}^2) + K_2\alpha_1{}^2\alpha_2{}^2\alpha_3{}^2; \qquad (69)$$

at room temperature $K_1 = 4.2 \times 10^5$ ergs/cm³ and $K_2 = 1.5 \times 10^5$ ergs/cm³. Results for iron at other temperatures are shown in Fig. 40; note that $K \to 0$ as $T \to T_c$. For nickel at room temperature $K_1 = -5 \times 10^4$ ergs/cm³.

Transition Region between Domains

A **Bloch wall** in a crystal is the transition layer which separates adjacent regions (domains) magnetized in different directions. The entire change in spin direction between domains does not occur in one discontinuous jump across a single atomic plane, but takes place in a gradual way over many atomic planes (Fig. 41). The exchange energy is lower when the change is distributed over many spins.

This behavior may be understood by interpreting the Heisenberg equation (6) classically; we also replace cos φ by $1 - \frac{1}{2}\varphi^2$. Then $w_{ex} = JS^2\varphi^2$ is the exchange energy between two spins making a small angle φ with each other; here J is the exchange integral and S is the spin quantum number. If a total change of π occurs in N equal steps, the angle between neighboring spins is π/N, and the exchange energy per pair of neighboring atoms is $w_{ex} = JS^2(\pi/N)^2$. The total exchange energy of a line of $N + 1$ atoms is

$$Nw_{ex} = JS^2\pi^2/N. \tag{70}$$

The wall would thicken without limit were it not for the anisotropy energy, which acts to limit the width of the transition layer. The spins contained within the wall are largely directed away from the axes of easy magnetization, so there is an anisotropy energy associated with the wall, roughly proportional to the thickness.

Let us consider a wall parallel to the cube face of a simple cubic lattice and separating domains magnetized in opposite directions. We wish to determine the number N of atomic planes contained within the wall.

The energy per unit area of wall is the sum of contributions from exchange and anisotropy energies: $\sigma_w = \sigma_{ex} + \sigma_{anis}$. The exchange energy is given approximately by (70) for each line of atoms normal to the plane of the wall. There are $1/a^2$ such lines per unit area, where a is the lattice constant. Thus $\sigma_{ex} = \pi^2 JS^2/Na^2$. The anisotropy energy is of the order of the anisotropy constant times the thickness Na, or $\sigma_{anis} \approx KNa$; therefore

$$\sigma_w \approx (\pi^2 JS^2/Na^2) + KNa. \tag{71}$$

This is a minimum with respect to N when

$$\partial\sigma_w/\partial N = 0 = -(\pi^2 JS^2/N^2a^2) + Ka \tag{72}$$

or

$$N = (\pi^2 JS^2/Ka^3)^{1/2}. \tag{73}$$

For order of magnitude, $N \approx 300$ in iron.

The total wall energy per unit area on our model is

$$\sigma_w = 2\pi(KJS^2/a)^{1/2}; \tag{74}$$

in iron $\sigma_w \approx 1$ erg/cm^2. Accurate calculation for a 180° wall in a (100) plane gives $\sigma_w = 2(2K_1JS^2/a)^{1/2}$.

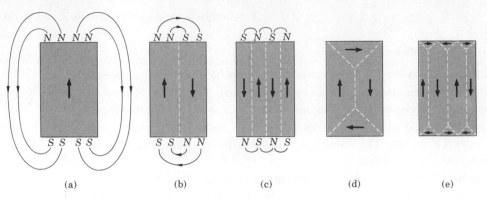

Figure 42 The origin of domains.

Origin of Domains

Landau and Lifshitz showed that domain structure is a natural consequence of the various contributions to the energy—exchange, anisotropy, and magnetic—of a ferromagnetic body. Direct evidence of domain structure is furnished by photomicrographs of domain boundaries obtained by the technique of magnetic powder patterns and by optical studies using Faraday rotation. The powder pattern method developed by F. Bitter consists in placing a drop of a colloidal suspension of finely divided ferromagnetic material, such as magnetite, on the carefully prepared surface of the ferromagnetic crystal under study. The colloid particles in the suspension concentrate strongly about the boundaries between domains where strong local magnetic fields exist which attract the magnetic particles. The discovery of transparent ferromagnetic compounds has encouraged the use of optical observation.

We may understand the origin of domains by considering the structures shown in Fig. 42, each representing a cross section through a ferromagnetic single crystal. In (a) we have a single domain; as a consequence of the magnetic "poles" formed on the surfaces of the crystal this configuration will have a high value of the magnetic energy $(1/8\pi) \int H^2 \, dV$. The magnetic energy density for the configuration shown will be of the order of $M_s^2 \approx 10^6$ ergs/cm^3; here M_s denotes the saturation magnetization.

In (b) the magnetic energy is reduced by roughly one-half by dividing the crystal into two domains magnetized in opposite directions. In (c) with N domains the magnetic energy is reduced because of the reduced spatial extension of the field to approximately $1/N$ of the magnetic energy of (a).

In domain arrangements such as (d) and (e) the magnetic energy is zero. Here the boundaries of the triangular prism domains near the end faces of the crystal make equal angles—45°—with the magnetization in the rectangular domains and with the magnetization in the domains of closure. The component of magnetization normal to the boundary is continuous across the boundary and there is no magnetic field associated with the magnetization.

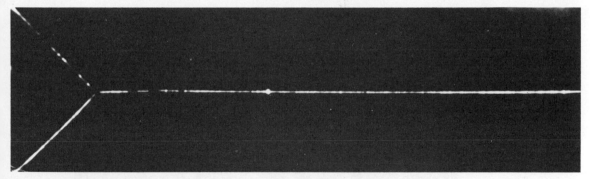

Figure 43   Domain of closure at the end of a single crystal iron whisker. The face is a (100) plane; the whisker axis is [001]. (Courtesy of R. V. Coleman, C. G. Scott, and A. Isin.)

The flux circuit is completed within the crystal—thus giving rise to the phrase **domains of closure** for surface domains which act to complete the flux circuit, as in Fig. 43.

Domain structures are often more complicated than our simple examples, but *domain structure always has its origin in the possibility of lowering the energy of a system by going from a saturated configuration with high magnetic energy to a domain configuration with a lower energy.*

Coercive Force and Hysteresis

The coercive force is the field $-H_c$ required to reduce the induction B to zero (Fig. 37). It is the most sensitive property of ferromagnetic materials which is subject to control. The coercive force may range from the value of 600 G in a loudspeaker permanent magnet (Alnico V) and 20,000 G in a special high stability magnet (Fe-Pt) to 0.5 G in a commercial power transformer (Si-Fe) or 0.004 G in a pulse transformer (Supermalloy). In a transformer low hysteresis is desired; this means a low coercive force.

The coercive force decreases as the impurity content decreases and also as internal strains are removed by annealing (slow cooling). Alloys which contain a precipitated phase may have a high coercivity, as in Fig. 44.

The high coercivity of materials composed of very small grains or fine powders is well understood. A sufficiently small particle, with diameter less than 10^{-5} or 10^{-6} cm, is always magnetized to saturation as a single domain because the formation of a flux-closure configuration is energetically unfavorable[38] (Problem 6).

In a sufficiently small single domain particle it will not be possible for magnetization reversal to take place by means of the process of boundary

[38] L. Néel, Compt. rend. **224**, 1488 (1947), C. Kittel, Phys. Rev. **70**, 965 (1946). A review of permanent magnet technology is given by F. E. Luborsky, Electro-Technology **70** (1962)—see No. 1, p. 100; No. 2, p. 94; No. 3, p. 107.

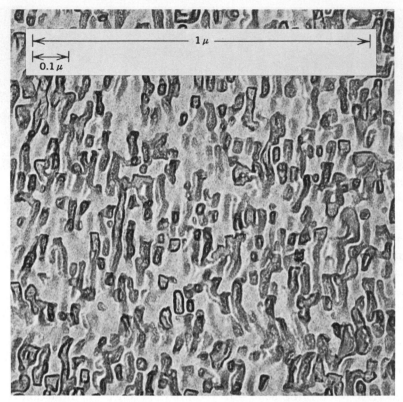

Figure 44 Microstructure of Alnico V in its optimum state as a permanent magnet. (Courtesy of F. E. Luborsky.)

displacement; which usually requires relatively weak fields; instead the magnetization of the particle must rotate as a whole, a process which may require large fields depending on the anisotropy energy of the material and the shape of the particle.

The coercive force of fine iron particles is expected theoretically to be about 500 oersteds on the basis of rotation opposed by the crystalline anisotropy energy, and this is of the order of the value reported by several observers. Higher coercivities have been reported for elongated iron particles, the rotation here being opposed by the shape anisotropy of the demagnetization energy. The high coercivity of powders of MnBi ($_{M}H_{c} > 14,000$), investigated by Guillaud, suggests that anisotropy energy is the factor opposing rotation.

Problems

1. **Magnon dispersion relation.** Derive the magnon dispersion relation (27) for a spin S on a simple cubic lattice, $z = 6$. Hint: Show first that (21a) is replaced by

$$dS_\rho^x/dt = (2JS/\hbar)(6S_\rho^y - \sum_\delta S_{\rho+\delta}^y),$$

where the central atom is at ρ and the six nearest neighbors are connected to it by six vectors δ. Look for solutions of the equations for dS_ρ^x/dt and dS_ρ^y/dt of the form $\exp(i\mathbf{k}\cdot\rho - i\omega t)$.

2. **Heat capacity of magnons.** Use the approximate magnon dispersion relation $\omega = Ak^2$ to find the leading term in the heat capacity of a three-dimensional ferromagnet at low temperatures $k_B T \ll J$. The result is $0.113\, k_B(k_B T/\hbar A)^{3/2}$, per unit volume. An experimental curve is given in Fig. 45; the heat capacity here is made up of a magnon contribution proportional to $T^{3/2}$ and a phonon contribution proportional to T^3.

3. **Néel temperature.** Taking the effective fields on the two-sublattice model of an antiferromagnetic as

$$H_A = H - \mu M_B - \epsilon M_A; \qquad H_B = H - \mu M_A - \epsilon M_B,$$

show that

$$\theta/T_N = (\mu + \epsilon)/(\mu - \epsilon).$$

4. **Magnetoelastic coupling.** In a cubic crystal the elastic energy density is, according to Chapter 4,

$$U_{el} = \tfrac{1}{2}C_{11}(e_{xx}^2 + e_{yy}^2 + e_{zz}^2) + \tfrac{1}{2}C_{44}(e_{xy}^2 + e_{yz}^2 + e_{zx}^2)$$
$$+ C_{12}(e_{yy}e_{zz} + e_{xx}e_{zz} + e_{xx}e_{yy}),$$

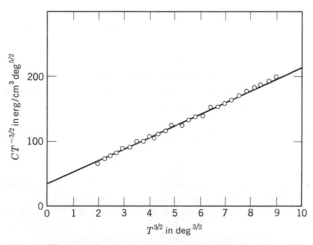

Figure 45 Heat capacity of yttrium iron garnet, $Y_3Fe_5O_{12}$, after S. Shinozaki, Phys. Rev. **122**, 388 (1961). A plot of $C/T^{3/2}$ versus $T^{3/2}$ will be a straight line if the heat capacity is of the form $C = aT^{3/2} + bT^3$, where $aT^{3/2}$ is the magnon contribution and bT^3 is the phonon contribution.

and the leading term in the magnetic anisotropy energy density is, from (69),

$$U_K \cong K_1(\alpha_1{}^2\alpha_2{}^2 + \alpha_2{}^2\alpha_3{}^2 + \alpha_3{}^2\alpha_1{}^2).$$

Coupling between elastic strain and magnetization direction may be taken formally into account by including in the total energy density a term

$$U_c \cong B_1(\alpha_1{}^2 e_{xx} + \alpha_2{}^2 e_{yy} + \alpha_3{}^2 e_{zz}) + B_2(\alpha_1\alpha_2 e_{xy} + \alpha_2\alpha_3 e_{yz} + \alpha_3\alpha_1 e_{zx})$$

arising from the strain dependence of U_K; here B_1 and B_2 are called **magnetoelastic coupling constants**. Show that the total energy is a minimum when

$$e_{ii} = B_1[C_{12} - \alpha_i{}^2(C_{11} + 2C_{12})]/[(C_{11} - C_{12})(C_{11} + 2C_{12})];$$
$$e_{ij} = -B_2\alpha_i\alpha_j/C_{44} \qquad (i \neq j).$$

This explains the origin of magnetostriction, the change of length on magnetization.

5. *Coercive force of a small particle.* Consider a small spherical single-domain particle of a uniaxial ferromagnet. Show that the reverse field along the axis required to reverse the magnetization is

$$H = 2K/M_s.$$

The coercive force of single-domain particles is observed to be of this magnitude. Take $U_K = K \sin^2 \theta$ as the anisotropy energy density and $U_M = -HM \cos \theta$ as the interaction energy density with the external field H; here θ is the angle between **H** and **M**. *Hint:* Expand the energies for small angles about $\theta = \pi$, and find the value of H for which $U_K + U_M$ does not have a minimum near $\theta = \pi$.

6. *Criterion for single domain particles.* Show that the magnetic energy of a saturated sphere of diameter d is $\approx M_s{}^2 d^3$. An arrangement with appreciably less magnetic energy has a single wall in an equatorial plane. The domain wall energy will be $\pi\sigma_w d^2/4$, where σ_w is the wall energy per unit area. *Estimate* for cobalt the critical radius below which the particles are stable as single domains, taking the value of JS^2/a as for iron.

°7. *Antiferromagnetism of fcc lattice.* Show that, for spins on a face-centered cubic lattice with antiferromagnetic nearest-neighbor interactions only, $\theta/T_N = 3$. *Hint:* Decompose the fcc lattice into four sc sublattices.

References

S. Chikazumi, *Physics of magnetism*, Wiley, 1964. (Elementary account of ferromagnetism.)

A. H. Morrish, *Physical principles of magnetism*, Wiley, 1965.

G. T. Rado and H. Suhl, eds., *Magnetism*, Academic Press, 1963, several volumes. (An encyclopedic work.)

R. M. Bozorth, *Ferromagnetism*, Van Nostrand, 1951.

C. Kittel and J. K. Galt, "Ferromagnetic domains," *Solid state physics* **3**, 437 (1956).

D. J. Craik and R. S. Tebble, *Ferromagnetism and ferromagnetic domains*, North Holland, 1966.

J. Smit and H. P. J. Wijn, *Ferrites*, Wiley, 1959.

F. Keffer, "Spin waves," *Encyclo. of physics* **18/2** (1966).

T. Nagamiya, K. Yosida, and R. Kubo, "Antiferromagnetism," *Adv. in Physics* **4**, 1 (1955).

J. B. Goodenough, *Magnetism and the chemical bond*, Interscience, 1963.

16

Magnetic Resonance

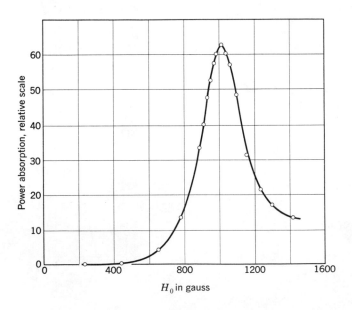

Figure 1 Electron spin resonance absorption in MnSO$_4$ at 298°K at 2.75 Gcs, after Zavoisky.

In this chapter we discuss dynamical magnetic effects associated with the spin angular momentum of nuclei and of electrons. Applications of magnetic spin resonance in solid state physics are of great importance. The principal phenomena are often identified in the literature by their initial letters, such as

NMR: nuclear magnetic resonance
NQR: nuclear quadrupole resonance
EPR: electron paramagnetic resonance (electron spin resonance)
FMR: ferromagnetic resonance
AFMR: antiferromagnetic resonance

Zavoisky[1] performed the earliest magnetic resonance experiments in a solid. He observed strong electron spin resonance absorption (Fig. 1) in several paramagnetic salts. Spin resonance experiments on nuclei in liquids and solids were carried out first by Purcell, Torrey, and Pound[2] and by Bloch, Hansen, and Packard.[3]

It is best to discuss NMR in some detail, as a basis for a brief account of the other resonance experiments. The references listed at the end of the chapter are exceptionally useful sources of further information.

NUCLEAR MAGNETIC RESONANCE

We consider a nucleus which possesses a magnetic moment μ and an angular momentum $\hbar\mathbf{I}$. The two quantities are parallel, and we may write

$$\mu = \gamma\hbar\mathbf{I}; \tag{1}$$

γ is a constant, as in Eq. (14.15). By convention $\mathbf{I}$ denotes the nuclear angular momentum measured in units of $\hbar$. The energy of interaction with an applied magnetic field $\mathbf{H}$ is

$$U = -\mu \cdot \mathbf{H}; \tag{2}$$

if $\mathbf{H} = H_0\hat{z}$,

$$U = -\mu_z H_0 = -\gamma\hbar H_0 I_z. \tag{3}$$

The allowed values of I_z are $m_I = I, I - 1, \ldots, -I$, whence $U = -m_I\gamma\hbar H_0$.

[1] E. Zavoisky, J. Phys. USSR 9, 211, 245, 447 (1945).
[2] E. M. Purcell, H. C. Torrey, and R. V. Pound, Phys. Rev. 69, 37 (1946).
[3] F. Bloch, W. W. Hansen, and M. Packard, Phys. Rev. 69, 127 (1946).

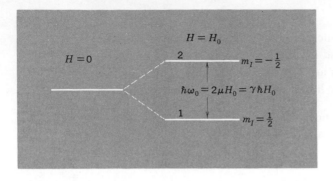

Figure 2 Energy level splitting of a nucleus of spin $I = \frac{1}{2}$ in a static magnetic field H_0.

In a magnetic field a nucleus with $I = \frac{1}{2}$ has two energy levels corresponding to $m_I = \pm\frac{1}{2}$, as in Fig. 2. If $\hbar\omega_0$ denotes the energy difference between the two levels, then $\hbar\omega_0 = \gamma\hbar H_0$ or

$$\omega_0 = \gamma H_0. \tag{4}$$

This is the fundamental condition for magnetic resonance absorption. For the proton[4] $\gamma = 2.68 \times 10^4$ sec^{-1} gauss^{-1}, so that ν (kilocycles/sec) $= 4.26$ H (gauss), where ν is the frequency. For the electron spin ν (megacycles/sec) $= 2.80\ H$ (gauss). Magnetic data for selected nuclei are given in Table 1.

Table 1   Nuclear magnetic resonance data for selected nuclei
(After Varian Associates NMR table)

Isotope	Natural abundance, %	NMR frequency, in Mcs per 10 kG	Magnetic moment μ, in multiples of $e\hbar/2M_pc$	Spin I	Electric quadrupole moment, in multiples of $e \times 10^{-24}$ cm^2
H^1	99.984	42.576	2.793	$\frac{1}{2}$	0
H^2	0.016	6.536	0.857	1	0.0027
Li^7	92.57	16.55	3.256	$\frac{3}{2}$	-0.1
C^{13}	1.11	10.71	0.702	$\frac{1}{2}$	0
F^{19}	100	40.06	2.63	$\frac{1}{2}$	0
Na^{23}	100	11.26	2.216	$\frac{3}{2}$	0.1
Si^{29}	4.70	8.46	-0.555	$\frac{1}{2}$	0
Cl^{35}	75.4	4.17	0.821	$\frac{3}{2}$	-0.08
K^{39}	93.08	1.99	0.391	$\frac{3}{2}$	-0.07
K^{41}	6.91	1.09	0.215	$\frac{3}{2}$	$-$
I^{127}	100.0	8.52	2.79	$\frac{5}{2}$	-0.75

[4] The magnetic moment of the proton is 1.410×10^{-23} erg/gauss, whence $\gamma \equiv 2\mu_p/\hbar = 2.68 \times 10^4$ sec^{-1} G^{-1}. The **nuclear magneton** μ_n is defined as $e\hbar/2M_pc$ and is equal to 5.050×10^{-24} erg/G; thus $\mu_p = 2.793$ nuclear magnetons.

Equations of Motion

The rate of change of angular momentum of a system is equal to the torque which acts on the system. The torque on a magnetic moment μ in a magnetic field $\mathbf{H}$ is $\mu \times \mathbf{H}$, so that we have the gyroscopic equation

$$\hbar \frac{d\mathbf{I}}{dt} = \mu \times \mathbf{H}; \tag{5}$$

or

$$\frac{d\mu}{dt} = \gamma \mu \times \mathbf{H}. \tag{6}$$

The nuclear magnetization $\mathbf{M}$ is defined as the sum $\Sigma \mu_i$ over all the nuclei in a unit volume. If only a single isotope is important, we consider only a single value of γ, so that

$$\boxed{\frac{d\mathbf{M}}{dt} = \gamma \mathbf{M} \times \mathbf{H}.} \tag{7}$$

We place the nuclei in a static field $\mathbf{H} = H_0 \hat{z}$. In thermal equilibrium at temperature T the magnetization will be along $\hat{z}$:

$$M_x = 0; \quad M_y = 0; \quad M_z = M_0 = \chi_0 H_0 = CH_0/T, \tag{8}$$

where the Curie constant $C = N\mu^2/3k_B$ as defined by (14.14). The magnetization of a system of spins with $I = \frac{1}{2}$ is related to the population difference $N_1 - N_2$ of the lower and upper levels in Fig. 2: $M_z = (N_1 - N_2)\mu$, where the N's refer to a unit volume. The population ratio in thermal equilibrium is just given by the Boltzmann factor

$$N_2{}^0/N_1{}^0 = \exp\left(-2\mu H_0/k_B T\right), \tag{9}$$

because the energy difference is $2\mu H_0$. The equilibrium magnetization is given by (14.20).

Suppose the magnetization component M_z is not in thermal equilibrium? We assume that M_z approaches equilibrium at a rate proportional to the departure from the equilibrium value $M_0 = \chi_0 H_0$:

$$dM_z/dt = (M_0 - M_z)/T_1. \tag{10}$$

In the standard notation T_1 is called the **longitudinal relaxation time** or the **spin-lattice relaxation time**.

If at $t = 0$ an unmagnetized specimen is placed in a magnetic field $H_0\hat{z}$, the magnetization will increase from the initial value[5] $M_z = 0$ to a final value

---

[5] Before and just after the specimen is placed in the field the population N_1 will be equal to N_2, as appropriate to thermal equilibrium in zero magnetic field. It is necessary to reverse some spins to establish the new equilibrium distribution in the field H_0.

504

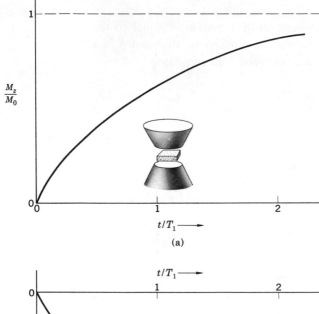

Figure 3a At time $t = 0$ an unmagnetized specimen $M_z(0) = 0$ is placed in a static magnetic field H_0. The magnetization increases with time and approaches the new equilibrium value $M_0 = \chi_0 H_0$. This experiment defines the longitudinal relaxation time T_1.

(a)

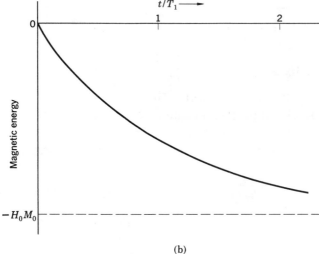

Figure 3b In the experiment of Fig. 3a the magnetic energy density $-\mathbf{M} \cdot \mathbf{H}$ decreases as part of the spin population moves into the lower level. The asymptotic value at $t \gg T_1$ is $-H_0 M_0$. The energy flows from the spin system to the system of lattice vibrations; thus T_1 is also called the spin-lattice relaxation time.

(b)

$M_z = M_0$. On integrating (10):

$$\int_0^{M_z} \frac{dM_z}{M_0 - M_z} = \frac{1}{T_1} \int_0^t dt, \tag{11}$$

or

$$\log \frac{M_0}{M_0 - M_z} = \frac{t}{T_1}; \qquad M_z(t) = M_0(1 - e^{-t/T_1}), \tag{12}$$

as in Fig. 3a. The magnetic energy $-\mathbf{H} \cdot \mathbf{M}$ decreases as M_z approaches its new equilibrium value (Fig. 3b).

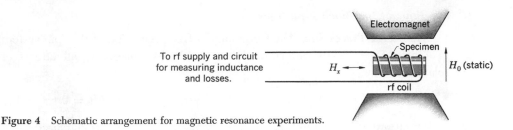

Figure 4   Schematic arrangement for magnetic resonance experiments.

Taking account of (10), the z component of the equation of motion (7) becomes

$$dM_z/dt = \gamma(\mathbf{M} \times \mathbf{H})_z + (M_0 - M_z)/T_1, \qquad (13a)$$

where $(M_0 - M_z)/T_1$ is an extra term in the equation of motion, arising from interactions not included in the magnetic field $\mathbf{H}$. That is, besides precessing about the magnetic field, $\mathbf{M}$ will relax to the equilibrium value $\mathbf{M}_0$.

If in a static field $H_0\hat{z}$ the transverse magnetization component M_x is not zero, then M_x will decay to zero, and similarly for M_y. The decay occurs because in thermal equilibrium the transverse components are zero. We can modify the equations to provide for transverse relaxation:

$$dM_x/dt = \gamma(\mathbf{M} \times \mathbf{H})_x - M_x/T_2; \qquad (13b)$$

$$dM_y/dt = \gamma(\mathbf{M} \times \mathbf{H})_y - M_y/T_2, \qquad (13c)$$

where T_2 is called the **transverse relaxation time**. The magnetic energy $-\mathbf{H} \cdot \mathbf{M}$ does not change as M_x or M_y changes, provided that $\mathbf{H}$ is along $\hat{z}$. No energy need flow out of the spin system for relaxation of M_x or M_y to occur,[6] so that the conditions which determine T_2 may be less strict than for T_1. Sometimes the two times are nearly equal, and sometimes $T_1 \gg T_2$, depending on local conditions. Two separate kinds of relaxation processes must be considered.

The set of equations (13) are called the **Bloch equations**. They are not symmetrical in x, y, and z because we have biased the system with a static magnetic field along $\hat{z}$. In the experiments an rf magnetic field is usually applied along the $\hat{x}$ or $\hat{y}$ axes. Our main interest is in the behavior of the magnetization in the combined rf and static fields, as in Fig. 4. The Bloch equations are plausible, but not exact; they do not describe all spin phenomena, particularly in solids.

[6] There is no static field component H_x or H_y, so that the magnetic energy $-\mathbf{H} \cdot \mathbf{M}$ does not involve M_x or M_y.

Solutions of the Bloch Equations

(a) *Free Precession.* The frequency of free precession of the spin system in a field $\mathbf{H} = H_0\hat{z}$ is determined from (13) by neglecting all effects of relaxation. Then

$$dM_x/dt = \gamma H_0 M_y; \qquad dM_y = -\gamma H_0 M_x; \qquad dM_z/dt = 0. \tag{14}$$

In this situation the magnetization vector $\mathbf{M}$ carries out a circular precession about the field direction. If m is the amplitude and ω the frequency of the precession, then

$$M_x = m \cos \omega t; \qquad M_y = -m \sin \omega t, \tag{15}$$

as in Fig. 5. On substitution of (15) in (14) we find

$$-\omega \sin \omega t = -\gamma H_0 \sin \omega t; \qquad -\omega \cos \omega t = -\gamma H_0 \cos \omega t, \tag{16}$$

so that the free precession frequency ω_0 is

$$\omega_0 = \gamma H_0. \tag{17}$$

This is identical with the result (4).

(b) *Steady state, weak rf field.* We are interested in the motion of the spin system in combined static and rf fields after all transient effects arising from the switching-on of the fields have decayed. Let

$$\mathbf{H} = H_1(\hat{x} \cos \omega t - \hat{y} \sin \omega t) + H_0\hat{z}; \tag{18}$$

this represents a static field $H_0\hat{z}$ and an rf field of constant amplitude H_1 which rotates in the x, y plane. The rotation is clockwise for $\omega > 0$. Then the Bloch equations (13) become, with $\omega_0 \equiv \gamma H_0$ and $\omega_1 \equiv \gamma H_1$,

$$dM_x/dt = \omega_0 M_y + \omega_1 M_z \sin \omega t - M_x/T_2; \tag{19a}$$

$$dM_y/dt = -\omega_0 M_x + \omega_1 M_z \cos \omega t - M_y/T_2; \tag{19b}$$

$$dM_z/dt = -\omega_1(M_x \sin \omega t + M_y \cos \omega t) + (M_0 - M_z)/T_1. \tag{19c}$$

If the rf magnetic field is sufficiently weak (we shall see later what restriction this puts on H_1), the transverse magnetization components will be small in comparison with M_z, and the terms in (19c) in $\omega_1 M_x$ and $\omega_1 M_y$ may be neglected[7] in comparison with the terms $\omega_1 M_z$, $\omega_0 M_x$, etc., in the other equations. Thus in the steady state (19c) has the solution $M_z = M_0$.

We look for solutions for M_x, M_y of the form

$$M_x = m \cos (\omega t + \varphi); \qquad M_y = -m \sin (\omega t + \varphi), \tag{20}$$

---

[7] Note that each of the two terms ω_1 and M_x in $\omega_1 M_x$ is proportional to the rf field H_1, because M_x is the response of the system to H_1. But $\omega_1 M_z$ is of first order in H_1 because $M_z \cong M_0$, independent of H_1.

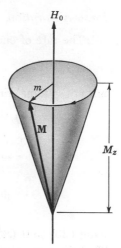

Figure 5 The magnetization **M** precesses about the static field H_0 at the frequency $\omega_0 = \gamma H_0$.

where φ is an angle to be determined; it is the azimuthal angle by which **M** leads **II**. Using (20) in (19a) we have, on setting $t = 0$ after differentiation,

$$-\omega m \sin \varphi = -\omega_0 m \sin \varphi - (m/T_2) \cos \varphi, \qquad (21)$$

whence

$$\tan \varphi = -\frac{1}{(\omega_0 - \omega) T_2}. \qquad (22)$$

From (19b) we have

$$-\omega m \cos \varphi = -\omega_0 m \cos \varphi + (m/T_2) \sin \varphi + \omega_1 M_z, \qquad (23)$$

or

$$m = \frac{\omega_1 M_z T_2}{(\omega_0 - \omega) T_2 \cos \varphi - \sin \varphi}. \qquad (24)$$

If we take[8]

$$\cos \varphi = \frac{(\omega_0 - \omega) T_2}{[1 + (\omega_0 - \omega)^2 T_2{}^2]^{1/2}}; \quad \sin \varphi = -\frac{1}{[1 + (\omega_0 - \omega)^2 T_2{}^2]^{1/2}}, \quad (25)$$

we satisfy (22), and we find from (24) that the transverse magnetization amplitude is given by

$$m = \frac{\gamma M_z T_2 H_1}{[1 + (\omega_0 - \omega)^2 T_2{}^2]^{1/2}}. \qquad (26)$$

This is a maximum when $\omega = \omega_0$. In the present approximation we may replace M_z by M_0 if we wish. The reason T_2 enters is that both m and T_2 refer to transverse effects.

---

[8] The minus sign is placed with the sine and not with the cosine in order to give conservation of energy—that is, to make the power absorption (28) positive. The same point arises in the theory of the motion of a driven harmonic oscillator.

Power Absorption

The rate of energy absorption by the nuclear spin system is

$$\mathcal{P} = \mathbf{H} \cdot d\mathbf{M}/dt \tag{27}$$

per unit volume. From (18) and (20) we have

$$
\begin{aligned}
\mathcal{P} &= (H_1 \cos \omega t)(-\omega m)(\sin \omega t \cos \varphi + \cos \omega t \sin \varphi) \\
&\quad + (-H_1 \sin \omega t)(-\omega m)(\cos \omega t \cos \varphi - \sin \omega t \sin \varphi) \\
&= -\omega H_1 m \sin \varphi \, (\cos^2 \omega t + \sin^2 \omega t),
\end{aligned} \tag{28}
$$

or

$$\mathcal{P} = -\omega H_1 m \sin \varphi = \frac{\omega \gamma M_z T_2 H_1{}^2}{1 + (\omega_0 - \omega)^2 T_2{}^2}, \tag{29}$$

using (25) and (26). The power absorption is a maximum close to $\omega = \omega_0$. The half-width of the resonance at half-power is

$$(\Delta \omega)_{1/2} = 1/T_2; \tag{30}$$

thus $1/T_2$ is a measure of the line width.

In the steady state the energy absorbed from the rf field usually will end up as lattice vibrations.

Change of Inductance near Resonance

The contribution of the nuclear magnetization to the inductance of a coil wound around the specimen is the subject of Problem 1. By the definition of inductance as relating flux to current (recall that H_1 is proportional to the current in the rf coils) we find that the inductance is proportional to the part of $\mathbf{M}$ which moves *in phase* with $\mathbf{H}$.

From (20) the transverse magnetization is given by

$$
\begin{aligned}
\mathbf{m}(t) = m\{ \hat{\mathbf{x}}(\cos \omega t \cos \varphi - \sin \omega t \sin \varphi) \\
- \hat{\mathbf{y}}(\sin \omega t \cos \varphi + \cos \omega t \sin \varphi)\}.
\end{aligned} \tag{31}
$$

The component of $\mathbf{m}(t)$ which moves in phase with a rotating field $\mathbf{H}_1(t) = H_1(\hat{\mathbf{x}} \cos \omega t - \hat{\mathbf{y}} \sin \omega t)$ is denoted by $\mathbf{m}'$; it is readily identified from (31) as

$$\mathbf{m}' = m \cos \varphi \, (\hat{\mathbf{x}} \cos \omega t - \hat{\mathbf{y}} \sin \omega t). \tag{31a}$$

There is a component of $\mathbf{m}(t)$ which is perpendicular to $\mathbf{H}_1(t)$; this out-of-phase component is denoted by $\mathbf{m}''$, where

$$\mathbf{m}'' = -m \sin \varphi \, (\hat{\mathbf{x}} \sin \omega t + \hat{\mathbf{y}} \cos \omega t). \tag{31b}$$

---

[9] Also (if complex notation is used) called the real and imaginary parts of the susceptibility: $\chi = \chi' + i\chi''$, as for the dielectric constant $\epsilon = \epsilon' + i\epsilon''$ in Chapter 12. We also call χ' the **dispersive part** and χ'' the **absorptive part** of the susceptibility.

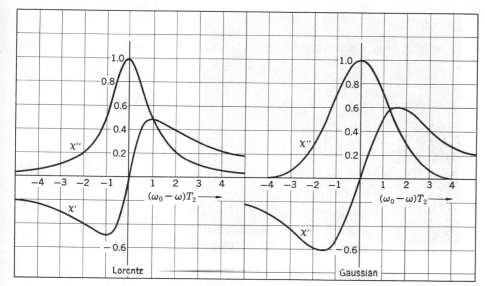

Figure 6   Plot of absorption χ'' and dispersion χ' components of the rf susceptibility in units of $\chi_0 \omega_0 T_2$ versus $(\omega_0 - \omega) T_2$. The rf field rotates at frequency ω. The Lorentzian line shape is defined by (33) and (69); the Gaussian by (67). (After Pake and Purcell.)

We define[9] the **in-phase susceptibility** χ' and **out-of-phase susceptibility** χ'' by

$$\chi'(\omega) \equiv (m \cos \varphi)/H_1; \qquad \chi'' \equiv -(m \sin \varphi)/H_1. \qquad (32)$$

We note that the power absorption (29) is given by $\mathcal{P} = \omega H_1^2 \chi''$.

Using m from (26), and $\cos \varphi$ and $\sin \varphi$ from (25) we have[10]

$$\chi'(\omega) = \chi_0 \cdot \frac{\omega_0 (\omega_0 - \omega) T_2^2}{1 + (\omega_0 - \omega)^2 T_2^2}; \quad \chi''(\omega) = \chi_0 \cdot \frac{\omega_0 T_2}{1 + (\omega_0 - \omega)^2 T_2^2}; \qquad (33)$$

here $\chi_0 = M_z/H_0$ is the static susceptibility, so that $\gamma M_z = \chi_0 \omega_0$. Note (Fig. 6) that χ' is an odd function of $\omega_0 - \omega$, whereas χ'' is an even function of $\omega_0 - \omega$. At resonance

$$\chi'(\omega_0) = 0; \qquad \chi''(\omega_0) = \chi_0 \cdot \omega_0 T_2 = \chi_0 \frac{\omega_0}{(\Delta \omega)_{1/2}}, \qquad (34)$$

using (30). We see that χ'' at resonance will be very much larger than the static susceptibility χ_0 if the line width $(\Delta \omega)_{1/2}$ is $\ll \omega_0$. We say that the "Q" of the resonance is given by $Q \equiv \omega_0/(\Delta \omega)_{1/2} = \omega_0 T_2$.

---

[10] In the NMR literature the susceptibilities are usually defined for a linearly polarized field $H_x = 2H_1 \cos \omega t$ by the relation $M_x(t) = 2H_1\{\chi'(\omega) \cos \omega t + \chi''(\omega) \sin \omega t\}$; the values of χ' and χ'' from (33) must be reduced by one-half to obtain the expressions in the literature; compare Slichter, p. 31, and Abragam, p. 48. We have treated the simpler problem of circular polarization.

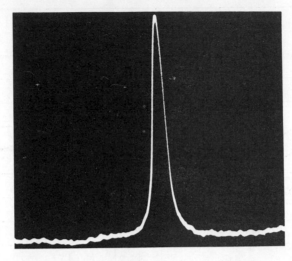

Figure 7 Proton resonance absorption in water. (Courtesy of E. L. Hahn.)

It is possible experimentally to measure χ' or χ'' separately. The component χ' of the susceptibility changes the inductance of a circuit; and χ'' changes the resistance, as in Problem 1. Figure 7 shows χ'' for protons in water.

Saturation at High rf Power

We now treat the behavior of the magnetization (and the power absorption) in strong rf fields. The discussion following (19) was predicated on a "sufficiently weak" rf magnetic field. The exact solutions[11] for an rf field of arbitrary strength are particularly simple at resonance. Guided by the approximate solutions (25), we now define resonance by $\cos \varphi = 0$ and $\sin \varphi = -1$, so that at resonance $\varphi = -\frac{1}{2}\pi$. Then from (20) the transverse magnetization components are

$$M_x = m \sin \omega_0 t; \qquad M_y = m \cos \omega_0 t, \qquad (35)$$

and (19c) becomes, at resonance,

$$dM_z/dt = -\omega_1 m(\sin^2 \omega_0 t + \cos^2 \omega_0 t) + (M_0 - M_z)/T_1. \qquad (36)$$

In the steady state $dM_z/dt = 0$, whence

$$M_z = M_0 - m\omega_1 T_1 = M_0 - M_z(\omega_1^2 T_1 T_2), \qquad (37)$$

from (24) with $\varphi = -\frac{1}{2}\pi$. Thus

$$M_z = \frac{M_0}{1 + \gamma^2 H_1^2 T_1 T_2}, \qquad (38)$$

as plotted in Fig. 8a. We see that the criterion for a weak rf field is $\gamma^2 H_1^2 T_1 T_2 \ll 1$.

_____

[11] The exact solutions for arbitrary values of $\omega - \omega_0$ are given in Abragam, p. 46; see also (53) below.

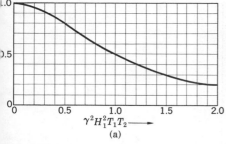
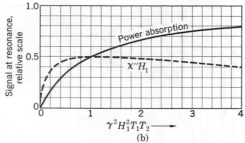

Figure 8a Decrease of M_z at high rf power. Here H_1 is the rf field; and T_1, T_2 are the longitudinal and transverse relaxation times, respectively.

Figure 8b Saturation of power absorption and $\chi''H_1$ at resonance; at sufficiently high rf fields the power absorbed becomes independent of the rf field intensity, and $\chi''H_1$ decreases. By definition $\chi''H_1$ is the transverse magnetization component which is $\pi/2$ out of phase with H_1.

With this value of M_z the transverse magnetization (26) at resonance is

$$m(\omega = \omega_0) = \frac{\gamma M_0 T_2 H_1}{1 + \gamma^2 H_1{}^2 T_1 T_2}, \tag{39a}$$

and (25) tells us that the definition of resonance as $\varphi = -\frac{1}{2}\pi$ is equivalent to the definition $\omega_0 = \gamma H_0$. Thus (33) becomes

$$\chi'(\omega_0) = 0; \qquad \chi''(\omega_0) = \chi_0 \frac{\omega_0 T_2}{1 + \gamma^2 H_1{}^2 T_1 T_2}. \tag{39b}$$

The power absorption is proportional to M_z, so that (38) substituted in (29) at resonance gives

$$\mathcal{P}(\omega_0) = \chi_0 \frac{\omega_0{}^2 T_2 H_1{}^2}{1 + \gamma^2 H_1{}^2 T_1 T_2}. \tag{40}$$

At high values of $H_1{}^2$ we see that

$$\mathcal{P}(\omega_0) \rightarrow \chi_0 H_0{}^2 / T_1, \tag{41}$$

inversely proportional to T_1 and independent of H_1. The phenomenon that the power absorption becomes independent of the rf field when

$$\gamma^2 H_1{}^2 T_1 T_2 \gg 1 \tag{42}$$

is known as **saturation** (Fig. 8b). The dispersion χ' does not saturate under the same conditions because the dispersion is usually observed at values of $\omega - \omega_0$ such that the absorption line shape function (Fig. 6) is much smaller than at $\omega = \omega_0$.

Often the signal detected experimentally is proportional to the out-of-phase magnetization component $H_1\chi''$. For large values of H_1 this signal

512

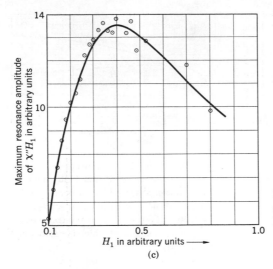

Figure 8c   Saturation of $\chi''H_1$ for protons in an aqueous solution of H_2F_2, after E. L. Hahn.

H_1 in arbitrary units $\longrightarrow$

(c)

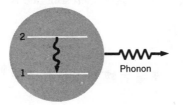

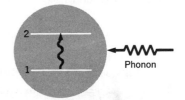

Figure 9   Transition of a spin $I = \frac{1}{2}$ between the states $m_I = \pm\frac{1}{2}$ with the emission or absorption of a phonon of energy $\hbar\omega_0$. The lattice phonons act as a thermal reservoir; by coupling of the spins with the lattice the spin system is brought to thermal equilibrium with the lattice in a time of the order of T_1.

decreases as $1/H_1$. Results for protons are shown in Fig. 8c. If H_1 is too large it is possible in an experiment to miss the resonance entirely.

We now consider saturation from another point of view: In the two-level spin system of Fig. 9 we let N_1, N_2 denote the concentrations in the lower and upper levels, respectively. The rate at which N_2 changes has the form

$$dN_2/dt = w_{21}N_1 - w_{12}N_2 = w_{21}N - (w_{21} + w_{12})N_2, \qquad (43)$$

using $N_1 + N_2 = N$. Here the coefficients w are rate constants which express the effect of longitudinal relaxation. The level 2 gains population by transitions from 1 to 2, and loses populations from 2 to 1. We shall relate the w's to T_1. For the change of N_1 we have

$$dN_1/dt = w_{12}N - (w_{21} + w_{12})N_1, \qquad (44)$$

whence

$$d(N_1 - N_2)/dt = (w_{12} - w_{21})N - (w_{21} + w_{12})(N_1 - N_2). \qquad (45)$$

In thermal equilibrium $N_1 = N_1{}^0$, $N_2 = N_2{}^0$, and $d(N_1 - N_2)/dt = 0$;

from (45) we have

$$(w_{12} - w_{21})N = (w_{21} + w_{12})(N_1{}^0 - N_2{}^0). \tag{46}$$

Thus (45) may be rewritten as

$$d(N_1 - N_2)/dt = (w_{21} + w_{12})[(N_1{}^0 - N_2{}^0) - (N_1 - N_2)]. \tag{47}$$

In equilibrium this rate is zero.

Because $M_z = (N_1 - N_2)\mu$ and $M_0 = (N_1{}^0 - N_2{}^0)\mu$ we rewrite (47) as

$$dM_z/dt = (M_0 - M_z)(w_{21} + w_{12}). \tag{48}$$

This agrees with (10) if we define

$$1/T_1 \equiv (w_{21} + w_{12}). \tag{49}$$

An rf field will induce transitions between the two levels at a rate proportional to the population difference:

$$\left(\frac{d(N_1 - N_2)}{dt}\right)_{\text{rf}} = -\alpha(N_1 - N_2). \tag{50}$$

Here α is a measure of the transition rate due to the rf field; α is proportional to $H_1{}^2$ and to the position and shape of the resonance line. We describe the line by a **line shape function** $g(\omega - \omega_0)$ which depends on the difference between the rf frequency ω and the resonance frequency ω_0. We expect $g(\omega - \omega_0)$ to be a maximum at $g(0)$.

It is customary to normalize $g(\omega - \omega_0)$ so that the transition rate is

$$\alpha = \pi\gamma^2 H_1{}^2 g(\omega - \omega_0). \tag{51}$$

This agrees with the standard quantum theory result for the transition rate if $\int d\omega \, g(\omega - \omega_0) = 1$. Adding (50) to (47) we have for (48):

$$\frac{dM_z}{dt} = \frac{M_0 - M_z}{T_1} - \pi\gamma^2 H_1{}^2 g(\omega - \omega_0)M_z. \tag{52}$$

That is, M_z changes by two competing processes, coupling with lattice vibrations or similar motions and coupling with the rf field.

In the steady state $dM_z/dt = 0$ and

$$M_z = \frac{M_0}{1 + \pi\gamma^2 H_1{}^2 g(\omega - \omega_0)T_1}. \tag{53}$$

This reduces to (38) for $\omega = \omega_0$ if

$$g(0) = T_2/\pi. \tag{54}$$

The farther ω is from ω_0, the smaller will be the value of $g(\omega - \omega_0)$ and the higher the value of H_1 needed to produce saturation. Particular forms of $g(\omega - \omega_0)$ are considered in (67) to (70).

LINE WIDTH AND SHAPE

The magnetic dipolar interaction is often the most important cause of line broadening. The interaction energy of two magnetic dipoles μ_1, μ_2 at separation r_{12} is

$$U_{\mathrm{dip}} = \frac{\mu_1 \cdot \mu_2}{r_{12}{}^3} - \frac{3(\mu_1 \cdot r_{12})(\mu_2 \cdot r_{12})}{r_{12}{}^5}, \tag{55}$$

from elementary magnetostatics. The magnetic field seen by one dipole due to all the other dipoles in the specimen is

$$\mathbf{H}_i = \sum_j{}' \frac{3\mathbf{r}_{ij}(\mu_j \cdot \mathbf{r}_{ij}) - \mu_j r_{ij}{}^2}{r_{ij}{}^5}, \tag{56}$$

by analogy with (12.4). This section is concerned primarily with the contribution to the line width of a field $\mathbf{H}_i$ due to a randomly oriented set of magnetic dipole moments.

Dipolar Line Width in a Rigid Lattice

Let identical nuclear moments with $I = \tfrac{1}{2}$ be randomly distributed[12] among the states $I^z = \pm\tfrac{1}{2}$. We first make a semiclassical estimate of the width and shape of the distribution of the random local field; the exact result is given by (66). Our tentative picture is that the spread of values of $\gamma H_i{}^z$ as seen by the different nuclei is to be identified with the width $\Delta\omega = 1/T_2$ of the resonance line, as in (30).

We take

$$\mu = \gamma \hbar I^z \hat{\mathbf{z}}, \tag{57}$$

neglecting μ_x and μ_y. Let H_i denote the z component of $\mathbf{H}_i$; then from (56)

$$H_i = \gamma \hbar \sum_j{}' \frac{3\cos^2 \theta_j - 1}{r_{ij}{}^3} I_j{}^z, \tag{58}$$

where θ_j is the angle between $\mathbf{r}_{ij}$ and the z axis.

The mean square value $\langle H_i{}^2 \rangle$ is obtained on squaring (58) and making use of the relation

$$\langle I_i{}^z I_j{}^z \rangle = \tfrac{1}{4}\delta_{ij}. \tag{59}$$

This follows from the assumption that the state $\uparrow$ or $\downarrow$ of different nuclei are

---

[12] The Boltzmann factor $\exp\left(-\mu H / k_B T\right)$ is usually very close to unity for nuclear moments, so that in estimating the line width we may neglect the slight preferential orientation of the moments.

uncorrelated or random. Then

$$\langle H_i^2 \rangle = \left(\frac{1}{2}\gamma\hbar\right)^2 \sum_j{}' \frac{(3\cos^2\theta_j - 1)^2}{r_{ij}^6}. \tag{60}$$

We call $\langle H_i^2 \rangle$ the **second moment** of H_i.

If the specimen is a powder composed of crystallites having random orientations, we may average (60) over all directions in space, giving

$$\langle H_i^2 \rangle = \tfrac{1}{5}(\gamma\hbar)^2 \sum_j{}' r_{ij}^{-6}. \tag{61}$$

For a sc crystal of lattice constant a the sum

$$\sum_j{}' r_{ij}^{-6} = 8.5/a^6; \tag{62}$$

a related sum for an fcc crystal was considered in (3.6). Combining (61) and (62),

$$\langle H_i^2 \rangle = 1.7(\gamma\hbar N)^2, \tag{63}$$

where $N = 1/a^3$ is the number of nuclei per unit volume.

The quantity $\Delta H_{\text{rms}} \equiv \langle H_i^2 \rangle^{1/2}$ is a measure of the spread in the values of the local magnetic field seen by the nuclei. Different nuclei will come into resonance at different values of the applied magnetic field, because each nucleus sees a different local field. Thus as a measure of the line width we have

$$\boxed{\Delta\omega = \gamma\,\Delta H_{\text{rms}} \approx \gamma^2\hbar N.} \tag{64}$$

For the nucleus F^{19} we have $I = \tfrac{1}{2}$ and $\gamma = 2.5 \times 10^4 \text{ sec}^{-1}\text{ G}^{-1}$ from Table 1. In the crystal CaF_2 the F^- ions form a sc lattice with $N = 5 \times 10^{22}$ F^- ions/cm^3. Nearly all the Ca nuclei have spin 0. Thus

$$\Delta H_{\text{rms}} \approx 2 \text{ G}; \quad \Delta\omega \approx 5 \times 10^4 \text{ sec}^{-1}; \quad T_2 \equiv 1/\Delta\omega \approx 2 \times 10^{-5} \text{ sec}, \tag{65}$$

in satisfactory agreement with the experimental values.[13]

For a simple cubic crystal the exact quantum mechanical value of the second moment[14] for arbitrary spin I is

$$\langle H_i^2 \rangle = 12.3(\gamma\hbar)^2 I(I+1)(1/a^6)(\alpha_1^4 + \alpha_2^4 + \alpha_3^4 - 0.187), \tag{66}$$

[13] G. E. Pake and E. M. Purcell, Phys. Rev. **74**, 1184 (1948); **75**, 535 (1949).

[14] J. H. Van Vleck, Phys. Rev. **74**, 1168 (1948).

where α_1, α_2, α_3 are the direction cosines of the applied field with respect to the crystal axes.

It is not always sufficient in estimating the line width to consider only the second moment $\langle H_i^2 \rangle$; it is sometimes essential to consider the higher moments. The fourth moment $\langle H_i^4 \rangle$ has also been calculated by Van Vleck. The satisfying agreement of calculated and experimental results for CaF_2 is shown in Table 2; here the dipolar interaction is clearly dominant because it accounts for the experimental results.

Table 2   Observed and calculated value of the second and fourth moments of the F^{19} resonance in CaF_2
(After Abragam)

Direction of H	$\langle H_i^2 \rangle^{1/2}$ in G		$\langle H_i^4 \rangle^{1/4}$ in G	
	Observed	Calculated	Observed	Calculated
[100]	3.47–3.68	3.60	4.13–4.19	4.31
[110]	2.17–2.25	2.24	2.65–2.76	2.73
[111]	1.52–1.77	1.53	1.88–1.96	1.88

It is shown in Problem 3 that $\langle H_i^4 \rangle / \langle H_i^2 \rangle^2 = 3$ for the **Gaussian line** defined by the shape function

$$g(\omega - \omega_0) = [1/\Delta(2\pi)^{1/2}] \exp\left[-(\omega - \omega_0)^2/2\Delta^2\right], \tag{67}$$

as in Fig. 6. For a simple cubic crystal with $I = \frac{1}{2}$ the exact calculated ratio of $\langle H_i^4 \rangle / \langle H_i^2 \rangle^2$ is 2.07 in the [100] direction and 2.30 in the [111] direction. These values of the ratio are near 3, which suggests that the dipolar line may be close to Gaussian.

The Bloch equations give a different line shape. From (33) we have

$$\chi''(\omega) \propto \frac{1}{1 + (\omega_0 - \omega)^2 T_2^2}. \tag{68}$$

This is called a **Lorentzian line;** the normalized line shape function is

$$g(\omega - \omega_0) = \frac{\delta}{\pi} \cdot \frac{1}{\delta^2 + (\omega - \omega_0)^2}, \tag{69}$$

with $\delta = 1/T_2$. Neither the second nor any higher moment of the Lorentzian line is convergent, so we cannot compare the ratio of the moments with experiment. The long tails of the Lorentzian line make it essentially different from the Gaussian line, for which the tails are very weak.

Many observed lines are of the Lorentzian form over the region of observation. The tails are usually hard to follow far from resonance because of noise. A crude representation of a convergent modification of a Lorentzian line is given by the shape function

$$g(\omega - \omega_0) = \frac{\delta}{\pi} \cdot \frac{1}{\delta^2 + (\omega - \omega_0)^2} \qquad \text{for } |\omega - \omega_0| \le \Omega$$
$$0 \qquad \text{for } |\omega - \omega_0| > \Omega. \tag{70}$$

Here Ω is called the cutoff frequency; we suppose that $\Omega \gg \delta$. We shall see that a good physical basis for the assumption of a cutoff frequency can often be found. As calculated in Problem 4 we have from (70):

$$\langle H_i{}^4 \rangle / \langle H_i{}^2 \rangle^2 = \pi\Omega/6\delta, \tag{71}$$

which can be very large.

When the value of the observed ratio of $\langle H_i{}^4 \rangle / \langle H_i{}^2 \rangle^2$ is close to 3, we usually represent the line by the Gaussian function, Eq. (67). If the value of the ratio is much larger than 3, we use the cutoff Lorentzian function of (70). We recall that the Lorentzian does satisfy the Bloch equations. In magnetically diluted rigid lattices with magnetic moments distributed at random on lattice points the line shape[15] is Gaussian at concentrations $f > 0.1$ and Lorentzian at $f < 0.01$.

[15] C. Kittel and E. Abrahams, Phys. Rev. **90**, 238 (1953); the method of this paper is applicable to a wide variety of random lattice problems. See also Abragam, pp. 125–128; S. J. Wyard, Proc. Phys. Soc. (London) **86**, 587 (1965).

Motional Narrowing

It is well established experimentally that the line width is decreased if the nuclei are in rapid motion relative to one another. The effect in solids is illustrated by Fig. 10: diffusion[16] ressembles a random walk process where atoms jump from one crystal site to another. An atom remains in one site for an average time τ which decreases as the temperature increases. In liquids the motional effects on line width are usually even more spectacular than in solids, because atoms are more mobile in a liquid.

We can estimate the motional effects on the line width $\Delta\omega = 1/T_2$ by an elementary argument. We know that for the rigid lattice T_2 measures the average time in which different spins become dephased by one radian, for $\Delta\omega \cdot T_2 \approx 1$, where $\Delta\omega$ is the width of the frequency distribution, as in (64). But if the atoms are in rapid relative motion, the local field H_i seen by a given spin will fluctuate rapidly in time. The local field may be caused by dipolar interactions with other spins. To take a simple model, suppose that the local field has a value H_i for a short time τ and then changes randomly to $\pm H_i$. This change could be caused by relative motion of atoms, as by a change of the angle θ in (58). In the time τ the spin will precess an extra phase angle $\delta\varphi = \pm\gamma H_i\tau$ relative to its precession in the applied field H_0. After n intervals of duration τ the mean square dephasing angle will be

$$\langle\varphi^2\rangle = n(\delta\varphi)^2 = n\gamma^2 H_i{}^2\tau^2, \tag{72}$$

by analogy with a random walk process: the mean square displacement after n steps of length l in random directions is $\langle r^2\rangle = nl^2$.

The number of steps necessary to dephase by one radian is $n = 1/\gamma^2 H_i{}^2\tau^2$, and this number of steps takes place in a time

$$T_2 = n\tau = 1/\gamma^2 H_i{}^2\tau, \tag{73}$$

quite different from the rigid lattice result $T_2 \cong 1/\gamma H_i$. From (73) we obtain

[16] A detailed study of T_1 and T_2 in alkali metals has been made by D. F. Holcomb and R. E. Norberg, Phys. Rev. **84**, 1074 (1955). Diffusion is discussed in Chap. 18.

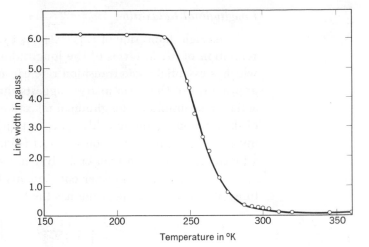

Figure 10 Effect of diffusion of nuclei on the Li[7] NMR line width in metallic lithium. At low temperatures the value of the second moment agrees with the theoretical value for a rigid lattice. As the temperature increases the diffusion rate increases and the line width decreases. [After H. S. Gutowsky and B. R. McGarvey, J. Chem. Phys. **20**, 1472 (1952).]

as the line width for rapid motion with a characteristic time τ:

$$\Delta\omega = 1/T_2 = (\gamma H_i)^2\tau, \tag{74}$$

or

$$\boxed{\Delta\omega = 1/T_2 = (\Delta\omega)_0{}^2\tau,} \tag{75}$$

where $(\Delta\omega)_0$ is the line width of the rigid lattice.

The argument assumes that $(\Delta\omega)_0\tau \ll 1$, as otherwise $\delta\varphi$ will not be $\ll 1$. Thus $\Delta\omega \ll (\Delta\omega)_0$. The shorter is τ, the narrower is the resonance line! This remarkable effect is known as **motional narrowing**.[17] The rotational relaxation time of water molecules at room temperature is known from dielectric constant measurements to be of the order of 10^{-10} sec; if $(\Delta\omega)_0 \approx 10^5$ sec^{-1}, then $(\Delta\omega)_0\tau \approx 10^{-5}$. Thus the motion narrows the proton resonance line to about 10^{-5} of the static width.

[17] The physical ideas are due to N. Bloembergen, E. M. Purcell, and R. V. Pound, Phys. Rev. **73**, 679 (1948). The result differs from the theory of optical line width caused by *strong* collisions between atoms (as in a gas discharge), where a short τ gives a broad line. In the nuclear spin problem the collisions are weak.

Longitudinal Relaxation

The right-hand side of Eq. (52) has two terms, one which describes the relaxation of M_z in terms of the longitudinal relaxation rate $1/T_1$, and one which is essentially the transition rate caused by the incident rf power. The appearance of the term in $H_1{}^2$ suggests that we might represent the interactions responsible for longitudinal relaxation in terms of the power spectrum of the random magnetic fields which act on the spins. The power absorption involves the square of the transverse rf field, so that we look at $H_x{}^2 + H_y{}^2$ as a function of time. We Fourier-analyze in frequency what we see.

The spectrum of Fourier components has some important general features. We assume the spectrum has the form shown in Fig. 11:

$$J(\omega) = \frac{2}{\pi} \frac{\tau}{1 + \omega^2\tau^2}; \qquad \int_0^\infty d\omega \, J(\omega) = 1. \tag{76}$$

This equation means that if we analyze $H_x{}^2(t) + H_y{}^2(t)$ into Fourier components, then in a unit frequency range[18] at the spin resonance frequency ω_0 we have

$$\langle H_x{}^2 \rangle \cdot \frac{2}{\pi} \cdot \frac{\tau}{1 + \omega_0{}^2\tau^2}, \tag{77}$$

where $\langle H_x{}^2 \rangle$ is the time average. Equation (77) is just the power at ω_0 which induces transitions between the two spin levels separated in energy by ω_0. Thus by comparison with (51) the transition rate due to the random fields involves

$$\boxed{\frac{1}{T_1} \approx \gamma^2 \langle H_x{}^2 \rangle \frac{\tau}{1 + \omega_0{}^2\tau^2}.} \tag{78}$$

Our argument has been sketchy, but the result is essentially correct. The variation of (78) with τ is very interesting: for rapid motion $\omega_0\tau \ll 1$ and

$$1/T_1 \approx \gamma^2 \langle H_x{}^2 \rangle \tau, \tag{79}$$

closely similar to (75) for $1/T_2$. For slow motion ($\omega_0\tau \gg 1$) the spins see only the high frequency tail of the power spectrum and

$$\frac{1}{T_1} \approx \frac{\langle H_x{}^2 \rangle}{H_0{}^2} \cdot \frac{1}{\tau}. \tag{80}$$

Contrast the τ dependence in the different limits, as given by (79) and (80). Experimental results are shown in Fig. 12. Notice also that the criteria for fast or slow differ for $1/T_1$ and $1/T_2$; one involves the value of $\omega_0\tau$ and the other involves $(\Delta\omega)_0\tau$.

---

[18] The standard quantum expression for the transition rate involves the power per unit frequency range.

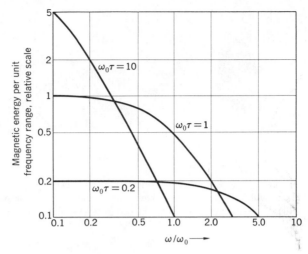

Figure 11 Log-log plot of assumed normalized power spectrum of $\langle H_x^2 \rangle$ versus ω/ω_0. The function plotted is $\tau/(1 + \omega^2\tau^2)$; curves are given for three values of the correlation time τ. Observe that at $\omega = \omega_0$ the power spectrum is higher for $\omega_0\tau = 1$ than for $\omega_0\tau = 0.2$ or 10. The longitudinal relaxation rate $1/T_1$ decreases for fast motion ($\omega_0\tau \ll 1$) because the spectrum is spread out over a wide frequency range; the rate also decreases for slow motion ($\omega_0\tau \gg 1$) because the power is concentrated near zero frequencies and the resonance line sees only the tail of the spectrum.

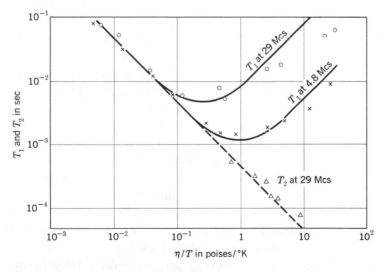

Figure 12 Relaxation times T_1 and T_2 for proton resonance in glycerin as a function of the viscosity η divided by the temperature T. The ratio η/T is proportional to the rotational correlation or hopping time τ. Note that the transverse relaxation time $T_2 \propto 1/\tau$, as expected from (75). Note also the minimum in T_1, as expected from Fig. 11 and (78); the position of the minimum varies with ω_0. (After N. Bloembergen.)

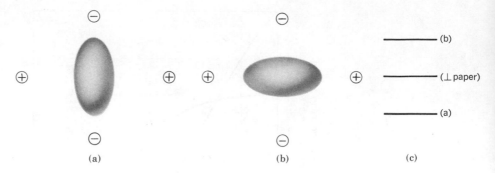

Figure 13 (a) Lowest energy orientation of a nuclear quadrupole moment ($Q > 0$) in the local field of the four ions shown. The electrons of the ion itself are not shown. (b) Highest energy orientation. (c) The energy level splitting for $I = 1$.

NUCLEAR QUADRUPOLE RESONANCE

Nuclei of spin $I \geq 1$ have an electric quadrupole moment. The quadrupole moment Q is a measure of the ellipticity of the distribution of charge in the nucleus. The quantity of interest is defined classically by[19]

$$eQ = \tfrac{1}{2} \int (3z^2 - r^2)\rho(\mathbf{r}) \, d^3x, \tag{81}$$

where $\rho(\mathbf{r})$ is the charge density. An egg-shaped nucleus has Q positive; a saucer-shaped nucleus has Q negative.

The nucleus when placed in a crystal will see the electrostatic field of its environment, as in Fig. 13. If the symmetry of this field is lower than cubic, then the nuclear quadrupole moment will lead to a set of energy levels with a splitting determined by the interaction of the quadrupole moment with the local electric field. Precisely this effect is discussed in Appendix H for an electronic quadrupole moment. There we do not use the term quadrupole moment; however, an electron in a p state ($L = 1$) has a quadrupole moment which is responsible for the crystal field splitting in the example treated.

The states which are split are the $2I + 1$ states of a spin I. The quadrupole splittings can often be observed directly because an rf magnetic field of the appropriate frequency can cause transitions between the levels. The term **nuclear quadrupole resonance** refers to observations of nuclear quadrupole splittings in the absence of a static magnetic field.

The quadrupole splittings are particularly large in covalently bonded molecules such as Cl_2, Br_3, and I_2; the splittings are of the order 10^7 or 10^8 cps.

[19] See Slichter, Chap. 6.

FERROMAGNETIC RESONANCE

Spin resonance at microwave frequencies in ferromagnets[20] is similar in principle to nuclear spin resonance. The total magnetic moment of the specimen precesses about the direction of the static magnetic field, and energy is absorbed strongly from the rf transverse field when its frequency is equal to the precessional frequency. We may equally well think of the macroscopic vector representing the total spin of the ferromagnet as quantized in the static magnetic field, with energy levels separated by the usual Zeeman frequencies; the selection rule $\Delta m_S = \pm 1$ allows transitions only between adjacent levels.

The unusual features of ferromagnetic resonance include the following:

a. The transverse susceptibility components χ' and χ'' are very large because the magnetization of a ferromagnet in a given static field is very much larger than the magnetization of electronic or nuclear paramagnets in the same field.

b. The shape of the specimen plays an important role. Because the magnetization is large, the demagnetization field[21] is large.

c. The strong exchange coupling between the ferromagnetic electrons tends to suppress[22] the dipolar contribution to the line width, so that the ferromagnetic resonance lines can be quite sharp (<1 G) under favorable conditions. The exchange-narrowing effect in the paramagnetic region is treated below under EPR.

d. Saturation effects are found to occur at relatively low rf power levels. It is not possible, as it is with nuclear spin systems, to drive a ferromagnetic spin system so hard that the magnetization M_z is reduced to zero or reversed. That is, we cannot carry out on a ferromagnet the experiment envisaged in Problem 2 for a nuclear spin system. The ferromagnetic resonance excitation breaks down into spin wave modes before the magnetization vector can be rotated appreciably from its initial direction.

Shape Effects in FMR

We treat the effects of specimen shape on the resonance frequency.[23] Consider a specimen of a cubic ferromagnetic insulator in the form of an ellipsoid with principal axes parallel to x, y, z axes of a Cartesian coordinate system. The **demagnetization factors** N_x, N_y, N_z are identical with the depolarization factors defined by (12.5). The components of the internal magnetic field $\mathbf{H}_i$ in the ellipsoid are related to the applied field $\mathbf{H}$ by

---

[20] Observed first by J. H. E. Griffiths, Nature **158**, 670 (1946).
[21] See depolarization field, Chapter 12.
[22] The effect for paramagnets is treated in (96) below.
[23] C. Kittel, Phys. Rev. **71**, 270 (1947); **73**, 155 (1948).

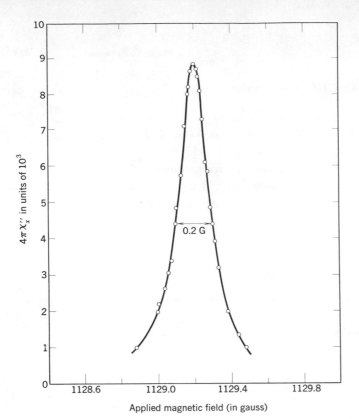

Figure 14 FMR in a polished sphere of yttrium iron garnet at 3.33 Gcs and 300°K, for $H_0 \parallel [111]$. The total line width at half-power is only 0.2 G. (After R. C. LeCraw and E. Spencer, unpublished.)

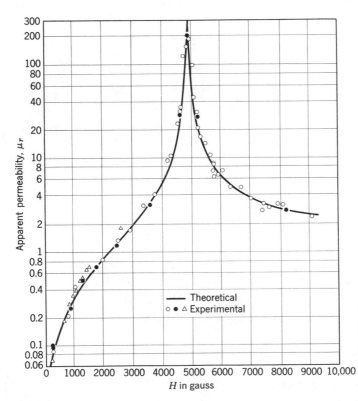

Figure 15 Resonance curve for Supermalloy, according to Yager and Bozorth; the vertical scale is that combination of the real and imaginary parts of the permeability which determines the eddy current losses.

$$H_x{}^i = H_x - N_x M_x; \qquad H_y{}^i = H_y - N_y M_y; \qquad H_z{}^i = H_z - N_z M_z. \quad (81)$$

These relations are of the form of (12.3) with the omission of the Lorentz field $4\pi M/3$. [We are now concerned with torques of the form $\mathbf{M} \times \mathbf{H}$; any term in $\mathbf{H}$ which may be written as a constant times $\mathbf{M}$ will not contribute because $\mathbf{M} \times \mathbf{M} = 0$. Thus the Lorentz (Chapter 12) and exchange (Chapter 15) fields do not usually contribute to the torque.]

With (81) the components of the spin equation of motion (7) become, for an applied static field $H_0 \hat{z}$,

$$
\begin{aligned}
dM_x/dt &= \gamma(M_y H_z{}^i - M_z H_y{}^i) = \gamma[M_y(H_0 - N_z M) - M(-N_y M_y)] \\
&= \gamma[H_0 + (N_y - N_z)M]M_y; \quad (82) \\
dM_y/dt &= \gamma[M(-N_x M_x) - M_x(H_0 - N_z M)] = -\gamma[H_0 + (N_x - N_z)M]M_x.
\end{aligned}
$$

To first order we may set $dM_z/dt = 0$ and $M_z = M$. Solutions of (82) with time dependence $e^{-i\omega t}$ will exist if

$$
\begin{vmatrix}
i\omega & \gamma[H_0 + (N_y - N_z)M] \\
-\gamma[H_0 + (N_x - N_z)M] & i\omega
\end{vmatrix} = 0, \quad (83)
$$

so that the ferromagnetic resonance frequency is

$$\omega_0{}^2 = \gamma^2[H_0 + (N_y - N_z)M][H_0 + (N_x - N_z)M]. \quad (84)$$

The frequency ω_0 is called the frequency of the **uniform mode,** in distinction to the frequencies of magnon and other nonuniform modes. In the uniform mode all the moments precess together with frequency ω_0.

For a sphere $N_x = N_y = N_z$, so that

$$\omega_0 = \gamma H_0. \quad (85)$$

A very sharp resonance line for this geometry is shown in Fig. 14.

For a flat plate with $\mathbf{H}_0$ perpendicular to the plate $N_x = N_y = 0$; $N_z = 4\pi$, whence

$$\omega_0 = \gamma(H_0 - 4\pi M). \quad (86)$$

If H_0 is parallel to the plane of the plate and the plate lies in the xz plane, then $N_x = N_z = 0$; $N_y = 4\pi$, and

$$\omega_0 = \gamma[H_0(H_0 + 4\pi M)]^{1/2}. \quad (87)$$

This is usually written as $\omega_0 = \gamma(BH)^{1/2}$. A resonance line for this geometry is shown in Fig. 15.

The experiments determine γ which is related to the spectroscopic splitting factor g by $-\gamma \equiv g\mu_B/\hbar$, as in Eq. (14.15a). Values of g for metallic Fe, Co, Ni at room temperature are 2.10, 2.18, and 2.21, respectively.

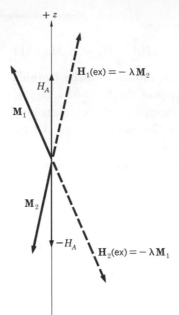

$+z$

$H_1(ex) = -\lambda M_2$

H_A

M_1

M_2

$-H_A$

$H_2(ex) = -\lambda M_1$

Figure 16 Effective fields in antiferromagnetic resonance. The magnetization M_1 of sublattice 1 sees a field $-\lambda M_2 + H_A\hat{z}$; the magnetization M_2 sees $-\lambda M_1 - H_A\hat{z}$. (Both ends of the crystal axis are "easy axes" of magnetization.)

ANTIFERROMAGNETIC RESONANCE

We consider a uniaxial antiferromagnet with spins on two sublattices, 1 and 2. We suppose that the magnetization M_1 on sublattice 1 is directed along the $+z$ direction by an anisotropy field $H_A\hat{z}$; the anisotropy field (Chapter 15) results from an anisotropy energy density $U_K(\theta_1) = K\sin^2\theta_1$, where θ_1 is the angle between M_1 and the z axis. As in Problem 6, $H_A = 2K/M$, where $M = |M_1| = |M_2|$. The magnetization M_2 is directed along the $-z$ direction by an anisotropy field[24] $-H_A\hat{z}$.

The exchange interaction between M_1 and M_2 is treated in the molecular field approximation. The exchange fields are

$$H_1(ex) = -\lambda M_2; \qquad H_2(ex) = -\lambda M_1, \tag{88}$$

where λ is positive. In the absence of an external magnetic field the total field acting on M_1 is $H_1 = -\lambda M_2 + H_A\hat{z}$; the total field on M_2 is $H_2 = -\lambda M_1 - H_A\hat{z}$, as in Fig. 16. In what follows we set $M_1^z = M$; $M_2^z = -M$.

The linearized equations of motion are

$$dM_1^x/dt = \gamma[M_1^y(\lambda M + H_A) - M(-\lambda M_2^y)];$$
$$dM_1^y/dt = \gamma[M(-\lambda M_2^x) - M_1^x(\lambda M + H_A)]; \tag{89}$$

$$dM_2^x/dt = \gamma[M_2^y(-\lambda M - H_A) - (-M)(-\lambda M_1^y)];$$
$$dM_2^y/dt = \gamma[(-M)(-\lambda M_1^x) - M_2^x(-\lambda M - H_A)]. \tag{90}$$

We define $M_1^+ = M_1^x + iM_1^y$; $M_2^+ = M_2^x + iM_2^y$. Then (89) and (90) be-

---

[24] If $+z$ is an easy direction of magnetization, so is $-z$. If one sublattice is directed along $+z$, the other will be directed along $-z$.

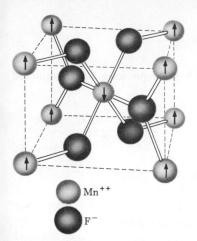

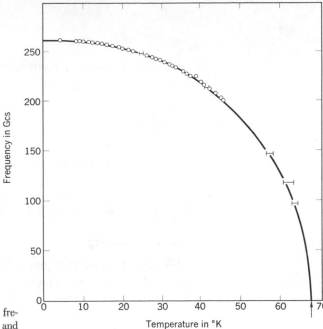

Figure 17 (*above*) Chemical and magnetic structure of MnF$_2$. The arrows indicate the direction and arrangement of the magnetic moments assigned to the manganese atoms.

Figure 18 (*right*) Antiferromagnetic resonance frequency for MnF$_2$ versus temperature, after Johnson and Nethercot.

come, for time dependence exp $(-i\omega t)$,

$$-i\omega M_1^+ = -i\gamma [M_1^+(H_A + \lambda M) + M_2^+(\lambda M)]; \qquad (91a)$$

$$-i\omega M_2^+ = i\gamma [M_2^+(H_A + \lambda M) + M_1^+(\lambda M)]. \qquad (91b)$$

These equations have a solution if, with $H_E \equiv \lambda M$,

$$\begin{vmatrix} \gamma(H_A + H_E) - \omega & \gamma H_E \\ \gamma H_E & \gamma(H_A + H_E) + \omega \end{vmatrix} = 0. \qquad (92)$$

Thus the AFMR frequency[25] is given by

$$\omega_0^2 = \gamma^2 H_A(H_A + 2H_E). \qquad (93)$$

Commonly the exchange field is much larger than the anisotropy field, so that

$$\omega_0 \cong \gamma(2H_A H_E)^{1/2} = \gamma(4\lambda K)^{1/2}, \qquad (94)$$

where $\lambda \equiv H_E/M$ is the molecular field constant and $K \equiv \frac{1}{2}H_A M$ is the anisotropy constant of a single sublattice.

MnF$_2$ is an extensively studied antiferromagnet. The structure is shown in Fig. 17. The observed variation of ω_0 with temperature is shown[26] in Fig. 18. Long before the first observations, careful estimates from empirical data were made by Keffer of H_A and H_E for MnF$_2$. He estimated $H_E = 540$ kG and $H_A = 8.8$ kG at $0°$K, whence $(2H_A H_E)^{1/2} = 100$ kG or 280 Gcs. The observed value is 93 kG or 261 Gcs. (1 Gcs $\equiv 10^9$ cps).

[25] T. Nagamiya, Prog. Theor. Phys. **6**, 342 (1951); C. Kittel, Phys. Rev. **82**, 565 (1951); F. Keffer and C. Kittel, Phys. Rev. **85**, 329 (1952).

[26] F. M. Johnson and A. H. Nethercot, Jr., Phys. Rev. **104**, 847 (1956); **114**, 705 (1959); S. Foner, Phys. Rev. **107**, 683 (1957).

Richards[27] has made a compilation of AFMR frequencies as extrapolated to 0°K:

Crystal	CoF_2	NiF_2	MnF_2	FeF_2	MnO	NiO
Frequency in cm^{-1}	28.5	31.1	8.68	52.7	27.6	36.5

ELECTRON PARAMAGNETIC RESONANCE

Electron spin resonance is now a vast area of research. We have space only to mention several isolated topics of considerable interest.

Exchange Narrowing

We consider a paramagnet with an exchange interaction J among nearest-neighbor electron spins. The temperature of the specimen is assumed to be well above any spin-ordering temperature T_c. It is observed under these conditions that the width of the spin resonance line is usually much narrower than expected from the result (64) for the dipole-dipole interaction. The effect is called **exchange narrowing**; there is a close analogy with motional narrowing.

Van Vleck[28] has shown that the second moment $\langle H_i^2 \rangle$ of the local random field does not contain the exchange interaction, but the fourth moment does:

$$\langle H_i^4 \rangle \approx H_E^2 \langle H_i^2 \rangle, \tag{95}$$

where $H_E \approx J/\mu_B$. Thus $\langle H_i^4 \rangle / \langle H_i^2 \rangle^2 \approx H_E^2 / \langle H_i^2 \rangle$, which may be $\gg 1$. By the argument following (71) we expect to find a Lorentzian line with a cut-off at $\pm J/\hbar$ on either side of the resonance line. By (95) and (71) the width of the exchange-narrowed line is

$$\Delta\omega \approx (\Delta\omega)_0^2 / \omega_{\text{ex}}, \tag{96}$$

where $(\Delta\omega)_0^2 = \gamma^2 \langle H_i^2 \rangle$ is the square of the static dipolar width in the absence of exchange and $\omega_{\text{ex}} \approx J/\hbar = \gamma H_E$. The similarity which exists between (96) and the motional-narrowing result (75) suggests that we may interpret ω_{ex} as a "hopping" frequency $1/\tau$, analogous to the frequency with which a diffusing atom changes lattice sites.

A useful and striking example of exchange narrowing is the paramagnetic organic crystal known as the g marker or DPPH.[29] This free radical has

---

[27] P. L. Richards, J. Appl. Phys. **34**, 1237 (1963).

[28] J. H. Van Vleck, Phys. Rev. **74**, 1168 (1948); F. Keffer, Phys. Rev. **88**, 686 (1952).

[29] Diphenyl picryl hydrazyl. The g value is 2.0036 ± 0.0002. Because of the sharp line width it is often used for calibration of the magnetic field; see A. N. Holden et al., Phys. Rev. **77**, 147 (1950).

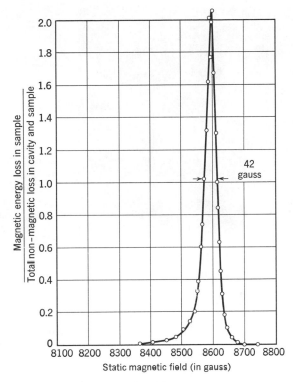

Figure 19   EPR in NiSiF$_6 \cdot$6H$_2$O at 24.45 Gcs. (After Holden, Kittel, and Yager.)

a 1.35 G half-width of the resonance line at half-power, only a few percent of the pure dipolar width.

Zero-field Splitting

A number of paramagnetic ions have crystal field splittings of their magnetic ground state energy levels in the range of 0.1 − 10 cm^{-1} which is conveniently accessible by microwave techniques.[30] An example is given in Fig. 19: the observed spectrum of the Ni^{++} ion can be interpreted to give a zero-field splitting $\Delta = 0.49$ cm^{-1} at room temperature.

The Mn^{++} ion is popular and has been studied in many crystals as an additive impurity. A ground state splitting in the range 0.001 to 0.020 cm^{-1} is observed, according to the environment.

---

[30] Much of the early work is due to B. Bleaney and co-workers at Oxford.

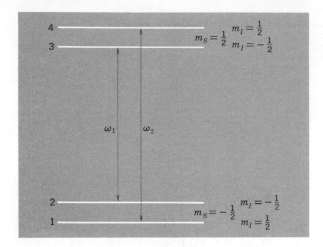

Figure 20 Energy levels in a magnetic field of a system with $S = \frac{1}{2}$, $I = \frac{1}{2}$. The diagram is drawn for the strong field approximation $\mu_B H \gg a$, where a is the hyperfine coupling constant, taken to be positive. The four levels are labeled by the magnetic quantum numbers m_S, m_I. The strong electronic transitions have $\Delta m_I = 0$.

Hyperfine Splitting

The hyperfine interaction is the interaction between the magnetic moment of the nucleus and the magnetic moment of the electron. For an electron in an s state ($L = 0$) the form of the interaction is

$$U = a\mathbf{I} \cdot \mathbf{S}, \tag{97}$$

where $\mathbf{I}$ is the nuclear spin in units of $\hbar$. Values of the hyperfine constant a for the ground states of several free atoms are

nucleus	H^1	Li^7	Na^{23}	K^{39}	K^{41}
I	$\frac{1}{2}$	$\frac{3}{2}$	$\frac{3}{2}$	$\frac{3}{2}$	$\frac{3}{2}$
a in gauss	507	144	310	83	85
a in Mcs	1420	402	886	231	127

The values in gauss as seen by an electron spin are found from a in ergs as $a/2\mu_B$.

In a strong magnetic field the energy level scheme of a free atom or ion is dominated by the Zeeman energy splitting of the electron levels; the hyperfine interaction gives an additional splitting which in strong fields is $U' \cong a m_s m_I$, where m_s, m_I are the magnetic quantum numbers. For the energy level diagram of Fig. 20 the two electronic transitions have frequencies $\omega = \gamma H_0 \pm a/2\hbar$. The nuclear transitions are not marked; they have $\Delta m_s = 0$, so that $\omega_{\text{nuc}} = a/2\hbar$. The frequency of the nuclear transition $1 \rightarrow 2$ is equal to that of $3 \rightarrow 4$.

Spin-lattice Relaxation

The dominant spin-lattice interaction of paramagnetic ions in crystals is by the phonon modulation of the crystalline electric field. Relaxation proceeds by three principal processes (Fig. 21): direct (emission or absorption of

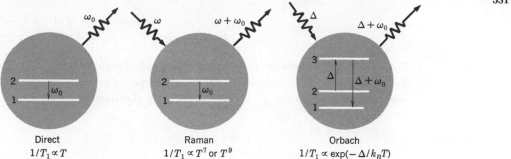

ω_0 ω $\omega + \omega_0$ Δ $\Delta + \omega_0$

Direct	Raman	Orbach
$1/T_1 \propto T$	$1/T_1 \propto T^7$ or T^9	$1/T_1 \propto \exp(-\Delta/k_B T)$

Figure 21 (*above*) Spin relaxation from $2 \rightarrow 1$ by phonon emission, phonon scattering, and a two-stage phonon process. The temperature dependence of the longitudinal relaxation time T_1 is shown for the several processes.

Figure 22 (*right*) Log of relaxation rate $1/T_1$ versus reciprocal temperature for 1 and 5 percent Nd in lanthanum double nitrate, after observations by Scott and Jeffries between 1.4 and $4.3°$K. The results are clear evidence for the Orbach process at the higher temperatures.

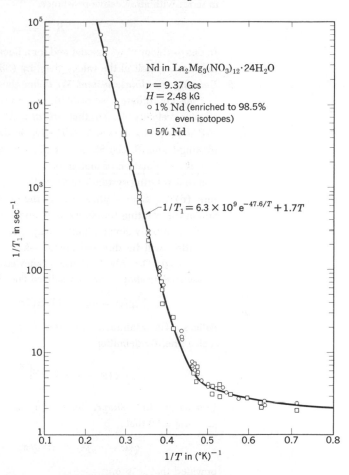

Nd in $La_2Mg_3(NO_3)_{12} \cdot 24H_2O$

$\nu = 9.37$ Gcs
$H = 2.48$ kG
○ 1% Nd (enriched to 98.5% even isotopes)
▫ 5% Nd

$$1/T_1 = 6.3 \times 10^9 \, e^{-47.6/T} + 1.7T$$

a phonon); Raman (scattering of a phonon); and Orbach[31] (intervention of a third state). A thorough experimental analysis of spin-lattice relaxation in several rare-earth salts of helium temperatures has been given by Scott and Jeffries;[32] they discuss evidence for the three processes and give useful references to the literature of paramagnetic relaxation. An example of the results is given in Fig. 22.

[31] C. B. P. Finn, R. Orbach, and W. P. Wolf, Proc. Phys. (London), **77**, 261 (1961).
[32] P. L. Scott and C. D. Jeffries, Phys. Rev. **127**, 32 (1962).

Problems

1. **Equivalent electrical circuit.** Consider an empty coil of inductance L_0 and resistance R_0; show if the coil is completely filled with a spin system characterized by the susceptibility components $\chi'(\omega)$ and $\chi''(\omega)$ that the inductance at frequency ω becomes

$$L = [1 + 4\pi\chi'(\omega)]L_0,$$

in series with an effective resistance

$$R = 4\pi\omega\chi''(\omega)L_0 + R_0.$$

In this problem χ', χ'' are defined for a linearly polarized rf field; it may be shown that they are one-half of the values given by (33).

2. **Rotating coordinate system.** We define the vector $\mathbf{F}(t) = F_x(t)\hat{x} + F_y(t)\hat{y} + F_z(t)\hat{z}$. Let the coordinate system of the unit vectors $\hat{x}$, $\hat{y}$, $\hat{z}$ rotate with an instantaneous angular velocity $\boldsymbol{\Omega}$, so that $d\hat{x}/dt = \Omega_y\hat{z} - \Omega_z\hat{y}$, etc. (a) Show that $d\mathbf{F}/dt = (d\mathbf{F}/dt)_R + \boldsymbol{\Omega} \times \mathbf{F}$, where $(d\mathbf{F}/dt)_R$ is the time derivative of $\mathbf{F}$ as viewed in the rotating frame R. (b) Show that (7) may be written $(d\mathbf{M}/dt)_R = \gamma\mathbf{M} \times (\mathbf{H} + \boldsymbol{\Omega}/\gamma)$. This is the equation of motion of $\mathbf{M}$ in a rotating coordinate system. The transformation to a rotating system is extraordinarily useful; it is exploited widely in the literature. (c) Let $\boldsymbol{\Omega} = -\gamma H_0\hat{z}$; thus in the rotating frame there is no static magnetic field. Still in the rotating frame, we now apply a dc pulse $H_1\hat{x}$ for a time t. If the magnetization is initially along $\hat{z}$, find an expression for the pulse length t such that the magnetization will be directed along $-\hat{z}$ at the end of the pulse. (Neglect relaxation effects.) (d) Describe this pulse as viewed from the laboratory frame of reference.

3. **Gaussian line shape.** The normalized line shape function

$$g(\omega - \omega_0) = [1/\Delta(2\pi)^{1/2}] \exp[-(\omega - \omega_0)^2/2\Delta^2]$$

defines a Gaussian line. Show that $\langle(\omega - \omega_0)^2\rangle = \Delta^2$ and $\langle(\omega - \omega_0)^4\rangle = 3\,\Delta^4$ for such a line. By definition

$$\langle(\omega - \omega_0)^n\rangle = \int_{-\infty}^{\infty} d\omega(\omega - \omega_0)^n g(\omega - \omega_0).$$

4. **Lorentzian line shape.** Show for the Lorentzian line (69) with a cutoff at $|\omega - \omega_0| = \Omega$ that

$$\langle(\omega - \omega_0)^2\rangle \cong 2\Omega\,\delta/\pi; \qquad \langle(\omega - \omega_0)^4\rangle \cong 2\Omega^3\,\delta/3\pi,$$

provided that $\Omega \gg \delta$.

5. **Hyperfine effects on ESR in metals.** We suppose that the electron spin of a conduction electron in a metal sees an effective magnetic field from the hyperfine interaction

of the electron spin with the nuclear spin. Let the z component of the field seen by the conduction electron be written

$$H_i = \left(\frac{a}{N}\right) \sum_{j=1}^{N} I_j^z,$$

where I_j^z is equally likely to be $\pm\frac{1}{2}$. (a) Show that $\langle H_i^2 \rangle = (a/2N)^2 N$. (b) Show that $\langle H_i^4 \rangle = 3(a/2N)^4 N^2$, for $N \gg 1$; (c) Show that these results are consistent with a Gaussian line shape and that the width $\to 0$ as $N \to \infty$.

6. *FMR in the anisotropy field.* Consider a spherical specimen of a uniaxial ferromagnetic crystal with an anisotropy energy density of the form $U_K = K \sin^2 \theta$, where θ is the angle between the magnetization and the z axis. We assume that K is positive. Show that the ferromagnetic resonance frequency in an external magnetic field $H_0 \hat{z}$ is $\omega_0 = \gamma(H_0 + H_A)$, where $H_A \equiv 2K/M_s$.

7. *Exchange frequency resonance.* Consider a ferrimagnet with two sublattices A and B of magnetizations $\mathbf{M}_A$ and $\mathbf{M}_B$, where $\mathbf{M}_B$ is opposite to $\mathbf{M}_A$ when the spin system is at rest. The gyromagnetic ratios are γ_A, γ_B and the molecular fields are $\mathbf{H}_A = -\lambda \mathbf{M}_B$; $\mathbf{H}_B = -\lambda \mathbf{M}_A$. Show that there is a resonance at

$$\omega_0^2 = \lambda^2 (\gamma_A |M_B| - \gamma_B |M_A|)^2.$$

This is called the exchange frequency resonance.[33]

8. *Paramagnetic maser.* A microwave cavity of unit volume is resonant at ω_0. The rate of energy loss to eddy currents in the cavity walls is $\approx (H_1^2/4\pi)(\omega_0/Q)$, where Q is the quality factor. A two-level system of electron spins (as in Fig. 2) is placed in the cavity. If spin-lattice relaxation is neglected ($T_1 \to \infty$), the rate of change of the spin population by coupling with the electromagnetic field is given by (50): $[d(N_1 - N_2)/dt]_{\text{rf}} = -\alpha(N_1 - N_2)$, where N_1, N_2 are the spin concentrations in the lower and upper states. At the maximum of the spin resonance line $\alpha = \gamma^2 H_1^2 T_2$. (a) Show that an inverted spin population ($N_2 > N_1$) will emit photons at a rate faster than the cavity walls can absorb them if

$$N_2 - N_1 > \Delta H / 8\pi g \mu_B Q,$$

where g is the spectroscopic splitting factor and ΔH is the line width. When this inequality is satisfied the spin system will emit a burst of rf energy.[34] (b) Estimate the excess population required. (c) How might the population be inverted?

---

[33] J. Kaplan and C. Kittel, J. Chem. Phys. **21**, 760 (1953); for experiments see the review by S. Foner listed in the references.

[34] Devices which utilize this principle of stimulated emission to amplify microwave signals are called **masers**; see C. H. Townes, "Production of coherent radiation by atoms and molecules," Science **149**, 831 (1965). Similar devices to amplify light are called **lasers**.

References

INTRODUCTION

C. P. Slichter, *Principles of magnetic resonance, with examples from solid state physics,* Harper and Row, 1963. (An excellent introduction.)

G. E. Pake, "Nuclear magnetic resonance," *Solid state physics* **2,** 1–91 (1956).

N. Bloembergen, E. M. Purcell, and R. V. Pound, "Relaxation effects in nuclear magnetic resonance absorption," Phys. Rev. **73,** 679–712 (1948).

NUCLEAR MAGNETIC RESONANCE

A. Abragam, *Nuclear magnetism,* Oxford, 1961. (Definitive and comprehensive.)

T. P. Das and E. L. Hahn, "Nuclear quadrupole resonance spectroscopy," *Solid state physics,* Supplement **1,** (1958).

V. Jaccarino, "Nuclear resonance in antiferromagnets," *Magnetism*[35] IIA.

A. M. Portis and R. H. Lindquist, "Nuclear resonance in ferromagnetic materials," *Magnetism* IIA, 357.

E. L. Hahn, "Spin echoes," Physics Today **6,** 4 (Nov. 1953).

ELECTRON RESONANCE

B. Bleaney and K. W. H. Stevens, "Paramagnetic resonance," Repts. Prog. Phys. **16,** 108 (1953).

K. D. Bowers and J. Owen, "Paramagnetic resonance II," Repts. Prog. Phys. **18,** 304 (1955).

J. W. Orton, "Paramagnetic resonance data," Repts. Prog. Phys. **22,** 204 (1959).

W. Low, "Paramagnetic resonance in solids," *Solid state physics,* Supplement **2,** 1960.

S. A. Al'tshuler and B. M. Kozyrev, *Electron paramagnetic resonance,* Academic Press, 1964.

FERRO- AND ANTIFERROMAGNETIC RESONANCE

M. Sparks, *Ferromagnetic relaxation theory,* McGraw-Hill, 1964.

S. Foner, "Antiferromagnetic and ferrimagnetic resonance," *Magnetism* I, 384.

C. W. Haas and H. B. Callen, "Ferromagnetic relaxation and resonance line widths," *Magnetism* I, 450.

R. W. Damon, "Ferromagnetic resonance at high power," *Magnetism* I, 552.

[35] Edited by G. T. Rado and H. Suhl, Academic Press.

17

Optical Phenomena in Insulators

COLOR OF CRYSTALS

Crystals which are electrical insulators at room temperature usually are transparent. A section 1 cm thick of such a single crystal appears clear to the eye, although rarely as clear as plate glass. To be clear a crystal can have no strong electronic or vibronic transitions in the visible spectral range from 7400 to 3600 Å, or 1.7 to 3.5 ev. In general, to have a very strong color a crystal must have an allowed electric dipole electronic transition in the visible region. (The strongest optical transitions are from electric dipoles.) We consider briefly the origin of the color exhibited by common solids. If the absorption is not strong, the color presented by a powder of small crystals is usually the color of light transmitted through the crystal.

(1) A pure perfect diamond is clear. In Table 10.1 the energy gap of diamond is given as 5.33 ev, so that electronic transitions from the valence band to the conduction band do not occur in the visible range. Diamonds can be colored by irradiation which produces lattice defects (Chapter 18).

(2) Cadmium sulfide is yellow-orange. The energy gap is 2.42 ev, so that the blue region of the spectrum is absorbed by the crystal.

(3) Silicon has a metallic luster because the band gap of 1.14 ev is below the visible region in energy: all wavelengths in the visible region cause electronic transitions[1] from the valence band to the conduction band. But a thin (<0.01 cm) section of silicon transmits weakly in the red, because the absorption process in silicon for frequencies near the gap involves a phonon as well as a photon and is not very intense. The threshold energy for direct absorption lies at 2.5 ev in the middle of the visible spectral region. Tin oxide is a semiconductor which is transparent in thin layers; it is often used as an electrode when transparency is required.

(4) Ruby is a dark red gem; sapphire is a blue gem. Both are impure crystals of Al_2O_3, which is colorless when pure. The color of ruby is caused by perhaps 0.5 percent of Cr^{3+}, which enters lattice sites normally occupied by an Al^{3+} ion. The blue color of sapphire is due to Ti^{3+} ions present as impurities in Al_2O_3.

(5) Many compounds containing transition elements are colored even though the crystals do not have energy gaps in the visible region. It is characteristic of many transition element ions to have electronic excited states at

---

[1] That is, the metallic appearance of silicon persists to 0°K and is not caused by any free charge carriers which may be present.

energies in the visible region. The excited state may be localized near or on the transition ion[2].

(6) Some crystals can be colored by radiation damage, that is, by bombardment with energetic particles, gamma rays, or ultraviolet light. Electrons or holes trapped at lattice defects often have absorption lines in the visible region, as discussed in Chapter 18.

(7) The precipitation of metallic impurities as fine colloidal particles throughout a crystal will cause coloration by virtue of the wavelength dependence of the scattering cross-section of the particles. The production of ruby-colored glass by the controlled precipitation of gold is the classic example.

EXCITONS

We saw in Chapter 10 that an electron-hole pair is produced when photons of energy greater than the energy gap E_g are absorbed in a crystal. The electron and hole produced in this way (Fig. 1) are free and may move independently through the crystal. But because an electron and hole have an attractive Coulomb interaction for each other it is possible for stable bound states of the two particles to be formed. The photon energy required to create a bound pair starting from a filled valence band will be less than the gap energy E_g.

The bound electron-hole pair (Fig. 2) is known as an **exciton;** it may move through the crystal transporting excitation energy but not charge. Thus an exciton[3] is a neutral excited mobile state of a crystal: an exciton can travel

[2] The sense in which such an excitation is localized is discussed later in the section on tightly bound excitons.

[3] Important original papers on excitons include J. Frenkel, Phys. Rev. **37**, 17, 1276 (1931); Physik. Z. Sowjetunion **9**, 158 (1936); R. Peierls, Ann. Physik **13**, 905 (1932); J. C. Slater and W. Shockley, Phys. Rev. **50**, 705 (1936); G. H. Wannier, Phys. Rev. **52**, 191 (1937); W. R. Heller and A. Marcus, Phys. Rev. **84**, 809 (1951); N. F. Mott, Trans. Faraday Soc. **34**, 500 (1938); D. L. Dexter and W. R. Heller, Phys. Rev. **84**, 377 (1951); A. S. Davydov, J.E.T.P. **18**, 210 (1948).

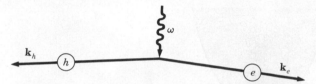

Figure 1 Absorption of a photon of frequency above the energy gap. The photon excites an electron from the valence band to the conduction band, leaving behind a hole in the valence band. The photon wavevectors are of negligible magnitude in the energy range of interest; thus $\mathbf{k}_h \cong -\mathbf{k}_e$.

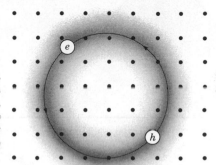

Figure 2 An exciton is a bound electron-hole pair, usually free to move together through the crystal. In some respects it is similar to an atom of positronium, which is formed from a positron and an electron. The exciton shown here is a Mott exciton: it is weakly bound, with an average electron-hole distance large in comparison with a lattice constant.

through a crystal, giving up its energy of formation on recombination.[4] Because of its charge neutrality it does not contribute directly to the electrical conductivity.

We consider excitons in two different limiting approximations, one due to Frenkel in which the exciton is considered as tightly bound, and the other due to Mott and Wannier in which the exciton is weakly bound, with an electron-hole interparticle distance large in comparison with a lattice constant.

---

[4] An exciton is said to recombine when the electron drops into the hole state from which it came.

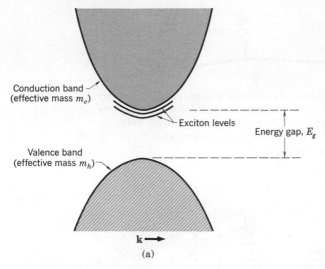

Conduction band
(effective mass m_e)

Exciton levels

Energy gap, E_g

Valence band
(effective mass m_h)

$\mathbf{k} \longrightarrow$

(a)

Figure 3a Exciton levels in relation to the conduction band edge, for a simple band structure with both conduction and valence band edges at $\mathbf{k} = 0$. An exciton can have translational kinetic energy, but if the translational energy is greater than the binding energy of the exciton, then the exciton is metastable with respect to decay into a free hole and free electron. All excitons are potentially unstable with respect to radiative recombination in which the electron drops down into the hole state in the valence band, accompanied by the emission of a photon or phonons.

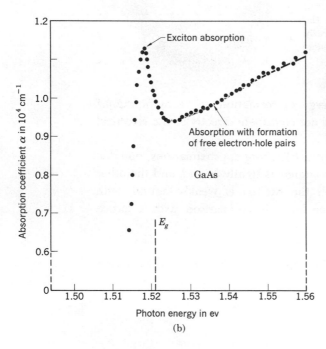

Exciton absorption

Absorption with formation
of free electron-hole pairs

GaAs

E_g

Absorption coefficient α in 10^4 cm^{-1}

Photon energy in ev

(b)

Figure 3b The observed effect of an exciton level on the optical absorption of a semiconductor for photons of energy near the band gap E_g. The optical absorption edge and the exciton absorption peak in gallium arsenide at 21°K, after M. D. Sturge, Phys. Rev. **127**, 768 (1962). The vertical scale is the intensity absorption coefficient, as in $I(x) = I_0 \exp(-\alpha x)$. The energy gap and exciton binding energy are deduced from the shape of the absorption curve: the gap E_g is 1.521 ev and the exciton binding energy is 0.0034 ev.

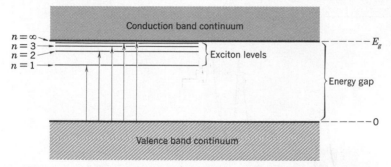

Figure 4 Energy levels of an exciton whose center of mass is at rest. Optical transitions from the top of the valence band are shown by the arrows; the longest corresponds to the ionization of the exciton and therefore to the energy gap between the edges of the conduction and valence bands. There is a continuum of levels associated with each exciton level shown because the center of mass of an exciton may be given translational energy. (Each exciton level forms an exciton band.) In direct optical transitions the total translational energy does not change appreciably; thus sharp exciton lines are possible. The zero of the energy scale at the right is taken at the top of the valence band.

Weakly Bound Excitons

We consider an electron in the conduction band of a crystal and a hole in the valence band. The electron and hole are attracted to each other by the attractive Coulomb potential

$$U(r) = -e^2/\epsilon r, \tag{1}$$

where r is the distance between the particles and ϵ is the appropriate dielectric constant.[5] There will be bound states (Figs. 3 and 4) of the exciton system having total energies lower than the bottom of the conduction band. The problem is much like the hydrogen atom problem if the energy surfaces for the electron and hole are spherical and nondegenerate. The energy levels referred to the top of the valence band are given by a modified Rydberg equation

$$E_n = E_g - \frac{\mu e^4}{2\hbar^2 \epsilon^2 n^2}. \tag{2}$$

Here n is the principal quantum number and μ is the reduced mass

$$\frac{1}{\mu} = \frac{1}{m_e} + \frac{1}{m_h} \tag{3}$$

formed from the effective masses m_e, m_h of the electron and hole. For general

[5] The lattice polarization contribution to the dielectric constant should not usually be included, as the lattice will not respond at the frequency of motion of the exciton. See W. Kohn, J. Phys. Chem. Solids **8**, 43 (1959); L. M. Roth and G. W. Pratt, J. Phys. Chem. Solids **8**, 47 (1959).

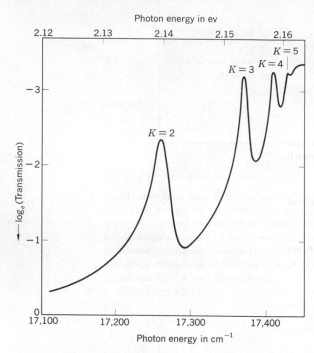

Figure 5 Logarithm of the optical transmission versus photon energy in cuprous oxide at 77°K, showing a series of exciton lines. [After P. W. Baumeister, Phys. Rev. **121**, 359 (1961).] Note that on the vertical axis the log is plotted decreasing upward; thus a peak corresponds to *low* transmission.

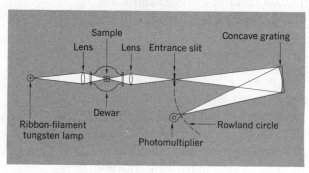

Figure 6 Apparatus used by Baumeister to measure the absorption coefficients of exciton lines in Cu_2O.

energy surfaces the exciton problem may be quite complicated, but there is little doubt that bound exciton states[6] almost always exist in insulators.

The exciton ground state energy is obtained on setting $n = 1$ in (2); this energy corresponds to the ionization energy required to break up the exciton from its lowest state. For $\epsilon = 5$ and $\mu = 0.5\ m$, the ionization energy is about 0.3 ev. It is difficult to produce excitons in sufficient concentration to observe directly transitions among the exciton levels, but it is possible to observe in optical absorption the transitions at $\hbar\omega_n = E_n$ between the valence band edge and an exciton level.

One crystal is known whose exciton spectrum satisfies (2) fairly accurately. Gross[7] and others have studied optical absorption lines in cuprous oxide Cu_2O at low temperatures, with results for the spacing of the exciton levels in surprisingly good agreement with the Rydberg equation (2), particularly for levels with $n > 2$. The results and experimental arrangement used by Baumeister are shown in Figs. 5 and 6. An empirical fit to the lines as observed by Apfel and Hadley is obtained with the relation $\nu(cm^{-1}) = 17{,}508 - (800/n^2)$. Taking $\epsilon = 10$, we find $\mu \cong 0.7\ m$ from the coefficient of $1/n^2$. Unfortunately no adequate independent values of m_e and m_h are available[8] for Cu_2O.

[6] It may not always be possible to separate internal and center-of-mass coordinates, although this can be done for ellipsoidal energy surfaces.

[7] E. F. Gross, B. P. Zakharchenya, and N. M. Reinov, Doklady Akad. Nauk S.S.S.R. **92**, 265 (1953); **97**, 57, 221 (1954); **99**, 231, 527 (1954); S. Nikitine, G. Perny, and M. Sieskind, Compt. rend. (Paris) **238**, 67 (1954); J. H. Apfel and L. N. Hadley, Phys. Rev. **100**, 1689 (1955); A. G. Samoilovich and L. L. Kornblit, Doklady Akad. Nauk S.S.S.R. **100**, 43 (1955); S. Nikitine, Helv. Phys. Acta **28**, 307 (1955).

[8] For further details of the interpretation of the exciton series in Cu_2O, see the articles by R. J. Elliott and by M. Grosmann in *Polarons and excitons*, Plenum, New York, 1963. The article by T. P. McLean in the same volume gives an excellent account of excitons in germanium. An exhaustive analysis of excitons in CdS has been given by D. G. Thomas and J. Hopfield, Phys. Rev. **124**, 657 (1961); their work includes a remarkable demonstration of the motion of excitons through the lattice.

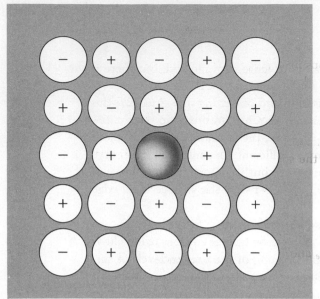

Figure 7 Schematic representation of a tightly bound or Frenkel exciton localized on one atom in the (100) plane of an alkali halide crystal. An ideal Frenkel exciton will travel as a wave throughout the crystal, but the electron is always close to the hole.

Tightly Bound Excitons

In a **Frenkel exciton** the excitation is localized on or near a single atom in the sense that the hole is usually on the same atom as the electron, although the pair may be anywhere in the crystal. A Frenkel exciton is essentially an excited state of a single atom, but the excitation can hop from one atom to another, according to the strength of the coupling between neighbors. The excitation wave travels through the crystal much as the reversed spin of a magnon travels through the crystal.

In alkali halide crystals (Fig. 7) the excitons of lowest energy are localized on the negative halogen ions: the negative ions have lower electronic excitation levels than the position ions. Alkali halide crystals when pure are transparent in the visible region of the spectrum, but in the vacuum ultraviolet region they show a considerable structure[9] in spectral absorption (Fig. 8). It is known (particularly from the work of L. Apker and E. Taft) that free electrons and holes are not produced when light is absorbed in the region of the lowest-energy absorption peak. It is very likely that this absorption results in the creation of excitons.

A doublet structure is particularly evident in the bromides. This structure, as noted by Mott, is similar to the doublet structure of the lowest excited states of the krypton atom, which has the same number of electrons as the Br^- ion. The resemblance of the doublet structures supports our identification of the lowest energy states in the alkali bromides as excitons on the Br^- ions.[10] The splitting is caused by the spin-orbit interaction.

[9] R. Hilsch and R. W. Pohl, Z. Physik **57**, 145 (1929); **59**, 812 (1930); N. F. Mott and R. W. Gurney, *Electronic processes in ionic crystals*, Oxford, 1948.

[10] For identification of the other peaks in the absorption spectra of alkali halides see J. C. Phillips, Phys. Rev. Letters **12**, 142 (1964); also R. S. Knox and N. Inchauspé, Phys. Rev. **116**, 1093 (1959); A. W. Overhauser, Phys. Rev. **101**, 1702 (1956).

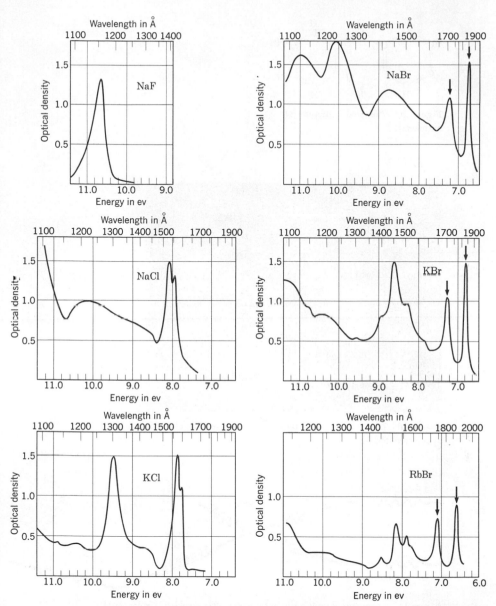

Figure 8 Optical absorption spectra of thin films of alkali halides at 80°K, after J. E. Eby, K. J. Teegarden, and D. B. Dutton, Phys. Rev. **116**, 1099 (1959). The vertical axes give the absorption on a relative scale. A doublet structure in the bromides is marked by arrows. The lowest excitations of the halogen ions are doublets: in Br⁻ the ground state is a $^1S_0$ state arising from the electron configuration $4p^6$; the lowest excited states arise from the configuration $4p^5 5s$. The $4p^5$ core may have total angular momentum $J = \frac{3}{2}$ or $\frac{1}{2}$, split by about 0.5 ev; the observed doublet structure results from this splitting.

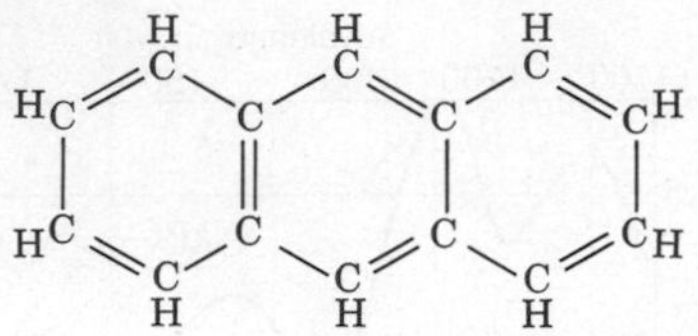

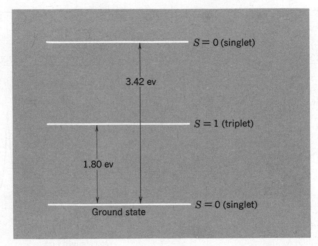

Figure 9 Chemical structure of anthracene.

Figure 10 Low-lying exciton states of anthracene. The electron spin is denoted by S.

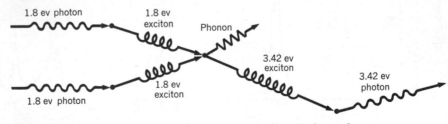

Figure 11 Detection of excitons in anthracene, after Avakian, Kepler, et al.

Excitons in Molecular Crystals

Molecular crystals also furnish examples of the Frenkel or tight-binding model of excitons. In molecular crystals the covalent binding within a molecule is strong in comparison with the van der Waals binding between molecules. Electronic excitation lines of an individual molecule will appear in the crystalline solid as an exciton, often with little shift in position. At low temperatures the lines in the solid are quite sharp, although there may be more structure to the lines in the solid than in the molecule.[11] In such solids the exciton energies are much more closely related to the spectroscopic properties of the isolated molecule than to the Mott-Wannier model discussed earlier.

Considerable interesting work has been done on excitons in crystals of anthracene (Fig. 9). The low-lying exciton levels of anthracene are indicated in Fig. 10. The optical transition between the ground state (singlet) and the lowest electronic excited state (triplet) is not an allowed electric dipole transition, but the transition probability is nonzero and a significant concentration of triplet excitons can be produced by irradiation of the crystal with an intense laser beam of photons of energy 1.79 ev. Two triplet excitons can combine[12] to form one singlet exciton of energy 3.42 ev, the excess energy being carried off by phonons. The 3.42 ev exciton is connected with the ground state by an allowed transition, and the emitted photon at 3.42 ev is detected in the experiments (Fig. 11).

Several systems, particularly certain ion radical salts of tetracyanoquinomethane, exist for which the molecular solid possesses triplet electronic excited states close enough in energy to a singlet ground state for the triplet exciton states to be densely populated at room temperature.[13] Electron spin resonance studies have been carried out on the triplet excitons. The absence of hyperfine broadening of the exciton resonance line (Problem 16.5) suggests that the excitons move fairly freely throughout the crystals.

[11] See, for example, the discussion of solid benzene by D. Fox and O. Schnepp, J. Chem. Phys. **23**, 767 (1955); the general theory is discussed by A. S. Davydov, J. Exptl. Theoret. Phys. (U.S.S.R.) **18**, 210 (1948); H. Winston, J. Chem. Phys. **19**, 156 (1951).

[12] R. G. Kepler, J. C. Caris, P. Avakian, and E. Abramson, Phys. Rev. Letters **10**, 400 (1963); P. Avakian and R. E. Merrifield, Phys. Rev. Letters **13**, 541 (1964).

[13] D. B. Chesnut and W. D. Phillips, J. Chem. Phys. **35**, 1002 (1961); D. B. Chesnut, J. Chem. Phys. **40**, 405 (1964).

PHOTOCONDUCTIVITY

Photoconductivity is the increase in electrical conductivity of an insulating crystal caused by radiation incident on the crystal. Much of the pioneering work in the field was done by Gudden, Pohl, and Rose. The photoconductive effect finds practical application in television cameras, infrared detectors, light meters, and indirectly in the photographic process. The direct effect of illumination is to increase the number of mobile charge carriers in the crystal. If the energy of the incident photon is higher than the energy gap E_g, then each photon absorbed in the crystal will produce a free electron-hole pair. The photon is absorbed by raising to the conduction band an electron originally in the valence band. Both the hole in the valence band and the electron in the conduction band may contribute to the conductivity.

The hole and electron will eventually recombine with each other, but they may have quite different histories before recombination. Each may spend various amounts of time trapped locally, perhaps on impurities and imperfections, in the crystal.[14] It is not usual to find that holes and electrons make comparable contributions to the photoconductivity in a given specimen.

The concept of trapping is of central importance in understanding the photoconductive response of a crystal. The mechanisms of the atomic processes occurring in traps are not always well understood, but we cannot understand the experimental facts of photoconductivity without invoking the presence of traps. Their role is treated in the following section.

If the energy of the incident photon is below the threshold for the production of pairs of holes and electrons, the photon may be able to cause ionization of donor and acceptor impurity atoms and in this way produce mobile electrons or holes, according to the nature of the impurity.

We discuss first the simplest possible model of a photoconductor. There exist few, if any, realizations of this model in actual crystals, but from the failure of the predictions to apply to real crystals we shall learn how to improve the model. The model (Fig. 12) supposes that electron-hole pairs are produced uniformly throughout the volume of the crystal by irradiation with an external light source. We suppose that recombination occurs by direct annihilation of electrons with holes. We suppose that electrons leaving the crystal at one electrode are replaced by electrons flowing in from the opposite electrode. It is convenient to neglect the mobility of the holes in comparison with the mobility of the electrons. In many photoconducting substances the mobility of the holes may often be neglected.

On this model the rate of change of the electron concentration n is given by

---

[14] Crystals (such as AgBr and AgCl) are known in which the hole is trapped immediately after an electron-hole pair is produced. It is believed that the hole may be trapped by any halide ion to form a stable V_K center (Chapter 18).

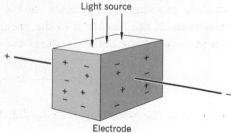

Light source

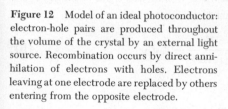

Figure 12 Model of an ideal photoconductor: electron-hole pairs are produced throughout the volume of the crystal by an external light source. Recombination occurs by direct annihilation of electrons with holes. Electrons leaving at one electrode are replaced by others entering from the opposite electrode.

Electrode

$$dn/dt = L - Anp = L - An^2, \qquad (4)$$

using $n = p$. Here L is the number of photons absorbed per unit volume of specimen per unit time. The term Anp is a bimolecular recombination rate, proportional to the product of hole and electron concentrations.

In the steady state $dn/dt = 0$, so that the steady-state electron concentration is

$$n_0 = (L/A)^{1/2}; \qquad (5)$$

the associated conductivity is

$$\sigma = n_0 e\mu = (L/A)^{1/2} e\mu, \qquad (6)$$

where μ is the electron mobility. This relation predicts that at a given voltage the photocurrent will vary with light level L as $L^{0.5}$; the actual exponents observed run between 0.5 and 1.0, or higher.

The decay of carriers if the light is switched off suddenly is described by

$$dn/dt = -An^2, \qquad (7)$$

which has the solution

$$n = \frac{n_0}{1 + Atn_0}, \qquad (8)$$

where n_0 is the concentration at $t = 0$ when the light was turned off. The carrier concentration drops to $\tfrac{1}{2}n_0$ in the time

$$t_0 = 1/An_0 = (LA)^{-1/2} = n_0/L. \qquad (9)$$

Thus the elementary theory predicts that the **response time** t_0 should be directly proportional to the photoconductivity at a given illumination level: sensitive photoconductors should have long response times.[15] The precise details of the predicted association of these properties is rarely observed in practice.

We define the **sensitivity** or gain factor G as the ratio of the number of

[15] Photographers know that the response time of a very sensitive cadmium sulfide light meter is several seconds.

carriers crossing the specimen to the number of photons absorbed in the specimen. If the thickness of the specimen is d and the cross-section area is unity, then a potential V produces the particle flux

$$J_N = \frac{n_0 \mu V}{d} = \frac{V\mu}{d^2 (AL)^{1/2}}(Ld), \tag{10}$$

using (5). The sensitivity $G \equiv J_N/Ld$, or

$$G = \frac{V\mu}{d^2 (AL)^{1/2}}. \tag{11}$$

The transit time T_d of a carrier between the electrodes is given by

$$T_d = \frac{d}{V\mu/d} = \frac{d^2}{V\mu}. \tag{12}$$

The lifetime T_e of an electron before recombination is given by t_0 in (9):

$$T_e = (LA)^{-1/2}. \tag{13}$$

The gain (11) may be expressed as

$$G = T_e/T_d; \tag{14}$$

that is, the gain is equal to the ratio of the carrier lifetime to the transit time of a carrier between electrodes. This expression for the gain is quite general and is not limited to the specific model just discussed. But if the lifetime T_e is taken as equal to the observed response time, the gains calculated from (14) are very much larger than observed experimentally, in some instances by a factor of 10^8. A new mechanism must be added to our picture of the photoconductive process. Traps supply the missing mechanism.

Traps

A trap is an atom or imperfection in the crystal capable of capturing an electron or hole. The captured carrier may be re-emitted at a subsequent time. It is convenient to discuss models in which at any instant the holes are entirely trapped and a fraction of the electrons nominally in the conduction band are trapped. We shall discuss only very simple models.

There is an operational distinction between two types of traps. One type acts principally as a recombination center as discussed in Chapter 10, helping electrons and holes to recombine and thereby assisting in the restoration of thermal equilibrium. Another type of trap affects principally the freedom of motion of charge carriers of one sign. It is this latter variety of trap which we treat.

We consider first a crystal with N electron trap levels per unit volume (Fig. 13). We suppose that the temperature is sufficiently low in relation to

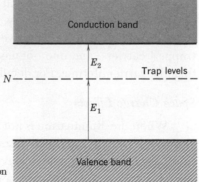

Figure 13 Model for photoconductivity with electron traps in concentration N.

the relevant ionization energies so that the concentration of thermal carriers may be neglected. For simplicity we assume that the recombination coefficient A is the same for electron-hole recombination as for electron-trap capture. Then

$$dn/dt = L - An(n + N), \qquad (15)$$

where n is the electron concentration in the conduction band. In (15) we have omitted the effect of thermal ionization of carriers from traps back into the conduction band. In the steady state

$$n_0(n_0 + N) = L/A. \qquad (16)$$

There are two limiting cases to discuss. It is difficult to grow crystals with trap concentrations N much less than 10^{14} cm^{-3}. At low current levels the carrier concentration n_0 may be very much less than this, perhaps only 10^8 or 10^{10} cm^{-3}. In the limit $n_0 \ll N$ we have the result

$$n_0 = L/AN, \qquad (17)$$

in place of (5). The photocurrent is now directly proportional to the illumination L. At high levels of illumination with $n_0 \gg N$ the response is given by $n_0 = (L/A)^{1/2}$, just as found earlier in the absence of traps. The experimental results indicate just such a change in the response with illumination level.

The decay of the system on switching off the light is given by the solution of the rate equation (15) with $L = 0$:

$$\log \frac{n + N}{n} - \log \frac{n_0 + N}{n_0} = NAt. \qquad (18)$$

If $N \gg n_0$, the solution reduces to $n = n_0 \exp(-NAt)$, and so the time for the signal to fall to e^{-1} of its initial value is

$$t_0 = 1/NA, \qquad (19)$$

in contrast with the earlier result (9) in the absence of traps. The presence of traps reduces the conductivity and the response time.

The model can be improved by taking account of the ionization of trapped carriers, and one obtains as observed a response time much longer than the carrier lifetime. For details consult the book by Rose (see references).

Space Charge Effects

When the illumination is not uniform throughout the crystal or when the electrodes cannot supply or drain off charge carriers freely in the crystal, space charges build up which may reduce the photocurrents severely. Suppose that 300 volts is applied across a crystal slab 1 cm thick by electrodes not in contact with the crystal. This electric field is equivalent to that produced by about 2×10^8 carriers/cm^2 drawn to opposite faces of the slab.

After this charge has collected on the crystal surfaces, the current will stop flowing because the electric field of the surface charges cancels the field applied by the electrodes. The currents and times involved in the production of the surface charge are not large. Polarization effects are a major obstacle to measurements of photoconductivity; thus pulse methods are often used. The crystal counter using a pulse of carriers is a useful tool in the investigation of mobility and trapping in crystals.

Crystal Counters

The crystal counter detects single ionizing particles by means of the pulse of charge carriers produced on passage of the particle through a crystal slab. The first practical crystal counter detected beta rays passing through a silver chloride crystal. The basic circuit is illustrated in Fig. 14.

The mechanism of counting is simple: the charge carriers produced by the ionizing particle drift under the influence of an applied electric field until they reach the electrodes or are trapped. The net displacement of charge parallel to the electric field induces a proportional charge on the electrodes. The electrode signal is then amplified.

We now analyze the voltage pulse induced by an alpha particle. The range of natural alpha particles in crystals is usually very small, of the order of 10^{-3} cm. Suppose that n free electrons are produced when one alpha particle penetrates the negative electrode and stops shortly thereafter. The contribution of the holes to the signal will be neglected, as they are swept up by the cathode near where they are produced. An electron moving a distance x across the crystal induces a charge $Q = ex/d$ on the electrodes,[16] where d is

[16] This appears obvious, but it is not trivial. For a proof, see W. Shockley, J. Appl. Phys. **9,** 635 (1938).

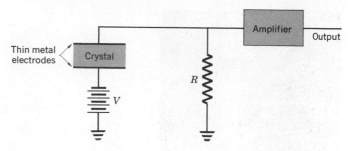

Figure 14   Schematic diagram of a crystal counter.

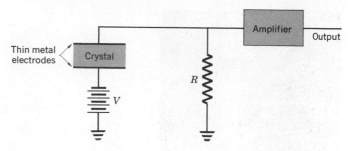

Figure 15 Induced charge on electrodes for an alpha particle incident on a crystal counter as a function of the ratio of electron range δ to crystal thickness d.

the thickness of the crystal. Electrons drifting toward the anode will be trapped along their path, with a trapping time T:

$$n = n_0 \exp\left(-t/T\right) = n_0 \exp\left(-x/\mu ET\right), \qquad (20)$$

because $x = \mu Et$, where μ is the mobility and E the electric field intensity. The number trapped in dx at x is $dn = dx \, (n_0/\mu ET) \exp\left(-x/\mu ET\right)$.

The total charge appearing on the capacitance is

$$Q = \frac{e}{d} \int x \, dn = \frac{n_0 e}{d\mu \, ET} \int_0^d x e^{-x/\mu ET} \, dx + n_0 e \exp\left(-d/\mu ET\right). \qquad (21)$$

The second term on the right arises from electrons which get all the way across the crystal to the anode. On integrating we find

$$Q = (n_0 e\mu ET/d)(1 - e^{-d/\mu ET}). \qquad (22)$$

The quantity $\delta = \mu ET$ is called the range of the carriers. A plot of Q versus δ/d is given in Fig. 15.

Measurements of the rise time give us the trapping time T, and measurements of the pulse height give us $\delta = \mu ET$; on combining the results we can determine the mobility.

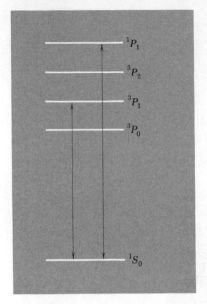

Figure 16 Ground and lowest excited states of the free Tl$^+$ ion, with transitions indicated.

LUMINESCENCE

Luminescence denotes the absorption of energy in matter and its re-emission as visible or near visible radiation. The initial excitation may be by light, particle bombardment, mechanical strain, chemical reaction, or heat. If the emission occurs during excitation, or within 10^{-8} sec of excitation, the process is commonly called **fluorescence.** The interval 10^{-8} sec is chosen as of the order of the lifetime of an atomic state for an allowed electric dipole transition in the visible region of the spectrum. If the emission occurs after excitation has ceased, the process may be called **phosphorescence** or **afterglow.** The delay period may be of the order of microseconds to hours. Crystalline luminescent solids are known as **phosphors.**

Many solids are luminescent with low efficiency for the conversion of other forms of energy into radiation. The ability of a given material to luminesce with high efficiency is frequently related to **activators,** which are special impurity atoms present in small proportions. Luminescent crystals may be divided into two classes: photoconductors (of which Cu-activated ZnS is the prototype), and crystals in which photoconductivity is incidental to the luminescent process.

Thallium-activated Potassium Chloride

Thallium-activated alkali halide phosphors have been studied extensively[17] and provide good examples of phosphors which are not photoconducting.

[17] The work is reviewed by F. E. Williams, Advances in Electronics **5**, 137 (1953); an early discussion was given by F. Seitz, J. Chem. Phys. **6**, 150 (1938).

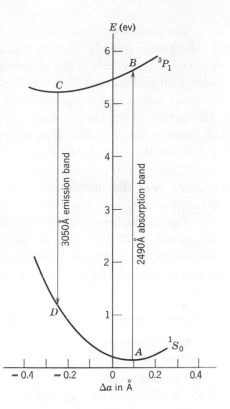

Figure 17 Two energy levels of Tl⁺ in KCl plotted as a function of the coordinate representing the symmetric displacement of the six neighboring Cl⁻ ions. The thallium ion in the ground state is close to point A, with some spread about this point caused by the thermal motion of the lattice. When the crystal is irradiated with light near 2490 Å, a transition to the upper state at B may take place. According to the Franck-Condon principle the absorption occurs with the lattice configuration characteristic of the ground state: thus the absorption occurs from A to B, rather than from A to C. After the transition a rearrangement of the neighboring ions takes place and the system assumes the equilibrium position C. The energy difference $B - C$ is dissipated by generation of lattice phonons. From C the ion emits light in a band around 3050 Å, passing to D, and, after giving energy to the lattice, returns to the equilibrium position A. (After F. E. Williams.)

Thallous ions Tl⁺ are believed to occupy at random positive ion sites in the lattice. The experimental situation is particularly simple for thallium concentrations of 0.01 percent or less.

The phosphor KCl:Tl consists of an ionic lattice containing Tl⁺ ions substituted for K⁺ ions. Optical absorption of the pure KCl crystal (Fig. 8) begins at 1650 Å and extends to shorter wavelengths. The thallium introduces two bell-shaped absorption bands centered about 1960 Å and 2490 Å, and a broad emission band centered about 3050 Å. The absorption and emission bands are associated with excited states of the Tl⁺ ion.

The electronic configuration of the ground state of Tl⁺ is $6s^2$, and the state is $^1S_0$. (The spins of the two s electrons are antiparallel.) The lowest excited states arise from the configuration $6s6p$ and consist (Fig. 16) of $^3P_0$, $^3P_1$, $^3P_2$, and $^1P_1$, each separated by the order of 1 volt. The spectroscopic selection rule against transitions from $J = 0$ to $J' = 0$ suggests that the transition $^1S_0 \leftrightarrow {}^3P_0$ does not occur, and the transition $^1S_0 \leftrightarrow {}^3P_2$ is excluded by the general selection rule $\Delta J = 0, \pm 1$. The selection rule $\Delta S = 0$ is not very effective and the transitions $^1S_0 \rightarrow {}^3P_1$ and $^1S_0 \rightarrow {}^1P_1$ have comparable intensities, the former leading to the 2490 Å absorption band and the latter to the 1960 Å absorption band. The emission at 3050 Å is associated with the downward transition $^3P_1 \rightarrow {}^1S_0$, as in Fig. 17.

The absorption from the ground state occurs with the neighboring ions in the lattice roughly fixed in position, according to the Franck-Condon[18] principle. The width of the absorption band is accounted for quite well by zero-point and thermal motions of the lattice; these motions cause transitions to occur over a certain spread of values of the configurational coordinate.[19] The lifetime of the excited state (say $^3P_1$) is 10^5 times longer than the period of a lattice vibration; thus after absorption and before re-emission the system can come to thermal equilibrium in the $^3P_1$ state. Luminescent emission occurs from the $^3P_1$ state to the $^1S_0$ state at the value of the configuration coordinate near the minimum energy position of the excited state. The rearrangement energy $B \rightarrow C$ and $D \rightarrow A$ is emitted as phonons.

The luminescence of phosphors activated with divalent manganese is somewhat parallel to that of the thallium-activated phosphors. Divalent manganese is an efficient activator in many crystals and finds application in fluorescent lamps and oscilloscope screens.

RECENT RESEARCH

Many recent optical studies are unfortunately beyond the scope of this book. We mention several briefly: (a) An important experimental approach to the overall band structure of semiconductors is provided by the Franz-Keldysh effect in which an applied electric field modulates the optical reflectance or transmission[20] of the semiconductor. (b) Optical absorption processes in antiferromagnetic crystals have been observed in which the photon creates two magnons or one magnon and one exciton.[21] (c) The theoretical interpretation of the observed optical properties of transition metals has contributed to the understanding of their band structures. (d) Studies of the light emitted by excited electrons (photo-emission) are valuable in band structure studies.

---

[18] The Franck-Condon principle states that atoms in molecules do not change their internuclear distances during an electronic transition.

[19] A configurational coordinate is any convenient linear combination of the position vectors of the nuclei of ions in the neighborhood of interest. In our problem Δa is defined as the symmetric displacement from the perfect KCl lattice positions of the six Cl^- ions bounding the Tl^+ ion.

[20] See, for example, B. O. Seraphin et al., Phys. Rev. Letters **14**, 138 (1965); **15**, 104 (1965).

[21] J. W. Halley and I. Silvera, Phys. Rev. Letters **15**, 654 (1965); R. L. Greene et al., Phys. Rev. Letters **15**, 656 (1965); S. J. Allen, Jr., R. Loudon, and P. L. Richards, Phys. Rev. Letters **16**, 463 (1966).

Problems

1. **Orbital g factor of exciton.** What is the orbital spectroscopic splitting factor of a Mott exciton composed of an electron and hole of effective masses m_e and m_h? (Find the center of mass; calculate the orbital angular momentum about the c.m. for a given angular velocity; calculate the total orbital magnetic moment, bearing in mind that the hole and electron act as if oppositely charged; finally, find g. Do the whole calculation classically.)

2. **Stark effect of Mott exciton.** (a) Taking $m_e = m_h = m$ and $\epsilon = 10$, estimate the electric field intensity required for an exciton to have a first-order Stark splitting of 1 cm^{-1} in the level $n = 2$. (b) Compare this field with that required for atomic hydrogen. (Make use of the *results* of the theory of the Stark effect as given in most elementary texts on quantum theory.)

3. **Sign of photoconducting carriers.** You are given a crystal slab in which the photoconductivity is known to be associated with one carrier type, holes or electrons, but just which is not known. Describe an experiment (using light of a wavelength strongly absorbed in a short distance in the crystal) which will identify the carrier type, without utilizing the Hall effect.

4. **Activator concentration.** Thallous ions Tl$^+$ are activators for luminescence in KCl. The thallous ions are believed to occupy at random alkali metal sites in the lattice. Let the ratio of concentrations $[Tl^+]/[K^+] \equiv c$. Only those Tl ions which do not have other Tl ions among their nearest cation neighbors are effective activators. Derive and plot an expression for the variation in the concentration c^* of effective activators as a function of c.

References

R. S. Knox, "Theory of excitons," *Solid state physics*, Supplement **5**, 1963.

C. G. Kuper and G. D. Whitfield, ed., *Polarons and excitons*, Plenum, New York, 1963.

D. S. McClure, "Electronic spectra of molecules and ions in crystals," *Solid state physics* **8**, 1 (1959).

H. C. Wolf, "The electronic spectra of aromatic molecular crystals," *Solid state physics* **9**, 1 (1959).

A. S. Davydov, *Theory of molecular excitons*, McGraw-Hill, 1962.

A. Rose, *Concepts in photoconductivity*, Interscience, 1963.

C. C. Klick and J. S. Schulman, "Luminescence in solids," *Solid state physics* **5**, 97 (1957).

D. Fox, M. M. Davis, and A. Weissburger, *Physics and chemistry of the organic solid state*, Interscience, 1963—, several vols.

18

Point Defects in Solids

From *Go fly a kite, Charlie Brown*, by kind permission of C. M. Schulz, © 1960 by United Features Syndicate, Inc.

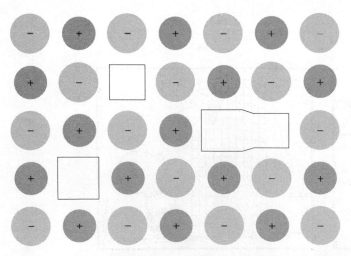

Figure 1 A plane of a pure alkali halide crystal, showing a vacant positive ion site, a vacant negative ion site, and a coupled pair of vacant sites of opposite sign.

Any deviation in a crystal from a perfect periodic lattice or structure is an imperfection. The common point imperfections are chemical impurities, vacant lattice sites, and interstitial atoms (extra atoms not in regular lattice positions). A point imperfection is localized near a point or atom in the structure, in contrast with a line or plane of imperfections. Line imperfections are considered in Chapter 19. Planar imperfections may occur in the initial stages of the formation of a new crystal structure within an existing crystal.

Real crystals are always imperfect in some respect. The nature of the imperfections are fairly well understood for some solids. Much work is concerned with the alkali and silver halides, germanium, silicon, copper, and alloys in general. An alloy represents a high concentration of point imperfections.

Many important properties of solids are controlled as much by imperfections as by the nature of the host crystal, which may act only as a vehicle or solvent or matrix for the imperfections. The conductivity of some semiconductors is due entirely to trace amounts of chemical impurities. The color of many crystals arises from imperfections. The luminescence of crystals is nearly always connected with the presence of impurities. Diffusion of atoms through solids may be accelerated enormously by impurities or imperfections. The mechanical and plastic properties of solids are usually controlled by imperfections.

LATTICE VACANCIES

The simplest imperfection is a **lattice vacancy**, which is a missing atom or ion, known as a **Schottky defect.** A lattice vacancy is often indicated in illustrations and in chemical equations by a square (Fig. 1). We create a Schottky defect in a perfect crystal by transferring an atom from a lattice site in the interior to a lattice site on the surface of the crystal.

In thermal equilibrium in an otherwise perfect crystal a certain number of lattice vacancies are always present, because the entropy is increased by the presence of disorder in the structure. At a finite temperature the equilibrium condition of a crystal is the state of minimum free energy[1] $F = E - TS$. In metals with close-packed structures the proportion of lattice sites vacant at temperatures just below the melting point is of the order of 10^{-3} to 10^{-4}. But in some alloys, in particular the very hard transition metal carbides such as TiC, the proportion of vacant sites of one component can be as high as 50 percent.

---

[1] For simplicity we assume the system is held at constant volume; it is not difficult to treat the system at constant pressure, for which $G = E - TS + pV$ is the appropriate thermodynamic potential.

We treat the statistics of the vacancy concentration in a monatomic crystal. We want to minimize the free energy with respect to the number of vacant lattice sites. Let E_V be the energy required to take an atom from a lattice site inside the crystal to a lattice site on the surface; then $E = nE_V$ is the increase in energy associated with the production of n isolated vacant sites.

Now consider the entropy S. The total number of ways in which we can pick n atoms from a crystal containing N atoms is

$$\frac{N(N-1) \cdots (N-n+1)}{n!} = \frac{N!}{(N-n)!\,n!}. \tag{1}$$

The $n!$ in the denominator occurs because the order in which the n vacancies are created is immaterial. According to Boltzmann the entropy is the log of the number of possible arrangements: the increase in entropy on creating n vacancies in a perfect crystal is

$$S = k_B \log \frac{N!}{(N-n)!\,n!}. \tag{2}$$

We neglect the smaller entropy associated with the lattice sites on the surface of the crystal. The change in the free energy is

$$F = E - TS = nE_V - k_BT \log \frac{N!}{(N-n)!\,n!}. \tag{3}$$

In thermal equilibrium at constant volume the free energy[2] F will be a minimum with respect to changes in n. The factorials in (3) are simplified by the Stirling approximation: $\log x! \cong x \log x - x$, for $x \gg 1$. Thus

$$\log \frac{N!}{(N-n)!\,n!} \cong (N \log N - N) - (N-n) \log (N-n)$$

$$+ (N-n) - (n \log n - n)$$

$$= N \log N - (N-n) \log (N-n) - n \log n. \tag{4}$$

In equilibrium we have from (3) and (4):

$$(\partial F/\partial n)_T = E_V - k_BT \log \frac{N-n}{n} = 0, \tag{5}$$

or

$$\log \frac{n}{N-n} = -E_V/k_BT. \tag{6}$$

---

[2] We neglect the elastic energy needed to keep the crystal at constant volume.

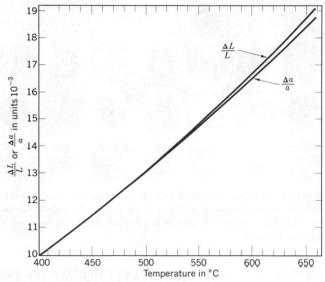

Figure 2 The *difference* between the linear dilation $\Delta L/L$ of the specimen on heating and the fractional lattice parameter change $\Delta a/a$ determined by x-ray diffraction is a measure of the concentration of vacant lattice sites. (The diffraction experiment is not significantly affected by a vacant site, but the length of the specimen is increased when atoms are taken out of lattice sites in the interior of the specimen and placed on the surface.) The graph gives results for aluminum, after R. O. Simmons and R. W. Balluffi, Phys. Rev. **117**, 52 (1960). The vertical scale is normalized to zero at 20°C.

For $n \ll N$ this result reduces to

$$n \cong N \exp\left(-E_V/k_B T\right). \tag{7}$$

If[3] $E_V \sim 1$ ev and $T \sim 1000°$K, then $n/N \sim e^{-12} \sim 10^{-5}$. The equilibrium concentration of vacancies decreases as the temperature decreases. The actual concentration of vacancies will be higher than the equilibrium value if the crystal is grown at an elevated temperature and then cooled suddenly, thereby freezing in the vacancies (see the discussion of diffusion below). The thermal generation of lattice vacancies in aluminum is shown in Fig. 2.

In ionic crystals it is usually favorable energetically to form roughly equal numbers of positive and negative ion vacancies. The formation of such pairs of vacancies keeps the crystal electrostatically neutral on a local scale. The number of ways in which we can form n separated pairs of positive and

---

[3] The energy of a nearest-neighbor bond in a solid is of the order of 1 ev.

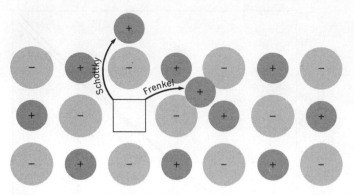

Figure 3 Schottky and Frenkel defects in an ionic crystal. The arrows indicate the displacement of the ions. In a Schottky defect the ion is moved to the surface of the crystal; in a Frenkel defect it is removed to an interstitial position.

negative ion vacancies is given by squaring[4] the quantity evaluated in Eq. (1). On following the exponent 2 through to the end of that calculation, we obtain

$$n \cong N \exp\left(-E_p/2k_BT\right), \tag{8}$$

for the number of pairs, where E_p is the energy of formation of a pair.

Another type of vacancy defect is the **Frenkel defect** (Fig. 3) in which an atom is transferred from a lattice site to an **interstitial position,** a position not normally occupied by an atom. The calculation of the equilibrium number of Frenkel defects proceeds along familiar lines (Problem 1). If the number n of Frenkel defects is much smaller than the number of lattice sites N and the number of interstitial sites N', the result is

$$n \cong (NN')^{1/2} \exp\left(-E_I/2k_BT\right), \tag{9}$$

where E_I is the energy necessary to remove an atom from a lattice site to an interstitial position.

It is believed from ionic conductivity studies and density measurements that in pure alkali halides the most common lattice vacancies are Schottky defects; in pure silver halides the most common vacancies are Frenkel defects. The production of Schottky defects lowers the density of the crystal because the volume is increased with no increase in mass. The production of Frenkel defects does not change the volume[5] of crystal; thus the density remains unchanged.

---

[4] We multiply probabilities.

[5] An interstitial atom takes up space, but the rest of the lattice is compressed. Under certain conditions elasticity theory predicts that the net volume change is zero.

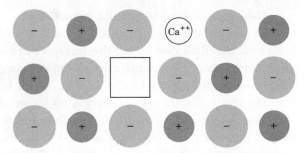

Figure 4 Production of lattice vacancy by the solution of $CaCl_2$ in KCl: to ensure electrical neutrality a positive ion vacancy is introduced into the lattice with each divalent cation Ca^{++}. The two Cl^- ions of $CaCl_2$ enter normal negative ion sites.

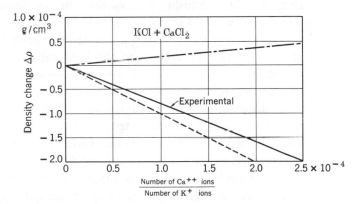

Figure 5 The change in density of KCl with controlled amounts of $CaCl_2$. The full line is experimental; the lower dashed line is the expected shift if the calcium ion plus vacancy occupies the same volume as two potassium ions. The upper hyphenated curve is the expected density if the densities of the two salts are additive.

Lattice vacancies in controlled concentrations are present in alkali halides containing additions of divalent elements. If a crystal of KCl is grown with controlled amounts of $CaCl_2$, the density varies as if a K^+ lattice vacancy were formed for each Ca^{++} ion in the crystal. The Ca^{++} enters the lattice in a normal K^+ site and the two Cl^- ions enter two Cl^- sites in the KCl crystal (Fig. 4). The net deficiency of one metal ion results in a vacant metal ion site. The experimental results (Fig. 5) show that the addition of $CaCl_2$ to KCl lowers the density of the crystal. The density would increase if no vacancies were produced, because Ca^{++} is a heavier and smaller ion than K^+.

The mechanism of electrical conductivity in alkali and silver halide crystals is usually the motion of ions and not the motion of electrons. This has been established by comparing the transport of charge with the transport of mass as measured by the material plated out on electrodes in contact with the crystal. Conductivity by the motion of ions is called **ionic conductivity**.

The study of ionic conductivity is an important tool in the investigation of lattice defects. Work on alkali and silver halides containing known additions of divalent metal ions such as Cd, Ca, Sr, Ba, Mg shows that at not too high temperatures the ionic conductivity is directly proportional to the amount of divalent addition. This is not because the divalent ions are intrinsically highly mobile; it is predominantly the monovalent metal ion which deposits at the cathode, rather than the divalent addition. Thus **the lattice vacancies introduced with the divalent ions are responsible for the enhanced diffusion** (Fig. 6c). The diffusion of a vacancy in one direction is equivalent to the diffusion of an atom in the opposite direction.

When lattice defects are generated thermally their energy of formation gives an extra contribution to the heat capacity of the crystal, as shown in Fig. 7.

Breckenridge[6] has noted that an associated pair of vacancies of opposite sign exhibits an electric dipole moment. He has observed contributions to the dielectric constant and dielectric loss at various frequencies in alkali halides which he attributes to the motion of pairs of vacancies; the dielectric relaxation time (Chapter 12) is a measure of the time required for one of the vacant sites to jump by one atomic position with respect to the other. (The dipole moment can change at low frequencies, but not at high.) In sodium chloride this relaxation frequency is 1000 cps at 85°C.

[6] R. G. Breckenridge, J. Chem. Phys. **16**, 959 (1948).

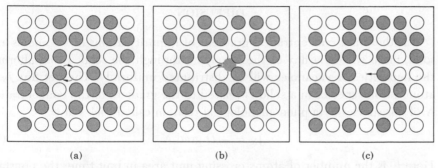

Figure 6 Three basic mechanisms of diffusion: (a) Interchange by rotation about a midpoint. More than two atoms may rotate together. (b) Migration through interstitial sites. (c) Atoms exchange position with vacant lattice sites. (From Seitz.)

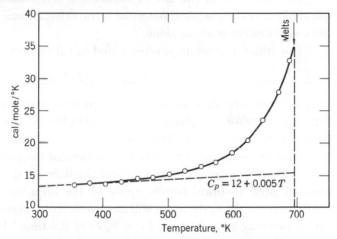

Figure 7 Heat capacity of silver bromide at constant pressure, exhibiting the excess heat capacity from the formation of lattice defects, after R. W. Christy and A. W. Lawson, J. Chem. Phys. **19**, 517 (1951).

DIFFUSION

If there is a concentration gradient of impurity atoms or vacancies in a solid, there will be a flux of these moving through the solid. In equilibrium the impurities or vacancies will be distributed uniformly. The net flux J_N of atoms of one species in a solid is related to the gradient of the concentration N of this species by a phenomenological relation called **Fick's law:**

$$\mathbf{J}_N = -D \text{ grad } N. \tag{9}$$

Here J_N is the number of atoms crossing unit area in unit time; the constant D is the **diffusion constant** or **diffusivity** and has the units cm^2/sec. The minus sign means that diffusion occurs away from regions of high concentration.

The form (9) of the law of diffusion is often adequate, but rigorously the gradient of the chemical potential is the driving force for diffusion and not the concentration gradient alone.[7]

The diffusion constant is often found to vary with temperature as

$$D = D_0 \exp{(-E/k_BT)}; \tag{10}$$

here E is the **activation energy** for the process. Experimental results on the diffusion of carbon in alpha iron are shown in Fig. 8. The data are represented by $E = 0.87$ ev, $D_0 = 0.020$ cm^2/sec.

In order to diffuse, an atom must surmount the potential energy barrier presented by its neighbors. We consider the diffusion of impurity atoms in interstitial sites; identical results apply to the diffusion of vacancies. If the barrier is of height E, the atom will have sufficient thermal energy to pass over the barrier only a fraction $\exp{(-E/k_BT)}$ of the time.[8] If ν is a characteristic atomic vibrational frequency in cycles per second, then the probability p that sometime during one second the atom will have enough thermal energy to pass over the barrier is

$$p \approx \nu \exp{(-E/k_BT)}. \tag{11}$$

In one second the atom makes ν passes at the barrier, with a probability $\exp{(-E/k_BT)}$ of surmounting the barrier on each try. The quantity p is also called the *jump frequency*. Values of ν are of the order of 10^{14} cps.

We consider two parallel planes of impurity atoms in interstitial sites. The planes are separated by lattice constant a. There are S impurity atoms on one plane and $(S + a \, dS/dx)$ on the other. The net number of atoms crossing be-

---

[7] See J. Bardeen and C. Herring, "Diffusion in alloys and the Kirkendall effect," *Imperfections in nearly perfect crystals,* Wiley, 1952.

[8] Quantum tunneling through a barrier is usually important only for the lightest nuclei, because for a given energy the de Broglie wavelength increases as the mass of the particle decreases.

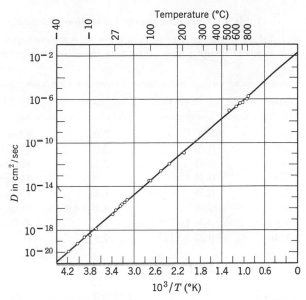

Figure 8   Diffusion coefficient of carbon in iron, after Wert. The logarithm of D is directly proportional to $1/T$.

tween the planes in one second is $\approx -pa\,dS/dx$. If N is the total concentration of impurity atoms, then $S = aN$ per cm² of a plane. The diffusion flux may now be written as

$$J_N \approx -pa^2\,dN/dx. \tag{12}$$

On comparison with (9) we have the result

$$\boxed{D = (\nu a^2)\exp(-E/k_BT),} \tag{13}$$

of the form of (10) with $D_0 = \nu a^2$.

If the impurities are charged, we may find the ionic mobility μ and the conductivity σ from the diffusivity by using the Einstein relation $k_BT\mu = qD$ from (10.34):

$$\mu = (q\nu a^2/k_BT)\exp(-E/k_BT); \tag{14}$$

$$\sigma = Nq\mu = (Nq^2\,\nu a^2/k_BT)\exp(-E/k_BT), \tag{15}$$

where now N is the concentration of impurity ions of charge q.

The proportion of vacancies is independent of temperature in the temperature range in which the number of vacancies is determined by the number of divalent metal ions. In this range the slope of a plot of $\log\sigma$ versus $1/k_BT$ gives E_+, the barrier activation energy for the jumping of positive ion

Table 1 Activation energy for motion of a positive ion vacancy

Values of the energy of formation of a vacancy pair, E_f, are also given. The numbers given in parentheses for the silver salts refer to interstitial silver ions.

Crystal	E_+(ev)	E_f(ev)	Workers
NaCl	0.86	2.02	Etzel and Maurer
LiF	0.65	2.68	Haven
LiCl	0.41	2.12	Haven
LiBr	0.31	1.80	Haven
LiI	0.38	1.34	Haven
KCl	0.89	2.1–2.4	Wagner; Kelting and Witt
AgCl	0.39 (0.10)	1.4°	Teltow
AgBr	0.25 (0.11)	1.1°	Compton

°For Frenkel defect.

vacancies (Table 1). At room temperature the jump frequency is of the order of 1 sec^{-1}, and at 100°K it is of the order of 10^{-25} sec^{-1}. We see that diffusion is very slow at low temperatures.

The proportion of vacancies in the temperature range in which the concentration of defects is determined by thermal generation is given by

$$f \cong \exp{(-E_f/2k_BT)}, \tag{16}$$

where E_f is the energy of formation of a vacancy pair, according to the theory of Schottky or Frenkel defects. Here the slope of a plot of log σ versus $1/k_BT$ will be $E_+ + \frac{1}{2}E_f$, according to (14) and (16). From measurements in different temperature ranges we determine the energy of formation of a vacancy pair E_f and the jump activation energy E_+.

The diffusion constant can be measured directly by radioactive tracer techniques. The diffusion of a known initial distribution of radioactive ions is followed as a function of time or distance. Values of the diffusion constant thus determined may be compared with values from ionic conductivities. The two sets of values do not usually agree within the experimental accuracy, so that there may also be present a diffusion mechanism which does not involve the transport of charge. For example, the diffusion of pairs of positive and negative ion vacancies or the diffusion of an associated complex of a divalent ion and a vacancy do not involve the transport of charge.

For the vacancy diffusion mechanism there should be a small difference between the diffusion constant as measured by radioactive atoms and as deduced from the ionic conductivity. Such differences were observed by Johnson.[9]

Metals

Self-diffusion in monatomic metals most commonly proceeds by lattice vacancies. **Self-diffusion** means the diffusion of atoms of the metal itself, and not of impurities. According to calculations by Huntington[9a] the activation energy for self-diffusion in copper is expected to be in the range 2.4 to 2.7 ev for diffusion through vacancies and 5.1 to 6.4 ev for diffusion through interstitial sites. Observed values of the activation energy are 1.7 to 2.1 ev.

Activation energies for diffusion in Li and Na can be determined from measurements of the temperature dependence of the nuclear resonance line width. As discussed in Chapter 16, the resonance line width narrows when the jump frequency of an atom between sites becomes rapid in comparison with the frequency corresponding to the static line width. The values 0.57 ev and 0.45 ev were determined by NMR for Li and Na by Holcomb and Norberg.[10] Self-diffusion measurements also give 0.45 ev for sodium.

COLOR CENTERS

Pure alkali halide crystals are transparent throughout the visible region of the spectrum. The crystals may be colored in a number of ways: (a) by the introduction of chemical impurities; (b) by introducing an excess of the metal ion (we may heat the crystal in the vapor of the alkali metal and then cool it quickly—an NaCl crystal heated in the presence of sodium vapor becomes yellow; a KCl crystal heated in potassium vapor becomes magenta); (c) by x-ray, γ-ray, neutron, and electron bombardment; and (d) by electrolysis.

A **color center** is a lattice defect which absorbs visible light. An ordinary lattice vacancy does not color alkali halide crystals, although it affects the absorption in the ultraviolet.

---

[9] W. A. Johnson, Trans. AIME **147**, 331 (1943). The diffusion constant is lower for diffusion of a tracer atom than for a diffusion of a vacancy. Suppose that a tracer atom has jumped forward by trading places with a vacancy. The tracer atom is not now in a random position with respect to the vacancy, for the vacancy is directly behind the tracer. There is consequently a probability that the vacancy will be filled by the tracer atom jumping backwards.

[9a] Vacancy formation in Cu has been reviewed by W. M. Lomer, *Prog. metal physics* **8** (1959).

[10] D. F. Holcomb and R. E. Norberg, Phys. Rev. **93**, 919 (1954).

F Centers

The simplest color center is an *F* center. The name comes from the German word for color, *Farbe*. We usually produce *F* centers by heating the crystal in excess alkali vapor or by x-irradiation. The central absorption band (*F* band) associated with *F* centers in several alkali halides are shown in Fig. 9, and the quantum energies are listed in Table 2. Experimental properties of *F* centers have been investigated in detail, originally by Pohl.

Table 2 Experimental *F* center absorption energies in ev

LiCl	3.1	NaBr	2.3
NaCl	2.7	KBr	2.0
KCl	2.2	RbBr	1.8
RbCl	2.0	LiF	5.0
CsCl	2.0	NaF	3.6
LiBr	2.7	KF	2.7

What is the electronic structure of an *F* center? The center has been identified by electron spin resonance as an electron bound at a negative ion vacancy (Fig. 10) in agreement with a model suggested by de Boer. When excess alkali atoms are added to an alkali halide crystal, a corresponding number of negative ion vacancies are created. The valence electron of the alkali atom is not bound to the atom; the electron migrates in the crystal and becomes bound to a vacant negative ion site. (A negative ion vacancy in a perfect periodic lattice has the effect of an isolated positive charge:[11] it attracts and binds an electron.)

The model is consistent with the experimental facts:

a. The *F* band optical absorption is characteristic of the crystal and not of the alkali metal used in the vapor; that is, the band in potassium chloride is almost exactly the same whether the crystal is heated in potassium or sodium vapor. (The role of the alkali vapor is to produce an *F* center in the host crystal.)

b. Crystals colored by heating in alkali vapor are found by chemical analysis to contain an excess of alkali metal atoms, typically 10^{16} to 10^{19} per cm^3. The integrated spectral absorption in the *F* band corresponds quantitatively to that expected from the known amount of excess alkali metal.

c. Colored crystals are less dense than uncolored crystals. This agrees with the elementary picture that the introduction of vacancies should lower the density.

---

[11] We can simulate the electrostatic effect of a negative ion vacancy by adding a positive charge q to the normal charge $-q$ of an occupied negative ion site.

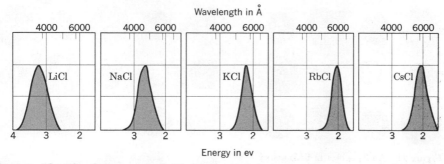

Figure 9 The *F* bands for several alkali halides: optical absorption versus wavelength for crystals which contain *F* centers.

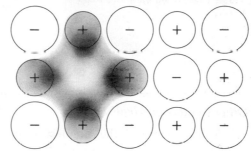

Figure 10 An *F* center is a negative ion vacancy with one excess electron bound at the vacancy. The distribution of the excess electron is largely on the positive metal ions adjacent to the vacant lattice site.

The width of the electron spin resonance line of an *F* center is determined essentially by the hyperfine interaction (Chapter 16) of the trapped electron with the nuclear magnetic moments of the alkali ions adjacent to the vacant lattice site. From the observed line width we may form a simple picture of the wavefunction of the electron. The electron is shared chiefly among the six alkali ions adjacent to the lattice vacancy.

If $\varphi(\mathbf{r})$ is the wavefunction of the valence electron on a single alkali ion, then in the first approximation[12]

$$\psi(\mathbf{r}) = C\sum_{P}\varphi(\mathbf{r} - \mathbf{r}_p), \tag{17}$$

where in the NaCl structure the index p runs over the six values of $\mathbf{r}_p$ at the alkali ion sites which bound the lattice vacancy. Here C is a normalization constant. The wavefunction is known to overlap somewhat the nearby halogen ions, so that (17) is not a complete description, but it is quite good.

---

[12] Kip, Kittel, Levy, and Portis, Phys. Rev. **91**, 1066 (1953); G. Feher, Phys. Rev. **105**, 1122 (1957). If the description (17) were complete, the width and shape of the EPR line would be determined from the hyperfine interaction of the electron with the nuclear magnetic moments of the six alkali ions. We assume the nuclear moments are oriented at random. For nuclear spin $I = \frac{3}{2}$ as for K^{39} there are $(2I + 1)^6 = 4^6$ possible spin arrangements distributed into $(12I + 1) = 19$ components.

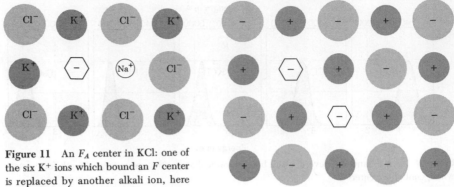

Figure 11 An F_A center in KCl: one of the six K⁺ ions which bound an F center is replaced by another alkali ion, here Na⁺. The hexagon is used here to denote a vacant negative ion site with a trapped electron.

Figure 12 An M center consists of two adjacent F centers.

Other Centers in Alkali Halides

The F center is the simplest trapped-electron center in alkali halide crystals. The optical absorption of an F center arises from an electric dipole transition to a bound excited state[13] of the F center.

Two absorption bands identify the F_A center, in contrast to the single absorption band of the F center. In the F_A center one of the six nearest neighbors of the F center has been replaced by a different[14] alkali ion, as in Fig. 11.

Complex trapped-electron centers are formed by groups of F centers, as in Figs. 12 and 13. Two adjacent F centers form an M center; three F centers form an R center. These and other centers are usually identified by their optical properties.

Holes may be trapped also to form color centers. Hole centers differ somewhat from electron centers: a hole in the filled p^6 shell of a halogen ion leaves the halogen in a p^5 electron configuration, whereas an electron added to the filled p^6 shell of an alkali ion leaves the ion in a p^6s configuration. The chemistry of the two configurations is different. The antimorph to the F center is a hole trapped at a positive ion vacancy, but no such center has been identified in experiments.

The best-known trapped-hole center is the V_K center (Fig. 14). It is believed that a hole may be trapped by any halogen ion in a perfect alkali halide crystal to form a V_K center. The structure of the V_K center is known from

[13] R. K. Swank and F. C. Brown, Phys. Rev. **130**, 34 (1963).
[14] F. Lüty and H. Pick, J. Phys. Soc. Japan Suppl. II **18**, 240 (1963).

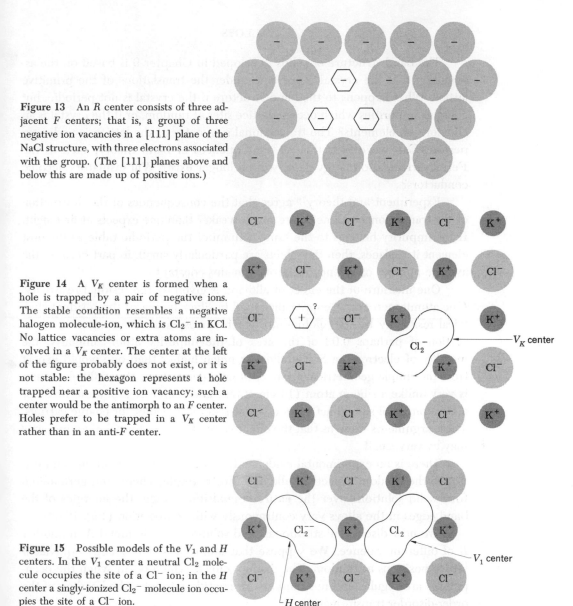

Figure 13 An *R* center consists of three adjacent *F* centers; that is, a group of three negative ion vacancies in a [111] plane of the NaCl structure, with three electrons associated with the group. (The [111] planes above and below this are made up of positive ions.)

Figure 14 A V_K center is formed when a hole is trapped by a pair of negative ions. The stable condition resembles a negative halogen molecule-ion, which is Cl_2^- in KCl. No lattice vacancies or extra atoms are involved in a V_K center. The center at the left of the figure probably does not exist, or it is not stable: the hexagon represents a hole trapped near a positive ion vacancy; such a center would be the antimorph to an *F* center. Holes prefer to be trapped in a V_K center rather than in an anti-*F* center.

Figure 15 Possible models of the V_1 and *H* centers. In the V_1 center a neutral Cl_2 molecule occupies the site of a Cl^- ion; in the *H* center a singly-ionized Cl_2^- molecule ion occupies the site of a Cl^- ion.

electron spin resonance experiments[15] to resemble a negative halogen molecule ion: in KCl the V_K center is like a Cl_2^- ion.

The anti-*F* center is not produced by heating a crystal in halogen vapor; other hole centers are produced instead. The V_1 and *H* centers of Fig. 15 involve Cl_2 and Cl_2^- in a Cl^- lattice site.

[15] W. Känzig, Phys. Rev. **99**, 1890 (1955); M. H. Cohen, Phys. Rev. **101**, 1432 (1958). The mechanism responsible for the trapping is the Jahn-Teller effect (Appendix H).

ALLOYS

The band structure of solids developed in Chapter 9 is based on the assumption that the crystal is periodic under the translations of the primitive lattice. What happens to the band structure if the crystal is not periodic, but contains impurities which occupy lattice sites at random, or if the crystal is an alloy of two elements? The translational symmetry of the lattice is no longer perfect. Can we expect that all consequences of band theory, such as the Fermi surface and energy gaps, will no longer exist? Will insulators become conductors?

Experiment and theory[16] agree that the consequences of the destruction of the translational symmetry are much weaker than one expects at first sight. If the impurity belongs to the same column of the periodic table as the host element it replaces, then the effects are particularly small, in part because the average number of valence electrons remains constant.

One measure of the effect of alloying is given by the residual resistivity. One atomic percent of copper dissolved in silver increases the residual electrical resistivity by 0.07 μohm-cm, which corresponds to a scattering cross-section of perhaps 0.03 of the area of the impurity atom. Similarly, the mobility of electrons in Si–Ge alloys is much higher than one would expect from the simple geometrical argument that a germanium atom (32 electrons) is very unlike a silicon atom (14 electrons) and therefore a Si atom in Ge or a Ge atom in Si should act as an efficient scattering center for charge carriers. These arguments show us that the effective scattering potential of an impurity may be very small.

There is no experimental evidence for an intrinsic reduction in band gap due to the random aspects of alloying. For example, silicon and germanium form solid solutions over the entire composition range; the energies of the band edges in the alloys vary continuously with composition (Fig. 16).

We now discuss substitutional solid solutions of one metal A in another B of different valence. We suppose that atoms A and B occupy equivalent lattice positions at random. The distinct effects which occur when the occupancies are regular and not random are considered under the heading of the order-disorder transformation.

Hume-Rothery has discussed empirical requirements for solid solutions

---

[16] These questions can be discussed using the method of orthogonalized plane waves and effective potentials described in Chapter 9. A low concentration of impurity atoms cannot have much effect on the Fourier components U_G of the potential $U(\mathbf{r})$ responsible for the band gaps and for the behavior of the energy surfaces near the band gap: An impurity will introduce Fourier components of $U(\mathbf{r})$ at wavevectors which are not reciprocal lattice vectors, but such components are never large if the impurity atoms are located at random. Thus one obtains sharp x-ray diffraction lines from random alloys.

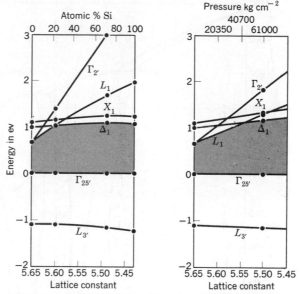

Figure 16 (a) Calculated variation of the major band edges in Ge-Si alloys as a function of the silicon concentration. The point $\Gamma_{25'}$ in **k** space is the valence band edge in both Ge and Si; L_1 is the conduction band edge in Si. (Compare with Figs. 10.12 and 10.13.) The calculations are by F. Bassani and D. Brust, Phys. Rev. **131**, 1524 (1963), who give extensive references to the experimental data. (b) The calculated variation as a function of pressure for pure Ge. Qualitatively the variation of the bands with pressure is similar to the variation with alloying, as we see by comparing energy values at equal values of the lattice constant.

to occur. One requirement is size. It is difficult to form solid solutions if the atomic diameters[17] of A and B differ by more than 15 percent. The sizes are favorable in the Cu (2.55 Å)–Zn (2.66 Å) system: zinc dissolves in copper as a fcc solid solution up to 38 atomic percent zinc. The sizes are somewhat unfavorable in the Cu (2.55 Å)–Cd (2.97 Å) system: only 1.7 atomic percent cadmium is soluble in copper. The atomic diameters referred to copper are 1.04 for zinc and 1.165 for cadmium.

Although the sizes may be favorable, solid solutions will not form if there is a strong tendency for A and B to form stable compounds of definite chemical proportions. If A is strongly electronegative and B strongly electropositive, it is likely that compounds such as AB and A_2B will precipitate out of solution. Although the atomic diameter ratio is favorable (1.02) for As in

[17] The atomic diameter is taken as the closest distance of approach in the crystal structure of the element (Table 1.4).

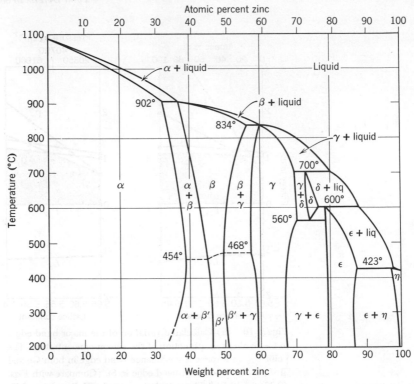

Figure 17 Equilibrium diagram of phases in the copper-zinc alloy system. The α phase is fcc; β and β' are bcc; γ is a complex structure; ϵ and η are both hcp, but ϵ has a c/a ratio near 1.56 and η (for pure Zn) has $c/a = 1.86$. The β' phase is ordered bcc, by which we mean that most of the Cu atoms occupy sites on one sc sublattice and most of the Zn atoms occupy sites on a second sc sublattice which interpenetrates the first sublattice. The β phase is disordered bcc: any site is equally likely to be occupied by a Cu or a Zn atom, almost irrespective of what atoms are in the neighboring sites.

Cu, only 6 percent As is soluble. The ratio is also favorable (1.09) for Sb in Mg, yet the solubility of Sb in Mg is very small.

Several aspects of the electronic structure of alloys can be discussed in terms of the average number[18] of conduction electrons per atom, denoted by n. The value of n in the alloy 50 percent Cu–50 percent Zn is 1.50; in 50 Cu–50 Al, $n = 2.00$. Some of the principal effects of alloying elements of different valence come from the change in electron concentration.[19] Hume-Rothery first drew attention to the importance of the average electron concentration as determining structural changes in certain alloy systems.

The phase diagram of the copper-zinc system[20] is shown in Fig. 17. The

---

[18] This number is often called the **electron concentration.**

[19] J. Friedel, Advances in Physics **3**, 446 (1954).

[20] The phases of interest are usually denoted by metallurgists by Greek characters: in the Cu-Zn system we have α (fcc), β (bcc), γ (complex cubic cell of 52 atoms), ϵ (hcp) and η (hcp); ϵ and η differ considerably in c/a ratio. The meaning of the characters depends on the alloy system.

fcc structure of pure copper ($n = 1$) persists on the addition of zinc ($n = 2$) until the electron concentration reaches 1.38. A bcc structure occurs at a minimum electron concentration of about 1.48. The γ phase exists for the approximate range of n between 1.58 and 1.66, and the hcp phase ϵ occurs near 1.75.

The term **electron compound** denotes an intermediate phase (such as the β phase of CuZn) whose crystal structure is determined by a fairly well-defined electron to atom ratio. The values of the ratio are called the **Hume-Rothery rules;** they are 1.50 for the β phase, 1.62 for the γ phase, and 1.75 for the ϵ phase. Representative experimental values are collected in Table 3, based on the usual chemical valence of 1 for Cu and Ag; 2 for Zn and Cd; 3 for Al and Ga; 4 for Si, Ge, and Sn.

The Hume-Rothery rules find a simple expression in terms of the band theory of nearly free electrons. The observed limit of the fcc phase occurs close to the electron concentration of 1.36 at which an inscribed Fermi sphere makes contact with the Brillouin zone boundary for the fcc lattice. The observed electron concentration of the bcc phase is close to the concentration 1.48 at which an inscribed Fermi sphere makes contact with the zone boundary for the bcc lattice. Contact of the Fermi sphere with the zone boundary for the γ phase is at the concentration 1.54. Contact for the hcp phase is at the concentration 1.69 for the ideal c/a ratio.

Why is there a connection between the electron concentration at which a new phase appears and the electron concentration at which the Fermi surface makes contact with the Brillouin zone boundary? It is costly in energy to add further electrons to an alloy once the filled states reach the zone boundary. Additional electrons can be accommodated only in states above the energy gap which occurs at the boundary or in the states of high energy near

Table 3   Electron/atom ratios of electron compounds

Alloy	fcc phase boundary	Minimum bcc phase boundary	γ-phase boundaries	hcp phase boundaries
Cu–Zn	1.38	1.48	1.58–1.66	1.78–1.87
Cu–Al	1.41	1.48	1.63–1.77	
Cu–Ga	1.41			
Cu–Si	1.42	1.49		
Cu–Ge	1.36			
Cu–Sn	1.27	1.49	1.60–1.63	1.73–1.75
Ag–Zn	1.38		1.58–1.63	1.67–1.90
Ag–Cd	1.42	1.50	1.59–1.63	1.65–1.82
Ag–Al	1.41			1.55–1.80

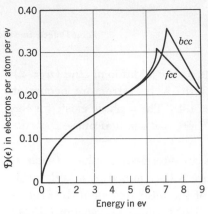

Figure 18 Number of free electron states per unit energy range for the first Brillouin zone of the fcc and bcc lattices, as a function of energy.

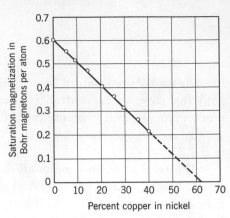

Figure 19 Bohr magneton numbers of ferromagnetic nickel-copper alloys.

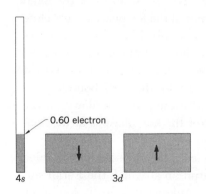

Figure 20 Distribution of electrons in the alloy 60Cu40Ni. The extra 0.6 valence electron provided by the copper has filled the d band entirely and increased slightly the number of electrons in the s band with respect to Fig. 15.7b.

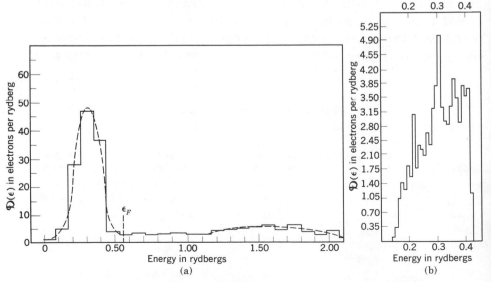

Figure 21 Density of states per atom in copper, after calculations by G. A. Burdick, Phys. Rev. 129, 138 (1963). (a) $\mathfrak{D}(\epsilon)$ for the bands arising from the 4s and 3d atomic states; (b) Fine structure of the hump in $\mathfrak{D}(\epsilon)$ due to the 3d band.

580

the corners of the lower zone. It may therefore be energetically favorable for the crystal structure to change to one which can contain a larger Fermi surface before contact. In this way the sequence fcc, bcc, γ, hcp was made plausible by H. Jones.

The transformation from fcc to bcc is illustrated by Fig. 18; this shows the number of states per unit energy range as a function of energy, for the fcc and bcc structures. As the number of electrons is increased, a point is reached where it is easier to accommodate additional electrons in the Brillouin zone of the bcc lattice rather than in the Brillouin zone of the fcc lattice. The figure is drawn for free electrons, and it may perhaps be objected that the actual density of states in pure fcc metals is somewhat different—see the Fermi surface of Cu in Figs. 9.24 and 9.32.

Nickel-copper alloys. We consider the relationship of the s and d bands in pure nickel at $0°K$ as suggested by Fig. 15.7b. There is a certain arbitrariness in the proposed distribution: we can transfer electrons from the d sub bands to the s band provided we take 0.54 more from one d sub-band than from the other d sub-band. Evidence that our particular choice may correspond to reality is provided by Fig. 19 which shows the effect on the magneton number of adding copper to nickel. We add one extra electron with each copper atom because the atomic number of copper is larger by one than the atomic number of nickel. The density of electron states in the d band is over ten times greater than in the s band, so that the extra electron goes at least 90 percent into the d band and less than 10 percent into the s band. The ferromagnetic magneton number is observed to go to zero at about 60 atomic percent copper.

At 60 atomic percent copper we have added about 0.54 electron per atom to the d band and about 0.06 electron to the s band. But 0.54 electron added to the d band of Fig. 15.7b will just fill both d sub-bands and will bring the magnetization to zero, in excellent agreement with observation. The distribution of electrons for 60Cu40Ni is shown in Fig. 20. At low Cu concentrations the decrease in magneton number from that of pure Ni should be a linear function of the concentration of copper, in agreement with Fig. 19.

For simplicity the block drawings show the density of states as uniform in energy. The actual density may be quite far from uniform: Fig. 21 gives the results of a calculation by Burdick for copper. The d band is characterized by a high density of states. The density of states at the Fermi surface is a rough indication of the enhancement of the electronic heat capacity and of the Pauli paramagnetic susceptibility which occurs in transition metals as compared with monovalent metals.

ORDER-DISORDER TRANSFORMATION[21]

The dashed horizontal line in the β phase region of the phase diagram of the Cu–Zn (Fig. 17) represents the transition temperature between ordered and disordered states of the alloy. Consider an alloy composed of equal numbers of two types of metal atoms, A and B. The alloy is said to be **ordered** if the A and B atoms have a regular periodic arrangement with respect to one another, as in Fig. 22a. The alloy is **disordered** if the A and B are randomly arranged, as in Fig. 22b. Many properties of an alloy are sensitive to the degree of order.

In the common ordered arrangement of an AB alloy with a bcc structure all the nearest-neighbor atoms of a B atom are A atoms, and vice versa. This arrangement results when the dominant interaction among the atoms is an attraction between A and B atoms. (If the dominant interaction is a repulsion between A and B atoms, a two-phase system is formed in which some crystallites have one chemical composition and other crystallites have a different composition.)

The alloy is completely ordered at absolute zero. It becomes less ordered as the temperature is increased, until a transition temperature is reached above which the structure is disordered. The transition temperature marks the disappearance of **long-range order,** which is order over many interatomic distances, but some **short-range order** or correlation among near neighbors may persist above the transition. The long-range order in an AB alloy is shown in Fig. 23a. Long- and short-range order for an alloy of composition AB_3 is given in Fig. 23b. The degree of order is defined below.

If an alloy is cooled rapidly from high temperatures to a temperature below the transition, a metastable condition may be produced in which a non-equilibrium disorder is frozen in the structure. The reverse effect occurs when an ordered specimen is disordered at constant temperature by heavy irradiation with nuclear particles.

The degree of order may be investigated experimentally by x-ray diffraction. The disordered structure in Fig. 22b has diffraction lines at the same positions as if the lattice points were all occupied by only one type of atom, because the effective scattering power of each plane is equal to the average of the A and B scattering powers. The ordered structure in Fig. 22a has extra diffraction lines not possessed by the disordered structure. The extra lines are called **superstructure lines.**

---

[21] For reviews see F. C. Nix and W. Shockley, Revs. Modern Phys. **10**, 1 (1938); H. Lipson, *Progress in metal physics* **2**, 1–52 (1950); T. Muto and Y. Takagi, *Solid state physics* **1**, 194 (1955).

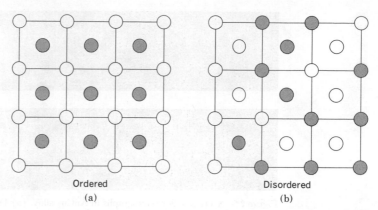

Figure 22 Ordered (a) and disordered (b) arrangements of AB ions in the alloy AB.

Ordered
(a)

Disordered
(b)

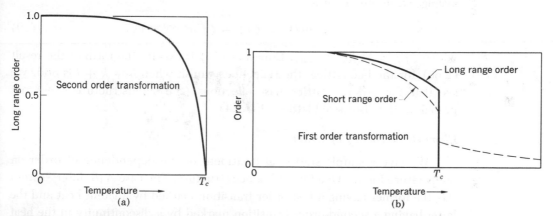

Figure 23 (a) Long-range order versus temperature for an AB alloy. The transformation is second order in the sense of Chapter 13. (b) Long-range and short-range order for an AB_3 alloy, after Nix and Shockley. The transformation for this composition is first order.

The structure of the ordered CuZn alloy is the cesium chloride structure (Fig. 1.26). The space lattice is simple cubic, and the basis has one Cu atom at $0\,0\,0$ and one Zn atom at $\frac{1}{2}\frac{1}{2}\frac{1}{2}$. The diffraction structure factor (2.65) becomes

$$S(hkl) = f_{Cu} + f_{Zn}e^{-i\pi(h+k+l)}. \qquad (18)$$

This cannot vanish because $f_{Cu} \neq f_{Zn}$; therefore all reflections of the simple cubic space lattice will occur.

In the disordered structure the situation is different: the basis is equally likely to have either Zn or Cu at $0\,0\,0$ and either Zn or Cu at $\frac{1}{2}\frac{1}{2}\frac{1}{2}$. Then the

Figure 24 X-ray powder photographs in AuCu$_3$ alloy. (a) Disordered by quenching from $T > T_c$; (b) ordered by annealing at $T < T_c$. (Courtesy of G. M. Gordon.)

average structure factor is

$$\langle \mathcal{S}(hkl) \rangle = \langle f \rangle + \langle f \rangle e^{-i\pi(h+k+l)}, \qquad (19)$$

where $\langle f \rangle = \frac{1}{2}(f_{Cu} + f_{Zn})$. Equation (19) is exactly the form of the result (2.66) for the bcc lattice; the reflections vanish when $h + k + l$ is odd. We see that the ordered lattice has reflections (the superstructure lines) not present in the disordered lattice (Fig. 24).

Elementary Theory of Order

We give a simple statistical treatment of the dependence of order on temperature for an AB alloy with a bcc structure. The case A_3B differs[22] from AB, the former having a first-order transition marked by a latent heat and the latter having a second-order transition marked by a discontinuity in the heat capacity (Fig. 25).

We introduce a measure of the long-range order. We call one simple cubic lattice a and the other b: the bcc structure is composed of the two interpenetrating sc lattices, and the nearest neighbors of an atom on one lattice lie on the other lattice. If there are N atoms A and N atoms B in the alloy, the **long-range order parameter** P is defined so that the number of A's on the lattice a is equal to $\frac{1}{2}(1 + P)N$. The number of A's on lattice b is equal to $\frac{1}{2}(1 - P)N$. When $P = \pm 1$, the order is perfect and each lattice contains only one type of atom. When $P = 0$, each lattice contains equal numbers of A and B atoms and there is no long-range order.

We consider that part of the internal energy associated with the bond

[22] The connection between composition and the order of the phase transition is discussed by S. Strässler and C. Kittel, Phys. Rev. **139**, A758 (1965).

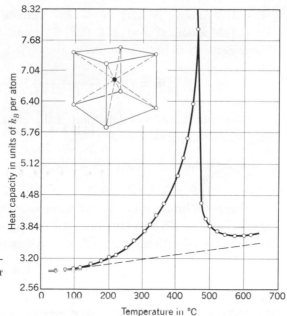

Figure 25   Heat capacity versus temperature of CuZn (β-brass) alloy, after Nix and Shockley.

energies of AA, AB, and BB nearest-neighbor pairs, although this concept is an oversimplification. The total bond energy is

$$E = N_{AA}U_{AA} + N_{BB}U_{BB} + N_{AB}U_{AB}, \tag{20}$$

where N_{ij} is the number of nearest-neighbor ij bonds, and U_{ij} is the energy of an ij bond.

The probability that an atom A on lattice a will have an AA bond is equal to the probability that an A occupies a particular nearest-neighbor site on b, times the number of nearest-neighbor sites, which is 8 for the bcc structure. We assume that the probabilities are independent. Thus, by the preceding expressions for the number of A's on a and b,

$$N_{AA} = 8[\tfrac{1}{2}(1 + P)N][\tfrac{1}{2}(1 - P)] = 2(1 - P^2)N;$$
$$N_{BB} = 8[\tfrac{1}{2}(1 + P)N][\tfrac{1}{2}(1 - P)] = 2(1 - P^2)N; \tag{21}$$
$$N_{AB} = 8N[\tfrac{1}{2}(1 + P)]^2 + 8N[\tfrac{1}{2}(1 - P)]^2 = 4(1 + P^2)N.$$

The energy (20) becomes

$$E = E_0 + 2NP^2U, \tag{22}$$

where

$$E_0 = 2N(U_{AA} + U_{BB} + 2U_{AB}); \qquad U = 2U_{AB} - U_{AA} - U_{BB}. \tag{23}$$

We now calculate the entropy S of this distribution of atoms. There are

$\frac{1}{2}(1 + P)N$ atoms A and $\frac{1}{2}(1 - P)N$ atoms B on lattice a; there are $\frac{1}{2}(1 - P)N$ atoms A and $\frac{1}{2}(1 + P)N$ atoms B on lattice b. The number of arrangements w of these atoms is

$$w = \left[\frac{N!}{[\frac{1}{2}(1 + P)N]! \, [\frac{1}{2}(1 - P)N]!} \right]^2. \tag{24}$$

From the Boltzmann definition of the entropy as $S = k_B \log w$, we have, using Stirling's approximation,

$$S = 2Nk_B \log 2 - Nk_B[(1 + P) \log (1 + P) + (1 - P) \log (1 - P)].$$

For $P = \pm 1$, $S = 0$; for $P = 0$, $S = 2Nk_B \log 2$.

The equilibrium order is determined by the requirement that the free energy $F = E - TS$ be a minimum with respect to the order parameter P. On differentiating F with respect to P, we have as the condition for the minimum

$$4NPU + Nk_BT \log \frac{1 + P}{1 - P} = 0. \tag{25}$$

The transcendental equation for P may be solved graphically; we find the smoothly decreasing curve shown in Fig. 23a. Near the transition we may expand (25), finding $4NPU + 2Nk_BTP = 0$. At the transition temperature $P = 0$, so that

$$T_c = -2U/k_B. \tag{26}$$

For a transition to occur, the effective interaction U must be negative (attractive).

The **short-range order parameter** r is a measure of the fraction of the average number q of nearest-neighbor bonds which are AB bonds. When completely disordered an AB alloy has an average of four AB bonds about each atom A. The total possible is eight. We may define[23]

$$r = (q - 4)/4, \tag{27}$$

so that $r = 1$ in complete order and $r = 0$ in complete disorder. Observe that r is a measure only of the local order about an atom, whereas the long-range order parameter P refers to the purity of the entire population on a given sublattice. Above the transition temperature T_c the long-range order is rigorously zero, but the short-range order decreases smoothly through the transition, as in Fig. 23b.

[23] A careful discussion of long- and short-range order is given by H. A. Bethe, Proc. Roy. Soc. (London) **A150**, 552 (1935).

Problems

1. **Frenkel defects.** Show that the number n of interstitial atoms in equilibrium with n lattice vacancies in a crystal having N lattice points and N' possible interstitial positions is given by the equation

$$E_I = k_B T \log \left[(N - n)(N' - n)/n^2 \right],$$

whence, for $n \ll N, N'$,

$$n \cong (NN')^{1/2} \exp(-E_I/2k_B T).$$

Here E_I is the energy necessary to remove an atom from a lattice site to an interstitial position.

2. **Schottky vacancies.** Suppose that the energy required to remove a sodium atom from the inside of a sodium crystal to the boundary is 1 ev. (a) Calculate the concentration of Schottky vacancies at 300°K. (b) If a sodium atom next to a vacancy has to move over a potential hill of 0.5 ev, and the atomic vibration frequency is 10^{12} cps, estimate the diffusion coefficient at room temperature for radioactive sodium in normal sodium.

3. **F Center.** (a) Treat an F center as a free electron of mass m moving in the field of a point charge e in a medium of dielectric constant $\epsilon = n^2$; what is the $1s$-$2p$ energy difference of F centers in NaCl? (b) Compare from Fig. 9 the F center excitation energy in NaCl with the $3s$-$3p$ energy difference of the free sodium atom.

4. **Superlattice lines in Cu_3Au.** Cu_3Au alloy (75% Cu, 25% Au) has an ordered state below 400°C, in which the gold atoms occupy the 0 0 0 positions and the copper atoms the $\frac{1}{2}\frac{1}{2}0$, $\frac{1}{2}0\frac{1}{2}$, and $0\frac{1}{2}\frac{1}{2}$ positions in a face-centered cubic lattice. Give the indices of the new x-ray reflections which appear when the alloy goes from the disordered to the ordered state. List all new reflections with indices ≤ 2.

5. **Configurational heat capacity.** Derive an expression in terms of $P(T)$ for the heat capacity associated with order/disorder effects in an AB alloy. (The entropy associated with (24) is called the configurational entropy).

References

J. H. Schulman and W. D. Compton, *Color centers in solids*, Pergamon, 1962.

L. A. Girifalco, *Atomic migration in crystals*, Blaisdell, New York, 1964. (Elementary treatment.)

P. G. Shewmon, *Diffusion in solids*, McGraw-Hill, 1963.

D. Lazarus, "Diffusion in metals," *Solid state physics* **10**, 71 (1960).

C. C. Klick, "Point defects in insulators," Science **150**, 451 (1965).

J. Friedel, "Electronic structure of primary solid solutions in metal," Advances in Physics **3**, 446 (1954).

W. Hume-Rothery, *Electrons, atoms, metals, and alloys*, 3rd ed., Dover, 1963.

L. Guttman, "Order-disorder phenomena in metals," *Solid state physics* **3**, 145 (1956).

19

Dislocations

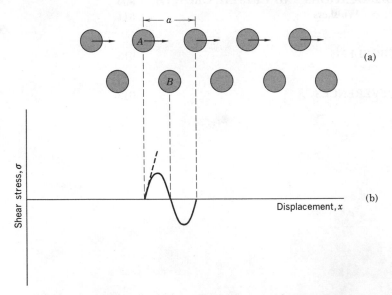

Figure 1 (a) Relative shear of two planes of atoms (shown in cross-section) in a uniformly strained crystal; (b) shear stress as a function of the relative displacement of the planes from their equilibrium position. The heavy broken line is drawn at the initial slope corresponding to the shear modulus G.

The present chapter is concerned principally with the interpretation of the plastic mechanical properties of crystalline solids in terms of the theory of dislocations. The plastic properties are those properties such as yield and slip associated with irreversible deformations; elastic properties are reversible.

The ease with which pure single crystals of many solids deform plastically is striking. This intrinsic weakness of crystals is exhibited in various ways, but there are few exceptions[1] to the rule that pure crystals are plastic and are not strong. Pure silver chloride melts at 455°C, yet at room temperature it has a cheeselike consistency and can be rolled into sheets. Pure aluminum crystals are elastic (follow Hooke's law) only to a strain of about 10^{-5}, after which they deform plastically. Theoretical estimates of the elastic limit of perfect crystals give values 10^3 or 10^4 higher than the lowest observed values, although a factor 10^2 is more usual.

SHEAR STRENGTH OF SINGLE CRYSTALS

Frenkel[2] gave a simple method of estimating the theoretical shear strength of a perfect crystal. We consider in Fig. 1 the force needed to make a shear displacement of two planes of atoms past each other. For small elastic strains the stress σ is related to the displacement x by

$$\sigma = Gx/d, \tag{1}$$

as in Chapter 4. Here d is the interplanar spacing, and G is the appropriate shear modulus; for example, $G = C_{44}$ for shear in a $\langle 100 \rangle$ direction on a $\{100\}$ plane in a cubic crystal.

When the displacement is large and has proceeded to the point that atom A is directly over atom B in the figure, the two planes of atoms are in a configuration of unstable equilibrium and the stress is zero. As a first approximation we might represent the stress-displacement relation by a sine function:

$$\sigma = (Ga/2\pi d) \sin (2\pi x/a), \tag{2}$$

where a is the interatomic spacing in the direction of shear. This relation reduces to (1) for small values of x/a.

The critical shear stress σ_c at which the lattice becomes unstable is given by the maximum value of σ, or

$$\sigma_c = Ga/2\pi d. \tag{3}$$

---

[1] It seems that exceptions really exist; for example, crystals of high purity germanium and silicon are not plastic at room temperature and fail or yield only by fracture. Glass fails only by fracture at room temperature, but it is not crystalline. The fracture of glass is caused by stress concentration at minute cracks, as proposed by A. A. Griffith, Phil. Trans. Roy. Soc. (London) A221, 163 (1921).

[2] J. Frenkel, Z. Physik 37, 572 (1926).

If $a \simeq d$, then $\sigma_c \simeq G/2\pi$. This calculation leads therefore to the result that the ideal critical shear stress is of the order of $\frac{1}{6}$ of the shear modulus.

The observations in Table 1 show the experimental values of the elastic limit much smaller than (3) would suggest. The theoretical estimate (3) may be improved by consideration of the actual form of the intermolecular forces and by consideration of other configurations of mechanical stability available to the lattice as it is sheared. Mackenzie has shown that these two effects may reduce the theoretical ideal shear strength to about $G/30$, corresponding to a critical shear strain angle of about 2 degrees.[3]

The observed low values of the shear strength cannot be explained without the presence of imperfections that can act as sources of mechanical weakness in real crystals. It is now known that special crystal imperfections called dislocations exist in almost all crystals, and their movement is responsible for slip at very low applied stresses.

Slip

Plastic deformation in many crystals occurs by **slip**, an example of which is shown in Fig. 2. In slip one part of the crystal slides as a unit across an adjacent part. The surface on which slip takes place is often a plane, and this is known as the slip plane. The direction of motion in slip is known as the slip direction.

The great importance of lattice properties (rather than continuum properties) for plastic strain is indicated by the highly anisotropic nature of

Table 1 Comparison of shear modulus and elastic limit
(After Mott)

	Shear modulus G, in dynes/cm^2	Observed elastic limit σ_c, in dynes/cm^2	G/σ_c
Sn, single crystal	1.9×10^{11}	1.3×10^7	15,000
Ag, single crystal	2.8×10^{11}	6×10^6	45,000
Al, single crystal	2.5×10^{11}	4×10^6	60,000
Al, pure, polycrystal	2.5×10^{11}	2.6×10^8	900
Al, commercial drawn	$\sim2.5 \times 10^{11}$	9.9×10^8	250
Duralumin	$\sim2.5 \times 10^{11}$	3.6×10^9	70
Fe, soft, polycrystal	7.7×10^{11}	1.5×10^9	500
Heat-treated carbon steel	$\sim8 \times 10^{11}$	6.5×10^9	120
Nickel-chrome steel	$\sim8 \times 10^{11}$	1.2×10^{10}	65

[3] J. K. Mackenzie, thesis, Bristol, 1949. W. L. Bragg and W. M. Lomer, Proc. Roy. Soc. (London) **196**, 171 (1949) have shown that the observed shear strength of a perfect two-dimensional raft of bubbles is of this order.

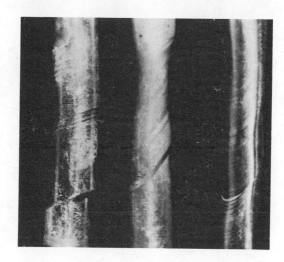

Figure 2 Translational slip in zinc single crystals. (Courtesy of E. R. Parker.)

slip. Even in the cubic metals displacement takes place along well-defined crystallographic planes with a set of small Miller indices, such as the {111} planes in fcc metals and the {110}, {112}, and {123} planes in bcc metals. Under most conditions the slip direction is observed to lie in the line of closest atomic packing, ⟨110⟩ in fcc metals and ⟨111⟩ in bcc metals.

To maintain the crystal structure after slip, the displacement or slip vector must equal a lattice translation vector. The shortest lattice translation vector expressed in terms of the lattice constant a in a fcc structure is of the form $(a/2)(\hat{x} + \hat{y})$; in a bcc structure it is $(a/2)(\hat{x} + \hat{y} + \hat{z})$. But in fcc crystals one also observes partial displacements which upset the regular sequence $ABCABC\ldots$ of closest-packed planes (Chapter 1), to produce a **stacking fault** such as $ABCABABC\ldots$. The result is then a "mixture" of fcc and hcp stacking.

Deformation of a crystal by slip is observed to be inhomogeneous. Large shear displacements occur on a few widely separated slip planes, while parts of the crystal lying between slip planes remain essentially undeformed. An incidental property of slip is the Schmid law of the critical shear stress: slip takes place along a given slip plane and direction when the corresponding *component* of shear stress reaches the critical value.

Slip is one mode of plastic deformation. A second mode of plastic deformation, called **twinning,** is observed in some crystals, particularly in hcp and bcc structures. During the slip process a considerable amount of displacement occurs on a few widely separated slip planes. During twinning a partial displacement occurs successively on each of many neighboring crystallographic planes. After deformation by twinning, the deformed part of the crystal is a mirror image of the undeformed part. Although both slip and twinning are caused by the motion of dislocations, we shall be concerned primarily with slip.

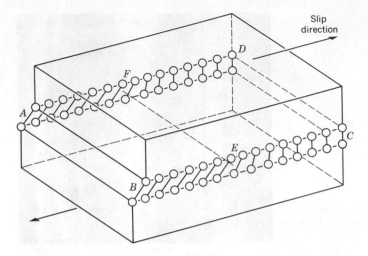

Figure 3 An edge dislocation *EF* in the glide plane *ABCD*. The figure shows the slipped region *ABEF* in which the atoms have been displaced by more than half a lattice constant and the unslipped region *FECD* with displacement less than half a lattice constant.

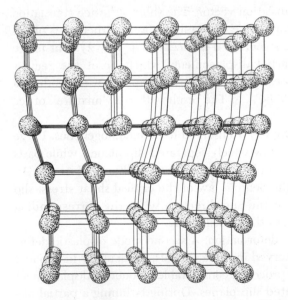

Figure 4 Structure of an edge dislocation. The deformation may be thought of as caused by inserting an extra plane of atoms on the upper half of the *y* axis. Atoms in the upper half-crystal are compressed by the insertion; those in the lower half are extended.

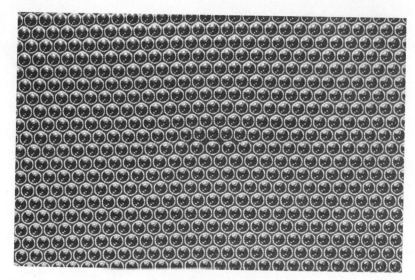

Figure 5   A dislocation in a two-dimensional bubble raft. The dislocation is most easily seen by turning the page by 30° in its plane and sighting at a low angle. (Courtesy of W. M. Lomer, after Bragg and Nye.)

DISLOCATIONS

The low observed values of the critical shear stress can be explained in terms of the motion through the lattice of a particular type of line imperfection known as a dislocation. The idea that slip propagates by the motion of dislocations was published in 1934 independently by Taylor, Orowan, and Polanyi; the concept of dislocations was introduced into physics somewhat earlier by Prandtl and Dehlinger.

There are several basic types of dislocations. We first describe an **edge dislocation.** Figure 3 shows a simple cubic crystal in which slip of one atom distance has occurred over the left half of the slip plane but not over the right half. The boundary between the slipped and unslipped regions is called the dislocation. Its position is marked by the termination of an extra vertical half-plane of atoms crowded into the upper half of the crystal as shown in Fig. 4. Near the dislocation the crystal is highly strained. The simple edge dislocation extends indefinitely in the slip plane in a direction normal to the slip direction. In Fig. 5 we show a photograph of a dislocation in a two-dimensional soap bubble raft obtained by the method of Bragg and Nye.[4]

[4] W. L. Bragg and J. F. Nye, Proc. Roy. Soc. (London) **A190,** 474 (1947); W. L. Bragg and W. M. Lomer, Proc. Roy. Soc. (London) **A196,** 171 (1949).

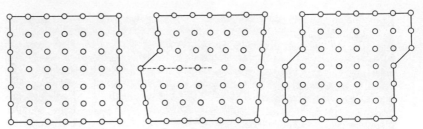

Figure 6 Motion of a dislocation under a shear tending to move the upper surface of the specimen to the right. (After Taylor.)

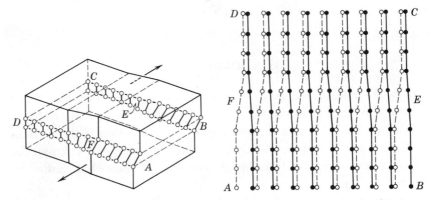

Figure 7 A screw dislocation. A part *ABEF* of the slip plane has slipped in the direction parallel to the dislocation line *EF*. A screw dislocation may be visualized as a helical arrangement of lattice planes, such that we change planes on going completely around the dislocation line. (After Cottrell.)

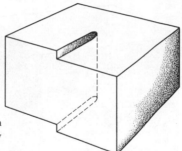

Figure 8   Another view of a screw dislocation. The broken vertical line which marks the dislocation is surrounded by strained material.

The mechanism responsible for the mobility of a dislocation is shown in Fig. 6. The motion of an edge dislocation through a crystal is analogous to the passage of a ruck or wrinkle across a rug: the ruck moves more easily than the whole rug, but passage of the ruck across the rug gives the same displacement as sliding the whole rug on the floor. If atoms on one side of the slip plane are moved with respect to those on the other side, atoms at the slip plane will experience repulsive forces from some neighbors and attractive forces from others across the slip plane. These forces cancel to a first approximation.

The external stress required to move a dislocation has been calculated and is quite small, probably below 10^5 dynes/cm^2, provided that the bonding forces in the crystal are not highly directional. Thus dislocations may make a crystal very plastic. Passage of a dislocation through a crystal is equivalent to a slip displacement of one part of the crystal.

The second simple type of dislocation is the **screw dislocation,** sketched in Figs. 7 and 8. A screw dislocation marks the boundary between slipped and unslipped parts of the crystal. The boundary *parallels* the slip direction, instead of lying perpendicular to it as for the edge dislocation. The screw dislocation may be thought of as produced by cutting the crystal partway through with a knife and shearing it parallel to the edge of the cut by one atom spacing. A screw dislocation transforms successive atom planes into the surface of a helix; this accounts for the name of the dislocation.

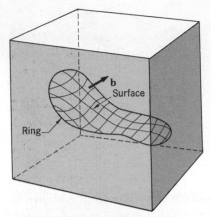

Figure 9 General method of forming a dislocation ring in a medium. The medium is represented by the rectangular block. The ring is represented by the closed curve in the interior in the block. A cut is made along the surface bounded by the curve and indicated by the contoured area. The material on one side of the cut is displaced relative to that on the other by vector distance **b**, which may be oriented arbitrarily relative to the surface. Forces will be required to effect the displacement. The medium is filled in or cut away so as to be continuous after the displacement. It is then joined in the displaced state and the applied forces are relaxed. Here **b** is the Burgers vector of the dislocation. (After Seitz.)

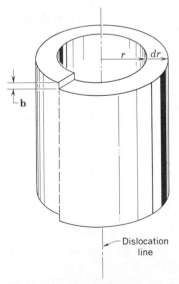

Figure 10 Shell of elastically distorted crystal surrounding screw dislocation with Burgers vector **b**.

Burgers Vector

Other dislocation forms may be constructed from segments of edge and screw dislocations. Burgers has shown that the most general form of a linear dislocation pattern in a crystal can be described as shown in Fig. 9. We consider any closed curve not necessarily planar within a crystal, or an open curve terminating on the surface at both ends: (a) Make a cut along any simple surface bounded by the line. (b) Displace the material on one side of this surface by a vector **b** relative to the other side; here **b** is called the **Burgers vector.** (c) In regions where **b** is not parallel to the cut surface, this relative displacement will either produce a gap or cause the two halves to overlap. In these cases we imagine that we either add material to fill the gap or subtract material to prevent overlap. (d) Rejoin the material on both sides. We leave the strain displacement intact at the time of rewelding, but afterwards we allow the medium to come to internal equilibrium. The resulting strain pattern is that of the dislocation characterized jointly by the boundary curve and the Burgers vector. The Burgers vector must be equal to a lattice vector in order that the rewelding process will maintain the crystallinity of the material.

The Burgers vector of a screw dislocation (Figs. 7 and 8) is parallel to the dislocation line; that of an edge dislocation (Figs. 3 and 4) is perpendicular to the dislocation line and lies in the slip plane.

Stress Fields of Dislocations

The stress field of a screw dislocation is particularly simple. Figure 10 shows a shell of material surrounding an axial screw dislocation. It is evident that the shell of diameter $2\pi r$ has been sheared by an amount b in the circumferential direction θ, giving a shear strain component $e_{r\theta} = b/2\pi r$. The corresponding shear stress in an elastic continuum is

$$\sigma_{r\theta} = Ge_{r\theta} = Gb/2\pi r. \tag{4}$$

This expression cannot hold in the region immediately around the dislocation line, as the strains here are too large for continuum or linear elasticity theory to apply.

The elastic energy of the shell is $dE_s = \frac{1}{2}Ge_{r\theta}{}^2 \, dV = (Gb^2/4\pi) \, dr/r$ per unit length. The total elastic energy per unit length of screw dislocation is found on integration to be

$$E_s = (Gb^2/4\pi) \log (R/r_0), \tag{5}$$

where R and r_0 are appropriate upper and lower limits for the variable r. A reasonable value of r_0 is comparable to the magnitude b of the Burgers vector or to the lattice constant; the value of R cannot exceed the dimensions of the crystal. In many applications R should be considerably smaller than

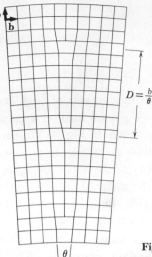

$$D = \frac{b}{\theta}$$

Figure 11 Low-angle grain boundary. (After Burgers.)

the dimensions of the crystal. The value of the ratio R/r_0 is not very important because it enters in a log term.

We now calculate the energy of an edge dislocation at the origin of the coordinate system (Fig. 4). We let σ_{rr} and $\sigma_{\theta\theta}$ denote the tensile stresses in the radial and circumferential directions, and we let $\sigma_{r\theta}$ denote the shear stress. In an isotropic elastic continuum σ_{rr} and $\sigma_{\theta\theta}$ are proportional to $(\sin \theta)/r$: we need a function which falls off as $1/r$ and which changes sign when y is replaced by $-y$. The shear stress $\sigma_{r\theta}$ is proportional to $(\cos \theta)/r$: considering the plane $y = 0$ we see from Fig. 4 that the shear stress is an odd function of x. On dimensional grounds the constants of proportionality in the stress are proportional to the shear modulus G and to the Burgers vector b of the displacement. The final result, which is derived in the books cited in the references, is

$$\sigma_{rr} = \sigma_{\theta\theta} = -\frac{Gb}{2\pi(1-\nu)}\frac{\sin \theta}{r}, \qquad \sigma_{r\theta} = \frac{Gb}{2\pi(1-\nu)}\frac{\cos \theta}{r}, \qquad (6)$$

where ν is the Poisson ratio defined in Problem 4.1 ($\nu \approx 0.3$ for most crystals). The strain energy of a unit length of edge dislocation is

$$E_e = [Gb^2/4\pi(1-\nu)] \log (R/r_0). \qquad (7)$$

We want an expression for the shear stress component σ_{xy} on planes parallel to the slip plane in Fig. 4. From the stress components σ_{rr}, $\sigma_{\theta\theta}$, and $\sigma_{r\theta}$ evaluated on the plane a distance y above the slip plane, we find

$$\sigma_{xy} = \frac{Gb}{2\pi(1-\nu)}\frac{\sin 4\theta}{4y}. \qquad (8)$$

It is shown in Problem 3 that the force caused by a uniform shear stress σ is $F = b\sigma$ per unit length of dislocation. This result holds also for the force that one dislocation exerts upon another. As a result, the force that an edge dis-

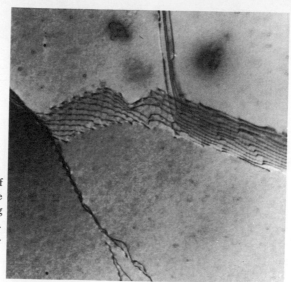

Figure 12 Electron micrograph of dislocation structures in small-angle grain boundaries in an Al–7% Mg solid solution. Magnification ×17,000. (Courtesy of R. Goodrich and G. Thomas.)

location at the origin exerts upon a similar one at the location (y, θ) is

$$F = b\sigma_{xy} = \frac{Gb^2}{2\pi(1 - \nu)} \frac{\sin 4\theta}{4y} \tag{9}$$

per unit length.[5]

Low-angle Grain Boundaries

Burgers[6] suggested that low angle boundaries between adjoining crystallites or crystal grains consist of arrays of dislocations. A simple example of the Burgers model of a grain boundary is shown in Fig. 11. The boundary occupies a (010) plane in a simple cubic lattice and divides two parts of the crystal that have a [001] axis in common. Such a boundary is called a pure tilt boundary: the misorientation can be described by a small rotation θ about the common [001] axis of one part of the crystal relative to the other. The tilt boundary is represented as an array of edge dislocations of spacing $D = b/\theta$, where b is the Burgers vector of the dislocations.

Experiments have substantiated this model. Figure 12 shows the distribution of dislocations along small-angle grain boundaries, as observed with an electron microscope. Further, Read and Shockley[7] derived a theory of the interfacial energy as a function of the angle of tilt, with results in excellent agreement with measurements. We note that the region of elastic distortion near a grain boundary does not extend very far into the two crystals, but is essentially confined to a slab whose thickness equals the dislocation spacing D. Each dislocation is surrounded by its own strain field and by the strain fields

---

[5] Strictly speaking, F is the component of force in the slip direction. There is another component of force perpendicular to the slip direction, but it is of no importance at low temperatures where the only possible motion of a dislocation is in the slip plane.

[6] J. M. Burgers, Proc. Koninkl. Ned. Akad. Wetenschap. **42**, 293 (1939); Proc. Phys. Soc. (London) **52**, 23 (1940).

[7] W. T. Read and W. Shockley, Phys. Rev. **78**, 275 (1950).

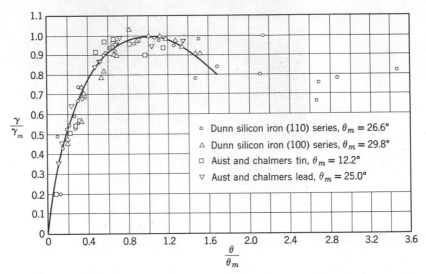

Figure 13   Comparison of theoretical curve with measurements of relative grain-boundary energy as function of the angle between grains. The theoretical curve is given by $\gamma/\gamma_m = (\theta/\theta_m)\ [1 - \log\ (\theta/\theta_m)]$. (By permission from *Dislocations in crystals*, by W. T. Read, Jr. Copyright, 1953. McGraw-Hill Book Company, Inc.)

of dislocations above and below it. The latter strain fields nearly cancel each other, being equal in magnitude and opposite in sign, so that the strain energy near each dislocation results primarily from its own strain field. In this approximation (7) gives the elastic strain energy per unit length of dislocation in the boundary as $[Gb^2/4\pi(1 - \nu)]\ \log\ (\alpha D/b)$, where r_0 has been set equal to b and α is a number near 1. There are $1/D = \theta/b$ dislocations per unit length of boundary, so that the grain boundary energy is

$$\gamma = - \left(\frac{Gb}{4\pi(1 - \nu)}\right)\theta(\log\theta + \log\alpha). \tag{10}$$

The grain boundary energy γ is zero when θ is zero, and rises with an initial vertical slope as θ increases. With further increase in θ, γ reaches a maximum γ_m and begins to decline. If we let θ_m be the value of θ for which $\gamma = \gamma_m$, (10) reduces to

$$\gamma/\gamma_m = (\theta/\theta_m)\ [1 - \log\ (\theta/\theta_m)]. \tag{11}$$

This equation is compared in Fig. 13 with the experimental measurements of relative grain boundary energy as a function of θ. The agreement is remarkably good up to $\theta \geq 30°$; this is beyond the point where the dislocation model is expected to apply.

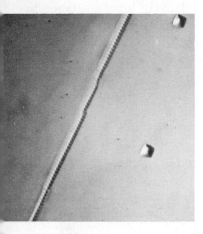

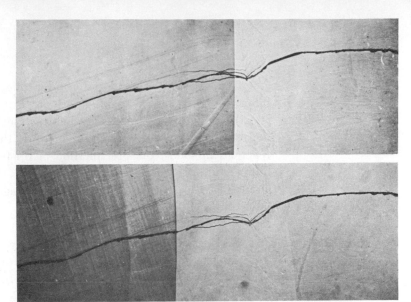

Figure 14 Dislocation etch pits in low-angle boundary on (100) face of germanium; the angle of the boundary is 27.5 sec. The boundary lies in a (0$\overline{1}$1) plane; the line of the dislocations is [100]. The Burgers vector is the shortest lattice translation vector, or |**b**| = $a/\sqrt{2}$ = 4.0 Å. [After F. L. Vogel, Jr., Acta Metallurgica **3**, 245 (1955).]

Figure 15 Motion of a small-angle grain boundary under stress. The boundary is the straight vertical line, and it is photographed under vertical illumination, thereby making evident the 2° angular change in the cleavage surface of the zinc crystal at the boundary. The irregular horizontal line is a small step in the cleavage surface which serves as a reference mark. The crystal is clamped at the left; at the right it is subject to a force normal to the plane of the page. *Top,* original position of boundary; *bottom,* moved back 0.4 mm. (Courtesy of J. Washburn and E. R. Parker.)

Direct verification of the Burgers model is provided by the quantitative x-ray and optical studies of low-angle boundaries in germanium crystals by Vogel[8] and co-workers. By counting etch pits along the intersection of a low-angle grain boundary with an etched germanium surface (Fig. 14), they determined the dislocation spacing D. They assumed that each etch pit marked the end of a dislocation. The angle of tilt calculated from the relation $\theta = b/D$ agrees well with the angle measured directly by means of x-rays.

The interpretation of low-angle boundaries as arrays of dislocations is further supported by the fact that pure tilt boundaries move normal to themselves on application of a suitable stress. The motion has been demonstrated in a beautiful experiment by Washburn and Parker (Fig. 15). The specimen is a bicrystal of zinc containing a 2° tilt boundary, with dislocations about thirty atomic planes apart. One side of the crystal was clamped, and a force was applied at a point on the opposite side of the boundary. Motion of the boundary took place by cooperative motion of the dislocations in the array, each dislocation moving an equal distance in its own slip plane. The motion was produced by stresses of the order of magnitude of the yield stress for zinc crystals, a fact that gives strong evidence that ordinary deformation results from the motion of dislocations.

[8] F. L. Vogel, W. G. Pfann, H. E. Corey, and E. E. Thomas, Phys. Rev. **90**, 489 (1953); F. L. Vogel, Jr., Acta Met. **3**, 245 (1955).

Grain boundaries and dislocations offer relatively little resistance to diffusion of atoms in comparison with diffusion in perfect crystals. Diffusion is known to be greater in plastically deformed material than in annealed crystals. Diffusion along grain boundaries controls the rates of some precipitation reactions in solids: the precipitation of tin from lead-tin solutions at room temperature proceeds about 10^8 times faster than expected from diffusion in an ideal lattice. A dislocation is an open passage for diffusion.

Dislocation Densities

The density of dislocations is the number of dislocation lines that intersect a unit area in the crystal. The density ranges from 10^2 to 10^3 dislocations/cm^2 in the best germanium and silicon crystals to 10^{11} or 10^{12} dislocations/cm^2 in heavily deformed metal crystals. The methods available for estimating dislocation densities are compared in Table 2. The book by Amelinckx is an excellent reference for all present methods of observing dislocations.

The actual dislocation configurations in cast or annealed (slowly cooled) crystals correspond either to a group of low-angle grain boundaries or to a three-dimensional network of dislocations arranged in cells, as shown in Fig. 16.

The dislocation density in heavily deformed crystals may be estimated from the increased internal energy that results from plastic deformation. From (5) and (7), the energy per unit length of a dislocation is about $(Gb^2/4\pi)$ log (R/r_0). We take R comparable to the dislocation spacing and $r_0 \approx b$, and so $R/r_0 \approx 10^3$. The dislocation energy then is about 5×10^{-4} erg/cm, or about 8 ev per atom plane through which the dislocation passes. The maximum energy stored in lattice distortions as a consequence of severe plastic deformation, as by twisting, filing, or compressing, has been measured thermally for several metals. If the deformation is not too great, about 10 per-

Table 2   Methods for estimating dislocation densities*

Technique	Specimen thickness	Width of image	Maximum practical density, per cm^2
Electron microscopy	$>$1000 Å	$\sim$100 Å	10^{11}–10^{12}
X-ray transmission	0.1–1.0 mm	5μ	10^4–10^5
X-ray reflection	$<2\mu$ (min.) $-$ 50μ (max.)	2μ	10^6–10^7
Decoration	$\sim$10μ (depth of focus)	0.5μ	2×10^7
Etch pits	no limit	0.5μ†	4×10^8

*Based on W. G. Johnston. Prog. Ceramic Sci. **2**, 1 (1961).
†Limit of resolution of etch pits.

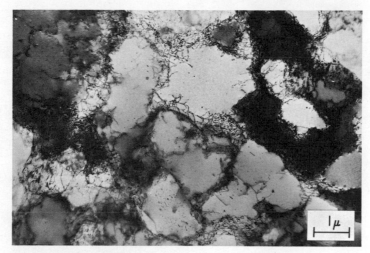

Figure 16   Cell structure of three-dimensional tangles of dislocations in deformed aluminum. (Courtesy of P. R. Swann.)

cent of the energy expended in plastic flow is stored in the lattice. Upon continued plastic flow, however, the stored energy approaches a saturation value. The observed values of the stored energy are about 10^8 ergs/cm^3. If the energy per unit length of dislocations is 5×10^{-4} erg/cm, then there must be about 10^{11} cm of dislocation lines per cubic centimeter of crystal, or about 10^{11} dislocations/cm^2. This is about one dislocation per square 100 atoms on a side. Such a concentration is characteristic of severely deformed metals.

A problem is posed by the presence of dislocations in cast and annealed crystals. No dislocations can be present in thermal equilibrium, because their energy is much too great in comparison with the increase in entropy that they produce. Dislocations must therefore be introduced in a nonequilibrium manner during the solidification of crystals from the melt, and the dislocations must remain even during the most careful annealing. The mechanism of their introduction during solidification is not known, although it is thought to be associated with the precipitation of lattice vacancies as the crystal cools.

Lattice vacancies which precipitate along an existing edge dislocation will eat away a portion of the extra half-plane of atoms and cause the dislocation to climb, which means to move at right angles to the slip direction. If no dislocations are present, the crystal will become supersaturated with lattice vacancies; their precipitation in penny-shaped vacancy plates may be followed

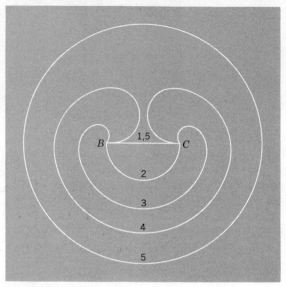

Figure 17 Electron micrograph of dislocation loops formed by aggregation and collapse of vacancies in Al–5% Mg quenched from 550°C. The helical dislocations are formed by the "climb" of screw dislocations as a result of the precipitation of vacancies. Mag. ×43,000. (Courtesy of A. Eikum and G. Thomas.)

Figure 18 Frank-Read mechanism for multiplication of dislocations, showing successive stages in the generation of a dislocation loop by the segment BC of a dislocation line. The process can be repeated indefinitely.

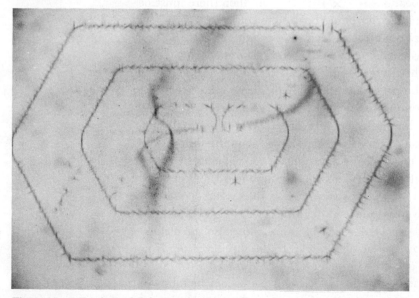

Figure 19 A Frank-Read dislocation source in silicon, decorated with copper precipitates and viewed with infrared illumination. Two complete dislocation loops are visible, and the third, innermost loop is near completion. (After W. C. Dash, *Dislocations and Mechanical Properties of Crystals,* Fisher et al. (eds.), Wiley, 1957, pp. 57–68.)

by collapse of the plates and formation of dislocation rings which grow with further vacancy precipitation, as in Fig. 17.

A second problem discussed below is posed by the very great increase in dislocation density that is caused by plastic deformation. Dislocation density measurements typically show an increase from about 10^8 to about 10^{11} dislocations/cm^2 during deformation, a 1000-fold increase. Equally striking is the fact that, if a dislocation were to move completely across its slip plane, an offset of only one atom spacing would be produced, whereas offsets of as much as 100 to 1000 atom spacings are actually observed.

Dislocation Multiplication and Slip

Consider a closed circular dislocation loop of radius r surrounding a slipped area of the same radius. A dislocation loop will have to be partly edge, partly screw, and mostly intermediate in character. Because the strain energy of the dislocation of loop increases in proportion to its circumference, the loop will tend to shrink. However, if a shear stress that favors slip is acting, the loop will tend to expand. A dislocation segment pinned at each end (Fig. 18) is called a **Frank-Read source**,[9] and as in the figure it can lead to the generation of a large number of concentric dislocation loops on a single slip plane. This and related types of dislocation multiplication mechanisms give rise to slip and to the increased density of dislocations during plastic deformation. A beautiful example of a dislocation source is shown in Fig. 19.

STRENGTH OF ALLOYS

Pure crystals are very plastic and yield at very low stresses. There appear to be four important ways of increasing the yield strength of an alloy so that it will withstand shear stresses as high as 10^{-2} G. They are mechanical blocking of dislocation motion, pinning of dislocations by solute atoms, impeding dislocation motion by short-range order, and increasing the dislocation density so that tangling of dislocations results. All four strengthening mechanisms depend for their success upon impeding dislocation motion. A fifth mechanism, that of removing all dislocations from the crystal, may operate for certain fine hairlike crystals (whiskers) that are discussed in the section on crystal growth.

Mechanical blocking of dislocation motion can be produced most directly by introducing tiny particles of a second phase into a crystal lattice. This process is followed in the hardening of steel, where particles of iron carbide are precipitated into iron, and in hardening aluminum, where particles of Al_2Cu are precipitated.

---

[9] The classical Frank-Read source is not observed as often as certain modifications: see G. Thomas, J. of Metals, Apr. 1964.

In strengthening by the addition of small particles there are two cases to be considered: either the particle can be deformed with the matrix, which requires that the particle can be traversed by the dislocation, or the particle cannot be traversed by the dislocation. If the particle cannot be cut[10] the stress necessary to force a dislocation between particles spaced L apart on a slip plane should be approximately

$$\sigma/G = b/L. \tag{12}$$

The smaller the spacing L, the higher is the yield stress σ. Before particles precipitate, L is large and the strength is low. Immediately after precipitation is complete and many small particles are present, L is a minimum and the strength is a maximum. If the alloy is then held at a high temperature, some particles grow at the expense of others, so that L increases and the strength drops.

The strength of dilute solid solutions is believed to result from the pinning of dislocations by solute atoms. Cottrell pointed out that the solubility of a foreign atom will be greater in the neighborhood of a dislocation than elsewhere in a crystal. For example, an atom that tends to expand the crystal will dissolve preferentially in the expanded region near an edge dislocation. A small atom will tend to dissolve preferentially in the contracted region near the dislocation—a dislocation offers both expanded and contracted regions. As a result of the affinity of solute atoms for dislocations, each dislocation will collect a cloud of associated solute atoms during cooling, at a time when the mobility of solute atoms is high. At still lower temperatures diffusion of solute atoms effectively ceases, and the solute atom cloud becomes fixed in the crystal. When a dislocation moves, leaving its solute cloud behind, the energy of the crystal must increase. The increase in energy can only be provided by an increased stress acting on the dislocation as it pulls away from the solute atom cloud, and so the presence of the cloud strengthens the crystal.

The passage of a dislocation across a slip plane in pure crystals does not alter the binding energy across the plane after the dislocation is gone. The internal energy of the crystal remains unaffected. The same is true for random solid solutions, because the solution is equally random across a slip plane after slip. Most solid solutions, however, contain short-range order, as defined in Chap. 18. Atoms of different species are not arranged at random on the lattice sites, but tend to have an excess or a deficiency of pairs of unlike atoms. Thus in ordered alloys dislocations tend to move in pairs: the second dislocation reorders the local disorder left by the first dislocation.

The strength of a crystalline material increases with plastic deformation. The phenomenon is called **work-hardening** or **strain-hardening.** The strength is believed to increase because of the increased density of dislocations and the

---

[10] Hard intermetallic phases, such as refractory oxides, cannot be cut by dislocations.

greater difficulty of moving a given dislocation across a slip plane that is threaded by many dislocations. The difficulty is particularly acute when one screw dislocation tries to cross another; lattice vacancies and interstitial atoms may be generated in the process. Strain-hardening frequently is employed in the strengthening of materials, but its usefulness is limited to low enough temperatures so that annealing does not occur.

The important factor in strain-hardening is not the total density of dislocations, but their arrangement. In most metals dislocations tend to form cells (Fig. 16) of dislocation-free areas of dimensions of the order of 1 micron. But unless we can get a uniform high density of dislocations we cannot strain-harden a metal to its theoretical strength, because of slip in the dislocation-free areas. A uniform density is accomplished by explosive deformation or by special thermal-mechanical treatments.[11]

Each of the mechanisms of strengthening crystals can raise the yield strength to the order of 10^{-3} G to 10^{-2} G. All mechanisms begin to break down at temperatures where diffusion can occur at an appreciable rate. When diffusion is rapid, precipitated particles dissolve; solute clouds drift along with dislocations as they glide; short-range order repairs itself behind slowly moving dislocations; and dislocation climb and annealing tend to decrease the dislocation density. The resulting time-dependent deformation is called **creep.** This irreversible motion precedes the elastic limit. The search for alloys for use at very high temperatures is a search for reduced diffusion rates, so that the four strengthening mechanisms will survive to high temperatures.

DISLOCATIONS AND CRYSTAL GROWTH

It has been shown by Frank[12] and his collaborators that in some cases the presence of dislocations may be the controlling factor in crystal growth. When crystals are grown in conditions of low supersaturation, of the order of 1 percent, it has been observed that the growth rate is enormously faster than that calculated for an ideal crystal. The actual growth rate is explained by Frank in terms of the effect of dislocations on growth.

The theory of growth of ideal crystals predicts that in crystal growth from vapor a supersaturation (pressure/equilibrium vapor pressure) of the order of 10 is required to nucleate new crystals, of the order of 5 to form liquid drops, and of 1.5 to form a two-dimensional monolayer of molecules on the face of a perfect crystal. Volmer and Schultze observed growth of iodine crystals at vapor supersaturations down to less than 1 percent, where the growth rate should have been down by the factor e^{-3000} from the rate defined as the

[11] V. F. Zackay, "Strength of steel," Sci. Amer. **209**, 71 (August, 1963).

[12] For a full review of this field see Neugebauer, ed., *Growth and perfection of crystals*, Wiley, 1959; also Chap. 7 of J. Friedel, *Dislocations*, Addison-Wesley, 1964.

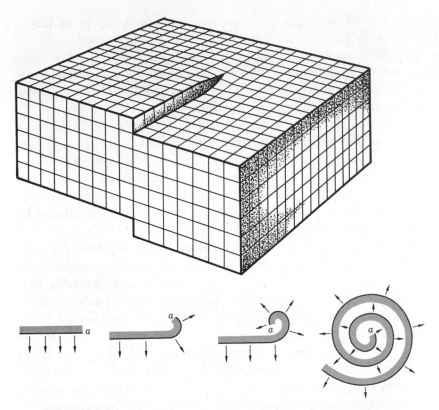

Figure 20 Development of a spiral step produced by intersection of a screw dislocation with the surface of a crystal. Each cube represents a molecule. (After F. C. Frank.)

minimum observable growth. This is a substantial disagreement between observation and theory.

The large disagreement expresses the difficulty of nucleating a new monolayer on a completed surface of an ideal crystal. But if a screw dislocation is present (Fig. 20) it is never necessary to nucleate a new layer: the crystal will grow in spiral fashion at the *edge* of the discontinuity shown. (An atom can be bound to a step more strongly than to a plane.) The calculated growth rates for this mechanism are in good agreement with observation. We expect that nearly all crystals in nature grown at low supersaturation will contain dislocations, as otherwise they could not have grown.

Spiral growth patterns have been observed on a large number of crystals. A beautiful example of the growth pattern from a single screw dislocation is given in Fig. 21.

If the growth rate is independent of direction of the edge in the plane of the surface, the growth pattern is an Archimedes spiral,

$$r = a\theta, \tag{13}$$

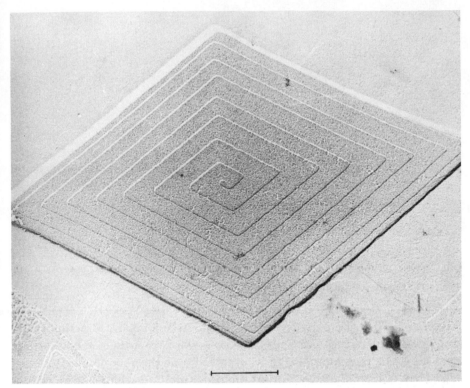

Figure 21 Growth pattern from single dislocation on single crystal of paraffin $n\text{-}C_{36}H_{74}$. [Electron micrograph courtesy of H. F. Kay and B. J. Appelbe, after Dawson and Vand, Proc. Roy. Soc. (London) **A206**, 555 (1951).]

where a is a constant. The limiting minimum radius of curvature near the dislocation is determined by the supersaturation. If the radius of curvature is too small, atoms on the curved edge evaporate until the equilibrium curvature is attained. Away from the origin each part of the step acquires new atoms at a constant rate, so that $dr/dt = \text{const}$.

Whiskers

Fine hairlike crystals or **whiskers** have been observed to grow under conditions of high supersaturation without the necessity for more than perhaps one dislocation. It may be that these crystals contain a single axial screw dislocation that aids their essentially one-dimensional growth. From the absence of dislocations we would expect these crystal whiskers to have high yield strengths, of the order of the calculated value $G/30$ discussed earlier in this chapter. A single axial screw dislocation, if present, could not cause yielding because in bending the crystal the dislocation is not subjected to a shear

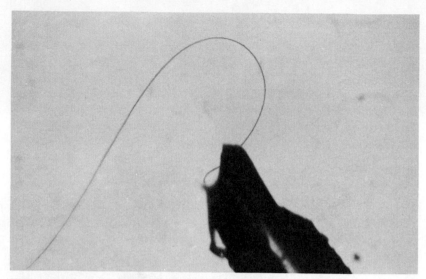

Figure 22 Copper whisker strained 1.5 percent. (Courtesy of S. S. Brenner.)

stress parallel to its Burgers vector. That is, the stress is not in a direction which can cause slip. Herring and Galt[13] observed whiskers of tin of radius $\sim 10^{-4}$ cm with elastic properties near those expected from theoretically perfect crystals. They observed yield strains of the order of 10^{-2}, which correspond to shear stresses of order 10^{-2} G, about 1000 times greater than in bulk tin, thereby confirming the early estimates of the strength of perfect crystals.

Theoretical or ideal elastic properties have been observed for a number of materials. Elastic deformation of a whisker of copper at a high strain is shown in Fig. 22. Ferromagnetic domain structures on whiskers of iron were illustrated in Chapter 15.

[13] C. Herring and J. K. Galt, Phys. Rev. **85**, 1060 (1952); W. W. Piper and W. L. Roth, Phys. Rev. **92**, 503 (1953).

Problems

1. **Lines of closest packing.** Show that the lines of closest atomic packing are $\langle 110 \rangle$ in fcc structures and $\langle 111 \rangle$ in bcc structures.

2. **Dislocation pairs.** (a) Find a pair of dislocations equivalent to a row of lattice vacancies; (b) find a pair of dislocations equivalent to a row of interstitial atoms.

3. **Force on dislocation.** Consider a crystal in the form of a cube of side L containing an edge dislocation of Burgers vector **b**. If the crystal is subjected to a shear stress σ on the upper and lower faces in the direction of slip, show by considering energy balance that the force acting on the dislocation is $F = b\sigma$ per unit length.

References

J. Friedel, *Dislocations*, Addison-Wesley, 1964. (A thorough modern discussion.)

J. Weertman and J. R. Weertman, *Elementary dislocation theory*, Macmillan, 1964. (A good introduction.)

S. Amelinckx, *Direct observation of dislocations*, Academic Press, 1964.

G. Thomas and J. Washburn, ed., *Electron microscopy and strength of crystals*, Wiley, 1963.

G. Thomas, *Transmission electron microscopy of metals*, Wiley, 1962.

Appendix

A. PROPAGATION OF ELECTROMAGNETIC WAVES IN A CRYSTAL

We study the normal modes of the electromagnetic field in an infinite crystal,[1] in order to obtain the dispersion relation $\omega(\mathbf{k})$ for the frequency as a function of the wave-vector $\mathbf{k}$. The dispersion relation exhibits forbidden bands at values of $\mathbf{k}$ which satisfy the Bragg relation $2\mathbf{k} \cdot \mathbf{G} = G^2$. For frequencies within a forbidden band the wavevectors are not real; this means that an undamped wave cannot propagate in the crystal when the Bragg relation is satisfied. We use a powerful Fourier-analysis method which clarifies in a natural way the role of the crystal structure factor and the atomic structure factor.

Our basic assumption is that the polarization $\mathbf{P}(\mathbf{x})$, the electric dipole moment per unit volume, is linearly related to the electric field intensity $\mathbf{E}(\mathbf{x})$ by

$$\mathbf{P}(\mathbf{x}) = \chi(\mathbf{x})\mathbf{E}(\mathbf{x}), \tag{1}$$

where $\chi(\mathbf{x})$ is the dielectric susceptibility (Chapter 12) of the crystal at the point $\mathbf{x}$.

In writing (1) we have assumed for convenience that the connection between $\mathbf{P}$ and $\mathbf{E}$ is *local;* that is, the polarization at $\mathbf{x}$ is determined by the electric field at $\mathbf{x}$ and not by the electric field at other points $\mathbf{x}'$. At x-ray frequencies χ is generally of the order of 10^{-4} or less. The susceptibility may be a function both of position $\mathbf{x}$ and frequency ω, but except for the frequencies near an x-ray absorption edge or an optical resonance we need not concern ourselves here with the frequency dependence of χ.

In a perfect crystal we may analyze the susceptibility in a Fourier series as

$$\chi(\mathbf{x}) = \sum_{\mathbf{G}} \chi_{\mathbf{G}} e^{i\mathbf{G}\cdot\mathbf{x}}, \tag{2}$$

where $\mathbf{G}$ runs over all reciprocal lattice vectors, including $\mathbf{G} = 0$. It is easily seen that $\chi_{\mathbf{G}}$ must equal $\chi^*_{-\mathbf{G}}$ if $(\mathbf{x})$ is real. The reason that only reciprocal lattice vectors enter in (2) was shown in Problem 2.6.

---

[1] This problem is discussed in several papers, including K. Forsterling, Ann. d. Phys. **19**, 261–289 (1934); E. Fues, Z. Physik **109**, 14–24 and 236–259 (1938).

Structure Factors

The Fourier components $\chi_{\mathbf{G}}$ of the susceptibility are of central importance because they are related directly to the x-ray structure factors. Within each unit cell of the crystal there are s atoms, not necessarily identical. We suppose that the center of the jth atom lies at $\mathbf{x}_j$, and we suppose that the local susceptibility $\chi_j(\mathbf{x})$ of this atom is a function only of the distance $|\mathbf{x} - \mathbf{x}_j|$ from the center of the atom. For convenience in notation we assume that the charge densities of different atoms do not overlap, but this is not essential. Within a cell

$$\chi(\mathbf{x}) = \sum_{j=1}^{s} \chi_j(|\mathbf{x} - \mathbf{x}_j|), \tag{3}$$

so that

$$\chi_{\mathbf{G}} = V_c^{-1} \int_{V_c} d^3x \, \chi(\mathbf{x}) e^{-i\mathbf{G}\cdot\mathbf{x}} = V_c^{-1} \sum_{j=1}^{s} e^{-i\mathbf{G}\cdot\mathbf{x}_j} \int_{V_c} d^3x \, \chi_j(|\mathbf{x} - \mathbf{x}_j|) e^{-i\mathbf{G}\cdot(\mathbf{x}-\mathbf{x}_j)}, \tag{4}$$

where V_c is the volume of a cell.[2]

We define the **atomic susceptibility structure factor** of the jth atom as

$$A_j(\mathbf{G}) \equiv \int d^3x \, \chi_j(|\mathbf{x} - \mathbf{x}_j|) e^{-i\mathbf{G}\cdot(\mathbf{x}-\mathbf{x}_j)} = 2\pi \int r^2 \, dr \, d(\cos\theta) \chi_j(r) e^{-iGr\cos\theta}, \tag{5}$$

where $r = |\mathbf{x} - \mathbf{x}_j|$ and θ is the angle between $\mathbf{G}$ and $\mathbf{x} - \mathbf{x}_j$. Thus

$$A_j(G) = \frac{4\pi}{G} \int r \, dr \, \chi_j(r) \sin Gr, \tag{6}$$

which is identical with the definition of the atomic form factor $f_j(G)$, except that $\chi_j(r)$ appears in place of the charge density $\rho_j(r)$. For x-rays we assume that $\chi_j(r)$ is directly proportional to $\rho_j(r)$, so that our $A_j(G)$ differs only by a constant from $f_j(G)$. Equation (4) becomes, using the definition of $A_j(G)$,

$$\chi_{\mathbf{G}} = V_c^{-1} \sum_j A_j(G) e^{-i\mathbf{G}\cdot\mathbf{x}_j} \propto \sum_j f_j(G) e^{-i\mathbf{G}\cdot\mathbf{x}_j} = \mathcal{S}_{\mathbf{G}}, \tag{7}$$

where $\mathcal{S}_{\mathbf{G}}$ is just the geometrical structure factor of (2.63).

---

[2] Here we have used a result for $\chi_{\mathbf{G}}$ in terms of $\chi(\mathbf{x})$. To obtain the result, multiply both sides of (2) by $e^{-i\mathbf{G}'\cdot\mathbf{x}}$ and integrate over the volume V of the crystal (or over the volume V_c of a unit cell):

$$\int d^3x \, \chi(\mathbf{x}) e^{-i\mathbf{G}'\cdot\mathbf{x}} = \sum_{\mathbf{G}} \chi_{\mathbf{G}} \int d^3x \, e^{i(\mathbf{G}-\mathbf{G}')\cdot\mathbf{x}} = \chi_{\mathbf{G}'} V,$$

because the integral of $\exp[i(\mathbf{G} - \mathbf{G}')\cdot\mathbf{x}]$ is V if $\mathbf{G} = \mathbf{G}'$ and zero otherwise. To see that it is zero otherwise, consider the example of a one-dimensional lattice of N cells of lattice constant a. Then $G - G' = 2\pi h/a$, where h is an integer, and

$$\int_0^{Na} dx \, e^{i2\pi hx/a} = (1/2\pi iha)(e^{i2\pi Nh} - 1) = 0,$$

because Nh is an integer. We can also integrate only over a single cell to obtain the same result.

Electromagnetic Wave Equation

The electromagnetic field in a crystal need not be periodic under a lattice translation, so that the general Fourier analysis of the electric field vector in an infinite crystal will require a Fourier integral:

$$E(x) = \int d^3K E(K) e^{iK \cdot x}. \tag{8}$$

On substituting (2) and (8) in (1) we find

$$P(x) = \sum_G \chi_G e^{iG \cdot x} \int d^3k E(k) e^{ik \cdot x} = \sum_G \chi_G \int d^3K E(K - G) e^{iK \cdot x}, \tag{9}$$

where we have written $K = k + G$ as the integration variable.

We are concerned with the electromagnetic wave equation

$$c^2 \nabla^2 E = \frac{\partial^2}{\partial t^2} (E + 4\pi P). \tag{10}$$

We look for a solution of (10) for which all Fourier components $E(K - G)$ have the identical time dependence $e^{-i\omega t}$. Such solutions are the normal modes of the electromagnetic field in the crystal. Now, from (8),

$$c^2 \nabla^2 E = -c^2 \int d^3K \, K^2 E(K) e^{iK \cdot x} \tag{11}$$

and, from (8) and (9),

$$\frac{\partial^2}{\partial t^2} (E + 4\pi P) = -\omega^2 \int d^3K \{ (1 + 4\pi\chi_0) E(K) + 4\pi \sum_G' \chi_G E(K - G) \} e^{iK \cdot x}. \tag{12}$$

The wave equation (10) will be satisfied if the coefficients of $e^{iK \cdot x}$ in (11) and (12) are equal. Thus

$$\boxed{c^2 K^2 E(K) = \omega^2 \sum_G \epsilon_G E(K - G),} \tag{13}$$

where we denote $1 + 4\pi\chi_0$ by ϵ_0 and $4\pi\chi_G$ by ϵ_G. This is a set of linear homogeneous algebraic equations which depend on the structure of the crystal through the Fourier coefficients ϵ_G. We now look for approximate solutions of (13) in the x-ray region. We assume $\epsilon_0 \gg \epsilon_G$.

Bragg Reflection

For x-rays the wavevector k may be of the order of magnitude of a nonzero G. The most interesting situation occurs when for a particular G it happens that

$$(k - G)^2 = k^2, \tag{14}$$

or

$$2k \cdot G = G^2, \tag{15}$$

which is the condition for Bragg diffraction. When this condition is nearly satisfied both $c^2(k - G)^2$ and c^2k^2 can be nearly equal to the same value of $\omega^2\epsilon_0$. Then the dominant waves in the crystal are $E(k)$ and $E(k - G)$. Thus (13) reduces to, with k written for K,

$$c^2k^2 E(k) = \omega^2 [\epsilon_0 E(k) + \epsilon_G E(k - G)] \tag{16}$$

and, with $\mathbf{k} - \mathbf{G}$ written for $\mathbf{K}$,

$$c^2(\mathbf{k} - \mathbf{G})^2\mathbf{E}(\mathbf{k} - \mathbf{G}) \cong \omega^2[\epsilon_0\mathbf{E}(\mathbf{k} - \mathbf{G}) + \epsilon_{-\mathbf{G}}\mathbf{E}(\mathbf{k})]. \qquad (17)$$

We may replace $\epsilon_{-\mathbf{G}}$ by $\epsilon_{\mathbf{G}}^*$ by the argument following (2).

Equations (16) and (17) are two coupled linear equations in the field amplitudes $\mathbf{E}(\mathbf{k})$ and $\mathbf{E}(\mathbf{k} - \mathbf{G})$. They have a nontrivial solution when the determinant

$$\begin{vmatrix} c^2k^2 - \omega^2\epsilon_0 & -\omega^2\epsilon_{\mathbf{G}} \\ -\omega^2\epsilon_{\mathbf{G}}^* & c^2(\mathbf{k} - \mathbf{G})^2 - \omega^2\epsilon_0 \end{vmatrix} = 0, \qquad (18)$$

or

$$\omega^4(\epsilon_0^2 - |\epsilon_{\mathbf{G}}|^2) - \omega^2\epsilon_0c^2[k^2 + (\mathbf{k} - \mathbf{G})^2] + c^4k^2(\mathbf{k} - \mathbf{G})^2 = 0. \qquad (19)$$

The Bragg condition is satisfied when $(\mathbf{k} - \mathbf{G})^2$ is exactly equal to k^2. Let $\mathbf{k}_0$ denote such a value of $\mathbf{k}$. Then (19) reduces to

$$\omega^4(\epsilon_0^2 - |\epsilon_{\mathbf{G}}|^2) - 2\omega^2\epsilon_0c^2k_0^2 + c^4k_0^4 = 0. \qquad (20)$$

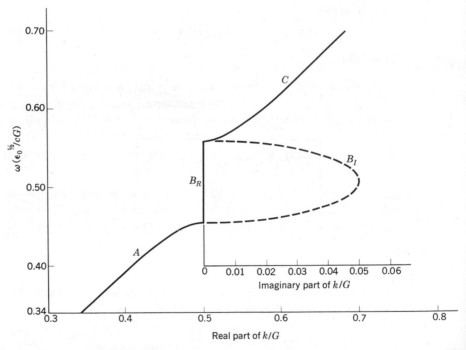

Figure A.1 Frequency gap for Bragg reflection. If we substitute real frequencies in Eq. (19) and solve for the wavevector k, we find that k is real on the branches A and C of the dispersion relation. Branch A runs from zero to just below $k = \frac{1}{2}G$; branch C starts just above $k = \frac{1}{2}G$. Branch B at $k = \frac{1}{2}G$ is complex: the real part of k on branch B is always equal to $k = \frac{1}{2}G$; the imaginary part of k on branch B is plotted as B_I. The dispersion relation is plotted for $\epsilon_G = 0.2\epsilon_0$.

On solving for ω^2 we have the two roots

$$\omega_\pm^2 = \frac{c^2 k_0^2}{\epsilon_0 \pm |\epsilon_G|}. \tag{21}$$

For real values of ω between ω_+ and ω_- the roots of (19) for k are complex, corresponding to waves damped in space. The roots are shown in Fig. A.1. The frequencies between ω_+ and ω_- are said to lie in a **forbidden band**. Waves in this frequency region do not propagate in the crystal, but are reflected strongly.

This is most easily exhibited by an example in which $\mathbf{k}$ and $\mathbf{k} - \mathbf{G}$ are nearly equal in magnitude but exactly opposite in direction. In (19) we set $k = \frac{1}{2}G + \delta$, where $\delta \ll \frac{1}{2}G$. Then

$$\delta^4 - 2\delta^2(\tfrac{1}{4}G^2 + \omega^2\epsilon_0/c^2) + (\tfrac{1}{4}G^2)^2 - 2(\tfrac{1}{4}G^2)(\omega^2\epsilon_0/c^2)$$
$$+ (\omega^4/c^4)(\epsilon_0^2 - |\epsilon_G|^2) = 0. \tag{22}$$

We neglect the term in δ^4. Let us solve for δ at the arbitrary frequency $\omega^2 = (\tfrac{1}{2}Gc)^2/\epsilon_0$, which lies between ω_+ and ω_-. Equation (22) becomes

$$-2\delta^2(\tfrac{1}{2}G^2) + [-(\tfrac{1}{4}G^2)^2 + (\tfrac{1}{4}G^2/\epsilon_0)^2(\epsilon_0^2 - \epsilon_G^2)] = 0 \tag{23}$$

or

$$4\delta^2 = -(\tfrac{1}{4}G^2)(\epsilon_G/\epsilon_0)^2; \qquad \delta = \pm i(\tfrac{1}{2}G)(\epsilon_G/2\epsilon_0), \tag{24}$$

so that at a frequency near the middle of the forbidden band the wavevector is given by

$$k = \tfrac{1}{2}G(1 \pm i\epsilon_G/2\epsilon_0). \tag{25}$$

The spatial attenuation of the mode is governed essentially by ϵ_G, the component of the dielectric constant at the reciprocal lattice vector $\mathbf{G}$.

B. QUANTUM-MECHANICAL EXPRESSION FOR THE POLARIZABILITY

We calculate the energy of interaction of an atomic system with an applied static electric field and set this equal to the macroscopic expression for the energy, which is

$$\Delta U = -\int P \, dE = -\tfrac{1}{2}\alpha E^2. \tag{1}$$

The result of second-order perturbation theory is

$$\Delta U = -\sum_j{}' e^2 |x_{ij}|^2 E^2 / \hbar\omega_{ij} \tag{2}$$

when the perturbing energy is eEx and $\hbar\omega_{ij} = \epsilon_j - \epsilon_i$. Therefore

$$\alpha = \sum_j{}' 2e^2 |x_{ij}|^2 / \hbar\omega_{ij}, \tag{3}$$

which is the expression to which (12.21) reduces when $\omega = 0$. The association of the polarizability with the second-order perturbation energy of a single atomic level i depends for its validity on the condition $\hbar\omega_{ij} \gg k_B T$; that is, only the ground state i is significantly populated at the temperature considered.

C. FERMI-DIRAC DISTRIBUTION

Complete derivations of the Fermi-Dirac distribution are found in elementary text-books on statistical mechanics.[1] We derive the distribution here by a device due to F. Bloch. We consider the inelastic collisions of a conduction electron with a "two-level" impurity atom with which the electron may be imagined to interact. The electron state is labeled by its wavevector $\mathbf{k}$. The impurity atom has two energy states 0 and Δ, as indicated in Fig. C.1; the occupation probabilities of the two levels will be written as $p(0)$ and $p(\Delta)$. We examine those inelastic collisions which connect the electron state $\mathbf{k}$ at electron energy ϵ with the electron state $\mathbf{k}'$ at electron energy $\epsilon + \Delta$.

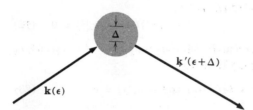

Figure C.1 An electron in a state $\mathbf{k}$ of energy ϵ collides inelastically with an impurity atom initially in an excited state of energy Δ. In the final state shown the electron is in a state $\mathbf{k}'$ with energy $\epsilon + \Delta$. In such collisions the atom loses energy Δ.

The transition rate for a collision in which the electron starts at $\mathbf{k}$ and ends at $\mathbf{k}'$ will be proportional to

$$f(\epsilon)p(\Delta)[1 - f(\epsilon + \Delta)],$$

where $f(\epsilon)$ is the probability that the initial state at $\mathbf{k}$ is occupied; $p(\Delta)$ is the probability the impurity atom is in the state Δ so that it can give up its energy Δ to the electron, and $1 - f(\epsilon + \Delta)$ is the probability that the electron state $\mathbf{k}'$ at $\epsilon + \Delta$ is vacant so that it can receive the scattered electron. The final state $\mathbf{k}'$ *must be vacant if the scattering event is to take place;* this is the special feature introduced by the Pauli principle.

The transition rate for the reverse collision $\mathbf{k}' \rightarrow \mathbf{k}$ is proportional to

$$f(\epsilon + \Delta)p(0)[1 - f(\epsilon)],$$

just reversing the steps in Fig. C.1 and in the preceding argument.

Now in thermal equilibrium the transition rates $\mathbf{k} \rightarrow \mathbf{k}'$ and $\mathbf{k}' \rightarrow \mathbf{k}$ must be equal, so that the two population factors must be equal:[2]

$$f(\epsilon)p(\Delta)[1 - f(\epsilon + \Delta)] = f(\epsilon + \Delta)p(0)[1 - f(\epsilon)], \tag{1}$$

where the averages are understood to be for thermal equilibrium at a common tempera-

---

[1] C. Kittel, *Elementary statistical physics,* Wiley, 1958.

[2] The constants of proportionality in the rates of the direct and the inverse processes are exactly equal by the principle of detailed balance, which follows directly from quantum theory.

ture T. The Boltzmann distribution applies to the population of the states of the impurity atom, so that

$$\frac{p(\Delta)}{p(0)} = \exp\left(-\Delta/k_B T\right). \tag{2}$$

Thus (1) becomes

$$\frac{f(\epsilon + \Delta)}{1 - f(\epsilon + \Delta)} \cdot \frac{1 - f(\epsilon)}{f(\epsilon)} = \exp\left(-\Delta/k_B T\right). \tag{3}$$

This equation is easily seen to have a solution for all T if

$$\frac{1 - f(\epsilon)}{f(\epsilon)} = e^{(\epsilon - \mu)/k_B T}, \tag{4}$$

where μ is a constant independent of ϵ. From (4) we have the Fermi-Dirac distribution law

$$f(\epsilon) = \frac{1}{e^{(\epsilon - \mu)/k_B T} + 1}. \tag{5}$$

The quantity μ is the chemical potential, as discussed in Chapter 7.

D. TIGHT BINDING APPROXIMATION FOR ELECTRONS IN METALS

It is useful to look at the formation of allowed and forbidden electron bands in another way. We start from the energy levels of the neutral separated atoms and watch the changes in the levels as the charge distributions of adjacent atoms overlap when the atoms are brought together to form the metal. We can understand the origin of the splitting of free atom energy levels into bands as the atoms are brought together by considering two hydrogen atoms, each with its electron in the 1s (ground) state. In Fig. D.1 the wavefunctions ψ_A, ψ_B on the separated atoms are shown in (a). As the atoms are brought closer together and their wavefunctions overlap, we are led to consider the two combi-

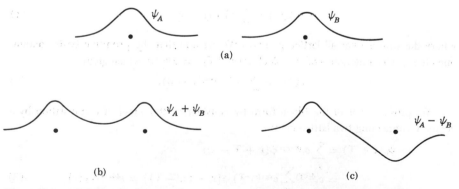

Figure D.1   (a) Schematic drawing of wavefunctions of electrons on two hydrogen atoms at large separation. (b) Ground state wavefunction at closer separation. (c) Excited state wavefunction.

nations $\psi_A \pm \psi_B$. Each combination shares the electrons equally as between the two protons, but an electron in the state $\psi_A + \psi_B$ will have a somewhat lower energy than in the state $\psi_A - \psi_B$, for the following reason. In the state $\psi_A + \psi_B$ shown in (b) the electron spends part of the time in the region midway between the two protons, and in this region it is under the influence of the attractive potential of both protons at once, thereby increasing the binding energy. In the state $\psi_A - \psi_B$ shown in (c) the probability density vanishes midway between the nuclei; an extra contribution to the binding does not appear. Thus as two atoms are brought together two separated energy levels are formed for each level of the isolated atom. For N atoms, N levels are formed for each level of the isolated atom and these N levels will be associated with one or more bands.

As free atoms are brought together the Coulomb interaction between the atom cores and the overlapping parts of the electron distribution will split the energy levels of the combined system, spreading the levels out into bands. A state of quantum number ns of the free atom is spread out in the metal into a band of energies. Here n denotes the principal quantum number, and s indicates zero orbital angular momentum. The width of the band is proportional to the strength of the interaction or overlap between neighboring atoms, each in the state ns. There will also be bands formed from $p, d, \ldots$ states ($l = 1, 2, \ldots$) of the free atoms. The ($2l + 1$) states degenerate in the free atom will form ($2l + 1$) bands. Each of these bands will not have in general the same energy as any other band over any substantial proportion of the range of the wavevector. Two or more bands may coincide in energy at certain values of $\mathbf{k}$ in the Brillouin zone.

The approximation which starts out from the wavefunctions of the free atoms is known as the **tight binding approximation.** A simple example of its use appears below. The tight binding approximation is thought to be quite good for the inner electrons of atoms, but it is not often a good description of the conduction electrons themselves. It is used to describe approximately the d bands of some of the transition metals and the valence bands of inert gas crystals.

Suppose that the ground state of an electron moving in the potential $U(r)$ of an isolated atom is $\phi(\mathbf{r})$ and that the energy is E_0; suppose further that ϕ is an s state. The treatment of bands arising from degenerate ($p, d, \ldots$) atomic levels is more complicated. If the influence of one atom on another is small, we obtain an approximate wavefunction for one electron in the whole crystal by taking

$$\psi_\mathbf{k}(\mathbf{r}) = \sum_j C_{\mathbf{k}j}\phi(\mathbf{r} - \mathbf{r}_j), \tag{1}$$

where the sum is over all lattice points. (We assume that the primitive basis contains one atom.) This function is of the Bloch form if $C_{\mathbf{k}j} = e^{i(\mathbf{k}\cdot\mathbf{r}_j)}$, which gives

$$\psi_\mathbf{k}(\mathbf{r}) = \sum_j e^{i(\mathbf{k}\cdot\mathbf{r}_j)}\phi(\mathbf{r} - \mathbf{r}_j). \tag{2}$$

We prove (2) is of the Bloch form by considering the effect of a translation by a vector $\mathbf{T}$ connecting two lattice points:

$$\psi_\mathbf{k}(\mathbf{r} + \mathbf{T}) = \sum_j e_i^{(\mathbf{k}\cdot\mathbf{r}_j)} \phi(\mathbf{r} + \mathbf{T} - \mathbf{r}_j)$$
$$= e_i^{(\mathbf{k}\cdot\mathbf{T})}\sum_j e^{i\mathbf{k}\cdot(\mathbf{r}_j - \mathbf{T})} \phi[\mathbf{r} - (\mathbf{r}_j - \mathbf{T})] = e^{i(\mathbf{k}\cdot\mathbf{T})}\psi_\mathbf{k}(\mathbf{r}) \tag{3}$$

which is exactly the Bloch requirement.

We find the first-order energy by calculating the diagonal matrix elements of the perturbation $H'(\mathbf{r})$ which expresses the difference between the potential in the crystal and the potential of an isolated atom. We have

$$\langle \mathbf{k}|H'|\mathbf{k}\rangle = \sum_j \sum_m e^{i\mathbf{k}\cdot(\mathbf{r}_j-\mathbf{r}_m)}\langle \phi_m|H'|\phi_j\rangle, \tag{4}$$

where $\phi_m \equiv \phi(\mathbf{r} - \mathbf{r}_m)$. Writing $\rho_m = \mathbf{r}_m - \mathbf{r}_j$,

$$\langle \mathbf{k}|H'|\mathbf{k}\rangle = N\sum_m e^{-i\mathbf{k}\cdot\rho_m}\int dV\,\phi(\mathbf{r}-\rho_m)H'\phi(\mathbf{r}). \tag{5}$$

If now we neglect all integrals in (5) except those between nearest neighbors connected by ρ and write, for a crystal of N atoms,

$$\int dV\phi^*(\mathbf{r})H'\phi(\mathbf{r}) = -\alpha/N; \qquad \int dV\phi^*(\mathbf{r}-\rho)H'\phi(\mathbf{r}) = -\gamma/N; \tag{6}$$

we get

$$\langle \mathbf{k}|H'|\mathbf{k}\rangle = -\alpha - \gamma\sum_m e^{-i\mathbf{k}\cdot\rho_m}.$$

Thus the first-order energy is given by

$$\epsilon_k = E_0 - \alpha - \gamma\sum_m e^{i(\mathbf{k}\cdot\rho_m)}. \tag{7}$$

For a simple cubic lattice the nearest-neighbor atoms are at the positions

$$\rho_m = (\pm a, 0, 0); \qquad (0, \pm a, 0); \qquad (0, 0, \pm a), \tag{8}$$

so that (7) becomes

$$\epsilon_\mathbf{k} = E_0 - \alpha - 2\gamma(\cos k_x a + \cos k_y a + \cos k_z a). \tag{9}$$

Thus the energies are confined to a band of width 12γ. For $ka \ll 1$,

$$\epsilon_\mathbf{k} \cong E_0 - \alpha - 6\gamma + \gamma k^2 a^2. \tag{10}$$

The energy at the bottom of the band is independent of the direction of motion. The effective mass is

$$m^* = \hbar^2/2\gamma a^2. \tag{11}$$

When the overlap integral γ is small the band width is narrow and the effective mass is high.

For every state of an electron in the free atom there exists a band of energies in the crystal. We have considered here one state of the free atom and have obtained one band. The number of states in the zone which corresponds to a nondegenerate atomic level is equal to $2N$, where N is the number of atoms. We see this directly: (9) is periodic in $\mathbf{k}$, and thus only values of $\mathbf{k}$ lying within the first Brillouin zone in $\mathbf{k}$ space will define independent wavefunctions. In the simple cubic case the polyhedron is defined by $-\pi/a < k_x < \pi/a$, etc. The volume of the polyhedron is $8\pi^3/a^3$; but the number of states (counting both spin orientations) per unit volume of $\mathbf{k}$ space is $1/4\pi^3$, so that the number of states is $2/a^3 = 2N$.

E. BCS THEORY OF THE SUPERCONDUCTING ENERGY GAP

The BCS theory in its original form[1] is not difficult to understand, and it appears even simpler with the help of the spin-analog method of P. W. Anderson. A careful discussion is given in QTS, Chap. 8. The essence of the theory of the ground state can be understood without great mathematical complications by making further simplifications in the assumptions. We first consider a mathematical problem which establishes useful background for what comes later. The problem we treat first is *not* the superconductivity problem, but the connection is close.

A Special Eigenvalue Problem

Consider an unperturbed one-particle system with an energy level spectrum such that one of the levels is R-fold degenerate and well separated in energy from all other levels. That is, we consider R independent states of the system, all having the same energy. Now let there be an additional interaction, a weak perturbation. The perturbation may split up the R states so that they occupy a certain range of energy, instead of all having the same energy.

We denote the R states associated with the degenerate level as φ_1, φ_2, . . . , φ_R. These states satisfy the Schrödinger equation of the unperturbed problem. We may choose the zero of energy so that $H_0\varphi = 0$ for these φ. In the first approximation the new states of the system in the presence of a perturbation U may be written as linear combinations of the old states:[2]

$$\psi_j = \sum_{s=1}^{R} c_{js}\varphi_s. \tag{1}$$

Suppose that the ψ's formed in this way are exact solutions of the Schrödinger equation of the perturbed problem:

$$(H_0 + U)\psi_j = U\psi_j = \epsilon_j\psi_j. \tag{2}$$

Here $H_0\psi_j = 0$ because of the choice of the zero of energy. Using (1), we may write (2) as

$$\sum_s c_{js}U\varphi_s = \epsilon_j\sum_s c_{js}\varphi_s. \tag{3}$$

We now multiply both sides of (3) by any φ_m^* and integrate over the volume. Using the matrix element notation $\langle m|U|s \rangle$ for the integral involving U, we have

$$\sum_s c_{js}\langle m|U|s \rangle = \epsilon_j c_{jm}, \tag{4}$$

where the term on the right follows from the orthogonality and normalization of the φ's.

There are R equations of the form of (4), one for each of the R possible choices of the φ_m^* by which we multiply (3). For each j we have an identical set of R independent simultaneous equations in the R unknowns c_{jm}. These equations have a nontrivial solution only if the determinant of the coefficients of the c_{jm} vanishes:

$$\begin{vmatrix} \langle 1|U|1 \rangle - \epsilon & \cdots & \langle 1|U|R \rangle \\ \vdots & & \\ \langle R|U|1 \rangle & \cdots & \langle R|U|R \rangle - \epsilon \end{vmatrix} = 0. \tag{5}$$

---

[1] J. Bardeen, L. N. Cooper, and J. R. Schrieffer, Phys. Rev. **106**, 162 (1957); **108**, 1175 (1957).
[2] This is just first-order degenerate perturbation theory in quantum mechanics.

The problem is to find the roots ϵ of this determinant; this may be a complicated numerical problem.

There is, however, one particularly simple case for which the roots can be found by informed inspection. Suppose every matrix element is equal to unity. Then (5) reduces to

$$
\begin{vmatrix}
1 - \epsilon & 1 & \cdots & 1 \\
1 & 1 - \epsilon & \cdots & 1 \\
\vdots & & & \\
1 & 1 & \cdots & 1 - \epsilon
\end{vmatrix} = 0. \tag{6}
$$

We can find the eigenvalues of (6) by a simple device.

A mathematical theorem states that the sum of all the roots of a determinant is equal to the sum of all the diagonal elements $\langle j|U|j\rangle$. The sum of the diagonal elements of (6) is R, so that

$$
\sum_{j=1}^{R} \epsilon_j = R. \tag{7}
$$

Another theorem states that the sum of the squares of all the roots of a determinant is equal to the sum of the squares of all the elements of the determinant. Thus

$$
\sum_{j=1}^{R} \epsilon_j^2 = R^2. \tag{8}
$$

We now assert that the determinant (6) has one root, say ϵ_1, equal to R and the other $R - 1$ roots are all equal to zero. This solution satisfies both theorems (7) and (8). We verify that there is actually one root equal to R. Form the symmetrical combination of the basis vectors φ_s:

$$
\psi_1 = R^{-1/2} \sum_s \varphi_s, \tag{9}
$$

for which the energy is

$$
\epsilon_1 = \langle \psi_1|U|\psi_1\rangle = \frac{1}{R}\sum_{js} \langle j|U|s\rangle = \frac{1}{R} R^2 = R. \tag{10}
$$

But this root exhausts the sum in (8), so that all other roots must be zero. Q.E.D.

If the potential U is an attractive and highly localized interaction, the matrix elements in (4) and (5) will be negative and nearly equal. Suppose that

$$
\langle j|U|s\rangle = -\delta \tag{11}
$$

for all states j, s. Here δ is a positive constant. Then the appropriate modification of (6), (8), and (10) gives

$$
\epsilon_1 = -R\delta. \tag{12}
$$

As shown in Fig. E.1 this single-state is split off below the rest of the spectrum; there exists an energy gap $R\delta$ between the ground state and the first excited state. We see the remarkable stabilization of a single state; even though the interaction δ may be weak, $R\delta$ may be large if the degeneracy R is high.

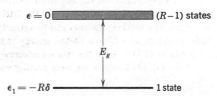

Figure E.1 Energy eigenvalue spectrum for R states connected by a perturbation U with equal matrix elements $\langle j|U|s\rangle = -\delta$, for all states j and s. Notice that a single state is split off with an energy gap $E_g = R\delta$.

Electron Pairs and the Superconducting State

In the problem just treated the states φ_s were states of a one-particle system. Suppose that we have a system of N free electrons, initially without mutual interaction. The various states Φ of the N-particle system can be specified by giving the occupancy (between zero and one, because of the Pauli principle) of the one-electron states. We may label a one-electron state as $\mathbf{k}\uparrow$; this means that the wavevector is $\mathbf{k}$ and the spin is up. It is convenient to label a state of the total N-particle system in terms of one-particle states by giving the labels of the *occupied* one-particle states. In the absence of interactions among the electrons each one-particle state is either occupied or vacant. We might write

$$\Phi_s \equiv \mathbf{k}_1\uparrow; \ \mathbf{k}_2\downarrow; \ \mathbf{k}_3\downarrow; \ \ldots; \ \mathbf{k}_N\uparrow, \tag{13}$$

where the subscripts on the $\mathbf{k}$'s denote specific values of the wavevector according to some arbitrary code or assignment.

We now let the electrons interact with each other by some interaction[3] between all pairs of electrons:

$$\mathcal{U} = \sum_{nm} U(\mathbf{r}_m - \mathbf{r}_n). \tag{14}$$

Each term of the sum acts to scatter two electrons (say those in the p and r positions in the wavefunction Φ_s) into two vacant one-electron states, states not represented as occupied in Φ_s. That is, one scattering event takes the system from the N-particle state Φ_s to some other N-particle state Φ_u.

Can we possibly make the drastic assumption as we did before[4] that matrix elements of the interaction $\mathcal{U}$ are equal between all states Φ_s, Φ_u? No, this is not possible in general. In the first place, we cannot scatter at all from $\Phi_s \equiv \mathbf{k}_1\uparrow; \ \mathbf{k}_2\downarrow; \ \mathbf{k}_3\downarrow \ldots$ to a state with different total spin, such as $\Phi_v \equiv \mathbf{k}_a\downarrow; \ \mathbf{k}_b\downarrow \ \mathbf{k}_3\downarrow \ldots$, because the interaction (14) does not contain spin operators and therefore cannot change the total spin of the system. That is, particles in $\mathbf{k}_1\uparrow$ and $\mathbf{k}_2\downarrow$ cannot be scattered to $\mathbf{k}_a\downarrow$ and $\mathbf{k}_b\downarrow$; therefore the matrix element of $\mathcal{U}$ between Φ_s and Φ_v will be zero. In the second place, matrix elements can appear with either $+$ or $-$ signs: if the particles in $\Phi_s \equiv \mathbf{k}_1\uparrow; \ \mathbf{k}_2\downarrow; \ \mathbf{k}_3\downarrow \ldots$ are scattered to $\Phi_w \equiv \mathbf{k}_c\uparrow; \ \mathbf{k}_d\downarrow; \ \mathbf{k}_3\downarrow \ldots$ with a positive matrix element, they can also be scattered to $\Phi_x \equiv \mathbf{k}_d\downarrow; \ \mathbf{k}_c\uparrow; \ \mathbf{k}_3\downarrow \ldots$. But Φ_x differs from Φ_w only in the interchange of the order of $\mathbf{k}_c\uparrow$ and $\mathbf{k}_d\downarrow$. According to the Pauli exclusion principle the interchange of the order of two states or two electrons in a wavefunction changes the sign of the wavefunction. Thus

$$\langle w|\mathcal{U}|s\rangle = -\langle x|\mathcal{U}|s\rangle; \tag{15}$$

this means that all matrix elements cannot have the same sign.

There is an ingenious way in which we can arrange for all matrix elements to have the same sign. We can find a many-body problem for which all matrix elements can be

---

[3] In superconductors the important contributions to U are from the Coulomb repulsion and the indirect coupling of two electrons by the lattice distortions associated with the electron-phonon interaction. The total interaction can be attractive among electrons near the Fermi surface, particularly among those within a Debye energy $\pm\hbar\omega_D$ of the Fermi surface. It is these electrons which cooperate in (16) to form the superconducting ground state.

[4] See Eq. (11), where we were dealing with a one particle problem.

allowed to be equal. Let us agree to consider *only* those many-body states which are occupied by pairs of electrons. We can agree on a definition of a pair: the usual definition is $\mathbf{k}\uparrow$; $-\mathbf{k}\downarrow$. That is, if $\mathbf{k}\uparrow$ is occupied, we insist that $-\mathbf{k}\downarrow$ be occupied.[5] The many-particle states we consider are of the form

$$\Phi_A \equiv \mathbf{k}_1\uparrow;\ -\mathbf{k}_1\downarrow;\ \mathbf{k}_2\uparrow;\ -\mathbf{k}_2\downarrow;\ \ldots. \tag{16}$$

These states form only a subspace of the problem, but by restricting ourselves to the subspace we get a problem we can solve. It has been shown that the restriction introduces errors only of order $1/N$, where N is the number of electrons.

Within the subspace of pair states of the form of (16) it is not unreasonable to take all matrix elements of $\mathcal{U}$ as equal. Then by direct analogy with the earlier solution (12) we obtain a spectrum which has a single ground state separated by an energy gap E_g from the excited states. Our discussion has neglected the kinetic energy of the unperturbed electrons[6] so that the original states are degenerate, but BCS show that inclusion of the kinetic energy does not destroy the energy gap.

F. QUANTUM THEORY OF DIAMAGNETISM OF MONONUCLEAR SYSTEMS

The magnetic vector potential $\mathbf{A}$ is defined by the relation $\mathbf{H} = \text{curl } \mathbf{A}$. In a magnetic field the generalized momentum $\mathbf{p}$ of a particle of charge e is

$$\mathbf{p} = \mathbf{p}_{\text{kin}} + \mathbf{p}_{\text{pot}} = m\dot{\mathbf{r}} + e\mathbf{A}/c; \tag{1}$$

so the kinetic energy is

$$\begin{aligned} K &= \frac{1}{2}m(dr/dt)^2 = \frac{1}{2m}\left(\mathbf{p} - \frac{e}{c}\mathbf{A}\right)^2 \\ &= \frac{1}{2m}p^2 - \frac{e}{mc}\mathbf{p}\cdot\mathbf{A} + \frac{e^2}{2mc^2}A^2. \end{aligned} \tag{2}$$

In quantum mechanics in the Schrödinger coordinate representation the momentum $\mathbf{p}$ is the operator $-i\hbar\nabla$. The effect of a magnetic field is to add to the Hamiltonian the terms

$$\mathcal{H}' = \frac{ie\hbar}{2mc}(\nabla\cdot\mathbf{A} + \mathbf{A}\cdot\nabla) + \frac{e^2}{2mc^2}A^2, \tag{3}$$

which for an atomic electron may usually be treated as a small perturbation. If the magnetic field is uniform and in the z direction, we may write

$$A_x = -\tfrac{1}{2}yH, \qquad A_y = \tfrac{1}{2}xH, \qquad A_z = 0,$$

and (3) becomes

$$\mathcal{H}' = \frac{ie\hbar H}{2mc}\left(x\frac{\partial}{\partial y} - y\frac{\partial}{\partial x}\right) + \frac{e^2 H^2}{8mc^2}(x^2 + y^2). \tag{4}$$

The first term on the right is proportional to the orbital angular momentum component L_z if $\mathbf{r}$ is measured from the nucleus. In mononuclear systems this term gives rise only to

[5] We could form pairs with parallel spin, as $\mathbf{k}\uparrow$; $-\mathbf{k}\uparrow$, but their energy is higher because of exchange energy effects.

[6] This approximation is known as the strong-coupling approximation.

paramagnetism. The second term gives for a spherically symmetric system a contribution

$$E' = \frac{e^2 H^2}{12mc^2}\langle r^2\rangle \tag{5}$$

to the first-order perturbation energy. The associated magnetic moment is

$$\mu = -\partial E'/\partial H = -(e^2\langle r^2\rangle/6mc^2)H, \tag{6}$$

in agreement with the classical result. For further details see the book by Van Vleck.

G. VAN VLECK TEMPERATURE-INDEPENDENT PARAMAGNETISM

We consider an atomic or molecular system which has no magnetic moment in the ground state, by which we mean that the diagonal matrix element of the magnetic moment operator μ_z is zero.

Suppose that there is a nondiagonal matrix element $\langle s|\mu_z|0\rangle$ of the magnetic moment operator, connecting the ground state 0 with the excited state s of energy $\Delta = E_s - E_0$ above the ground state. Then by standard perturbation theory the wavefunction of the ground state in a weak field $(\mu_z H \ll \Delta)$ becomes

$$\psi_0' = \psi_0 + (H/\Delta)\langle s|\mu_z|0\rangle\psi_s, \tag{1}$$

and the wavefunction of the excited state becomes

$$\psi_s' = \psi_s - (H/\Delta)\langle 0|\mu_z|s\rangle\psi_0. \tag{2}$$

The perturbed ground state now has a moment

$$\langle 0'|\mu_z|0'\rangle = 2H|\langle s|\mu_z|0\rangle|^2/\Delta, \tag{3}$$

and the upper state has a moment

$$\langle s'|\mu_z|s'\rangle = -2H|\langle s|\mu_z|0\rangle|^2/\Delta. \tag{4}$$

There are two interesting cases to consider:

Case (a). $\Delta \ll k_B T$. The surplus population in the ground state over the excited state is approximately equal to $N\Delta/2k_B T$, so that the resultant magnetization is

$$M = \frac{2H|\langle s|\mu_z|0\rangle|^2}{\Delta} \cdot \frac{N\Delta}{2k_B T},$$

which gives for the susceptibility

$$\chi = N|\langle s|\mu_z|0\rangle|^2/k_B T. \tag{5}$$

Here N is the number of molecules per unit volume. The contribution (5) is of the usual Curie form, although the mechanism of magnetization here is by polarization of the states of the system, whereas with free spins the mechanism of magnetization is the redistribution of ions among the spin states. We note that the splitting Δ does not enter in (5).

Case (b). $\Delta \gg k_B T$. Here the population is nearly all in the ground state, so that

$$M = 2NH|\langle s|\mu_z|0\rangle|^2/\Delta. \tag{6}$$

The susceptibility is

$$\chi = 2N|\langle s|\mu_z|0\rangle|^2/\Delta, \tag{7}$$

independent of temperature. This type of contribution is known as Van Vleck paramagnetism.

H. QUENCHING OF THE ORBITAL ANGULAR MOMENTUM BY CRYSTALLINE ELECTRIC FIELDS

We consider a single electron with orbital quantum number $L = 1$ moving about a nucleus, the whole being placed in an inhomogeneous crystalline electric field. We omit electron spin.

In a crystal of orthorhombic symmetry (Chapter 1) the charges on neighboring ions will produce an electrostatic potential V about the nucleus of the form

$$eV = Ax^2 + By^2 - (A + B)z^2, \tag{1}$$

where A and B are constants. This expression is the lowest degree polynomial in x, y, z which is a solution of the Laplace equation $\nabla^2 V = 0$ compatible with the symmetry of the crystal.

In free space the ground state is three-fold degenerate, with magnetic quantum numbers $m_L = 1, 0, -1$. In a magnetic field these levels are split by energies proportional to the field H, and it is this field-proportional splitting which is responsible for the normal paramagnetic susceptibility of the ion. In the crystal the picture may be different. We take as the three wavefunctions associated with the unperturbed ground state of the ion

$$U_x = xf(r); \qquad U_y = yf(r); \qquad U_z = zf(r). \tag{2}$$

These wavefunctions are orthogonal, and we assume that they are normalized. Each of the U's can be shown to have the property

$$\mathcal{L}^2 U_i = L(L + 1)U_i = 2U_i, \tag{3}$$

where $\mathcal{L}^2$ is the operator for the square of the orbital angular momentum, in units of $\hbar$. The result (3) confirms that the selected wavefunctions are in fact p functions, having $L = 1$.

We observe now that the U's are diagonal with respect to the perturbation, as by symmetry the nondiagonal elements vanish:

$$\langle U_x|eV|U_y\rangle = \langle U_x|eV|U_z\rangle = \langle U_y|eV|U_z\rangle = 0. \tag{4}$$

Consider for example

$$\langle U_x|eV|U_y\rangle = \int xy|f(r)|^2\{Ax^2 + By^2 - (A + B)z^2\}\,dx\,dy\,dz; \tag{5}$$

the integrand is an odd function of x (and also of y) and therefore the integral must be zero. The energy levels are then given by the diagonal matrix elements:

$$\begin{aligned} \langle U_x|eV|U_x\rangle &= \int |f(r)|^2\{Ax^4 + By^2x^2 - (A + B)z^2x^2\}\,dx\,dy\,dz \\ &= A(I_1 - I_2), \end{aligned} \tag{6}$$

where

$$I_1 = \int |f(r)|^2 x^4 \, dx \, dy \, dz; \qquad I_2 = \int |f(r)|^2 x^2 y^2 \, dx \, dy \, dz. \tag{7}$$

In addition,

$$\langle U_y|eV|U_y \rangle = B(I_1 - I_2); \qquad \langle U_z|eV|U_z \rangle = -(A + B)(I_1 - I_2). \tag{8}$$

The three eigenstates in the crystal field are p functions with their angular lobes directed along each of the x, y, z axes, respectively.

The orbital moment of each of the levels is zero, because

$$\langle U_x|L_z|U_x \rangle = \langle U_y|L_z|U_y \rangle = \langle U_z|L_z|U_z \rangle = 0.$$

This effect is known as **quenching**. The level still has a definite total angular momentum, since $\mathcal{L}^2$ is diagonal and gives $L = 1$, but the spatial components of the angular momentum are not constants of the motion and their time average is zero in the first approximation. Therefore the components of the orbital magnetic moment also vanish in the same approximation. The role of the crystal field in the quenching process is to split the originally degenerate levels into nonmagnetic levels separated by energies $\gg \mu H$, so that the magnetic field is a small perturbation in comparison with the crystal field.

At a lattice site of cubic symmetry there is no term in the potential of the form (1), that is, quadratic in the electron coordinates. Now the ground state of an ion with one p electron (or with one hole in a p shell) will be triply degenerate. However, the energy of the ion will be lowered if the ion displaces itself with respect to the surroundings, thereby creating a noncubic potential such as (1). Such a displacement is known as a **Jahn-Teller effect** and is often large and important, particularly with the Mn^{3+} and Cu^{2+} ions[1] and with holes in alkali and silver halides.

[1] See L. Orgel, *Introduction to transition metal chemistry*, Wiley, 1960; extensive references are given by M. D. Sturge, Phys. Rev. **140**, A880 (1965).

Author Index

Subject Index